THE THEORY OF GROUP REPRESENTATIONS

BY

FRANCIS D. MURNAGHAN

PH.D. (JOHNS HOPKINS)
D.SC. (NATIONAL UNIVERSITY OF IRELAND)
CONSULTANT IN MATHEMATICS
THE DAVID TAYLOR MODEL BASIN

NEW YORK
DOVER PUBLICATIONS, INC.

Published in the United Kingdom by Constable and Company Limited, 10 Orange Street, London W.C. 2.

This Dover edition, first published in 1963, is an unabridged and corrected republication of the work first published by the Johns Hopkins Press in 1938.

Library of Congress Catalog Card Number: 63-21677

Manufactured in the United States of America

Dover Publications, Inc.
180 Varick Street
New York 14, N. Y.

PREFACE

The function of a preface is to entice readers to a perusal of the book, to which it is written, by explaining its object and scope. In the present instance this explanation may be given quite briefly. We have attempted to give a quite elementary and self-contained account of the theory of group representations with special reference to those groups (particularly the symmetric group and the rotation group) which have turned out to be of fundamental significance for quantum mechanics (especially nuclear physics). We have devoted particular attention to the theory of group integration (as developed by Schur and Weyl); to the theory of two-valued or spin representations; to the representations of the symmetric group and the analysis of their direct products; to the crystallographic groups; and to the Lorentz group and the concept of semi-vectors (as developed by Einstein and Mayer). We had originally planned a chapter devoted to actual applications of the theory to concrete problems in nuclear physics and had secured the coöperation of Professor J. A. Wheeler, whose distinguished work in this field is so well known. However, considerations of space have prevented the inclusion of this chapter in the present volume; we hope to give an account of these applications in a future publication.

The three outstanding names in the theory of group representations are Frobenius, Schur, and Weyl. Any formal dedication would be presumptuous, but we hope that some of the flavor of their work may have been caught in the present book.

If this work possesses merit, it is due to the following circumstances. In the first place, we are fortunate in having as colleagues at Johns Hopkins, O. Zariski, A. Wintner, J. Williamson, E. R. van Kampen, and O. F. G. Schilling, and owe much to their friendly coöperation. Secondly the Institute for Advanced Study, Princeton, N. J., generously invited us to be a guest member during 1936-37; amongst our many debts incurred during our association with the Institute, we must here record those to Weyl and Wedderburn. We highly appreciate the painstaking care and efficiency of the J. H. Furst Company in this somewhat difficult piece of printing; and we wish to thank the manager of the Johns Hopkins Press for his courteous service which has made our relations with the Press so agreeable.

In the days when Ireland was known as the Land of Saints and Scholars the usual inscription on an illuminated missal or literary effort was "To the Glory of God and Honor of Ireland." In imitation of this pious practice we close our preface with the inscription:

TO THE GLORY OF GOD, HONOR OF IRELAND

AND

FAME OF AMERICA

F. D. MURNAGHAN

Baltimore,
August, 1938

CONTENTS

CHAPTER I

GROUPS AND MATRICES

CHAPTER II

REDUCIBILITY

CHAPTER III

GROUP CHARACTERS

CHAPTER IV

THE SYMMETRIC GROUP

CHAPTER V

THE CHARACTERS OF THE SYMMETRIC GROUP

CHAPTER VI

THE ALTERNATING GROUP

CHAPTER VII

LINEAR GROUPS

CHAPTER VIII

GROUP INTEGRATION

CHAPTER IX

THE ORTHOGONAL GROUP

CHAPTER X

SPIN REPRESENTATIONS OF THE ROTATION GROUP

CHAPTER XI

THE CRYSTALLOGRAPHIC GROUPS

CHAPTER XII

THE LORENTZ GROUP

CHAPTER ONE

GROUPS AND MATRICES

The object of this work is a study of those groups which are of importance in quantum mechanics (particularly, nuclear physics) and our main interest is in the theory of the representations of these groups by *linear* groups. We proceed, therefore, to explain what is meant by a group; by a linear group; by a representation of a group; and we list the particular groups in which we shall be interested.

1. The group concept.

We suppose that we have a collection C, finite or infinite, of elements $s, t, u, \cdots$ and an associative law of combination, termed product, which associates with any two of these elements (s, t), say, taken in a definite order, a third element u in C. When this is the case we say that the collection C *possesses the group property.* If, *in addition to* possessing the group property, C possesses another property which we shall shortly describe, we shall term it a group; but before describing this second property, we think it desirable to say a few words concerning the law of combination which we term product and denote by ts. As remarked above, the order in which the elements s, t are taken is, in general, material so that ts is not, necessarily, identifiable with st. We term, therefore, st the product of t *by* s and ts the product of s *by* t; the order in which the *factors* s, t of the product are named, or taken, being from *right* to *left.* The product ts is itself an element of C: $ts = u$; but it is *not* assumed that t and s are distinct nor that u is different from either s or t. Thus ss (written s^2) is an element u of C and it may happen that $u = s$. Expressed somewhat technically, ts is a function *on* ordered pairs of elements (s, t) of C to elements of C. It is essential that the function ts be one-valued; i. e. when s and t are given u is *uniquely* determined. The adjective associative means the following: if s, t, u are any three elements of C we may first form the product $v = ts$ of s by t and then the product $w = uv$ of v by u: $w = uv = u(ts)$; but we may also first form the product $x = ut$ of t by u and then the product $y = xs$ of s by x: $y = xs = (ut)s$. The product function is termed associative when $w = y$; i. e. when $u(ts) = (ut)s$ for every triad of elements s, t, u of C. The parentheses may, accordingly, be omitted and we may write simply uts for the common value of $u(ts)$ and $(ut)s$. It is clear that if s, t, u, v are any four elements of C we have

$$v(uts) = v(u(ts)) = (vu)(ts) = (vut)s$$

and in general if $s_1, s_2, \cdots s_n$ are any n elements of C, $n = 3, 4, 5, \cdots$

$$s_1(s_2 \cdots s_n) = (s_1s_2)(s_3 \cdots s_n) = (s_1s_2s_3)(s_4 \cdots s_n) = \cdots$$
$$= (s_1s_2 \cdots s_{\lambda_1})(s_{\lambda_1+1} \cdots s_{\lambda_1+\lambda_2})(s_{\lambda_1+\lambda_2+1} \cdots)(\cdots s_n)$$

where $\lambda_1, \lambda_2, \cdots \lambda_k$ is any partition of n into positive integers:

$$n = \lambda_1 + \lambda_2 + \cdots + \lambda_k.$$

This associative law is very significant and important. A product uts may be complicated to evaluate in the form $u(ts)$ but trivially easy in the form $(ut)s$.

As has been emphasized above the order of the factors s, t in the product is, in general, material so that there is no presumption that $st = ts$. If, however, our collection C of elements $(s, t, u, \cdots)$ possesses the additional property relative to the product function ts that $st = ts$, every s, t in C, we term the collection C *commutative* or *Abelian* relative to the given product function.

Examples

1. If the elements $s, t, u, \cdots$ of C are numbers, real or complex, and the law of combination, which we *term* product, is ordinary addition (e. g. $3.5 = 8$, *not* 15) we have as obvious collections possessing the group property

(a) C, the collection of all complex numbers (b) C, the collection of all real numbers (c) C, the collection of all integers, positive, negative, or zero (d) C, the collection of all real numbers $\geq p$ where p is any non-negative number (e) C, the collection of all even integers, including zero.

2. If the elements of C are as in Ex. 1 but the law of combination is ordinary multiplication all of the collections of Ex. 1 save (d) possess the group property. (d) will possess the group property if $p \geq 1$.

3. If the elements of C are $m \times n$ matrices (i. e. matrices of m rows and n columns) and the law of combination is ordinary matrix addition: $(ts)_k{}^j = t_k{}^j + s_k{}^j$, where $s_k{}^j$ denotes the element in the j-th row and k-th column of s: then the collection of all such matrices with complex (or real) elements possesses the group property.

All of the collections, possessing the group property, of Examples 1, 2, 3 are Abelian. As an important example of a non-Abelian collection, we cite

4. The elements of C are $n \times n$ matrices (or, as we shall say, matrices of dimension n) and the law of combination is ordinary matrix multiplication:

$$(ts)_k{}^j = t_a{}^j s_k{}^a$$

(the double use of the *Greek* label α indicating summation over the range 1 to n; thus $t_\alpha{}^j s_k{}^\alpha$ is an abbreviation for $t_1{}^j s_k{}^1 + t_2{}^j s_k{}^2 + \cdots + t_n{}^j s_k{}^n$): then the collection of all such matrices with complex (or real) elements possesses the group property. That the associative law is obeyed follows from

$$(u(ts))_k{}^j = u_\alpha{}^j(t_\beta{}^\alpha s_k{}^\beta) = (u_\alpha{}^j t_\beta{}^\alpha)s_k{}^\beta = ((ut)s)_k{}^j$$

(the occurrence of the two Greek labels α, β indicating a double summation where α, β take, independently, all values from 1 to n so that there are n^2 terms in the double summation).

It is clear that the collection is not Abelian for $s_\alpha{}^j t_k{}^\alpha$ is not, in general, the same as $t_\alpha{}^j s_k{}^\alpha$. If, however, we consider the collection of all n-dimensional diagonal matrices; i. e. of all matrices s of dimension n whose non-diagonal elements are all zero: $s_k{}^j = \lambda_k$ if $j = k$; $s_k{}^j = 0$ if $j \neq k$: and if the law of combination is ordinary matrix multiplication then the collection possesses the group property and is Abelian. In fact on writing $t_k{}^j = \mu_k$ if $j = k$; $t_k{}^j = 0$ if $j \neq k$ we have

$$(ts)_k{}^j = t_\alpha{}^j s_k{}^\alpha = 0 \text{ unless } j = k \text{ in which case it} = \mu_k \lambda_k$$

so that ts is diagonal and $st = ts$ If s is diagonal and, *in addition*, has all its diagonal elements equal:

$$\lambda_1 = \lambda_2 = \cdots = \lambda_n$$

we term it *scalar*. It is clear that the collection of all scalar matrices of a given dimension n possesses the group property (with respect to either ordinary matrix addition or ordinary matrix multiplication as the law of combination).

The additional requirement we impose upon a collection C of elements $(s, t, u, \cdots)$, which possesses the group property relative to a given law of combination ts, before we agree to term the collection a *group* is the following: we demand that for every s in C there exists an e in C with the property $se = s$ and also a t_s in C such that $st_s = e$. (The placing of the subscript s on t is to emphasize the fact that t_s will vary with s). As far as this imposed requirement is concerned we would be satisfied if e or/and t_s is/are not unique; we shall see, however, immediately that the already imposed requirement (that C possesses the group property) guarantees the uniqueness of e and t_s. We may express our second requirement as follows: we demand the existence of (at least) one right unit and of (at least) one right inverse of each s relative to this unit; the sense of the word right being that the unit and inverse elements are taken *first* in forming the products.

If s is an arbitrary element of C there exists a t_s such that $st_s = e$ and so $t_s st_s = t_s e = t_s$. If u_s is a right inverse of t_s with respect to e (the existence of u_s being guaranteed by our second requirement) we have

$$t_s st_s u_s = t_s u_s = e$$

and writing the left hand side in the form $(t_s s)(t_s u_s)$ it evaluates as $(t_s s)e = t_s s$ so that $t_s s = e$. In other words the assumed right inverse of s, with respect to e, is at the same time a left inverse of s with respect to e. Furthermore $es = (st_s)s = s(t_s s) = se = s$ so that the assumed right unit e is also a left unit. The uniqueness of e is then evident; for suppose there existed a second right unit e' : $se' = s$: then, in particular, $ee' = e$; but we have already shown $es = s$, and, in particular, $ee' = e'$. Hence $e = e'$. In other words the postulated right unit e is unique and is at the same time, a left unit. There is no *other* left unit e'; for from $e's = s$ we obtain $e = st_s = (e's)t_s = e'(st_s) = e'e = e'$. In other words there exists in C a unique right and left unit e: i. e., a unique element e such that for every s in C

$$se = es = s.$$

It follows also that the assumed right inverse t_s of s, which is also a left inverse of s, is unique. More precisely there is no other right inverse nor left inverse of s. In fact let t'_s be a second, assumed, right inverse: $st'_s = e$. Then $t_s = t_s e = t_s(st'_s) = (t_s s)t'_s = et'_s = t'_s$ so that there is no other right inverse of s than t_s. Let u be *any* left inverse of s: $us = e$; then $t_s = et_s = (us)t_s = u(st_s) = ue = u$ proving the uniqueness of the left inverse of s. Hence associated with each element s of C is a uniquely determinate element of C (which we term *the* inverse of s and which we denote by s^{-1}) satisfying the equations

$$ss^{-1} = s^{-1}s = e.$$

It follows that not only is the product $u = ts$ a one-valued function of its arguments s, t but $s = t^{-1}u$ is a one-valued function of u, t and $t = us^{-1}$ is a one-valued function of s, u. The essential feature of this result is the following: if t is any fixed element of the group G (we denote by G a collection C possessing the group property which is *at the same time* a group) then as s runs over G so also does ts and st there being a one-to-one correspondence between the elements s of G and the elements $u = ts$, $v = st$ of the two *rearrangements* of G.

The following collections of elements, possessing the group property, also satisfy the second requirement and, hence, constitute groups

1) The collection of all complex (or of all real) numbers with ordi-

nary addition as the law of combination; the unit $e = 0$ and $s^{-1} = -s$. Here $ts = t + s$ is obtained from s by the *translation* t. This word is carried over into the general case and the rearrangement of G indicated by $s \rightarrow ts$ is termed the left-translation of G induced by t; the rearrangement indicated by $s \rightarrow st$ being termed the *right translation* induced by t. For Abelian groups (to which belongs the present example) both translations, right and left, are the same.

2) The collection of all integers (or of all fractions = rational numbers) with ordinary addition as the law of combination; the unit $e = 0$ and $s^{-1} = -s$.

3) The collection of all complex numbers, or of all real numbers, or of all rational numbers, *with the exception of zero,* with ordinary multiplication as the law of combination; the unit $e = 1$ and $s^{-1} = 1 \div s$.

4) The collection of all *non-singular* matrices, of dimension n, with complex elements with ordinary matrix multiplication as the law of combination; the unit $e = E_n$ where E_n is the n-dimensional diagonal matrix all of whose elements are unity. The inverse s^{-1} of s is constructed as follows: set up the matrix of the cofactors of s, transpose it (i. e., interchange its rows and columns) and divide it (i. e. divide each of its elements) by $\det s$, the determinant of s. This particular group, and various subgroups of it, will engage a considerable portion of our attention and we shall refer to it as the *full linear group* (of dimension n); the subgroup of it which consists of all *non-singular* matrices, of dimension n, with *real* elements we term the *real* linear group. The collections of all non-singular diagonal matrices, of dimension n, with complex elements (or with real elements) are Abelian subgroups of the full linear or real linear group, respectively; neither the full linear group, nor the real linear group, being themselves Abelian (= commutative). Similarly the collection of all non-singular scalar matrices of dimension n with complex elements (or with real elements) constitutes an Abelian group, the law of combination being ordinary matrix multiplication; we refer to this group as the scalar group (complex or real as the case may be) of dimension n.

2. The symmetric group.

Of fundamental importance for us is the *symmetric* group or the group whose elements are the $n!$ permutations on n symbols $(1, \cdots, n)$. It must be clearly understood that the elements of the group are not the sets of n letters but the operations involved in passing from a standard arrangement, say $(1, \cdots, n)$, to *any* arrangement of these n letters. A typical element s may be indicated thus:

$$s = \uparrow\begin{pmatrix} s_1, s_2, \cdots, s_n \\ 1, 2, \cdots, n \end{pmatrix} = \uparrow\begin{pmatrix} s_j \\ j \end{pmatrix}$$

the notation implying that the operation s replaces 1 by s_1, 2 by $s_2, \cdots$, n by s_n where each of the symbols $s_1, \cdots, s_n$ assumes one of the values $(1, \cdots, n)$ *no two of them assuming the same value.* It is clear that if

$$t = \uparrow\begin{pmatrix} t_1, \cdots, t_n \\ 1, \cdots, n \end{pmatrix} = \uparrow\begin{pmatrix} t_j \\ j \end{pmatrix}$$

is *any* permutation of our collection s may be represented by

$$s = \uparrow\begin{pmatrix} s_{t_1}, s_{t_2}, \cdots, s_{t_n} \\ t_1, t_2, \cdots, t_n \end{pmatrix} = \uparrow\begin{pmatrix} s_{t_j} \\ t_j \end{pmatrix}$$

since this means that s replaces t_1 by s_{t_1}, t_2 by s_{t_2} and, in general t_k by s_{t_k}; since 1 is in the set t_k this means that s replaces 1 by s_1 and, similarly, 2 by s_2 and so on. Hence the operation indicated by $\uparrow\begin{pmatrix} s_{t_j} \\ t_j \end{pmatrix}$ is really a permutation (i. e. the values assumed by the symbols s_{t_j} lie in the set $1, \cdots, n$, *and are all different*) and is, in fact, the permutation $\uparrow\begin{pmatrix} s_j \\ j \end{pmatrix}$. By the law of combination ts we understand that we *first* perform the operation s on the symbols $(1, \cdots, n)$ and then follow this by the operation t. Since j is sent by s into s_j and s_j is sent by t into t_{s_j} the sequence of the two operations, in the order first s then t, sends j into t_{s_j}. It is, therefore, by the remark just made, itself a permutation so that the collection C whose elements s are the permutation operators s (of which there are $n!$) is a collection possessing the group property relative to a law of combination which is defined by mere *sequential performance.* That the collection is a group follows at once from the observation that

$$e = \uparrow\begin{pmatrix} 1, \cdots, n \\ 1, \cdots, n \end{pmatrix} = \uparrow\begin{pmatrix} j \\ j \end{pmatrix}$$

is a right unit and that

$$s = \uparrow\begin{pmatrix} 1, \cdots, n \\ s_1, \cdots, s_n \end{pmatrix} = \uparrow\begin{pmatrix} j \\ s_j \end{pmatrix}$$

is a right inverse of $s = \uparrow\begin{pmatrix} s_j \\ j \end{pmatrix}$ with respect to e. A permutation which sends t_j, $j = 1, \cdots, n-1$ into t_{j+1} and t_n into t_1 (i. e. where each of the letters $t_1, t_2, \cdots, t_n$, supposed arranged along a circle, is sent into its successor) is termed a cycle on n letters and is conveniently denoted by the symbol $(t_1, t_2, \cdots, t_n)$:

$$(t_1, \cdots, t_n) = \uparrow \begin{pmatrix} t_2, t_3, \cdots, t_1 \\ t_1, t_2, \cdots, t_n \end{pmatrix} = \uparrow \begin{pmatrix} t_{j+1} \\ t_j \end{pmatrix}$$

and it is immediately clear that

$$(t_1, \cdots, t_n) = (t_2, t_3, \cdots, t_n, t_1) = \cdots = (t_n, t_1, \cdots, t_{n-1}).$$

In other words it is immaterial with which of its letters a cycle starts off; what is significant is the sequence in which the letters are written. It is also clear that the inverse of the cycle $t = (t_1, \cdots, t_n)$ is itself a cycle, namely, the cycle t with the sense reversed:

$$(t^{-1}) = \uparrow \begin{pmatrix} t_1, t_2, \cdots, t_n \\ t_2, \quad \cdots, t_1 \end{pmatrix} = (t_2, t_1, t_n, t_{n-1}, \cdots, t_3) = \cdots = (t_n, t_{n-1}, \cdots, t_1).$$

It is also clear that any permutation whatever can be written in a unique manner as the product of cycles; the order in which the factor cycles are written being immaterial (since no two of the cycles have a common letter). E. g., $n = 5$, $s = \uparrow \begin{pmatrix} 3, 5, 1, 2, 4 \\ 1, 2, 3, 4, 5 \end{pmatrix} = (254)(13) = (13)(254)$; where we understand by a cycle on less than 5 letters, such as (13) or (245) the permutation on 5 letters in which the letters not written down are unchanged. Thus

$$(13) = \uparrow \begin{pmatrix} 3,2,1,4,5 \\ 1,2,3,4,5 \end{pmatrix}. \quad \text{Similarly} \uparrow \begin{pmatrix} 2,3,1,4,5 \\ 1,2,3,4,5 \end{pmatrix} = (123)(4)(5) = (123).$$

We shall denote by α_1 the number of unary cycles (i. e. cycles on one letter, or fixed letters), by α_2 the number of binary cycles (= cycles on two letters or *transpositions*) and so on. Thus for $s = \uparrow \begin{pmatrix} 3,5,1,2,4 \\ 1,2,3,4,5 \end{pmatrix}$ $\alpha_1 = 0$, $\alpha_2 = 1$, $\alpha_3 = 1$, $\alpha_4 = 0$, $\alpha_5 = 0$ whilst for

$$s = \uparrow \begin{pmatrix} 2, 3, 1, 4, 5 \\ 1, 2, 3, 4, 5 \end{pmatrix} \alpha_1 = 2, \ \alpha_2 = 0, \ \alpha_3 = 1, \ \alpha_4 = 0, \ \alpha_5 = 0.$$

Since for any permutation s on n letters the total number of letters in the various cycles into which it is factored (including the unary cycles) is n we have the basic relation

$$\alpha_1 + 2\alpha_2 + \cdots + n\alpha_n = n. \tag{1.1}$$

We say that a permutation s which factors into α_1 unary cycles, α_2 binary cycles etc., has the cycle structure (α) and we shall refer to the collection of permutations each of which has a stated common cycle structure (α) as the *class* (α) of permutations on n letters. It follows then that the number of distinct classes is the number of distinct solutions in integers (positive or zero) of the equation (1.1). It is important for us to notice that this is precisely the number of partitions of n into integers positive or zero; in fact if we write

$$(1.2)\qquad \begin{aligned} \alpha_1 + \alpha_2 + \cdots + \alpha_n &= \lambda_1 \\ \alpha_2 + \cdots + \alpha_n &= \lambda_2 \\ &\cdots \\ \alpha_n &= \lambda_n \end{aligned}$$

it is clear that

$$\lambda_1 + \lambda_2 + \cdots + \lambda_n = n; \qquad \lambda_1 \geq \lambda_2 \geq \cdots \geq \lambda_n \geq 0.$$

Conversely given any such partition of n we may associate with it a solution (α) of (1.1) defined by

$$(1.3)\qquad \alpha_1 = \lambda_1 - \lambda_2;\ \alpha_2 = \lambda_2 - \lambda_3;\ \cdots, \alpha_n = \lambda_n.$$

It is convenient to omit the zeros which may occur at the end of a partition of n; thus if $\lambda_k > 0$, $\lambda_{k+1} = \lambda_{k+2} = \cdots = \lambda_n = 0$ we denote the partition $(\lambda_1, \cdots, \lambda_n)$ of n by $(\lambda_1, \cdots, \lambda_k)$ using an exponential notation when two or more adjacent λ's are equal. Thus the partition $(3, 2, 2, 1, 1, 1, 0, 0, 0, 0)$ of 10 is written $(3, 2^2, 1^3)$. For small values of n the various partitions of n and their number r are as follows:

$n = 1$; (1); $r = 1$.
$n = 2$; (2), (1^2); $r = 2$
$n = 3$; (3), $(2, 1)$, (1^3); $r = 3$
$n = 4$; (4), $(3, 1)$, (2^2), $(2, 1^2)$, (1^4); $r = 5$
$n = 5$; (5), $(4, 1)$, $(3, 2)$, $(3, 1^2)$, $(2^2, 1)$, $(2, 1^3)$, (1^5); $r = 7$
$n = 6$; (6), $(5, 1)$, $(4, 2)$, $(4, 1^2)$, (3^2), $(3, 2, 1)$, $(3, 1^3)$, (2^3), $(2^2, 1^2)$, $(2, 1^4)$, (1^6); $r = 11$

. . . .

The number of partitions of n, and hence of classes of the symmetric group, increases rapidly with n. For $n = 10$ it is 42, for $n = 16$ it is 231 whilst for $n = 20$ it is 627. It is convenient to arrange, as has been done above, the partitions of n in *dictionary order:* $(\lambda_1, \cdots, \lambda_n)$ precedes $(\lambda'_1, \cdots, \lambda'_n)$ if the *first* of the differences $\lambda_1 - \lambda'_1, \lambda_2 - \lambda'_2, \cdots, \lambda_n - \lambda'_n$ which does not vanish is positive.

It is important to know, and easy to find, the number of permutations s which belong to the class (α). We imagine the unary cycles written first, the binary cycles next, the ternary cycles next etc., and examine any particular permutation s of the class (α). All permutations of this class will be found in the collection obtained by subjecting the n letters appearing in the cycle description of s to the $n!$ permutations of the symmetric group; but since the order in which the unary cycles, or the binary cycles, or the ternary cycles etc. are written is immaterial, each permutation will be found (at least) $\alpha_1!\, \alpha_2! \cdots, \alpha_n!$ times in this collection. In addition since each of the binary cycles may start off with either of its two letters, and since each of the ternary cycles may start off with any one of its three letters, and so forth, without affecting the permutation having the indicated cycle structure, the number just written must be multiplied by $2^{\alpha_2}3^{\alpha_3} \cdots n^{\alpha_n}$; any other permutation of the letters appearing in the cycles will change the permutation furnished by their product so that the number of permutations of the symmetric group on n letters which belong to the class (α) is

$$n_{(\alpha)} = \frac{n!}{\alpha_1!\, 2^{\alpha_2} \cdot \alpha_2!\, 3^{\alpha_3} \cdot \alpha_3! \cdots n^{\alpha_n} \cdot \alpha_n!} \tag{1.4}$$

(where we follow the usual convention according to which $0! = 1$).

The reciprocal of any permutation s may be obtained by analysing s into a product of cycles (there being no letter common to any two of the factor cycles) and so s^{-1} and s have the same cycle structure. In other words *each class contains the reciprocal of each of the permutations contained in it.* Again if s and p are any two permutations of the symmetric group on n letters:

$$s = \uparrow \binom{s_j}{j}, \quad p = \uparrow \binom{p_j}{j}; \quad p^{-1} = \uparrow \binom{j}{p_j}$$

we have

$$psp^{-1} = \uparrow \binom{p_j}{j} \uparrow \binom{s_j}{j} \uparrow \binom{j}{p_j} = \uparrow \binom{p_{s_j}}{s_j} \uparrow \binom{s_j}{j} \uparrow \binom{j}{p_j} = \uparrow \binom{p_{s_j}}{p_j}$$

(since in forming the product we read from *right* to *left* so that first $p_j \to j$ and secondly $j \to s_j$ and then, finally, $s_j \to p_{s_j}$). The cycle structure of $\uparrow \binom{p_{s_j}}{p_j}$ depends only on s and not at all on p; in particular it must be the same as the cycle structure of $\uparrow \binom{e_{s_j}}{e_j} = \uparrow \binom{s_j}{j} = s$. In other words *all permutations of the form psp^{-1}, s fixed, p variable, have the same cycle structure or, as we express it, belong to the same class.* For a reason which will be made clear in the next paragraph we term psp^{-1} the *transform* of s *by* p^{-1}. Our argument shows that if s and t are permutations with the same cycle structure and if the factor cycles of s and t are arranged in the same order (so that if $(s_p, s_{p+1}, \cdots, s_{p+k})$ is a factor cycle of s then $(t_p, t_{p+1}, \cdots, t_{p+k})$ is a factor cycle of t) then

$p^{-1} = \uparrow\begin{pmatrix} s_1, \cdots, s_n \\ t_1, \cdots, t_n \end{pmatrix} = \uparrow\begin{pmatrix} s_j \\ t_j \end{pmatrix}$ transforms s into t: $t = psp^{-1}$; in fact p^{-1} sends t_j into s_j, after which s sends s_j into s_{j+1} and finally p sends s_{j+1} into t_{j+1} so that psp^{-1} sends t_j into t_{j+1}. Thus $p^{-1} = \uparrow\begin{pmatrix} 1\,2\,3\,4\,5 \\ 4\,2\,1\,3\,5 \end{pmatrix}$ $= (134)$ transforms $s = (123)(45)$ into $t = (421)(35)$. Of course the transforming permutation p^{-1} is not unique (owing to the variety of possibilities in writing the cycle factorisation of either s or t). Thus in the example given we may write t in the forms $(214)(35)$, $(142)(35)$, $(421)(53)$, $(214)(53)$, $(142)(53)$ so that in addition to the transforming permutation $p^{-1} = (134)$ already given we have the transforming permutations $(12)(34)$, (234), (1354), $(12)(354)$, (2354).

If $(x_1, \cdots, x_n)$ are n indeterminates we denote by $\Delta(\boldsymbol{x})$ the difference product

$$\prod_{j<k} (x_j - x_k) = (x_1 - x_2)(x_1 - x_3) \cdots (x_{n-1} - x_n)$$

and it is clear that any permutation p of the subscripts $1, \cdots, n$ attached to the x's can, at most, change the sign of $\Delta(\boldsymbol{x})$, since this is all it can do to each of the factors $(x_j - x_k)$. If p contains but *one* cycle on $m \leq n$ letters (in addition to $n - m$ unary cycles, if $m < n$) i. e. if p is of the form $(t_1, t_2, \cdots, t_m)$ we can analyse it into the product of $m - 1$ binary cycles (transpositions) thus:

$$p = (t_1, t_2, \cdots, t_m) = (t_1, t_m)(t_1, t_{m-1}) \cdots (t_1, t_2).$$

Of course this is not a cycle analysis of the type considered above (where no two cycle factors had a common letter) since each of the $m - 1$ binary cycles has the common letter t_1. Since each of the $m - 1$ transpositions $(t_1, t_m), \cdots, (t_1, t_2)$ changes the sign of $\Delta(\boldsymbol{x})$, p will change the sign of $\Delta(\boldsymbol{x})$ if m is even and leave it unaltered if m is odd. Hence a general permutation, of cycle structure (α), will leave $\Delta(\boldsymbol{x})$ unaltered if $\alpha_2 + \alpha_4 + \cdots$ is even and will change its sign if $\alpha_2 + \alpha_4 + \cdots$ is odd. We shall term a permutation *even* if it leaves $\Delta(\boldsymbol{x})$ unaltered and *odd* if it changes the sign of $\Delta(\boldsymbol{x})$. We see then that a class (α) contains only even permutations if $\alpha_2 + \alpha_4 + \alpha_6 + \cdots$ is even and we refer to such a class as an even *class*; the classes for which $\alpha_2 + \alpha_4 + \alpha_6 + \cdots$ is odd being termed odd. It is clear from the definition of evenness that the collection of all *even* permutations on n letters possesses the group property; and that it is a group (since it contains the unit permutation e and since the reciprocal of any even permutation p is even belonging, as it does, to the same class as p). If t is an odd permutation the left translation of the symmetric group induced by $t: s \to ts$ translates the even permutations into odd permutations and the odd permutations into even permutations so that there are exactly as many even permutations as odd ones in the symmetric group on n letters. The group of $n!/2$ even permutations on n letters is known as the *alternating group* on n letters. We refer to a group containing a finite number of elements as a *finite group*; and term the finite number of elements in the group the *order* of the group. Thus the symmetric group on n letters is a finite group of order $n!$; whilst the alternating group on n letters is a subgroup of the symmetric group on n letters of order $n!/2$.

3. The full linear group.

Before we can describe this group (which, with its subgroups and the symmetric group, will principally engage our attention) it is necessary to say some words about what is meant by a *linear vector space.* This is, in the first place, an Abelian group containing elements $s, t, u, \cdots$ with a law of combination *termed* addition (rather than multiplication as before) and denoted by $+$ (thus we write $t + s$ instead of the previous symbol ts); the Abelian nature of the group is described by the formula $s + t = t + s$, every s, t, and we denote the unit e of the group by $0: s + 0 = s$, every s. In the second place we assume that the operation of multiplication by any complex number is defined over the group and that the group is closed with respect to it; in other words if s is any element of the group and α any complex number then αs has a meaning and is, in fact, itself a member of the group. Terming the process of multiplication by a complex number an operator we may say that a linear vector space is, firstly, an Abelian group over which there is defined an operator (*on* elements s of the group *to* elements t of the group), namely, multiplication by an arbitrary complex number $\alpha: t = \alpha s$. Thus, briefly, a linear vector space is an instance of a *group with an operator.* As properties of the operator we assume the following:

(a) $(\alpha + \beta)s = \alpha s + \beta s$; $\beta(\alpha s) = (\beta\alpha)s$; every s of the group and every pair of complex numbers α, β.

(b) $\alpha s = s$, every s, when $\alpha = 1$; that $\alpha s = 0$ (the unit of the group), every s, when α is the complex number zero follows from (a) on setting $\beta = 0$.

(c) $\alpha(t + s) = \alpha t + \alpha s$; every s, t of the group and every complex number α.

We refer to the elements $(s, t, \cdots)$ of the group as *vectors* and to the multiplying complex numbers as *scalars.*

On setting $t = 0$ in (c) it is clear that $\alpha 0 = 0$, every α and so the group consisting of the single vector 0 is a linear vector space; we refer to it as the *zero dimensional space*, or briefly, the *zero space*. If there exists a vector s other than 0, whilst every vector of the space is of the form αs, we term the linear vector space one-dimensional; and we say that any two vectors αs and βs of the one-dimensional linear vector space are *linearly dependent*. In general n vectors $s_1, s_2, \cdots, s_n$ of a linear vector space are termed linearly dependent if there exists a linear relation $\alpha^1 s_1 + \alpha^2 s_2 + \cdots + \alpha^n s_n = 0$ (*other* than the obvious, but trivial, one which obtains when *all* the scalar coefficients $\alpha^1, \alpha^2, \cdots, \alpha^n$ are zero) amongst the n vectors; in the contrary case, i. e. when no such non-trivial linear relation exists, we say that the n vectors $s_1, \cdots, s_n$ are *linearly independent*. In other words a hypothecated relation $\alpha^1 s_1 + \alpha^2 s_2 + \cdots + \alpha^n s_n = 0$ together with the datum that the n vectors $s_1, \cdots, s_n$ are linearly independent forces the conclusion: all $\alpha^k = 0, k = 1, 2, \cdots, n$. When a linear vector space contains n *and not more than* n linearly independent vectors we term it n *dimensional*. If $s_1, \cdots, s_n$ are n linearly independent vectors of an n dimensional linear vector space and t is any vector of the space we can hypothecate the relation $\alpha t + \alpha^1 s_1 + \cdots + \alpha^n s_n = 0$ and be assured that there exists a *non-trivial* relation of this type (since the $n + 1$ vectors $t, s_1, \cdots, s_n$ are by hypothesis linearly dependent). In such a non-trivial relation $\alpha \neq 0$ for if $\alpha = 0$,

$$\alpha^1 s_1 + \alpha^2 s_2 + \cdots + \alpha^n s_n = 0$$

and this would force $\alpha^1 = 0, \alpha^2 = 0, \cdots, \alpha^n = 0$ since $s_1, \cdots, s_n$ are, by hypothesis, linearly independent; but, then, the *non-trivial* relation would be trivial. On multiplying through by α^{-1} and transposing we obtain

$$t = t^1 s_1 + \cdots + t^n s_n; \qquad (t^k = - \alpha^k/\alpha)$$

($t = s$ being equivalent to $t - s = 0$). In other words every vector t of an n-dimensional linear vector space is expressible as a linear combination of *any* n linearly independent vectors $(s_1, \cdots, s_n)$ and the linear combination is unique; for if $t = t^1 s_1 + \cdots + t^n s_n = \tau^1 s_1 + \cdots + \tau^n s_n$ are two such analyses of t we have $(t^1 - \tau^1) s_1 + \cdots + (t^n - \tau^n) s_n = 0$ and the linear independence of $(s_1, \cdots, s_n)$ then forces $\tau^k = t^k$, $k = 1, \cdots, n$. The n linearly independent vectors $(s_1, \cdots, s_n)$ are said to form a *basis*; the individual vectors being termed the basis vectors. The complex numbers $(t^1, \cdots, t^n)$ are termed the *coordinates* of the vector t *relative to the basis* $(s_1, \cdots, s_n)$. It is clear that an n dimensional linear vector space has many bases; in fact if $(u_1, \cdots u_n)$ is one such basis (the existence of one basis being assured by hypothesis) the set $(v_1, \cdots, v_n)$ defined by

$$v_j = t_j{}^1 u_1 + \cdots + t_j{}^n u_n = t_j{}^\alpha u_\alpha; \qquad (j = 1, 2, \cdots, n);$$

is a second basis if $T = (t_j{}^k)$ is *any* non-singular n dimensional matrix. In fact an hypothecated relation $c^\beta v_\beta = 0$ would appear as $c^\beta t_\beta{}^\alpha u_\alpha = 0$ (double summation!) and the linear independence of the n vectors $(u_1, \cdots, u_n)$ would force $t_\beta{}^j c^\beta = 0$, $j = 1, \cdots, n$; finally the non-singularity of the matrix T (i. e. the non-vanishing of its determinant) would then force $c^k = 0$, $k = 1, 2, \cdots, n$. In other words there does not exist a single *non-trivial* relation $c^\beta v_\beta = 0$ so that the vectors $(v_1, \cdots, v_n)$ are linearly independent and, hence, constitute a basis. It is convenient to indicate the n vectors $(u_1, \cdots, u_n)$ of a basis by the single symbol $\boldsymbol{u}$ so that $\boldsymbol{u}$ is a $1 \times n$ matrix whose elements are *vectors.* Then the equations $v_j = t_j{}^\alpha u_\alpha$ which furnish the new basis $\boldsymbol{v}$ appear in the convenient form (note carefully the order of the factor matrices $\boldsymbol{u}$ and T)

$$\boldsymbol{v} = \boldsymbol{u}T. \tag{1.5}$$

It is clear that *all* bases are obtainable in this way from a given basis $\boldsymbol{u}$; for if $\boldsymbol{v}$ is *any* basis and $(t_j{}^1, \cdots, t_j{}^n)$ denote the coordinates of v_j relative to the basis $\boldsymbol{u}$ we have, by the very definition of coordinates, $v_j = t_j{}^1 u_1 + \cdots + t_j{}^n u_n$; $j = 1, \cdots, n$; i. e. $\boldsymbol{v} = \boldsymbol{u}T$. That T must be non-singular is evident since the columns of T are the coordinates, relative to the basis $\boldsymbol{u}$, of the vectors $(v_1, \cdots, v_n)$; if T were singular there would exist at least one non-trivial linear relation connecting the vectors $(v_1, \cdots, v_n)$ (it being known from the elementary theory of determinants that if the rank of T is r there are $n - r$ independent such relations and the statement that T is singular implying $r \leq n - 1$).

The essential thing to keep in mind is that the coordinates of a vector are *not properties of the vector*; they describe the *relationship* of the vector *to a basis.* When the basis is changed the coordinates will change whilst the vector remains the same. If the coordinates of a vector t relative to a given basis $\boldsymbol{u}$ be written as an $n \times 1$ matrix $x = (x^1, \ldots, x^n)$ we have

$$t = u_1 x^1 + \cdots + u_n x^n = \boldsymbol{u}x$$

and if the coordinates of the same vector t relative to a new basis $\boldsymbol{v} = \boldsymbol{u}T$ are $y = (y^1, \cdots, y^n)$ we have $t = \boldsymbol{v}y = \boldsymbol{u}Ty$ so that $\boldsymbol{u}x = \boldsymbol{u}Ty$. The linear independence of the vectors of the basis $\boldsymbol{u}$ then forces

$$x = Ty; \qquad y = T^{-1}x. \tag{1.6}$$

In other words the change of basis $\boldsymbol{u} \to \boldsymbol{v} = \boldsymbol{u}T$ induces the change of coordinates $x \to y = T^{-1}x$. In particular the vector whose coordinates relative to the basis $\boldsymbol{u}$ are Tx has coordinates x relative to the basis $\boldsymbol{v}$. On denoting by $T(t)$ the vector whose coordinates relative to the basis $\boldsymbol{v}$ are the same as those of t relative to the basis $\boldsymbol{u}$, it is clear that the coordinates of $T(t)$ relative to the basis $\boldsymbol{u}$ are Tx. Writing the one-to-one relationship between a vector t and its matrix of coordinates x *in a given basis* $\boldsymbol{u}$ in the form $t \to x, x \to t$ we have $T(t) \to Tx$. If α is any complex number we have $\alpha t \to \alpha x$ and so $T(\alpha t) \to T(\alpha x) = \alpha Tx \to \alpha T(t)$; if $s \to y$ is any other vector of our n-dimensional linear vector space $s + t \to y + x$ and so $T(s + t) \to T(y + x) = Ty + Tx \to T(s) + T(t)$. In other words the transformation $t \to T(t)$ *on* vectors of our space *to* vectors of our space possesses the two basic properties:

$$(1.7) \qquad T(\alpha t) = \alpha T(t); \qquad T(s + t) = T(s) + T(t).$$

We shall term any transformation of the vectors of our space which possesses these two properties *linear*; and so we have the theorem: given any two bases $\boldsymbol{u}, \boldsymbol{v}$ the transformations from vectors t to vectors $T(t)$ which have the same coordinates with respect to the bases $\boldsymbol{u}$ and $\boldsymbol{v}$, respectively, is *linear*. If the coordinates of t relative to the basis of $\boldsymbol{u}$ are furnished by the $n \times 1$ matrix x the coordinates of $T(t)$ relative to the same basis are Tx where the connecting relation between the two bases is $\boldsymbol{v} = \boldsymbol{u}T$. We say that the non-singular $n \times n$ matrix T presents, in the basis $\boldsymbol{u}$, the linear transformation $t \to T(t)$. If $\boldsymbol{w} = \boldsymbol{u}P$ is another basis the coordinates of t relative to $\boldsymbol{w}$ are furnished by the $n \times 1$ matrix $P^{-1}x$ (by (1.6)); and $x \to Tx$ induces $P^{-1}x \to P^{-1}Tx = P^{-1}TP \cdot P^{-1}x$. In other words the transformation $t \to T(t)$ from vectors t of our space to vectors $T(t)$ which have the same coordinates with respect to the bases $\boldsymbol{u}$ and $\boldsymbol{v}$, is presented in the basis $\boldsymbol{w}$ by the $n \times n$ matrix $P^{-1}TP$; the relationships between the various bases being $\boldsymbol{v} = \boldsymbol{u}T$; $\boldsymbol{w} = \boldsymbol{u}P$. Although the two matrices T and $P^{-1}TP$ which present the linear transformation $t \to T(t)$ in the bases $\boldsymbol{u}, \boldsymbol{w}$, respectively, are different, *the linear transformation is the same.* Regarded, therefore, in the rôle of presenting linear transformations the two matrices T and $P^{-1}TP$ are not essentially different; we term them *equivalent* and say that $P^{-1}TP$ is the transform of T by P.

The non-singularity of T assures us that the linear transformation $t \to T(t)$ of our n-dimensional linear vector space is exhaustive: as t runs over the entire space so does $T(t)$. In fact if the $n \times 1$ matrix x furnishes the coordinates of an *arbitrary* vector of our space in the basis $\boldsymbol{u}$ we obtain this vector in the collection $T(t)$ by choosing for t the vector whose coordinates relative to the basis $\boldsymbol{u}$ are furnished by the $n \times 1$ matrix $T^{-1}x$. It is convenient to refer to the linear transformation of the vector space into itself as a *linear mapping* of the vector space on itself; and to term the linear vector space itself the *carrier space* of the linear mapping or the carrier space in which *the representative matrices* $T, P^{-1}TP$ *of the linear mapping operate.*

It is immediately evident that *all* linear mappings of the carrier space are of the type just described. In fact if $t \to L(t)$ is an arbitrary linear transformation of the carrier space and $\boldsymbol{u}$ an arbitrary basis we denote $L(u_j)$ by (v_j); if the $n \times 1$ matrix x furnishes the coordinates of t relative to the basis $\boldsymbol{u}$ we have $t = \boldsymbol{u}x$ so that $L(t) = L(u_\alpha)x^\alpha = v_\alpha x^\alpha = u_\beta t_\alpha{}^\beta x^\alpha$ where $(t_j{}^1, \cdots, t_j{}^n)$ denote the coordinates of v_j relative to the basis $\boldsymbol{u}$. Hence the coordinates of $L(t)$ are furnished by the matrix Tx.

The collection of all linear mappings $(s, t, u, \cdots)$ of an n-dimensional linear vector space into itself is a collection possessing the group property relative to the law of combination which is defined by mere sequential performance; by this we mean that if s is presented in a basis $\boldsymbol{u}$ by the $n \times n$ matrix S and t is presented in the same basis by the $n \times n$ matrix T (so that under s an arbitrary vector whose coordinates relative to the basis $\boldsymbol{u}$ are furnished by the $n \times 1$ matrix x goes into the vector whose coordinates relative to the same basis are presented by the $n \times 1$ matrix Sx) then ts is presented in the basis $\boldsymbol{u}$ by the $n \times n$ matrix TS. In fact $x \to Sx$ under s and $Sx \to T \cdot Sx = TS \cdot x$ under t so that $x \to TSx$ under ts. The argument shows that linear transformations of our carrier vector space whose presenting matrices T are singular (and which are, accordingly, not mappings of the carrier space on itself but which, rather, transform the carrier space into a linear subspace of itself of dimension $< n$) may be included as far as "possessing the group property" is concerned. Such linear transformations are termed singular and it is now clear that the collection of all non-singular linear transformations of our n-dimensional linear vector space into itself constitute a group (the law of combination being defined by mere sequential performance). In fact the identity transformation $x \to x$ (whose presenting matrix in *any* basis is the n-dimensional unit matrix E_n) is a right unit and $x \to T^{-1}x$ is a right inverse of $x \to Tx$. This group is known as the *full linear group* of dimension n; it is presented in *any* basis by the collection of all non-singular $n \times n$ matrices (with complex elements). If the elements of the $n \times n$ matrices are restricted so as to be real we have the *real linear group* of dimension n. We shall shortly enumerate certain important subgroups of the full linear group but we pass at once to a description of the main topic of the present work: the theory of *the representation of groups.*

4. Group representations.

Let C be a collection of elements $(s, t, u, \cdots)$ which possesses the group property relative to a law of combination ts; and let us suppose that we are able to associate with each element s of C an $n \times n$ matrix $D(s)$ having the property that $D(ts) = D(t)D(s)$, every s, t in C. Then it is a triviality that the collection of $n \times n$ matrices $D(s)$ possesses the group property relative to ordinary matrix multiplication as the law of combination. We term the collection of $n \times n$ matrices $D(s)$ a *representation* (of dimension n) of the collection C of elements $s, t, \cdots$. Observe that we do not require any more than we have said; we do not, for example, require that $t \neq s$ implies $D(t) \neq D(s)$; nor do we require that any or all of the matrices $D(s)$ be non-singular; but we do require that $D(s)$ be unambiguously determined by s. A quite trivial representation of any collection (possessing the group property) is found by assigning to each element s the n-dimensional zero matrix. A less trivial but equally evident representation (one-dimensional) of any collection which possesses the group property is found by assigning to each element s the one-dimensional unit matrix i. e. the number unity. We shall refer to this one-dimensional representation as the *identity representation.*

When the collection C not only possesses the group property but actually is a group G (i. e. possesses a unit e and an inverse s^{-1} of each of its elements) the $n \times n$ matrices $D(s)$ constitute an n-dimensional representation of the group G provided they are all non-singular. It is clear that the representation contains, as the representative of the unit element e, the $n \times n$ unit matrix E_n. In fact from $se = s$ follows $D(s)D(e) = D(s)$ and this implies, on multiplication on the left by $D^{-1}(s)$, $D(e) = E_n$. Also $s^{-1}s = e$ implies $D(s^{-1})D(s) = D(e) = E_n$ so that the collection of matrices $D(s)$ contains the reciprocal of each of its members. Hence the distinct elements of the collection $D(s)$ form a group.

If the elements s of G are non-singular $n \times n$ matrices the association $D(s) = s$ furnishes an n-dimensional representation of G; so that G is an n-dimensional representation of itself. In particular the full linear group of dimension n is an n-dimensional representation of itself. We shall devote considerable attention to the problem of determining all representations (of a certain very general class) of the full linear group but we pass now to a representation of dimension n, of the symmetric group on n letters.

5. Representation of the symmetric group by permutation matrices.

Let $s = \uparrow\begin{pmatrix} s_1, s_2, \cdots, s_n \\ 1, 2, \cdots, n \end{pmatrix} = \uparrow\begin{pmatrix} s_j \\ j \end{pmatrix}$ be a typical element of the symmetric group ($=$ group of $n!$ permutations) on n letters. Denote by $D(s)$ the $n \times n$ matrix of which all the elements in the j-th column are zero save the one in the s_j-th row which is unity: $D(s) = (\sigma_j{}^k)$ where $\sigma_j{}^k = 0$ unless $k = s_j$, $j = 1, 2, \cdots, n$. Then the matrices $D(s)$ furnish a representation, of dimension n, of the symmetric group. In fact the element in the k-th row and j-th column of the product $D(t)D(s) = \tau_a{}^k\sigma_j{}^a$ and this will be zero unless the labels k, j are such that we can have simultaneously $\alpha = s_j$, $k = t_a = t_{s_j}$. Hence $D(t)D(s)$ is the matrix associated with the permutation $\uparrow\begin{pmatrix} t_{s_j} \\ j \end{pmatrix} = \uparrow\begin{pmatrix} t_{s_j} \\ s_j \end{pmatrix}\uparrow\begin{pmatrix} s_j \\ j \end{pmatrix} = ts$; i.e. $D(t)D(s) = D(ts)$. The matrices $D(s)$ are termed permutation matrices; all elements in each column are zero, by definition, save one which is unity. And since the numbers $(s_1, \cdots, s_n)$ are all different all elements in each *row* of $D(s)$ are zero, save one which is unity. If $\boldsymbol{u}$ is any basis in our carrier space and we introduce the basis $\boldsymbol{v} = \boldsymbol{u}D(s)$ we have $v_j = u_a\sigma_j{}^a = u_{s_j}$ so that the j-th vector of the new basis $\boldsymbol{v}$ is the s_j-th vector of the original basis $\boldsymbol{u}$. In other words the basis transformation associated with $D(s)$ amounts merely to a *renumbering of the basis vectors.*

If $T = (t_k{}^j)$ is any $n \times n$ matrix and P is the permutation matrix $D(p)$ associated with the permutation $p = \uparrow\begin{pmatrix} p_j \\ j \end{pmatrix}$ the transform of T by P, namely $P^{-1}TP$ is readily calculated. In fact $p^{-1} = \uparrow\begin{pmatrix} j \\ p_j \end{pmatrix}$ and $P^{-1} = D(p^{-1})$ so that the element in the k-th row and j-th column of $P^{-1}TP = (t_{p_k}^{p_j})$ all terms but one vanishing in the double summation $(P^{-1})_a{}^k t_\beta{}^a (P)_j{}^\beta$. In other words $P^{-1}TP$ is obtained from T by applying the *same* permutation $p^{-1} = \uparrow\begin{pmatrix} j \\ p_j \end{pmatrix}$ to the rows and columns of T. Conversely, a fact which is of importance to us later, two matrices which are such that one is obtainable from the other by applying the *same* permutation to its rows and columns are transformable, one into the other, by means of a permutation matrix.

6. Linear metric spaces.

In order to describe certain subgroups of the full linear group which are of importance for us it is necessary to discuss certain classes of linear vector spaces which we term *metric*. We say that a linear vector space is metric when we can associate with each ordered pair of vectors of the space a complex number (known as the scalar product of the first of the two vectors by the second) and having the properties about to be given. We shall denote the scalar product of the vector s by the vector t by the symbol $(s|t)$; so that $(s|t)$ is a function *on* ordered pairs of vectors of our linear vector space *to* complex numbers. In describing the postulated properties of the scalar product we shall denote, as is usual, the conjugate complex of a given complex number by superposing a bar on the symbol for the number. The postulated properties are as follows:

(1) $(s_1 + s_2|t) = (s_1|t) + (s_2|t)$

(2) $(t|s) = \overline{(s|t)}$

(3) $(\alpha s|t) = \alpha(s|t)$; α any complex number

(4) $(s|s) \geq 0$; the equality implying $s = 0$.

It is easy to draw a series of immediate implications of these postulates. Thus (1) implies $(s_1 + s_2 + \cdots + s_n|t) = (s_1|t) + (s_2|t) + \cdots + (s_n|t)$. Combining (1) and (2) we obtain $(s|t_1 + t_2) = (s|t_1) + (s|t_2)$ and, generally, $(s|t_1 + t_2 + \cdots + t_m) = (s|t_1) + (s|t_2) + \cdots + (s|t_m)$ and this combined with the previous generalization yields $((\sum_{j=1}^{n} s_j)|(\sum_{k=1}^{m} t_k)) = \sum_{j=1}^{n}\sum_{k=1}^{m}(s_j|t_k)$. A combination of (2) and (3) yields $(s|\alpha t) = \bar{\alpha}(s|t)$ and so if α^j, β^k are arbitrary complex numbers $((\sum_{j=1}^{n}\alpha^j s_j)|(\sum_{k=1}^{m}\beta^k t_k)) = \sum_{j=1}^{n}\sum_{k=1}^{m}\alpha^j\bar{\beta}^k(s_j|t_k)$. It follows at once that if our linear vector space is n dimensional we can express $(s|t)$ as a function of the coordinates of s and t relative to any basis; the function being linear in the coordinates of s and linear in the coordinates of t. In fact if the coordinates of s in the basis $\boldsymbol{u}$ are furnished by the $n \times 1$ matrix x whilst those of t in the same basis are furnished by the $n \times 1$ matrix y we have $s = \boldsymbol{u}x$, $t = \boldsymbol{u}y$ so that

$$\begin{aligned}(s|t) = (\boldsymbol{u}x|\boldsymbol{u}y) &= (u_\alpha x^\alpha|u_\beta y^\beta)\\ &= x^\alpha\bar{y}^\beta(u_\alpha|u_\beta).\end{aligned}$$

We denote by H the $n \times n$ matrix of which the element in the j-th row and k-th column is $(u_k|u_j)$ and observe that H is Hermitian: $H = H^*$; the star or adjoint A^* of any given $n \times m$ matrix A being the $m \times n$ matrix obtained from A by interchanging its rows and columns and then taking the conjugate complex of each of the elements. Thus the (j, k) element of A^* i. e. the element in the j-th row and k-th column is given by $a^{*}{}_{k}{}^{j} = \bar{a}_{j}{}^{k}$; it being an immediate consequence that $(AB)^* = B^*A^*$. In particular the star of the $n \times 1$ matrix ($=$ vector) y is the $1 \times n$ matrix y^* whose elements are $\bar{y}^1, \bar{y}^2, \cdots, \bar{y}^n$. In this notation, then, $(s \mid t) = \bar{y}^\beta h_\alpha{}^\beta x^\alpha = y^*Hx$ and we may term H the metrical matrix relative to the basis $\boldsymbol{u}$. It is clear from (2) that $(s \mid s)$ is real and we express the postulate that $(s \mid s) = x^*Hx$ is ≥ 0, the equality implying $x = 0$, by the statement that the Hermitian matrix H is *positively definite.* It is clear that if we introduce a *new* basis $\boldsymbol{v} = \boldsymbol{u}T$ the new *metrical matrix* will be T^*HT; for if z, w are the new presentations of s and t, respectively, we have $x = Tz$, $y = Tw$ so that $y^*Hx = w^*T^*HTz$. If T has the property that T^* is the reciprocal of T (in which case we shall term it unitary and denote it by U) the new metrical matrix is merely the transform of H by U: U^*HU. The collection of unitary $n \times n$ matrices is defined by

$$U^*U = UU^* = E_n$$

and it is clear that this collection possesses the group property: in fact if

$$U_1{}^*U_1 = U_1U_1{}^* = E_n \quad \text{and} \quad U_2{}^*U_2 = U_2U_2{}^* = E_n$$

then

$$(U_1U_2)^*(U_1U_2) = (U_2{}^*U_1{}^*)U_1U_2 = U_2{}^*(U_1{}^*U_1)U_2 = U_2{}^*U_2 = E_n$$

and

$$(U_1U_2)(U_1U_2)^* = (U_1U_2)(U_2{}^*U_1{}^*) = U_1(U_2U_2{}^*)U_1{}^* = U_1U_1 = E_n.$$

Moreover the collection contains the unit $E_n (E_n{}^* = E_n!)$ and the reciprocal U^* of any of its elements $((U^*)^* = U!)$. Hence the collection of all $n \times n$ unitary matrices U constitute a group; this is an important subgroup of the full linear group and is known as the *n-dimensional unitary group.* If we observe that $\det(A^*) = \overline{\det A}$, A *any* $n \times n$ matrix, and that $\det(AB) = \det A \det B$, A, B *any* two $n \times n$ matrices, it is clear that the defining equation $U^*U = UU^* = E_n$ implies that $\mid \det U \mid = 1$; i.e. $\det U$ is, for every element of the n-dimensional unitary group, a complex number of unit modulus. If we select from the n-dimensional unitary group those matrices whose determinants are actually unity (and not merely of modulus unity) we obtained a collection obviously possessing the group property and actually constituting a group; this subgroup of the n-dimensional unitary group (and, hence, also of the full linear group) is *termed the n-dimensional unimodular unitary group.* The subgroup of the full linear group obtained by taking all $n \times n$ matrices (unitary or not) of determinant unity is known, similarly, as the *n-dimensional full unimodular group.* If we take that subgroup of the n-dimensional unitary group which consists of all unitary matrices O with *real* elements we have the *n-dimensional full, real orthogonal group.* Since the elements of O are real O^* is simply the transpose O' of O (i.e. the matrix obtained from O by interchanging its rows and columns) and we may write

$$O'O = OO' = E_n.$$

Since $\det O$ is real and of unit modulus (O being unitary) we have $\det O = \pm 1$; the subgroup of the real orthogonal group obtained by selecting the real $n \times n$ orthogonal matrices whose determinant $= 1$ (i.e. the unimodular real orthogonal group) is known as the *proper real orthogonal group* or the *rotation group* (of dimension n) and we shall denote it by the symbol R_n; the same symbol with an attached prime, i.e. R'_n being used to denote the full real orthogonal group which contains not only the real $n \times n$ unitary matrices of determinant unity (= proper orthogonal matrices or rotations) but also the real $n \times n$ unitary matrices of determinant -1 (= improper orthogonal rotations or *reflexions*). The full orthogonal group (as opposed to the full real orthogonal group) consists of all $n \times n$ matrices O satisfying $O'O = OO' = E_n$. Any element of the full orthogonal group has its determinant $= \pm 1$ so that we may speak of proper and improper orthogonal matrices (even when the elements are complex) and we observe that the proper orthogonal matrices constitute a group known as the *proper orthogonal group.* One should clearly notice that an orthogonal matrix is not, in general, unitary; a *real* orthogonal matrix is, however, unitary: the terms real unitary and real orthogonal being synonymous.

It is important to notice that we can always find a basis in which the metrical (Hermitian) matrix is the unit matrix E_n so that $(s \mid t) = y^*x$. This fact rests on the following theorem: *every positively definite Hermitian matrix H can be presented in the form T^*T where T is a non-singular matrix.* The factorisation is evidently not unique since if $S = UT$, U *any* unitary $n \times n$ matrix,

$$S^*S = (T^*U^*)(UT) = T^*(U^*U)T = T^*T.$$

We shall prove the theorem with the additional condition that T is triangular, i.e. all elements below the principal diagonal vanish. We first remark that all diagonal elements $h_k{}^k$ of a positively definite Hermitian matrix are not only real but *positive.* In fact if x is the vector all of whose components are zero save the k-th, which is unity, we have $x^*Hx = h_k{}^k$ and hence, by the very definition of positive definiteness, $h_k{}^k > 0$. Next we observe that our theorem is true when $n = 1$; in this case H is the 1×1 matrix $h_1^1 > 0$ and we have merely to take $T = T^* = \sqrt{h_1^1}$. To prove the theorem we argue by induction with respect to n; i. e. we assume the theorem true for a given value $n-1$ and deduce its validity for n. Now H being a positively definite $n \times n$ Hermitian matrix the matrix obtained by erasing the last row and column of H is a positively definite $n-1 \times n-1$ Hermitian matrix H_{n-1}; in fact the form x^*Hx in the n variables $x = (x^1, \cdots, x^n)$ reduces, on setting $x^n = 0$, to the form $\xi^* H_{n-1} \xi$ in the $n-1$ variables $\xi = (x^1, \cdots, x^{n-1})$ and so $\xi^* H_{n-1} \xi \geqq 0$, every ξ, the equality implying $\xi = 0$. In other words H_{n-1} is a positively definite $n-1 \times n-1$ Hermitian matrix. Hence by the induction hypothesis $H_{n-1} = T_{n-1}{}^* T_{n-1}$ where T_{n-1} is a non-singular $n-1 \times n-1$ triangle matrix. We adjoin a last column whose first $n-1$ elements constitute an undetermined $n-1 \times 1$ matrix ξ and whose last element $t_n{}^n$ is an undetermined positive number, obtaining in this way an $n \times n$ triangle matrix

$$T_n = \begin{pmatrix} T_{n-1} & \xi \\ 0 & t_n{}^n \end{pmatrix}$$

(T_{n-1} an $n-1 \times n-1$ triangle matrix, 0 the zero $1 \times n-1$ matrix, ξ an undetermined $n-1 \times 1$ *matrix*). It is clear that

$$T^*{}_n = \begin{pmatrix} T^*{}_{n-1} & 0^* \\ \xi^* & t_n{}^n \end{pmatrix}$$

where 0^* is the zero $n-1 \times 1$ matrix and the ordinary rules of matrix multiplication yield

$$T^*{}_n T_n = \begin{pmatrix} T^*{}_{n-1}\, T_{n-1} & T^*{}_{n-1}\, \xi \\ \xi^* \quad T_{n-1} & \xi^* \xi + (t_n{}^n)^2 \end{pmatrix}$$

(The reader will note for future use the following trivially evident fact: let A and B be any two matrices (not necessarily square) for which AB has a meaning (i. e. A has as many columns as B has rows) and let A, B be divided up into submatrices thus:

$$A = \begin{pmatrix} A_1 & A_2 \\ A_3 & A_4 \end{pmatrix} \qquad B = \begin{pmatrix} B_1 & B_2 \\ B_3 & B_4 \end{pmatrix}.$$

Here (A_1, A_3) have the same number of columns as have also (A_2, A_4) and similarly (A_1, A_2) have the same number of rows as have also (A_3, A_4) and the same remarks are applicable to the submatrices B_1, B_2, B_3, B_4. Furthermore A_1 has the same number of columns as B_1 has rows and A_2 has the same number of columns as B_3 has rows. Then the very definition of matrix multiplication shows that

$$AB = \begin{pmatrix} A_1B_1 + A_2B_3 & A_1B_2 + A_2B_4 \\ A_3B_1 + A_4B_3 & A_3B_2 + A_4B_4 \end{pmatrix}$$

the indicated matrix products A_1B_1 etc. all having a meaning). Let η be the $n-1 \times 1$ matrix formed by the first $n-1$ elements of the last column of H and set $\xi = (T^*_{n-1})^{-1}\eta$ which is possible since T_{n-1} and, hence, T^*_{n-1} is non-singular. Our proof by induction will be finished when we show that a positive number $t_n{}^n$ exists whose square is $h_n{}^n - \xi^*\xi = h_n{}^n - \eta^*(T_{n-1})^{-1}(T^*_{n-1})^{-1}\eta = h_n{}^n - \eta^*H_{n-1}{}^{-1}\eta$. In other words we have to show that $h_n{}^n - \eta^*H_{n-1}{}^{-1}\eta > 0$. Writing $H_{n-1}{}^{-1}\eta = \zeta$ we have to show, since $\eta = H_{n-1}\zeta$, that $h_n{}^n - \zeta^*H_{n-1}\zeta > 0$. If u is the $n \times 1$ matrix whose first $n-1$ elements are furnished by ζ and whose last element is -1 we have $u^*H_nu = \zeta^*H_{n-1}\zeta - \zeta^*\eta - \eta^*\zeta + h_n{}^n = h_n{}^n - \zeta^*H_{n-1}\zeta$. Since u is not the zero vector $u^*H_nu > 0$ and our induction proof is complete.

If, then, in a certain basis $\boldsymbol{u}$, $(s\,|\,t) = y^*Hx = y^*(T^*T)x = (y^*T^*)Tx$ we introduce the basis $\boldsymbol{v} = \boldsymbol{u}T^{-1}$ in which s is presented by the $n \times 1$ matrix $Tx = \xi$ and t by the $n \times 1$ matrix $Ty = \eta$. Hence $(s\,|\,t) = \eta^*\xi$. It is clear that there are many bases in which the scalar product $(s\,|\,t)$ has this particularly simple, or *canonical*, presentation $\eta^*\xi$. If $\boldsymbol{u}$ is such a basis and we write $\boldsymbol{v} = \boldsymbol{u}U^*$ so that s is presented in the basis $\boldsymbol{v}$ by $U\xi = \lambda$ and t by $U\eta = \mu$ we have $(s\,|\,t) = \eta^*\xi = \mu^*\lambda$; conversely all of the *privileged* or *preferred* bases (i. e. bases in which $(s\,|\,t)$ has the simple or canonical form y^*x) are obtainable from any one of them by a unitary transformation: $\boldsymbol{v} = \boldsymbol{u}U^*$. For, writing, momentarily, $\boldsymbol{v} = \boldsymbol{u}T^{-1}$, the postulated identity $(s\,|\,t) = y^*x = \eta^*\xi$ coupled with $\xi = Tx$, $\eta = Ty$, yields $y^*T^*Tx = y^*x$. This being an identity in x, y we must have $T^*T = E_n$ so that T and $T^{-1} = T^*$ are unitary. We shall term these privileged bases *unitary* and we see that *all* unitary bases are derivable from *any one* of them by a unitary transformation. When we agree, as we shall generally do, to restrict ourselves to the use of *unitary* bases we refer to the linear metric space (plus this restriction on the choice of a basis) as a *unitary space.* The reader will observe that when our space is *real,* i. e. when the components of all vectors are real, the canonical presentation of the metric is $(s\,|\,t) = y'x$ so that

$$(s\,|\,s) = x'x = (x^1)^2 + \cdots + (x^n)^2.$$

In this case the space is termed rectangular *Cartesian* and the basis orthogonal (so that rectangular Cartesian means Euclidean plus a restriction on the choice of axes of reference). We extend the geometrical language familiar in Cartesian geometry to unitary spaces. Thus $(s\,|\,s) = x^*x$ is termed the squared magnitude of s and s, t are termed mutually orthogonal when $(s\,|\,t) = 0$ (a condition implying, by the postulate (2), $(t\,|\,s) = 0$). It follows that the n vectors which are presented in a unitary basis by the n columns of a unitary matrix are each of unit magnitude and any two of them are mutually orthogonal. We shall term a set of n vectors which possesses these properties a *unitary set.*

A further observation is of significance. The statement that all unitary bases are obtainable from any given one of them by a unitary transformation may be expressed in the following equivalent form: If s and t are any two vectors of our unitary space and if they are subjected to the same arbitrary unitary transformation U then their scalar product remains unaltered; $(s|t) = (Us|Ut)$. In fact if the vectors s and t are presented (in a unitary basis) by the $n \times 1$ matrices x, y, respectively Us, Ut are presented, in the same basis, by the matrices Ux, Uy, respectively; and so

$$(Us|Ut) = (Uy)^*Ux = (y^*U^*)Ux = y^*(U^*U)x = (y^*x) = (s|t).$$

Hence the group of $n \times n$ unitary matrices may be defined as the collection of $n \times n$ matrices which present, in a unitary basis, those linear transformations which leave invariant the scalar product $(s|t) = y^*x$ of any two vectors of the n-dimensional linear metric space.

Before leaving this brief introduction to the theory of linear metric spaces we must prove Schwarz' inequality and the triangle inequality. Denoting by $|s|$ the number $= +\sqrt{(s|s)}$ (termed the norm of s) Schwarz' inequality is

$$(1.8) \qquad |(t|s)| \leq |t| \; |s|, \text{ every } s, t;$$

the equality implying $t = \alpha s$ where α is a *real* complex number. We first observe that, by postulates (3) and (2),

$$|e^{i\theta} s| = |s|, \qquad \theta \text{ real.}$$

If s, t are any two elements of the linear metric space and λ is a real parameter we have

$$(s + \lambda t|s + \lambda t) \geq 0; \text{ i.e. } (s|s) + \lambda\{(t|s) + (s|t)\} + \lambda^2(t|t) \geq 0$$

every λ. Hence $\{(t|s) + (s|t)\}^2 \leq 4(s|s)(t|t)$ and since $(t|s) + (s|t)$ is twice the real part of $(t|s)$ we have

$$\{\text{Real part of } (t|s)\}^2 \leq (s|s)(t|t); \quad |\text{Real part of } (t|s)| \leq |s| \; |t|.$$

The right-hand side is unaffected if we replace s by $e^{i\theta}s$ whilst the $(t|s)$ of the left-hand side is multiplied by $e^{-i\theta}$ (θ any real number). Hence on choosing θ equal to the argument of $(t|s)$ we find

$$|(t|s)| \leq |t| \; |s|.$$

The equality would imply $s + \lambda t = 0$, λ real, so that Schwarz' inequality has been completely proven.

The triangle inequality is expressed by the formula:

(1.09) $$|s+t| \leq |s|+|t|, \text{ every } s, t.$$

In fact

$$(s+t|s+t) = (s|s)+(t|s)+(s|t)+(t|t)$$
$$\leq (s|s)+2|s|\,|t|+(t|t) = \{|s|+|t|\}^2$$

proving the stated inequality. Since the right-hand side is unaffected on replacing t by $e^{i\theta}t$, θ real, we have

$$|s+te^{i\theta}| \leq |s|+|t|$$

and, in particular, on setting $\theta = \pi$

$$|s-t| \leq |s|+|t|.$$

The triangle inequality may be written in the equivalent form

$$|s| \geq |s+t|-|t|$$

or, on writing $s+t=u$, $s=u-t$,

$$|u-t| \geq |u|-|t| \text{ every } u, t$$

or, equivalently,

$$|u+t| \geq |u|-|t| \text{ every } u, t.$$

7. Canonical forms for matrices.

If $(x_1, \cdots, x_n)$ are n linearly independent vectors they constitute a basis $\boldsymbol{x}$. Denoting by X the $n \times n$ matrix whose columns are furnished by the coordinates of the various vectors $(x_1, \cdots, x_n)$ the statement that $\boldsymbol{x}$ is a basis is equivalent to (i. e. implies and is implied by) the statement that X is non-singular. Hence the matrix $H = X^*X'$ is a positively definite Hermitian matrix; the Hermitian nature is evident since $H^* = (X^*X)^* = X^*X^{**} = X^*X = H$ and the positive definiteness is readily proven as follows. Let the $n \times 1$ matrix y present an arbitrary vector; then $y^*Hy = y^*X^*Xy = z^*z$ where $z = Xy$. Hence the vanishing of y^*Hy implies the vanishing of z and hence of $y = X^{-1}z$ (it being here essential that X is non-singular). We can, accordingly, write $H = X^*X$ in the form T^*T where T is a non-singular triangle matrix: $X^*X = T^*T$. We introduce the matrix $U = XT^{-1}$ and readily see that U must be unitary; in fact $X = UT$, $X^* = T^*U^*$ so that $T^*U^*UT = T^*T$. On multiplying each side on the left by the reciprocal of T^* and on the right by the reciprocal of T we deduce $U^*U = E_n$ so that U is unitary. Hence *any* non-singular matrix X can be factored in the form $X = UT$ where U is unitary and T is a non-singular triangle matrix. This important result is known as *the orthogonalisation process of Schmidt*; it assures us that the individual vectors of any set of n

linearly independent vectors can be expressed, in a recurrent manner, as linear combinations of the vectors of a unitary set. In fact if $u_1, \cdots, u_n$ are the vectors presented by the columns of U (so that $u_1, \cdots, u_n$ form a unitary set) the matrix equation $X = UT$ is equivalent to the set of equations

$$x_1 = t_1{}^1 u_1; \ x_2 = t_2{}^1 u_1 + t_2{}^2 u_2; \ \cdots x_n = t_n{}^1 u_1 + t_n{}^2 u_2 + \cdots + t_n{}^n u_n.$$

We shall need in a moment a particular case of this result which may be phrased as follows: given an arbitrary vector $x_1 (\neq 0)$ we may construct a unitary set of which an appropriate multiple of x_1 is the first vector. We have merely to take at random $n - 1$ other vectors $x_2, \cdots, x_n$ such that $(x_1, \cdots, x_n)$ are linearly independent (i. e. such that the matrix X of their components is not zero; for instance if $x_1{}^1 \neq 0$ we may take $x_2 = e_2 = (0, 1, 0, 0, \cdots); \cdots x_n = e_n = (0, 0, \cdots 0, 1)$). Then the orthogonalisation process of Schmidt furnishes a unitary set whose first vector $u_1 = x_1/t_1{}^1$.

If A is an arbitrary $n \times n$ matrix (singular or not) there exists at least one direction in the carrier space in which A operates which is invariant under A; i. e. there exists a vector $x \neq 0$ such that $Ax = \lambda x$ where λ is an appropriate multiplier. In fact if λ is chosen as a root of the algebraic equation of degree n obtained by equating det $(A - \lambda E_n)$ to zero the set of n homogeneous equations implicit in $Ax = \lambda x$ has at least one non-trivial solution $x \neq 0$. We term λ a characteristic constant and x an associated characteristic vector of A. It is clear that if x is a characteristic vector associated with λ so also is αx (α any complex number $\neq 0$) and so there is no lack of generality in assuming that x is a unit vector: $x^* x = 1$ (a normalisation which leaves x still undetermined to the extent of a *phase factor* $e^{i\theta}$, θ real). We are now able to prove a fundamental theorem due to Schur:

An arbitrary matrix A may be transformed by means of a unitary matrix to triangle form. In other words there exists at least one unitary matrix U such that $U^* A U$ is a triangle matrix. The proof is most readily given by means of an induction with respect to n, the dimension of the matrix; the theorem is true for $n = 1$ ($U = E$!, since every one-dimensional matrix is triangular) and we assume it true for a given dimension $n - 1$ and then show it must be true for the next higher dimension n. Let x be any unit characteristic vector of A (the associated characteristic constant being λ); we can take x as the first vector of a unitary set $(u_1, \cdots, u_n)$. Hence if e_1 is the vector $(1, 0, 0, \cdots, 0)$ and U is the unitary matrix whose columns are the vectors $(u_1, \cdots, u_n)$ we have $Ue_1 = x$ so that the equation $Ax = \lambda x$ may be written

$AUe_1 = \lambda Ue_1$ or, equivalently, $U^*AUe_1 = \lambda e_1$. Hence U^*AU is of the form $\begin{pmatrix} \lambda & \xi^* \\ 0 & A_{n-1} \end{pmatrix}$ where ξ^* is an undetermined $1 \times n-1$ matrix and A_{n-1} is an $n-1 \times n-1$ matrix whilst 0 denotes the $n-1 \times 1$ zero matrix. We can, therefore, by the induction hypothesis, find an $n-1 \times n-1$ unitary matrix U_{n-1} such that $U^*_{n-1}A_{n-1}U_{n-1} = T_{n-1}$. The $n \times n$ matrix

$\begin{pmatrix} 1 & 0 \\ 0 & U_{n-1} \end{pmatrix} = V$ is unitary ($V^* = V^{-1}$) and

$$V^*U^*AUV = \begin{pmatrix} 1 & 0 \\ 0 & U^*_{n-1} \end{pmatrix} \begin{pmatrix} \lambda & \xi^* \\ 0 & A_{n-1} \end{pmatrix} \begin{pmatrix} 1 & 0 \\ 0 & U_{n-1} \end{pmatrix} = \begin{pmatrix} \lambda & \xi^* U_{n-1} \\ 0 & U^*_{n-1} A_{n-1} U_{n-1} \end{pmatrix}$$

$$= \begin{pmatrix} \lambda & \xi^* U_{n-1} \\ 0 & T_{n-1} \end{pmatrix} = T_n \tag{1.10}$$

finishing the proof by induction since UV, being the product of two $n \times n$ unitary matrices, is itself an $n \times n$ unitary mattrix.

If the triangle matrix T which is the canonical form of A (under unitary transformations) is such that $T^*T = TT^*$ it must be, not only triangular but diagonal. In fact the diagonal elements of T^*T are the squared magnitudes of the columns of T whilst the diagonal elements of TT^* are the squared magnitudes of the rows of T. Thus, for instance, $T^*T = TT^*$ implies that the squared magnitude of the first row of T equals the squared magnitude of the first column of T and this implies that the only non-zero element in the first row of T is the first one; turning then to the second row and column of T we see, by the same argument, that the only non-zero element in the second row of T is the second; and so forth. Since $T = U^*AU$ we have $T^* = U^*A^*U$ so that

$$T^*T = (U^*A^*U)(U^*AU) = U^*A^*(UU^*)AU = U^*(A^*A)U$$

and

$$TT^* = (U^*AU)(U^*A^*U) = U^*A(UU^*)A^*U = U^*(AA^*)U.$$

Hence if A is such that $A^*A = AA^*$ we can find a unitary matrix such that U^*AU is diagonal. The converse is obviously true: if U^*AU is a diagonal matrix D then the evident relation $D^*D = DD^*$ (the subset of the set of all $n \times n$ matrices which consists of all $n \times n$ diagonal matrices possesses the group property and is Abelian!) yields

$$U^*A^*AU = U^*AA^*U$$

and on multiplying both sides on the left by U and on the right by U^* we obtain $A^*A = AA^*$. Terming a matrix A which satisfies the condition $A^*A = AA^*$ *normal* we have the result that *every normal matrix can be transformed, by means of a unitary matrix, to diagonal form and,* *conversely, if a matrix can be transformed, by means of a unitary matrix, to diagonal form it is normal.*

It is clear that any Hermitian matrix is normal ($H^* = H$!) as is also any unitary matrix ($U^*U = UU^* = E_n$!). Of importance for us in the next section is the fact that any non-singular matrix A can be written as the product of two normal matrices; in fact we now prove, more specifically, that *any non-singular matrix A can be expressed, in a unique manner, in the form $A = UP$ where U is unitary and P is a positively definite Hermitian matrix.* In fact A^*A is a positively definite Hermitian matrix and hence, in particular, normal. Hence there exists a unitary matrix V such that $V^*A^*AV = D$ is diagonal. D is evidently Hermitian ($D^* = D$) but it is also positively definite; for if x is any $n \times 1$ matrix the relation $x^*Dx = 0$ is equivalent to $z^*A^*Az = 0$ where $z = Vx$. Hence, in turn,

$$Az = 0,\ z = A^{-1}(Az) = 0,\ x = V^{-1}z = 0$$

showing the positive definite character of D (it being evident that $x^*Dx = z^*A^*Az \geq 0$). Hence the diagonal elements of D are positive and we denote their positive square roots by $(p_1, \cdots, p_n)$. Let Δ denote the positively definite Hermitian matrix which is diagonal and whose diagonal elements are $(p_1, \cdots, p_n)$ and set $P = V\Delta V^*$. P is a positively definite Hermitian matrix and is such that $P^2 = A^*A$; in fact Δ^2 is, by construction, D and so

$$P^2 = (V\Delta V^*)(V\Delta V^*) = V\Delta^2V^* = VDV^* = A^*A.$$

We now set $U = AP^{-1}$ and prove at once that U is, as the notation implies *unitary*. In fact $U^*U = (P^{-1}A^*)(AP^{-1})$ (note that $P^* = P$) $= P^{-1}(A^*A)P^{-1} = P^{-1}(P^2)P^{-1} = (P^{-1}P)(PP^{-1}) = E_nE_n = E_n$. We have, therefore, proved the possibility of writing any non-singular matrix A in the form $A = UP$ where U is unitary and P positively definite. The second part of our announced theorem, namely the uniqueness of such a factorisation of A is trivially evident. In fact $A = UP$ forces $A^*A = P^2$ and so P^2 is uniquely determined by A; on presenting P^2 in its canonical diagonal form it is clear that P is uniquely determined by P^2 (owing to the positive definiteness of P); hence P, and consequently $U = AP^{-1}$ are uniquely determined by A. For 1×1 matrices (= complex numbers) U is of the form $e^{i\theta}$, θ real, and our theorem reduces to the polar factorisation $a = e^{i\theta}\, p, p > 0$, of any complex number $a \neq 0$. In this (degenerate) case we can interchange the order of the factors and write $a = pe^{i\theta}$ (both factors P and U being diagonal and hence commutative!). In general an arbitrary non-singular $n \times n$ matrix A can also be factored in a unique manner in the form $A = QV$; we merely factor A^* in the form $A^* = V^*Q$; and it follows at once that $V = U$. For $A = QV = UP$ yields $A = V \cdot V^*QV = U \cdot P$ and the positive definiteness of V^*QV (which is a direct consequence of the positive definiteness of Q) together with the uniqueness of the factorisation $A = UP$ of A forces $V = U$, $V^*QV = P$ i. e. $Q = UPU^*$. From the two unique factorisations $A = UP = QU$ we read $A^*A = P^2, AA^* = Q^2$ so that a matrix A is normal when and only when its two unique factorisations are $A = UP = PU$; for we have just seen that $P^2 = Q^2$ together with the assumed positive definiteness of P and Q force $P = Q$. We may say, briefly, *that an $n \times n$ non-singular matrix A is normal when and only when the two factors U, P in its polar factorisation are commutative:*

$$A = UP = PU.$$

Both U and P being themselves normal we have shown that *any non-singular $n \times n$ matrix may be written as the product of two normal matrices.*

We close this section by directing attention to a simple form for an arbitrary matrix (singular or not) under transforming matrices which are *not* restricted to the unitary group as this form will be useful to us in the next chapter. We first observe that since y^*x is unaffected by any permutation $p = \uparrow \begin{pmatrix} p_j \\ j \end{pmatrix}$ of the labels $(1, \cdots, n)$ any permutation matrix is unitary (and, being real, real orthogonal). We wish to show that under transformation by an arbitrary matrix of the full linear group an arbitrary given $n \times n$ matrix can be written in the block form

$$A = \begin{pmatrix} A_1 & 0 & 0 \\ 0 & A_2 & \\ & & A_k \end{pmatrix}$$

where A_j is a triangle square matrix with all its diagonal elements $= \lambda_j$ $j = 1, \cdots, k$, and no two of the complex numbers $\lambda_1, \cdots, \lambda_k$ are equal. The simplest proof is, as usual, by induction with respect to n, the dimension of A (the theorem being trivially evident when $n = 1$). We assume, accordingly, the truth of the theorem for the dimension $n - 1$ and show that this assumption implies its truth for the next higher dimension n. Let, then, A be any $n \times n$ matrix; it has, under transformation by *unitary* matrices, the Schur canonical form

$$U^*AU = \begin{pmatrix} \lambda_1 & \xi^* \\ 0 & T_{n-1} \end{pmatrix}$$

where λ_1 is a characteristic number of A, ξ^* is a $1 \times n-1$ matrix and T_{n-1} is an $n-1 \times n-1$ triangle matrix. By the induction hypothesis we can find a transforming matrix B_{n-1} such that $B_{n-1}^{-1}T_{n-1}B_{n-1}$ has the block form of the theorem and we can (by means of a further transformation by a permutation $n-1 \times n-1$ matrix, if necessary) arrange that if any of the blocks has λ_1 as its common diagonal element this block will appear first. Since the product of the diagonal elements of T_{n-1} (i. e. its determinant) is the same as the product of all the diagonal elements of the various blocks of the "block matrix" into which it is, by the induction hypothesis transformable (this product being also the determinant of the block matrix and $\det B_{n-1}^{-1}T_{n-1}B_{n-1} = \det T_{n-1}$!) it is clear that a block with λ_1 as its common diagonal element will certainly appear if λ_1 is a diagonal element of T_{n-1}; and, furthermore, the dimension of this block is precisely the number of times λ_1 appears as a diagonal element of T_{n-1}. Denoting, momentarily, by C the $n \times n$ matrix $\begin{pmatrix} 1 & 0 \\ 0 & B_{n-1} \end{pmatrix}$ we have

$$C^{-1}U^*AUC = \begin{pmatrix} 1 & 0 \\ 0 & B_{n-1}^{-1} \end{pmatrix}\begin{pmatrix} \lambda_1 & \xi^* \\ 0 & T_{n-1} \end{pmatrix}\begin{pmatrix} 1 & 0 \\ 0 & B_{n-1} \end{pmatrix}$$
$$= \begin{pmatrix} \lambda_1 & \xi^* B_{n-1} \\ 0 & B_{n-1}^{-1}T_{n-1}B_{n-1} \end{pmatrix}.$$

This matrix will have almost but not quite the form stated in the theorem; the deficiency being that across the *top* row there will be, in general, non-zero (instead of zero) elements in the columns occupied by the 2nd, 3rd etc. blocks. In other words $C^{-1}U^*AUC$ will have the form

$$\begin{pmatrix} \lambda_1 & \eta^*_1 & \eta^*_2 & \cdots \\ 0 & B_1 & 0 & \cdots \\ 0 & 0 & B_2 & \\ \cdot & \cdot & \cdot & \cdot \end{pmatrix}$$

where $\eta_1^*, \eta_2^*, \cdots$ are one row matrices whose numbers of columns are, respectively, the dimensions of $B_1, B_2, \cdots$ (these indicating the various blocks of the matrix into which T_{n-1} is, by the induction hypothesis, transformable). In order to remove the unwanted $\eta_2^*, \eta_3^*, \cdots$ we multiply on the right by the matrix $D = \begin{pmatrix} 1 & \xi^*_1 \, \xi^*_2 \cdots \\ 0 & E_{n-1} \end{pmatrix}$ and on the left by its reciprocal $D^{-1} = \begin{pmatrix} 1 & -\xi^*_1 - \xi^*_2 \cdots \\ 0 & E_{n-1} \end{pmatrix}$. The reader will observe that D is not unitary (save in the trivial case $D = E_n$); the induction would not go through, failing precisely at this point, if we restricted ourselves to *unitary* transforming matrices. Denoting UCD by F we have

$$F^{-1}AF = \begin{pmatrix} \lambda_1 & \xi^*_1(\lambda_1 - B_1) + \eta^*_1 & \xi^*_2(\lambda_1 - B_2) + \eta^*_2 & \cdot & \cdot & \cdot \\ 0 & B_1 & 0 & \cdot & \cdot & \cdot \\ 0 & 0 & B_2 & \cdot & \cdot & \cdot \\ \cdot & \cdot & \cdot & \cdot & \cdot & \cdot \end{pmatrix}$$

The matrices $\lambda_1 - B_2, \lambda_1 - B_3, \cdots$ are non-singular (whilst, on the other hand, $\lambda_1 - B_1$ is singular) where λ_1 denotes, in each instance, the scalar matrix of *appropriate dimension* whose common diagonal element is λ_1. Hence on setting $\xi^*_2 = -\eta^*_2(\lambda_1 - B_2)^{-1}, \xi^*_3 = -\eta^*_3(\lambda_1 - B_3)^{-1}, \cdots$ and so forth the unwanted non-zero elements of the top row are removed. On writing $\begin{pmatrix} \lambda_1 & \xi^*_1(\lambda_1 - B_1) + \eta^*_1 \\ 0 & B_1 \end{pmatrix} = A_1,\ B_2 = A_2, \cdots$ we have

$$F^{-1}AF = \begin{pmatrix} A_1 & 0 & 0 & \cdot \\ 0 & A_2 & 0 & \cdot \\ 0 & 0 & \cdot & \cdot \end{pmatrix} \tag{1.11}$$

and the induction proof is finished. It is clear, since ξ_1^* is arbitrary, that the various component blocks can be further simplified. In fact each block $A_1, A_2, \cdots$, which is already a triangle matrix with a common diagonal element, may be presented, by a proper choice of basis, by a matrix all of whose elements are zero save those in the main diagonal (which are all equal) and those one step above the main diagonal, these latter being sets of 1's, each set being separated from the next by a zero), followed, possibly, by a set of zeros. The sets of 1's can, by means of a transforming permutation matrix, if necessary, be arranged in order of non-increasing length and then we have the basic result: two $n \times n$ matrices A, B are transformable, one into the other, by an element of the *full* linear group of dimension n, when and only when their blockstructure is the same; i. e. when $A_j = B_j$, $j = 1, 2, \cdots$. The equality implies first that the dimension of A_j = the dimension of B_j; next that $\lambda_j = \mu_j$ and finally that the sets of 1's, together with the concluding set of zeros, if such exists, are the same for each. But this basic result, which is the goal of the theory known as *elementary divisor* theory, is not essential for us and we relegate its derivation (which is, now, fairly simple) to an appendix.

8. The rational one-dimensional representations of the full linear group.

After the preliminaries of the preceding section we are easily able to find *all* the one-dimensional representations of the full linear group which are of the type known as *rational*; whilst the problem is simple, just because the representations are restricted to be one-dimensional (i.e. to representations by 1×1 matrices or numbers), the method of argument is typical and the result of some importance for us. Denoting the elements of the full linear group of dimension n by $s, t, u, \cdots$ (so that s, for instance, is a non-singular $n \times n$ matrix) and the elements of an m dimensional representation Γ of the group by $D(s), D(t), \cdots$ (so that $D(s)$ is a non-singular $m \times m$ matrix) we say that the representation Γ is *continuous* if *each* of the m^2 elements of $D(s)$ is a continuous function of the n^2 elements of s, every s. If each of the elements of $D(s)$ is a polynomial function of the n^2 elements of s the representation Γ is certainly continuous; we term it *rational integral.* If we allow the elements of $D(s)$ to be rational functions of the elements of s (i.e. each of the elements of $D(s)$ is a quotient of two polynomials in the elements of s, of which the one in the denominator does not vanish) we term the representation Γ a rational representation of the full linear group; it being clear from these definitions that every rational integral representation is rational and that every rational representation is continuous.

We now turn to the question at issue; namely, the determination of *all* rational one-dimensional representations of the full linear group. The fact that the representation is one-dimensional (so that $D(s)$ is a *number*, a function of the n^2 elements of s) introduces an essential simplification; the representation is Abelian:

$$D(st) = D(s)D(t) = D(t)D(s) = D(ts).$$

In particular $D(t^{-1}st) = D(stt^{-1}) = D(s)$. In other words $D(s)$ is known if we know $D(u)$ where $u = t^{-1}st$ is the transform of s by *any* element t of the full linear group. In particular if s is a *normal* matrix we know $D(s)$ if we know $D(u)$ where u is *any* diagonal matrix; but this implies that we know $D(s)$, s *any* element of the full linear group, if we know $D(u)$ where u is any diagonal matrix. In fact s can be written in the form $s = pq$ where p, q are normal matrices (p. 27) and the representation property yields $D(s) = D(p)D(q)$. The one-dimensional nature of the desired representation, therefore, simplifies the problem to that of determining $D(s)$ where s, instead of running over the *full* linear group, runs only over that *Abelian* subgroup of it, which consists of the non-singular diagonal $n \times n$ matrices. Denoting by $(s_1, s_2, \cdots, s_n)$ the diagonal elements of the diagonal matrix s, $D(s)$ is a function of the n variables $(s_1, \cdots, s_n)$ which satisfies the equation (derived from the basic relation $D(s)D(t) = D(st)$)

$$D(s_1, \cdots, s_n)D(t_1, \cdots, t_n) = D(s_1t_1, s_2t_2, \cdots, s_nt_n).$$

It is important to notice that $D(s_1, s_2, \cdots, s_n)$ is a *symmetric* function of its n arguments; in fact the diagonal matrix $(s_1, \cdots, s_n)$ transforms into the diagonal matrix $(s_{p_1}, s_{p_2}, \cdots, s_{p_n})$ under the permutation matrix P associated with the permutation $p = \uparrow\binom{p_j}{j}$. Writing $s_j = e^{\sigma_j}$ $j = 1, \cdots, n$, and $\log D(s) = f(\sigma)$ the function f of the n variables $(\sigma_1, \sigma_2, \cdots, \sigma_n)$ satisfies the equation

$$f(\sigma_1, \cdots, \sigma_n) + f(\tau_1, \cdots, \tau_n) = f(\sigma_1 + \tau_1, \cdots, \sigma_n + \tau_n).$$

It is an immediate consequence that

$$f(\sigma_1, \cdots, \sigma_n) = f_1(\sigma_1) + f_2(\sigma_2) + \cdots + f_n(\sigma_n)$$

where $f_1(\sigma_1)$ is an abbreviation for $f(\sigma_1, 0, 0, \cdots, 0)$, and so on; hence we have only to determine the n functions $f_1(x), \cdots, f_n(x)$ of a *single* variable x. Denoting *any* one of these by the unlabelled symbol $f(x)$ we have $f(x) + f(y) = f(x + y)$. If j is any positive integer it follows immediately that $f(jx) = jf(x)$; and on replacing x by x/j this yields $f\left(\frac{x}{j}\right) = \frac{1}{j}f(x)$. Combining these two results we see that if j, k are *any* two positive integers $f\left(\frac{k}{j}x\right) = kf\left(\frac{x}{j}\right) = \frac{k}{j}f(x)$ and, on setting $x = 1$, $f\left(\frac{k}{j}\right) = C\frac{k}{j}$ where C is the constant $f(1)$. It is clear from the basic relation $f(x) + f(y) = f(x + y)$ that $f(0) = 0$ and then that $f(-x) = -f(x)$ and it follows that $f\left(\frac{k}{j}\right) = C\frac{k}{j}$ if k is any integer positive, negative or zero and j is any positive integer. In other words the function $f(x) - Cx$ of the variable x vanishes when x is real and rational. If we assume first that $f(x)$ is a *continuous* function of x i. e. that the sought-for one-dimensional representation of the full linear group is continuous we see that $f(x) = Cx$ for all *real* values of x. In particular $f_1(\sigma_1) = C_1\sigma_1$ if σ_1 is real and, in terms of the original variables, this yields $D(s_1, 1, 1, \cdots, 1) = e^{f_1(\sigma_1)} = e^{C_1\sigma_1} = s_1{}^{C_1}$ *provided s_1 is real and positive.* The assumption that the sought for representation is not only continuous but *rational* "quantises" the undetermined constant C_1: it must be an *integer* positive, negative, or zero. Furthermore the difference $D(s_1, 1, \cdots, 1) - s_1{}^{C_1}$ is a rational function of the complex variable s_1 which vanishes for all real and positive values of the argument s_1; but a rational function of a single variable s_1 cannot vanish for more than a finite number of values of its argument (namely the number giving the degree of the polynomial in the numerator of the rational function) without vanishing identically. Hence $D(s_1, 1, \cdots, 1) = s_1{}^{C_1}$, or, equivalently, $f_1(\sigma_1) = C_1\sigma_1$ for *all* values of the complex variable σ_1. Arguing similarly for the other functions $f_2(\sigma_2), \cdots, f_n(\sigma_n)$ we obtain $f(\sigma_1, \cdots, \sigma_n) = C_1\sigma_1 + C_2\sigma_2 + \cdots + C_n\sigma_n$, or equivalently,

$$D(s_1, \cdots, s_n) = s_1^{C_1} s_2^{C_2} \cdots s_n^{C_n}$$

where $(C_1, C_2, \cdots, C_n)$ are integers positive, negative or zero. The fact that $D(s_1, \cdots, s_n)$ is a *symmetric* function of its arguments forces $C_1 = C_2 = \cdots = C_n = C$ (say) so that

$$D(s_1, \cdots, s_n) = (s_1 s_2 \cdots s_n)^C$$

or, equivalently, $D(s) = (\det s)^C$; s a diagonal element of the full linear group.

Since the determinant of a matrix is invariant under transformation of the matrix by any element of the full linear group it follows that $D(s) = (\det s)^C$; s any non-singular normal matrix. If s is any non-singular matrix we write $s = tu$ where t, u are normal and find

$$D(s) = D(t)D(u) = (\det t)^C (\det u)^C = (\det tu)^C = (\det s)^C.$$

We obtain thus the desired theorem:

All rational one-dimensional representations of the full linear group are obtained by taking a constant integral power, positive, negative or zero, of the determinants of the elements of the group. (The fact that rational one-dimensional representations of the full linear group are actually obtained in this way being trivially evident). We may readily deduce from this result the fact that all rational representations of a given dimension m of the full linear group are known when we know all rational *integral* representations of dimension m. In fact the elements of the matrices $D(s)$ of any rational representation have a lowest common denominator $\phi(s)$, say; so that $D(s) = P(s) \div \phi(s)$ where $\phi(s)$ and the elements of $P(s)$ are polynomials in the n^2 elements of s (the m^2 elements of $P(s)$ and $\phi(s)$ having no common factor and $\phi(s)$ being normalised, for convenience, by the condition $\phi(e) = 1$, e being the unit element of the full linear group). From the basic representation property $D(ts) = D(t)D(s)$ we read off

$$P(ts) \div \phi(ts) = P(t)P(s) \div \phi(t)\phi(s)$$

or, equivalently,

$$\phi(ts)P(s) \div \phi(s) = \phi(t)P^{-1}(t)P(ts).$$

The elements of the matrix on the right hand side are polynomials in the n^2 elements of s and therefore the elements of the matrix on the left hand side must also be polynomials in these n^2 variables. Since $\phi(s)$ denoted the *lowest* common denominator of the elements of $D(s)$ the elements of $P(s)$ and $\phi(s)$ have no common factor and so $\phi(ts)$ must be divisible by $\phi(s)$. Since they are of the same degree the quotient must be independent of s and on setting $s = e$ we find $\phi(ts) = \phi(t)\phi(s)$ so that $\phi(s)$ furnishes a one-dimensional rational, integral representation of the full linear group. We know, therefore, that $\phi(s) = (\det s)^C$ where C is an integer positive or zero and also that $P(ts) = P(t)P(s)$. In other words $P(s)$ furnishes a rational integral representation of the full linear group. Hence: *any rational representation of dimension m of the full linear group is obtainable by dividing the matrices $P(s)$ of a rational integral representation of the full linear group by a common integral power, positive or zero of the determinants of the elements of the group.*

Appendix to Chapter One

The canonical form for an $n \times n$ matrix A under transformation by an element of the full linear group of dimension n.

We have seen that A can be transformed by an element of the full linear group to block form

$$A = \begin{pmatrix} A_1 & 0 & \cdot \\ 0 & A_2 & 0 \\ \cdot & \cdot & \cdot \end{pmatrix}$$

where each component block A_j is a triangular square matrix with all its diagonal elements equal; we may, therefore, limit our attention to the problem of obtaining a canonical form for each such block. In fact if $C_1^{-1}A_1C_1 = B_1$, $C_2^{-1}A_2C_2 = B_2$ etc. and we denote by C the matrix

$$C = \begin{pmatrix} C_1 & 0 & 0 & \cdot \\ 0 & C_2 & 0 & \cdot \\ 0 & \cdot & \cdot & \\ \cdot & \cdot & \cdot & \cdot \end{pmatrix}$$

it is clear that

$$C^{-1}AC = \begin{pmatrix} B_1 & 0 & 0 & \cdot \\ 0 & B_2 & 0 & \cdot \\ \cdot & \cdot & \cdot & \end{pmatrix}$$

We consider, then, a matrix A of dimension m which is triangular and has all its diagonal elements $= \lambda$; the $m \times m$ matrix $B = A - \lambda E_m$ is therefore triangular and has all its diagonal elements zero. It is clear, then, that B^2 is a triangular $m \times m$ matrix with all its diagonal elements zero and in addition all elements which are one step above the diagonal zero; and that B^3 is a triangular $m \times m$ matrix with all its diagonal elements zero and in addition all elements which are either one step or two steps above the diagonal zero. Continuing in this way we see that $B^m = 0$ whilst, possibly, a lower power of B than the m-th may be the zero matrix. Let $k \leq m$ be the positive integer defined by $B^k = 0$, $B^{k-1} \neq 0$. If $k = 1$, $B = 0$, $A = \lambda E_m$ is already in its canonical form, no transformation being able to change it. We assume therefore $k > 1$. Then the collection of vectors u of our carrier space which are annihilated by B^{k-1}, i. e. which satisfy $B^{k-1}u = 0$, constitute a proper linear subspace S_1 of the carrier space. S_1 is a proper subspace of the carrier space since $B^{k-1} \neq 0$ and we denote by R_1, of dimension $p_1 > 0$, any subspace complementary to S_1; i. e. such that S_1 and R_1 have no common vector whilst any vector of the carrier space is of the form $r_1 + s_1$ where r_1 is in R_1 and s_1 is in S_1. Denoting by BR_1 the collection of vectors Br_1 it is clear that BR_1 constitutes a linear vector space which is a subspace of S_1: $BR_1 \subset S_1$. In fact $B^{k-1} \cdot Br_1 = B^k r_1 = 0$; hence R_1 and BR_1 have no common vector. The fact that no vector of R_1 is annihilated by B^{k-1} assures us that no vector of R_1 is annihilated by $B, B^2, \cdots, B^{k-2}$. Since no vector of R_1 is annihilated by B the space BR_1 has the same dimension p_1 as R_1; in fact if $(x_1, \cdots, x_{p_1})$ constitute a basis for R_1 $(Bx_1, \cdots, Bx_{p_1})$ constitute a basis for BR_1. Furthermore (if $k > 2$) no vector of the space $R_1 + BR_1$ (i. e. the linear space each of whose vectors is of the type $r_1 + Br'_1$, r_1 and r'_1 arbitrary vectors of R_1) is annihilated by B^{k-2} (since no vector of R_1 is annihilated by B^{k-1}); for an hypothecated relation $B^{k-2}\ (r_1 + Br'_1) = 0$ would yield, on multiplication by B, $B^{k-1}r_1 = 0$ implying $r_1 = 0$. Substituting this in the hypothecated relation we find $B^{k-1}r'_1 = 0$ implying $r'_1 = 0$. The vectors of the carrier space which are annihilated by B^{k-2} form a linear subspace S_2 which is also a linear subspace of S_1; we denote by R_2 a linear subspace of the carrier space which is complementary to S_2 and contains $R_1 + BR_1$. The remaining component $\bar{R}_2$, of dimension p_2, say, is contained in S_1: $R_1 + BR_1 + \bar{R}_2 = R_2$ (the dimension of R_2 being $2p_1 + p_2$). If $k > 3$ we proceed in exactly the same manner; we consider the space $B(BR_1 + \bar{R}_2)$ and make the following observations:

1) this space is a subspace of S_2 and hence has no vector in common with R_2; in fact it is annihilated by B^{k-2} because $BR_1 + \bar{R}_2$ is annihilated by B^{k-1} (being contained in S_1).

2) it has the same dimension $p_1 + p_2$ as $BR_1 + \bar{R}_2$; for an assumed relation $B^2r_1 + B\bar{r}_2 = 0$ forces $Br_1 + \bar{r}_2 = 0$ since no non-trivial vector of R_2 is annihilated by B (not being annihilated by B^{k-2}) and this forces

$Br_1 = 0$, $\bar{r}_2 = 0$ the spaces BR_1 and R_2 having, by definition of $\bar{R}_2$, no vector in common. Hence the space $R_2 + B(BR_1 + \bar{R}_2)$ is of dimension $3p_1 + 2p_2$. No vector of this space is annihilated by B^{k-3}; for an assumed relation $B^{k-3}\ [r_2 + B^2 r_1 + B\bar{r}_2]$ would force, on multiplication by B, $B^{k-2}r_2 + B^{k-1}\bar{r}_2 = 0$. Since $\bar{R}_2 \subset S_1$, $B^{k-1}\bar{r}_2 = 0$ and so $B^{k-2}r_2 = 0$ forcing $r_2 = 0$. Entering this in our hypothecated relation we find $B^{k-2}(Br_1 + \bar{r}_2) = 0$ forcing $Br_1 + \bar{r}_2 = 0$ and hence $\bar{r}_2 = 0$, $Br_1 = 0$ and finally $r_1 = 0$. The linear subspace S_3 of our carrier space which consists of the vectors annihilated by B^{k-3} is a subspace of S_2; we denote by R_3 a complementary space to S_3 which is spanned by $R_2 + B(BR_1 + \bar{R}_2) + \bar{R}_3$ where $\bar{R}_3$, of dimension p_3, say, lies in S_2 (the dimension of R_3 being $3p_1 + 2p_2 + p_3$). If $k > 4$ we proceed in exactly the same manner as before; to show how the construction ends we shall suppose (which implies, obviously, no real lack of generality) that $k = 4$. We consider the space $B\ (B^2R_1 + B\bar{R}_2 + \bar{R}_3)$ which is a subspace of S_3 and of the same dimension, namely $p_1 + p_2 + p_3$ as $B^2R_1 + B\bar{R}_2 + \bar{R}_3$. The space $R_3 + B(B^2R_1 + B\bar{R}_2 + \bar{R}_3)$ is, accordingly, of dimension $4p_1 + 3p_2 + 2p_3$; we denote by $R_4 \subset S_3$ a complementary space (of dimension p_4) to $R_3 + B(B^2R_1 + B\bar{R}_2 + \bar{R}_3)$ so that $R_3 + B(B^2R_1 + B\bar{R}_2 + \bar{R}_3) + R_4$ is the entire carrier space of dimension $m = 4p_1 + 3p_2 + 2p_3 + p_4$. Since $R_3 = R_2 + B(BR_1 + \bar{R}_2) + \bar{R}_3$ and $R_2 = R_1 + BR_1 + \bar{R}_2$ we have analysed our carrier space S as follows:

$$S = R_1 + BR_1 + B^2R_1 + B^3R_1 + R_2 + BR_2 + B^2R_2 + R_3 + BR_3 + R_4$$

where no two of the parts have a common vector and the first four parts have the common dimension p_1, the next three parts the common dimension p_2, the next two parts the common dimension p_3 and the last part the dimension p_4. Let us take an arbitrary basis $\boldsymbol{u}$ in R_1; then $B\boldsymbol{u}$ is a basis in BR_1, $B^2\boldsymbol{u}$ is a basis in B^2R_1 and $B^3\boldsymbol{u}$ is a basis in B^3R_1. We choose the vectors of $B^3\boldsymbol{u}$ as the 1st, 5th, 9th, $\cdots$ vectors $e_1, e_5, e_9, \cdots$ of a basis for the entire space; the vectors of $B^2\boldsymbol{u}$, in the same order, being taken as the 2nd, 6th, 10th, $\cdots$ vectors $e_2, e_6, e_{10}, \cdots$ of the basis for the entire space. Since $Be_1 = B^4u_1 = 0$ the first column of B is the zero vector; since $Be_2 = B^3u_1 = e_1$ the second column of $B = e_1$ and so on. Proceeding similarly with bases $\boldsymbol{v}$, $\boldsymbol{w}$, $\boldsymbol{t}$ for R_2, R_3, R_4 we obtain a basis $\boldsymbol{e}$ for the entire carrier space in which the matrix B appears in the form

$$
(1.12)\quad B = \left|\begin{array}{cccccccccccc}
0 & 1 & & & & & & & & & & \\
 & 0 & 1 & & & & & & & & & \\
 & & 0 & 1 & & & & & & & & \\
 & & & 0 & \multicolumn{8}{l}{\Big\}\, p_1 \text{ times}} \\
 & & & & 0 & 1 & & & & & & \\
 & & & & & 0 & 1 & & & & & \\
 & & & & & & 0 & \multicolumn{5}{l}{\Big\}\, p_2 \text{ times}} \\
 & & & & & & & 0 & 1 & & & \\
 & & & & & & & & 0 & \multicolumn{3}{l}{\Big\}\, p_3 \text{ times}} \\
 & & & & & & & & & 0\} & p_4 \text{ times} &
\end{array}\right|
$$

The original matrix $A = \lambda E_m + B$ follows from this by replacing the common diagonal element 0 by λ. The numbers $k, p_1, p_2, \cdots, p_k$ (of which both k and $p_1 > 0$) are evidently invariant under any transformation by the full linear group and so two matrices are equivalent under the full linear group when and only when they have the same canonical block structure, i. e. the same numbers $m, k, p_1, \cdots, p_k$ for each block. The numbers m are the multiplicities of the various characteristic numbers of the matrix. The invariant numbers $m, k, p_1, p_2, \cdots p_k$ are connected by the relation $kp_1 + (k-1)p_2 + \cdots + p_k = m$. If $k = m$ the only possibility is $p_1 = 1$, $p_2 = p_3 = \cdots = p_k = 0$; in other words two $m \times m$ matrices, both of which have but one characteristic number, are transformable one into the other by an element of the m-dimensional full linear group if the common characteristic number λ is the same for both and if the $(m-1)$-st power of the difference between each matrix and λE_m is not the zero matrix. The dimensions of the blocks which actually occur are termed the degrees of the *elementary divisors* of the matrix. Thus when $k = m$ there is but one elementary divisor of degree m.

CHAPTER TWO

REDUCIBILITY

We shall concern ourselves in the present chapter with canonical or normal forms for certain *collections* of $n \times n$ matrices which are regarded as representing, in a given basis, linear operators in a given n-dimensional carrier space; the normal forms being obtained by an intelligent choice of a basis which is appropriate for the entire collection. In the applications which we shall wish to make the collections of matrices will generally be collections possessing the group property; usually the collection will constitute a representation of some group in which we are interested. But the general remarks we wish first to make have no special reference to the *group* property; they apply to any collection whatever of $n \times n$ matrices.

1. Reducibility.

Let A be a typical matrix of our collection and s a typical vector of the carrier space. If S_1 is a linear subspace of the carrier space S which possesses the property that when s is in S_1 so also is As (a property conveniently indicated by $AS_1 \subset S_1$) we say that S_1 is an invariant space of the linear operator which is presented by the matrix A; and if S_1 is an invariant space of all the linear operators which are presented by the various matrices of our collection we say that S_1 is an invariant space of the collection. Every collection of $n \times n$ matrices possesses two *trivial* invariant spaces; namely the entire carrier space and the zero space. We shall refer to any *other* invariant space as a *proper* invariant space. Let now S_1 be a proper invariant space (of dimension m) of our collection and let us introduce a basis whose first m vectors $(e_1, \cdots, e_m)$ lie in S_1. Since Ae_j has for its components the elements of the j-th column of A (i. e. since Ae_j is presented by the j-th column of A) the statement that S_1 is an invariant space is equivalent to the statement that *each* of the *first* m columns of *each* matrix A of our collection has its *last* $n - m$ elements zero. In other words when the basis is so chosen that its first m vectors lie in the m-dimensional invariant space S_1 each and every matrix A of our collection has the form

$$A = \begin{pmatrix} A_m^m & \alpha_{n-m}^m \\ 0 & A_{n-m}^{n-m} \end{pmatrix}$$

where A_m^m is an $m \times m$ matrix, α_{n-m}^m is an $m \times n - m$ matrix, and 0 is the $n - m \times m$ zero matrix. When this is the case we term the collection of matrices A *reducible*; and when it is not the case we term the collection *irreducible.* In other words reducibility is equivalent to the existence of a common proper invariant subspace for the collection. If, *in addition to being reducible,* our collection has the further property that it possesses a second invariant subspace S_2 complementary to the first (and hence of dimension $n-m$) we choose as our basis one whose first m vectors $(e_1, \cdots, e_m)$ lie in S_1 and whose last $n-m$ vectors $(e_{m+1}, \cdots, e_n)$ lie in S_2. The statement that S_2 is an invariant space of the collection is equivalent to the statement that *each* of the *last* $n-m$ columns of each matrix A of our collection has its first m elements zero; in other words when the basis is so chosen that its first m vectors lie in S_1 whilst its last $n-m$ vectors lie in S_2 each and every matrix A of our collection has the form

$$A = \begin{pmatrix} A_m^m & 0^* \\ 0 & A_{n-m}^{n-m} \end{pmatrix}$$

where 0 is the zero $n-m \times m$ matrix whilst 0^* is the zero $m \times n-m$ matrix. When this is the case we term the collection of matrices A *completely reducible* or *analysable*; and when it is not the case we term the collection *non-completely-reducible* or *non-analysable.* In other words complete reducibility or analysability is equivalent to the existence of a common pair of complementary invariant spaces for the collection. It is a triviality that complete reducibility or analysability implies reducibility but the converse is not in general true; we shall see, however, that the converse *is* true for most of the groups in which we shall be interested (being true, in particular, for *every* finite group). We shall be particularly concerned with non-completely-reducible (= non-analysable) collections and we prove at once a basic theorem: *any matrix which is commutative with each and every matrix of a non-analysable collection has all its characteristic numbers equal.* Thus, in particular, if the matrix is normal it is scalar $(=\lambda E_n)$. (The reader will note carefully the hypotheses of the theorem: the collection is assumed *non-analysable*; it may well be reducible unless reducibility implies *complete* reducibility.) In fact let P be the $n \times n$ matrix which is commutative with all the matrices A of our non-analysable collection and present P in the form

$$P = \begin{pmatrix} P_1 & & & & \\ & P_2 & & & \\ & & \cdot & & \\ & & & \cdot & \\ & & & & \cdot \\ & & & & & P_j \end{pmatrix}$$

of Chapter 1, p. 28; P_k being an $m_k \times m_k$ triangular matrix with all its diagonal elements $= \lambda_k$, $k = 1, \cdots, j$, and $\lambda_k \neq \lambda_p$ if $k \neq p$. We section A into blocks indicated by the structure of P:

$$A = \begin{pmatrix} A_1{}^1 & A_2{}^1 & \cdots \\ A_1{}^2 & \cdots & \\ \cdot & \cdot & \cdot \end{pmatrix} \text{ where } A_p{}^q \text{ is an } m_q \times m_p \text{ matrix.}$$

Then

$$AP = \begin{pmatrix} A_1{}^1P_1 & A_2{}^1P_2 & \cdots \\ A_1{}^2P_1 & \cdots & \\ \cdot & \cdot & \cdot \end{pmatrix}$$

(the *columns* (block) of A being multiplied on the *right* by $P_1, P_2, \cdots, P_j$, respectively) whilst

$$PA = \begin{pmatrix} P_1A_1{}^1 & P_1A_2{}^1 & \cdots \\ P_2A_1{}^2 & \cdots & \\ \cdot & \cdot & \cdot \end{pmatrix}$$

(the *rows* (block) of A being multiplied on the *left* by $P_1, P_2, \cdots, P_j$, respectively). The assumed commutativity of P and A gives us a series of equalities and we examine more closely one of these, namely $A_2{}^1P_2 = P_1A_2{}^1$. It is quickly seen that this implies $A_2{}^1 = 0$; in fact the last row of $P_1A_2{}^1$ is λ_1 times the last row of $A_2{}^1$ and on comparing this with the last row of $A_2{}^1P_2$ it is clear that the last row of $A_2{}^1$ is zero (it being an essential requirement for this step of the argument to go through that $\lambda_2 \neq \lambda_1$); the same argument then shows, since we now know that the last row of $A_2{}^1$ is zero, that the next to the last row of $A_2{}^1$ is zero; and so forth. The same argument shows, in general, that $A_p{}^q = 0$, $p \neq q$ so that A has the same structure as P implying that the collection is, contrary to hypothesis, completely reducible. Hence all the characteristic numbers of P are equal. If the non-completely-reducible collection is Abelian each of its matrices is commutative with all the matrices of the collection and hence each matrix of the collection must have all its characteristic numbers equal; and if the matrices are normal they must, accordingly, all be scalar. But this would imply the complete reducibility of the collection save in one case: namely the case when the matrices are *one-dimensional. Hence a non-analysable Abelian collection of normal matrices is necessarily one-dimensional.* In particular a non-completely-reducible representation of an Abelian group by normal (e. g. unitary) matrices is necessarily one-dimensional.

When a collection of $n \times n$ matrices A is completely reducible (so that each matrix A is presentable in the form

$$A = \begin{pmatrix} A_1 & 0^* \\ 0 & A_2 \end{pmatrix}$$

A_1 an $m \times m$ matrix and A_2 an $n - m \times n - m$ matrix) we say that the collection $\{A\}$ is the direct sum of the two collections whose typical matrices are A_1 and A_2, respectively, and we denote the direct sum thus

$$A = A_1 \dotplus A_2.$$

If either A_1 or A_2, or both, are completely reducible we may, by proper choice of basis in each of the carrier spaces of A_1 and A_2, respectively, present them as a direct sum, and so on. The process must finally stop since each analysis lowers the dimension of the carrier space; we end therefore with the analysis

$$A = A_1 \dotplus A_2 \dotplus \cdots \dotplus A_k$$

where each of the component collections $\{A_j\}$ is non-completely-reducible.

We now turn our attention to the case where the collection of matrices A is an n-dimensional representation $\Gamma = \{D(s)\}$ of a group G with elements $s, t, u, \cdots$. If the collection is *reducible* (not necessarily completely reducible) each matrix $D(s)$ may, by choice of an appropriate basis, be presented in the form

$$D(s) = \begin{pmatrix} D_1(s) & \alpha(s) \\ 0 & D_2(s) \end{pmatrix}$$

where $D_1(s)$ is an $m \times m$ and $D_2(s)$ an $n - m \times n - m$ matrix whilst $\alpha(s)$ is an $m \times n - m$ matrix and 0 denotes the $n - m \times m$ zero matrix. Since $\det D(s) = \det D_1(s) \det D_2(s)$ the non-singularity of $D(s)$ assures us of the non-singularity of both $D_1(s)$ and $D_2(s)$, every s. Furthermore a direct application of the definition of matrix multiplication yields

$$D(st) = D(s)D(t) = \begin{pmatrix} D_1(s)D_1(t) & D_1(s)\alpha(t) + \alpha(s)D_2(t) \\ 0 & D_2(s)D_2(t) \end{pmatrix}$$

so that $D_1(st) = D_1(s)D_1(t)$; $D_2(st) = D_2(s)D_2(t)$. Hence the collections of matrices $D_1(s)$, $D_2(s)$ furnish representations Γ_1, Γ_2 of dimensions m and $n - m$, respectively, of our group G. We term $\Gamma_1 = \{D_1(s)\}$ the representation of G which is induced by Γ in its invariant subspace (here spanned by $e_1, \cdots, e_m$). In the particular case where the original representation Γ is not only reducible, but also completely reducible, we may write $D(s) = D_1(s) \dotplus D_2(s)$ i. e.

$$D(s) = \begin{pmatrix} D_1(s) & 0^* \\ 0 & D_2(s) \end{pmatrix}$$

and we term Γ the sum of Γ_1 and Γ_2 : $\Gamma = \Gamma_1 + \Gamma_2$. Since $D(s)$ may be transformed, by means of a permutation matrix P, into

$$P^{-1}D(s)P = \begin{pmatrix} D_2(s) & 0^* \\ 0 & D_1(s) \end{pmatrix} \text{ i. e. } P^{-1}D(s)P = D_2(s) \dotplus D_1(s)$$

and since the representation of G furnished by the matrices $P^{-1}D(s)P$ is the *same* as that furnished by the matrices $D(s)$ (the apparent difference in the individual matrices being due merely to a different choice of basis) we have $\Gamma = \Gamma_2 + \Gamma_1$. In other words the process of addition of representations is *commutative.* We define multiplication of a representation Γ_1 by a *positive integer* p as the addition of Γ_1 p times:

$$p\Gamma_1 = \Gamma_1 + \Gamma_1 + \cdots + \Gamma_1 \ (p \text{ terms}).$$

After analysing the completely reducible representation Γ in the form $\Gamma = \Gamma_1 + \Gamma_2$ we examine each of the representations Γ_1, Γ_2. If either is completely reducible we analyse it in the same manner as Γ and continue this process till it ends when none of the component representations $\Gamma_1, \Gamma_2, \cdots, \Gamma_k$ is completely reducible; this end is certainly reached since every one-dimensional representation is non-completely-reducible. When the analysis is finished: $\Gamma = c_1\Gamma_1 + c_2\Gamma_2 + \cdots + c_k\Gamma_k$ (c_j a positive integer or zero) we say that the completely reducible representation Γ is reduced and term the non-analysable representations Γ_j for which $c_j > 0$ the non-analysable (or irreducible *when reducibility implies complete reducibility*) components of Γ, the coefficients c_j being termed the multiplicities of the various non-analysable components.

It is clear that when a collection of matrices A is reducible (or completely reducible) so also is the collection of matrices A^*. In fact the hypothesis that the collection $\{A\}$ is reducible assures us that each matrix A of the collection may be presented in the form

$$A = \begin{pmatrix} A_m^m & \alpha_{n-m}^m \\ 0 & A_{n-m}^{n-m} \end{pmatrix}$$

(where α_{n-m}^m is the $m \times n - m$ zero matrix when the collection is completely reducible). Hence A^* may be presented in the form

$$A^* = \begin{pmatrix} A_m^{m*} & 0^* \\ \alpha_{n-m}^{m}{}^* & A_{n-m}^{n-m*} \end{pmatrix}$$

and it is then clear that the collection of matrices A^* possesses as an invariant space the space spanned by the $n - m$ vectors $e_{m+1}, \cdots, e_n$ (and, in addition, if α_{n-m}^m is the $m \times n - m$ zero matrix, the complementary space spanned by the m vectors $e_1, \cdots, e_m$) proving the theorem stated.

2. The analysis of any rational integral representation of the full linear group into a sum of homogeneous such representations.

We have seen in Chapter 1, Section 8, that *any* rational representation, of dimension m, of the full linear group may be obtained by dividing the matrices of a rational *integral* representation, of dimension m, of the full linear group by an integral power (positive or zero) of the determinants of the matrices of the full linear group. We now show that *any* rational integral representation, of dimension m, of the full linear group may be written as a sum of *homogeneous* rational integral representations of the full linear group; a rational integral representation by matrices $D(s)$ being termed homogeneous of degree p when the elements of $D(s)$ are homogeneous polynomials of degree p in the n^2 elements of the matrix s. In other words, the rational integral representation whose matrices are $D(s)$ is homogeneous if and only if $D(xs) = x^p D(s)$, x any complex number. Since $D(E_n) = E_m$ it follows that a *necessary* condition for homogeneity is $D(xE_n) = x^p E_m$ and it is immediately seen that this necessary condition is *sufficient*. In fact the basic representation property, namely $D(ts) = D(t)D(s)$ tells us, on setting $t = xE_n$, that

$$D(xs) = D(xE_n)D(s) = x^p D(s).$$

We now consider the Abelian subgroup of the full linear group which consists of the linear operators which are presented in a given basis by non-singular *diagonal* matrices and we denote by $\boldsymbol{x}$ the non-singular diagonal matrix whose diagonal elements are $(x_1, \cdots, x_n)$; thus $\boldsymbol{xy}$ is the non-singular diagonal matrix whose elements are $(x_1y_1, \cdots, x_ny_n)$. Then the collection of matrices $D(\boldsymbol{x})$ may or may not (so far as we know at present) be completely reducible; if it is completely reducible we reduce it so that $P^{-1}D(\boldsymbol{x})P = D_1(\boldsymbol{x}) \dotplus \cdots \dotplus D_j(\boldsymbol{x})$ where each part $D_k(\boldsymbol{x})$, $k = 1, \cdots, j$, constitutes a non-analysable Abelian collection (P being some element of the m-dimensional full linear group). We consider, in particular, the collection $D_1(\boldsymbol{x})$ where it is understood that if the collection $D(\boldsymbol{x})$ is not completely reducible $D_1(\boldsymbol{x})$ stands for $D(\boldsymbol{x})$. Since $D_1(\boldsymbol{x})$ is a non-completely-reducible Abelian collection each of its matrices must have only one characteristic number $\phi_1(\boldsymbol{x})$, say. The elements of $D_1(\boldsymbol{x})$ are certain linear combinations of the elements of $D(\boldsymbol{x})$ and so $\phi_1(\boldsymbol{x})$ is a rational integral (= polynomial) function of the n variables $(x_1, \cdots, x_n)$; for the sum of the diagonal elements of $D_1(\boldsymbol{x})$ is the product of $\phi_1(\boldsymbol{x})$ by the dimension of $D_1(\boldsymbol{x})$. The characteristic vectors of $D_1(\boldsymbol{x})$ being all necessarily associated with the single characteristic number $\phi_1(\boldsymbol{x})$ of $D_1(\boldsymbol{x})$ constitute a linear vector space, S_1, say, of dimension k_1. If u is any vector of S_1 we have, by definition, $D_1(\boldsymbol{x})u = \phi_1(\boldsymbol{x})u$ and on multiplication on the left by $D_1(\boldsymbol{y})$ we find (owing to the commutativity of $D_1(\boldsymbol{x})$ and $D_1(\boldsymbol{y})$)

$$D_1(\boldsymbol{x})D_1(\boldsymbol{y})u = D_1(\boldsymbol{y})D_1(\boldsymbol{x})u = D_1(\boldsymbol{y})\phi_1(\boldsymbol{x})u = \phi_1(\boldsymbol{x})D_1(\boldsymbol{y})u$$

so that $D_1(\boldsymbol{y})u$ also lies in S_1; in other words S_1 is an invariant space of $D_1(\boldsymbol{y})$. Hence $D_1(\boldsymbol{y})$ has at least one characteristic vector in S_1 (as is at once seen on introducing a basis whose first k vectors lie in S_1). On denoting such a common characteristic vector of $D_1(\boldsymbol{x})$ and $D_1(\boldsymbol{y})$ by u we have

$$D_1(\boldsymbol{xy})u = D_1(\boldsymbol{x})D(\boldsymbol{y})u = \phi_1(\boldsymbol{y})D_1(\boldsymbol{x})u = \phi_1(\boldsymbol{x})\phi_1(\boldsymbol{y})u$$

so that $\phi_1(\boldsymbol{x})\phi_1(\boldsymbol{y})$ is a characteristic number of $D_1(\boldsymbol{xy})$; but $D_1(\boldsymbol{xy})$ has, like all the matrices of the collection $D_1(\boldsymbol{x})$, only one characteristic number, namely $\phi_1(\boldsymbol{xy})$ and hence $\phi_1(\boldsymbol{x})$ is a polynomial in the n variables $(x_1, \cdots, x_n)$ which satisfies the equation

$$\phi_1(x_1, \cdots, x_n)\phi_1(y_1, \cdots, y_n) = \phi_1(x_1y_1, \cdots, x_ny_n).$$

By the reasoning of Chapter 1, Section 8, it follows that $\phi_1(\boldsymbol{x}) = x_1^{c_1} \cdots x_n^{c_n}$ where c_j is an integer positive or zero, $j = 1, \cdots, n$. [The reader should carefully note that whilst in that section we were able to derive the *further* result $c_1 = c_2 = \cdots = c_n$ we are unable to do so here; the reason being clear. There we had a function defined for all elements of the full linear group and not, as here, merely for the *diagonal* elements. We were able to show, consequently, that $\phi(\boldsymbol{x})$ must be a *symmetric* function of its n arguments because the diagonal matrix $\boldsymbol{x} = (x_1, \cdots, x_n)$ can be transformed into $\boldsymbol{x}_p = (x_{p_1}, \cdots, x_{p_n})$ by a permutation matrix. But this permutation matrix is outside the diagonal subgroup of the full linear group (E_n being the only diagonal permutation matrix!) In other words no diagonal matrix is transformable into any other diagonal matrix by a diagonal matrix; simply because the diagonal subgroup is Abelian. We are unable, therefore, to say (it would be, in fact, false) that $\phi_1(\boldsymbol{x})$ is a symmetric function of its n arguments $(x_1, \cdots, x_n)$]. In particular $\phi_1(xE_n) = x^{p_1}$ where $p_1 = c_1 + \cdots + c_n$ is an integer, positive or zero. On factoring out x^{p_1} from $D_1(xE_n)$ we obtain a matrix $\psi_1(xE_n)$ (defined by $\psi_1(xE_n) = D_1(xE_n) \div x^{p_1}$) all of whose characteristic numbers are unity and which satisfies the equation $\psi_1(xE_n)\psi_1(yE_n) = \psi_1(xyE_n)$. We propose to show that $\psi_1(xE_n)$ is the unit m_1-dimensional matrix. Admitting this for the moment it follows that $D_1(xE_n) = x^{p_1}E_{m_1}$ and, generally, $D_k(xE_n) = x^{p_k}E_{m_k}$, $k = 1, \cdots, j$. If any of the integers $p_1, p_2, \cdots$ are equal we place the corresponding matrices $D_k(xE_n)$ together (by means of a permutation matrix) and so we know that there exists a basis in which $D(xE_n)$ has the form

$$x^{p_1}E_{q_1} + x^{p_2}E_{q_2} + \cdots + x^{p_r}E_{q_r}, \; p_1 > p_2 > \cdots > p_r \geq 0.$$

Since $D(s)$ is permutable with $D(xE_n)$ it follows that $D(s)$ is completely reducible:

$$D(s) = \begin{pmatrix} A_1(s) & 0 & \cdots & & \\ 0 & A_2(s) & & & \\ & & \cdot & & \\ & & & \cdot & \\ & & & & \cdot \\ & & & & A_r(s) \end{pmatrix}$$

where $A_j(s)$ is a $q_j \times q_j$ matrix. The matrices $A_j(s)$ constitute a representation of the full linear group which possesses the property

$$A_j(xs) = x^{p_j}A(s)$$

since $D(xs) = D(xE_n)D(s)$; in other words it is homogeneous. Hence we have the result: *every rational integral representation of the full linear group of dimension n is either homogeneous or else expressible as a sum of homogeneous rational integral representations of the full linear group.* Combining this with the theorem of Chapter 1, Section 8, we see that all rational representations of the full linear group are known when we know the homogeneous rational integral representations.

It remains to prove that the matrix $\psi_1(xE_n)$ is the unit matrix E_{m_1}. We write $x = e^{\xi}$ and denote $\psi_1(xE_n)$ by $f_1(\xi)$, so that $f_1(\xi) - E_{m_1}$ has all its characteristic numbers zero (as is at once seen on presenting $\psi_1(xE_n)$ in its Schur canonical form). Denoting the constant matrix $f_1(1) - E_{m_1}$ by A_1 we have $A_1{}^{m_1} = 0$ so that for *positive integral values* of ξ the matrix $g_1(\xi) = E_{m_1} + \xi A_1 + \binom{\xi}{2}A_1{}^2 + \cdots + \binom{\xi}{m_1 - 1}A_1{}^{m_1-1}$ $\left(\text{where } \binom{\xi}{k} \text{ is the binomial coefficient } \dfrac{\xi(\xi-1)\cdots(\xi-k+1)}{k!}\right)$ is identical with $(E_{m_1} + A_1)^{\xi}$. Hence $g_1(\xi)g_1(\eta) = g_1(\xi + \eta)$ where ξ, η are positive or zero integers. The difference $g_1(\xi + \eta) - g_1(\xi)g_1(\eta)$ is a polynomial in the two variables ξ, η and since it vanishes (for *any* given positive integral value of one of the variables) for an infinite number of values of the other it must vanish identically. In other words

$g_1(\xi+\eta)=g_1(\xi)g_1(\eta)$ for all complex values of ξ and η. The matrix $f_1(\xi)$ satisfies the same equation: $f_1(\xi+\eta)=f_1(\xi)f_1(\eta)$ and $f_1(1)=E_{m_1}+A_1=g_1(1)$ and this is sufficient to imply $f_1(\xi)=g_1(\xi)$, every ξ. In fact $g_1(k\xi)=\{g_1(\xi)\}^k$, k any positive integer, so that $g_1(k)=\{g_1(1)\}^k$ and similarly $f_1(k)=\{f_1(1)\}^k$ so that $g_1(k)=f_1(k)$, k any positive integer. Since both $f_1(\xi)$ and $g_1(\xi)$ are continuous functions of ξ the equality $f_1(\xi)=g_1(\xi)$ will be proved for all positive real values of ξ if we can show that it holds for all positive rational values of ξ; i. e. for all values $\xi=k/l$ where k and l are positive integers. Since $g_1(k/l)=\{g_1(1/l)\}^k$, $f_1(k/l)=\{f_1(1/l)\}^k$ it is sufficient to show that $f_1(1/l)=g_1(1/l)$, l any positive integer. Setting $f_1(1/l)=B_1$, $g_1(1/l)=C_1$ we have to prove $B_1C_1^{-1}=E_{m_1}$ (that C_1 is not singular is a consequence of $g_1(\xi)g_1(-\xi)=g_1(0)=E_{m_1}$ so that $g_1(\xi)$ is non-singular for all values of ξ); now $B_1{}^l=f_1(1)=E_{m_1}+A_1$ so that A_1 commutes with B_1; C_1 is a polynomial in A_1 so it also commutes with B_1 and hence $(B_1C_1^{-1})^l=B_1{}^lC_1{}^{-l}=f_1(1)g_1^{-1}(1)=E_{m_1}$. B_1, like all $f_1(\xi)$, has all its characteristic numbers unity, and C_1, being a polynomial in A_1 (all of whose characteristic numbers are zero) with first term E_{m_1}, has all its characteristic numbers unity. Hence C_1^{-1} has all its characteristic numbers unity (use the Schur canonical form!) and this implies that $B_1C_1^{-1}$ has all its characteristic numbers unity (since the commutativity of B_1 and C_1 implies that of B_1 and C_1^{-1}). Writing $B_1C_1^{-1}=E_{m_1}+F_1$ it follows that F_1 has all its characteristic numbers zero so that $F_1{}^{m_1}=0$. Let k_1 be the lowest power of F_1 which vanishes: $F_1{}^{k_1}=0$, $F_1{}^{k_1-1}\neq 0$; since $(B_1C_1^{-1})^l=E_{m_1}$ we have $(E_{m_1}+F_1)^l=E_{m_1}$ or $lF_1+\binom{l}{2}F_1{}^2+\cdots+F_1{}^l=0$. On raising this to the k_1-1-st power (if $k_1>1$) we find (on using $F_1{}^{k_1}=0$)$F_1{}^{k_1-1}=0$ contrary to the definition of k_1; the only way out of the dilemma is to have $k_1=1$, i. e. $F_1=0$ implying $B_1=C_1$, i. e. $f_1(1/l)=g_1(1/l)$ or, consequently, $f_1(k/l)=g_1(k/l)$, k, l any positive integers. The continuity of $f_1(\xi), g_1(\xi)$ then ensures $f_1(\xi)=g_1(\xi)$, ξ any positive number. Since $f_1(\xi)$ is a rational function of $x=e^\xi$ and $g_1(\xi)$ is a polynomial in $\xi=\log x$ the only way we can have $f_1(\xi)=g_1(\xi)$ for all positive values of ξ is to have $A_1=0$ so that the logarithms disappear from $g_1(\xi)$, this reducing to the constant matrix E_{m_1}. We then have $f_1(\xi)=E_{m_1}$ for all positive real values of ξ, i. e. $\psi_1(xE_n)=E_{m_1}$ for all real values of x which are >1. Since the elements of $\psi_1(xE_n)$ are polynomials in x it follows that $\psi_1(xE_n)=E_{m_1}$ for *all* complex values of x; which is what we had to prove.

3. Schur's Lemma.

A fundamental theorem concerning irreducible collections of matrices, known as Schur's Lemma, is the following:

If $\{A\}$ and $\{B\}$ are two irreducible collections of matrices, whose carrier spaces are of dimensions n and m, respectively, and if there exists an $n \times m$ matrix P such that $AP = PB$, every A, B (this equality meaning that given *any* A of the first collection a B of the second collection may be found such that $AP = PB$; and, vice versa, given *any* B of the second collection an A of the first collection may be found such that $AP = PB$) then we are confronted by a simple alternative: either

1) P is the zero $n \times m$ matrix; in which case B is evidently indeterminate when A is given and A indeterminate when B is given

or 2) P is square and *non-singular*; in which case the collection of matrices $B = P^{-1}AP$ is equivalent (under the full linear group) to the collection of matrices A.

The proof of this basic theorem is trivial: let the columns of P present the vectors $p_1, \cdots, p_m$; then the columns of AP present the vectors $Ap_1, \cdots, Ap_m$ whilst the columns of PB present certain linear combinations of the vectors $(p_1, \cdots, p_m)$. In other words the linear space spanned by the m vectors $(p_1, \cdots, p_m)$ is invariant under the collection of matrices A. Hence the granted irreducibility of this collection assures us that the linear space spanned by these m vectors $(p_1, \cdots, p_m)$ is *either* the zero space *or* the entire carrier space. In the first case P is the zero $n \times m$ matrix, whilst in the second $m \geq n$ and n of the m vectors $(p_1, \cdots, p_m)$ are linearly independent. Starring the given equality $AP = PB$ we find $B^*P^* = P^*A^*$ and we know that the new collections $\{A^*\}$ and $\{B^*\}$ are irreducible; hence, unless P is the zero $n \times m$ matrix (in which case P^* is the zero $m \times n$ matrix), the number of columns of P^* (namely n) $\geq$ the number of rows of P^* (namely m). Combining both results we obtain the stated theorem: either P is the zero matrix or P is square $(m = n)$ and non-singular (since the n vectors presented by its columns are linearly independent). The reader should note carefully the hypotheses of the theorem: both collections A and B are assumed *irreducible*. Non-analysability is not enough (unless, as is, for instance, the case for all representations of all finite groups) reducibility implies complete reducibility (= analysability).

It is clear, by the same argument, that if we are given but one irreducible collection of $n \times n$ matrices A and a fixed $n \times m$ matrix P such that $AP = 0$ then either P is the zero matrix or the vectors represented by the columns of P span the entire n-dimensional carrier space; in this case $Ae_1 = 0$, $Ae_2 = 0, \cdots, Ae_n = 0$ or, in other words, the columns of A all present the zero vector i. e. $\{A\}$ is the trivial collection which consists of the single zero matrix.

4. Burnside's Theorem.

In order to derive this consequence of Schur's lemma, it is necessary to say a few words about a concept which is fundamental in the theory of group representations, namely, the *trace* of a square matrix. This is the sum of the diagonal elements of the matrix:

$$Tr(A) = a_\alpha{}^\alpha. \tag{2.1}$$

Since the j-th diagonal element of the matrix product AB (A, B both $n \times n$ matrices) is $a_\alpha{}^j b_j{}^\alpha$ we have $Tr(AB) = a_\alpha{}^\beta b_\beta{}^\alpha$ and the symmetry of this in the symbols a, b yields the important result:

$$Tr(BA) = Tr(AB). \tag{2.2}$$

It follows that the trace of a matrix of dimension n is invariant (herein lies its importance) under transformation of the matrix by any element of the full linear group; in fact if P is any non-singular $n \times n$ matrix we have

$$Tr(P^{-1}AP) = Tr(P^{-1}A \cdot P) = Tr(P \cdot P^{-1}A) = Tr(PP^{-1} \cdot A) = TrA.$$

We see, then, on transforming A to its Schur canonical form, that $Tr(A) =$ the sum of the n characteristic numbers of A.

Let now Γ be an irreducible representation, of dimension n, by matrices $D(s)$, of a group G whose elements are $s, t, u, \cdots$ and let us suppose that there exists an $n \times n$ matrix P such that

$$Tr(P^*D(s)) = 0, \text{ every } s.$$

Since the collection of all $n \times m$ matrices constitutes an Abelian group, under addition as the law of combination, we may regard any $n \times m$ matrix as a vector in an nm dimensional linear vector space (the nm different matrices each of which has all elements zero save one, which is unity, being evidently linearly independent and every $n \times m$ matrix being a linear combination of these). If A, B are any two $n \times m$ matrices B^* is an $m \times n$ matrix and so B^*A is an $m \times m$ matrix whose j-th diagonal element is $b^*{}_\alpha{}^j a_j{}^\alpha = \sum_\alpha \bar{b}_j{}^\alpha a_j{}^\alpha$. Hence the trace of this product is

$$Tr(B^*A) = b^*{}_\alpha{}^\beta a_\beta{}^\alpha = \sum_{\alpha,\beta} \bar{b}_\beta{}^\alpha a_\beta{}^\alpha \tag{2.3}$$

and it is evident that

$$Tr(A^*B) = \overline{Tr(B^*A)}$$

(a relation which is a consequence of the trivially evident relation $Tr(A^*) = \overline{TrA}$). It is, then, evident that the nm dimensional linear vector space whose elements are $n \times m$ matrices may be assigned the metric

$$(2.4) \qquad (A \mid B) = Tr(B^*A).$$

(That $(A \mid A) \geqq 0$, the equality implying $A = 0$, is evident since $(A \mid A) = Tr(A^*A) = \sum_{\alpha,\beta} \bar{a}_\beta{}^\alpha a_\beta{}^\alpha$ and any term of this double summation, $\bar{a}_q{}^p a_q{}^p$ say, is positive or zero and, if zero, $a_q{}^p = 0$).

Our assumed relation $Tr(P^*D(s)) = 0$ may be expressed by the statement that there exists a vector P in the n^2 dimensional linear metric space (whose elements are $n \times n$ matrices) which is perpendicular to all the matrices $D(s)$ of an irreducible representation of a given group G (and hence to the linear vector space spanned by the matrices $D(s)$ of the given irreducible representation). The collection of vectors P, in this n^2 dimensional space, which are orthogonal to the linear vector space R spanned by the matrices $D(s)$, constitutes a linear vector space S (of dimension j, say, and spanned by the vectors $P_1, \cdots, P_j$, say) complementary to R. The definition of S is such that if $P \subset S$ $(D(s) \mid P) = 0$, every s; in particular $(D(st) \mid P) = 0$, every s, t, i. e. $(D(s)D(t) \mid P) = 0$. But this expresses the fact $Tr(P^*D(s)D(t)) = 0$ i. e. $Tr(Q^*D(t)) = 0$ where $Q = D^*(s)P$. Hence $(D(t) \mid Q) = 0$, every t, so that $Q \subset S$, every s. On setting $P = P_k$, $k = 1, \cdots, j$, in turn, we have $D^*(s)P_k = P_\alpha t_k{}^\alpha$, $k = 1, \cdots, j$, the $t_k{}^m$ being undetermined complex numbers which constitute a $j \times j$ matrix $T^*(s)$. Each of the j $n \times n$ matrices P_k contains n^2 elements so that there are jn^2 elements altogether in the set; we select from these the jn elements which lie in the same column, say the q-th, of the j matrices and consider the $n \times j$ matrix M_q of which the element in the l-th row and m-th column is $(P_m)_q{}^l$. Then our relation $D^*(s)P_k = P_\alpha t_k{}^\alpha$ appears in the form

$$D^*(s)M_q = M_q T^*(s); \qquad (q = 1, \cdots, n).$$

But the irreducibility of the collection $D(s)$ implies that of the collection $D^*(s)$ and so the columns of M_q are either zero or else $j \geqq n$ and the j vectors (of the carrier space of $D(s)$) constituted by the columns of M_q span the entire carrier space. If $T^*(s)$ is the zero matrix the non-singularity of $D^*(s)$ implies $M_q = 0$, every q (on multiplication on the left by $D^{*-1}(s)$). *If the collection of matrices $T^*(s)$ is irreducible* we star the relations written above, obtaining $T(s)M^*_q = M^*_q D(s)$ implying $n \geq j$ (unless all $M^*_q = 0$) and the fact that the n vectors (of the carrier space of $T(s)$) constituted by the columns of M^*_q span the entire carrier space. Combining the two results we see that either $M_q = 0$, every q, or else there exists one M_q which is a non-singular $n \times n$ matrix so that the matrices $T(s) = M^*_q D(s) M^{*-1}_q$ furnish the same representation Γ of G as the matrices $D(s)$. If the first alternative holds, i. e. $M_q = 0$, every q, we have, by definition of the M_q, $P_k = 0$, $k = 1, \cdots, j$ so that S is the zero space, its complementary space R being the entire n^2 dimensional space. *In other words the matrices $D(s)$ span the entire n^2-dimensional linear vector space* (whose elements are $n \times n$ matrices). If the other alternative holds, we transform $T(s)$, which is equivalent to $D(s)$, by introducing a new basis in S so that $T(s)$ becomes $D(s)$ and we know that there exists a non-singular $n \times n$ matrix M^*_q having the property

$$D(s)M^*_q = M^*_q D(s), \text{ every } s.$$

This is sufficient to imply that M^*_q is a scalar matrix; for evidently any scalar matrix $\lambda_q E_n$ satisfies the same relation:

$$D(s)\lambda_q E_n = \lambda_q E_n D(s)$$

so that $D(s)(M^*_q - \lambda_q E_n) = (M^*_q - \lambda_q E_n)D(s)$. If λ_q is a characteristic number of M^*_q the matrix $M^*_q - \lambda_q E_n$ is singular and hence, by Schur's Lemma, it must be the zero matrix. In other words $M^*_q = \lambda_q E_n$ and, by the very definition of M_q, it follows that $(P_m)_q{}^l = 0$ unless $l = m$ in which case it $= \bar{\lambda}_q$. The relation $(D(s) \mid P_m) = 0$ i. e. $\sum_{\alpha.\beta} \overline{(P_m)_\beta{}^\alpha} (D(S))_\beta{}^\alpha = 0$ reduces, therefore, to $\sum_\beta \lambda_\beta (D(s))_\beta{}^m = 0$ i. e. $D(s)\lambda = 0$ where λ is the vector, of the carrier space in which $D(s)$ operates, whose components are $(\lambda_1, \cdots, \lambda_n)$. The non-singularity of $D(s)$ forces $\lambda = 0$ so that all the matrices M^*_q, and hence all the matrices M_q, vanish; implying, as before, that the matrices $D(s)$ span the entire n^2 dimensional space. However, our proof of this fact rests on the assumption that the collection of matrices $T^*(s)$ is irreducible. If the collection $T^*(s)$ is reducible we present it, by proper choice of basis in the space S, in reduced form

$$T^*(s) = \begin{pmatrix} T^*_1(s) & Q^*(s) \\ 0 & T^*_2(s) \end{pmatrix}$$

where the square matrix $T^*_1(s)$ (of dimension $j_1 < j$) is a member of an irreducible collection (obtained by letting s run over G). Taking only the first j_1 of the j equations $D^*(s)P_k = P_\alpha t_k{}^\alpha$ we argue with these precisely as above where the irreducible collection $T^*_1(s)$ takes the place of the previously *assumed* irreducible collection $T^*(s)$. We find that all the vectors $P_1, \cdots, P_{j_1}$ must vanish contrary to the hypothesis that they span a space of dimension $j_1 \geqq 1$. Hence the theorem is true in general: *the matrices of an irreducible n-dimensional representation of any group contain n^2 linearly independent matrices* (Burnside's theorem). An equivalent statement is the following: the n^2 elements of the matrices $D(s)$ of an irreducible representation, of dimension n, of any group G are linearly independent, no non-trivial relation $Tr(P^*D(s)) = 0$, every s, existing between them. In the course of the proof we have derived the very useful result: *the only matrices commutative with all the matrices of an irreducible collection are scalar matrices.* The reader will compare this theorem with a previous theorem where a *weaker* assumption (non-analysability instead of irreducibility) led to the *weaker* result (all characteristic numbers equal instead of matrix being scalar).

Frobenius and Schur have given a useful generalisation of Burnside's theorem which runs as follows. Suppose we have several *non-equivalent* irreducible representations $\Gamma_1, \Gamma_2, \cdots, \Gamma_q$ of a given group G by matrices $D_1(s), D_2(s), \cdots, D_q(s)$ of dimensions $n_1, n_2, \cdots, n_q$, respectively. The ordered set $(A_1, \cdots, A_q)$ where A_j is any n_j dimensional matrix, $j = 1, \cdots, q$ constitutes an Abelian group under the law of combination $(A_1, \cdots, A_q) + (B_1, \cdots, B_q) = (A_1 + B_1, \cdots, A_q + B_q)$ and, furthermore, has defined over it the operation of multiplication by an arbitrary complex number α: $\alpha(A_1, \cdots, A_q) = (\alpha A_1, \alpha A_2, \cdots, \alpha A_q)$. It constitutes, therefore, a linear vector space and the dimension of this linear vector space is $n_1{}^2 + n_2{}^2 + \cdots + n_q{}^2$. If we denote by $\boldsymbol{A}$ the typical vector $(A_1, \cdots, A_q)$ of this linear vector space, the formula

$$(\boldsymbol{A} \mid \boldsymbol{P}) = Tr(P^*_1 A_1) + Tr(P^*_2 A_2) + \cdots + Tr(P^*_q A_q)$$

evidently defines a metric over the space. If the vectors $\boldsymbol{D}(s) = (D_1(s), \cdots, D_q(s))$ span a subspace R of the linear vector space, the vectors $\boldsymbol{P} = (P_1, \cdots, P_q)$ which are completely perpendicular to R span a complementary space S and if this is of dimension j and is spanned by $\boldsymbol{P}_1, \cdots, \boldsymbol{P}_j$ the typical vector of S is $\boldsymbol{P}_a x^a$; $x^1, \cdots, x^j$ arbitrary complex numbers. The statement $\boldsymbol{P} \subset S$ is equivalent to $(\boldsymbol{D}(s) \mid \boldsymbol{P}) = 0$, every s; and this implies $(\boldsymbol{D}(st) \mid \boldsymbol{P}) = 0$ every s, t. Written out this is

$$\sum_{k=1}^{q} Tr(P^*_k D_k(s) D_k(t)) = 0,$$

i. e. $(\boldsymbol{D}(t) \mid \boldsymbol{Q}) = 0$, every t, where $\boldsymbol{Q} = (D^*_1(s)P_1, D^*_2(s)P_2, \cdots, D^*_q(s)P_q)$. Hence $\boldsymbol{P} \subset S$ implies $\boldsymbol{Q} \subset S$. On setting $\boldsymbol{P}$ in turn $= \boldsymbol{P}_k$,

$k = 1, \cdots, j$ where $\boldsymbol{P}_k = (P_{k,1}, \cdots, P_{k,q})$ we find $D^*_m(s) P_{k,m} = P_{a,m} t_k^a(s)$, $m = 1, 2, \cdots, q$, the t_k^r being undetermined complex numbers which constitute a $j \times j$ matrix $T^*(s)$. For a fixed value of m, say $m = 1$, we repeat the argument used in the proof of Burnside's Theorem; the conclusion being first that all the matrices $P_{k,1}$ vanish or else that the matrices $T(s)$ furnish the same representation Γ_1 of G as do the matrices $D_1(s)$. In this latter case they do not furnish the same representation of G as $\Gamma_2, \Gamma_3, \cdots,$ or Γ_q and hence the matrices $P_{k,2}, \cdots, P_{k,q}$ vanish, every k. We are then back in the previous case (i. e. Burnside's Theorem) so that the matrices $P_{k,1}$ must vanish, every k. In other words the vectors $\boldsymbol{D}(s)$ span the entire $n_1^2 + n_2^2 + \cdots + n_q^2$ dimensional space; or, equivalently, the $n_1^2 + n_2^2 + \cdots n_q^2$ elements of the matrices $D_1(s), D_2(s), \cdots, D_q(s)$ are linearly independent, no non-trivial relation of the type $\sum_{k=1}^{q} Tr\{P^*_k D_k(s)\} = 0$, every s, existing between them.

5. Bounded representations of a given group G.

If Γ is an n-dimensional representation, by matrices $D(s)$, of a group G with elements $s, t, u, \cdots$ we may picture $D(s)$ by a point in a real $2n^2$-dimensional rectangular Cartesian space whose coördinates are the real and imaginary parts of the n^2 (complex) elements of $D(s)$. Then $(D(s) \mid D(s)) = TrD^*(s)D(s)$ is the squared distance of the representative point from the origin (which represents the zero matrix). We say the representation is bounded when the representative points all lie within some "sphere" with center at the origin; i. e. when there exists a fixed number M such that $Tr(D^*(s)D(s)) \leq M$, every s. It is clear that a collection of $n \times n$ matrices is bounded *when and only when* the set of elements of the matrices of the collection is bounded. For example every representation of a finite group is bounded; or if the elements $s, t, \cdots$ are described by a finite number of real parameters which run over a *closed* point set as s runs over G the representation is bounded if it is continuous, i. e. if the elements of $D(s)$ are continuous functions of the parameters which specify s (for any continuous function defined over a closed point set is bounded over the set). Terming such a group G compact we may say that any continuous representation of a *compact* group is bounded. The (Euclidean) squared distance between the representative points p, q of two $n \times n$ matrices A, B being $(A - B \mid A - B)$ it is clear that not only does $(A - B \mid A - B) = 0$ imply $A - B = 0$, i. e. $p = q$ but that $q \to p$ as $B \to A$ and vice versa. In fact the formula $\mid q - p \mid^2 = \sum_{a,\beta} (\bar{a}_\beta^a - \bar{b}_\beta^a)(a_\beta^a - b_\beta^a)$ shows that

$|q - p| < \epsilon$ implies $|a_k^j - b_k^j| < \epsilon$ every j, k; and, conversely, $|a_k^j - b_k^j| < \epsilon$, every j, k, implies $|q - p| < n\epsilon$. Furthermore not only does the Schwarz' inequality: $|(A \mid B)|^2 \leq (A \mid A)(B \mid B)$ hold (this inequality being valid for *every* linear metric space) but

$$(2.5) \qquad |AB| \leq |A| \, |B|$$

where $|A|$ (called the *norm* of A) denotes the positive square root of $(A \mid A)$. To see this we first make the trivially evident remark that the norm of a matrix is unaffected by multiplication of A, on the right or left, by any unitary matrix U:

$$|AU| = |VA| = |A|; \; U, V \text{ arbitrary unitary matrices.}$$

In fact

$$|AU|^2 = (AU \mid AU) = Tr[(AU)^*AU] = Tr[(AU)(AU)^*]$$
$$= Tr(AUU^*A^*) = TrAA^* = TrA^*A = |A|^2$$

and

$$|VA|^2 = (VA|VA) = Tr[(VA)^*VA] = Tr(A^*V^*VA) = TrA^*A = |A|^2.$$

Hence, in particular, the norm of a matrix is invariant under transformation by any element of the unitary group: $|U^*AU| = |A|$). In particular the norm of a *normal* matrix is the square root of the sum of the squared moduli of its characteristic numbers (the Schur canonical form of the normal matrix being diagonal). If the normal matrix is a non-negative Hermitian matrix P, with characteristic numbers $(\lambda_1, \cdots, \lambda_n)$ so that $\lambda_j \geq 0$, $j = 1, \cdots, n$, $|P|^2 = \lambda_1^2 + \lambda_2^2 + \cdots + \lambda_n^2 \leq (\lambda_1 + \lambda_2 + \cdots + \lambda_n)^2 = (TrP)^2$ so that, since $|P|$ and $Tr(P)$ are both non-negative, $|P| \leq Tr(P)$. Writing P in the form T^*T we have $|T^*T| \leq Tr(T^*T) = |T|^2$ and this result (valid for *any* $n \times n$ matrix T) leads at once to the stated inequality. Thus

$$|AB|^2 = Tr(B^*A^* \cdot AB) = Tr(BB^*A^*A) = (A^*A \mid BB^*)$$
$$\leq [(A^*A \mid A^*A)(BB^* \mid BB^*)]^{1/2} \text{ (Schwarz' inequality)}$$
$$= |A^*A| \, |BB^*| \leq |A|^2 \, |B|^2$$

implying $|AB| \leq |A| \, |B|$. It is evident that if either A or B is the zero matrix the inequality may be replaced by an equality (both sides being zero). If neither A nor B is zero and one of them A, say, is such that A^*A has at least two non-zero characteristic numbers, the weak inequality $|AB| \leq |A| \, |B|$ may be replaced by the strong inequality $|AB| < |A| \, |B|$ for then $|A^*A| < |A|^2$.

When A, B are 1×1 matrices ($=$ complex numbers) our inequality becomes the modulus equality

$$|AB| = |A|\ |B|.$$

As far as convergence questions (where the interest is centered on *dominations* rather than equalities) are concerned, the *inequality* $|AB| \leq |A|\ |B|$ is just as forceful as the *equality* $|AB| = |A|\ |B|$. Thus if we have a sequence of $n \times n$ matrices $A_1, A_2, \cdots, A_m, \cdots$ we *say* that the sequence converges to a limit matrix L when the sequence of norms $|L - A_1|, \cdots, |L - A_m|, \cdots$ (each of which is a non-negative real number) converges to the limit zero; it being evident that then each *element* of A_m converges to the corresponding element of L. From the triangle inequality we derive $|A_p - A_q| = |(L - A_q) - (L - A_p)| \leq |L - A_q| + |L - A_p|$ so that it is trivially evident that a necessary condition for convergence of the sequence $A_1, A_2, \cdots, A_m, \cdots$ is $|A_p - A_q| \to 0$ as p, q tend, independently of each other, to ∞. But this *necessary* convergence condition is *sufficient*, i. e. it serves as a *criterion* for convergence (Cauchy convergence principle!) In fact if we consider for a fixed p the sequence $A_p - A_{p+1}, \cdots, A_p - A_{p+m}, \cdots$ we know that we can choose p so that the norm of each and every one of these $< \epsilon$ where ϵ is an arbitrarily assigned positive number (say 1). Hence the sequence $A_{p+1}, A_{p+2}, \cdots, A_{p+m}, \cdots$ is bounded (the representative points all lying within the "unit sphere" whose center is at the representative point of A_p). The representative points possess, accordingly, at least one accumulation point and we denote by L the matrix represented by this accumulation point. Then, by definition of an accumulation point, we know that to any assigned ϵ we can find an m such that $|L - A_{p+m}| < \epsilon$ and if p is chosen large enough so that $|A_{p+m} - A_{p+q}| < \epsilon$, every q (which can always be done since $|A_j - A_k| \to 0$ as $j, k \to \infty$, by hypothesis) it follows, on applying again the triangle inequality, that $|L - A_{p+q}| < 2\epsilon$ every q, proving the *convergence* to the limit L of the sequence $A_1, \cdots, A_m, \cdots$ (and incidentally the uniqueness of L; since two L's would have to satisfy, again on account of the triangle inequality, $|L_1 - L_2| < 4\epsilon$, ϵ arbitrary, i. e. $L_1 - L_2 = 0$ or $L_2 = L_1$). If we have an infinite series $S = A_1 + A_2 + \cdots + A_m + \cdots$ whose elements are $n \times n$ matrices we say that the infinite series *converges to the value* S if the sequence of partial sums

$$S_1 = A_1, S_2 = A_1 + A_2, \cdots \qquad S_m = A_1 + A_2 + \cdots + A_m, \cdots$$

converges to the limit S. It is clear, for example, that the exponential series

$$\exp A = E_n + A + \frac{A^2}{1\cdot 2} + \cdots + \frac{A^m}{m!} + \cdots$$

converges for *every* $n \times n$ *matrix* A (simply because

$$\exp |A| = 1 + |A| + \frac{|A|^2}{1\cdot 2} + \cdots + \frac{|A|^m}{m!} + \cdots$$

converges for *every* non-negative number $|A|$). In fact

$$S_q - S_p = \frac{A^p}{p!} + \frac{A^{p+1}}{p+1!} + \cdots + \frac{A^{q-1}}{q-1!}$$

and so

$$\begin{aligned} |S_q - S_p| &= \left| \frac{A^p}{p!} + \cdots + \frac{A^{q-1}}{q-1!} \right| \\ &\leq \left| \frac{A^p}{p!} \right| + \cdots + \left| \frac{A^{q-1}}{q-1!} \right| \quad \text{(by the triangle inequality)} \\ &= \frac{1}{p!}|A^p| + \cdots + \frac{1}{q-1!}|A^{q-1}| \\ &\leq \frac{1}{p!}|A|^p + \cdots + \frac{1}{q-1!}|A|^{q-1} \end{aligned}$$

since a continued application of the basic inequality $|AB| \leq |A|\,|B|$ gives $|A^2| \leq |A|^2$, $|A^3| \leq |A|^3, \cdots$, $|A^k| \leq |A|^k$. Hence the convergence of the *numerical* series $\exp |A|$ implies the convergence of the matrix series $\exp A$. Similarly the series

$$\log (E + A) = A - \frac{A^2}{2} + \cdots + (-1)^{q-1}\frac{A^q}{q} + \cdots$$

converges if $|A| < 1$. It is clear that if $B = P^{-1}AP$ is the transform of A by any element of the full linear group $\exp B = \exp (P^{-1}AP) = P^{-1}(\exp A)P$. If A is normal P can be so determined that B is diagonal and then $\exp B$ is diagonal, the diagonal elements being $\exp d_1, \cdots, \exp d_n$ where $d_1, \cdots, d_n$ are the diagonal elements of the (diagonal) matrix B. If, for instance, $A = U$ is unitary, its characteristic numbers $\lambda_1, \cdots, \lambda_n$ are all of unit modulus: $\lambda_k = \exp (i\theta_k)$, $k = 1, \cdots, n$, θ_k real; hence, if V is the Schur canonical form of U, $V = \exp i\Theta$ where Θ is the diagonal (Hermitian) matrix whose diagonal elements are $(\theta_1, \cdots, \theta_n)$. This implies

$$U = \exp (iH)\,; \; H \text{ an Hermitian matrix.}$$

Conversely it is obvious that if H is an arbitrary Hermitian matrix $U = \exp (iH)$ is unitary; for $U^* = (\exp (iH))^* = \exp (-iH^*)$

$= \exp(-iH)$ and hence $UU^* = E_n$ (for the ordinary rule for multiplication of power series shows that $\exp A \exp B = \exp(A + B)$ *provided A and B are commutative*; in particular $\exp A \exp(-A) = \exp 0 = E_n$). The factorisation $A = UP = QU$ of any $n \times n$ matrix (Chapter 1, Section 7) may, therefore, be written in the form,

$$A = e^{iH}P = Qe^{iH},$$

a result which is a direct generalisation of the polar factorisation of complex numbers: $a = e^{i\theta}\rho = \rho e^{i\theta}$. In general if A is any $n \times n$ matrix it may be presented in the Schur canonical form (in which it appears in triangle form) with the characteristic numbers $(\lambda_1, \lambda_2, \cdots, \lambda_n)$ of A along the main diagonal; then $\exp A$ appears in triangle form with $\exp \lambda_1, \cdots, \exp \lambda_n$ along the main diagonal. Hence

$$\begin{aligned} \det(\exp A) &= \exp \lambda_1 \exp \lambda_2 \cdots \exp \lambda_n = \exp(\lambda_1 + \lambda_2 + \cdots + \lambda_n) \\ &= \exp(TrA). \end{aligned}$$

If therefore $TrA = 0$, $\exp A$ is unimodular and, conversely, if $\exp A$ is unimodular TrA is an integral (positive, negative or zero) multiple of $2\pi i$.

It is clear that the limit V of a convergent sequence of unitary matrices $U_1, U_2, \cdots, U_m, \cdots$ is itself unitary. For on writing $V = U_m + \epsilon$ we have

$$V^*V = (U^*_m + \epsilon^*)(U_m + \epsilon) = E_n + U^*_m\epsilon + \epsilon^*U_m + \epsilon^*\epsilon,$$

and so

$$\begin{aligned} |V^*V - E_n| &= |U^*_m\epsilon + \epsilon^*U_m + \epsilon^*\epsilon| \\ &\leq |U^*_m\epsilon| + |\epsilon^*U_m| + |\epsilon^*\epsilon| \text{ (Triangle inequality)} \\ &= |\epsilon| + |\epsilon^*| + |\epsilon^*\epsilon| \to 0 \text{ with } \epsilon. \end{aligned}$$

Hence $|V^*V - E_n|$, being independent of ϵ, $= 0$ and so $V^*V = E_n$. In other words the unitary subgroup of the full linear group is *compact*; so that *any continuous* representation of the unitary group is bounded. The same remarks apply to the full real orthogonal subgroup R'_n of the full linear group and to the proper real orthogonal subgroup R_n of the full linear group. The full linear group itself is not compact (since a sequence of points in the representative $2n^2$-dimensional real Euclidean space may not have an accumulation point but may $\to \infty$); nor is the full unimodular group compact if $n > 1$: For if A is any element of the unimodular group so is the matrix B obtained from A by multiplying any row of it by any complex number ($\neq 0$) and dividing any other row of it by the same complex number; hence $|B|$ may be as large as we wish (being certainly not less than the modulus of any single element of B).

We now proceed to prove a quite fundamental theorem: namely the theorem that *any bounded subgroup of the full linear group is equivalent to a unitary group.* Since any representation of any group G is a subgroup of the full linear group it follows that any bounded representation of any group G is equivalent to a unitary representation of G. In line with our agreement to regard equivalent representations as identical (the apparent difference being due to a quite accidental choice of basis) we may say: *all bounded representations are unitary.* An important consequence of this theorem is that, as far as bounded representations are concerned, there is no distinction between *reducibility* and *analysability* or *complete reducibility.* Let then $\{A\}$ be a bounded collection of $n \times n$ matrices constituting a group. The hypothesis of boundedness is expressed by

$$|A| \leq M$$

where M is a positive number *independent of* A. It is clear that the hypothesis of boundedness implies that any accumulation point of the collection $\{A\}$ is itself non-singular. In fact let L be any accumulation point of $\{A\}$ and let $\{A_m\}$, $m = 1, 2, \cdots$, be a convergent sequence from $\{A\}$ with limit L. The matrices A_m^{-1}, $m = 1, 2, \cdots$, are in $\{A\}$, since the collection $\{A\}$ is a group, and hence this sequence is bounded. Let K be an accumulation point of it and let $\{A_{p_m}^{-1}\}$, $m = 1, 2, \cdots$, be a convergent subsequence (from the sequence A_m^{-1}) whose limit is K. Then we have the relations

$$L = A_{p_m} + \Delta_m; \quad K = A_{p_m}^{-1} + D_m$$

where both $|\Delta_m|$ and $|D_m| < \epsilon$ (an arbitrary positive number) if m is large enough. Since

$$LK = E_n + \Delta_m A_{p_m}^{-1} + A_{p_m} D_m + \Delta_m D_m$$

we have

$$\begin{aligned} |LK - E_n| &= |\Delta_m A_{p_m}^{-1} + A_{p_m} D_m + \Delta_m D_m| \\ &\leq |\Delta_m| \, |A_{p_m}^{-1}| + |A_{p_m}| \, |D_m| + |\Delta_m| \, |D_m| \\ &\leq 2M\epsilon + \epsilon^2 \rightarrow 0 \text{ with } \epsilon. \end{aligned}$$

The left-hand side being independent of ϵ we have $|LK - E_n| = 0$ implying $LK = E_n$ so that L is non-singular. The *closure* of $\{A\}$, i. e. the collection of all matrices A together with all their accumulation points, is itself a subgroup of the full linear group. In fact if L is any accumulation point of $\{A\}$ which does not belong to $\{A\}$ we select a convergent sequence $\{A_m\}$, $m=1,2,\cdots$, with limit L and consider the sequence $\{A_mA\}$, A any element of the original group $\{A\}$. This sequence has an accumulation point K and we select the subsequence $\{A_{p_m}\}$ of $\{A_m\}$ such that $\{A_{p_m}A\}$ is a convergent sequence with limit K. Then we have $L=A_{p_m}+\Delta_m$; $K=A_{p_m}A+D_m$ where both $|\Delta_m|$ and $|D_m|<\epsilon$ (an arbitrary positive number) if m is large enough. Hence $LA-K=\Delta_mA-D_m$ implying $|LA-K|\leq|\Delta_m|\,|A|+|D_m|\leq(M+1)\epsilon\to 0$ with ϵ. Hence $LA=K$ so that LA belongs to the closure of $\{A\}$. If L_1, L_2 are two points of accumulation of $\{A\}$, neither of which belongs to $\{A\}$ we consider two convergent sequences $\{A_m\}\to L_1$ and $\{B_m\}\to L_2$; the sequence $\{A_mB_m\}$ has an accumulation point K and we select the convergent subsequence $\{A_{p_m}B_{p_m}\}\to K$. Then, exactly as before, we find $L_1L_2=K$. Hence the closure of $\{A\}$ possesses the group property; it actually is a group since it contains E_n (already a member of $\{A\}$) and the inverse of each of its elements. The closure of $\{A\}$ is evidently *closed*; in fact if J is any accumulation point of it each neighborhood of J contains at least one element of the closure of $\{A\}$ other than, possibly, J itself. But this implies that each neighborhood of J contains at least one element of $\{A\}$ other than, possibly, J itself; for if L is a member of the closure of $\{A\}$ which does not itself belong to $\{A\}$ there are members of $\{A\}$ arbitrarily near L. Finally the closure of $\{A\}$ is bounded, for $|A_m|\leq M$ implies $|L|\leq M$ where $\{A_m\}$ is a convergent sequence with limit L; in fact $|L|\leq|L-A_m|+|A_m|\leq M+\epsilon$ and the fact that $|L|$ is independent of ϵ forces $|L|\leq M$.

The useful implication of the discussion of the previous paragraph is the following: if we can show that any bounded *and closed* subgroup of the full linear group is equivalent to a unitary group this will imply that any bounded subgroup of the full linear group is equivalent to a unitary group. For if the closure of $\{A\}$ is equivalent to a unitary group, $\{A\}$ itself, being contained in its closure is, à fortiori, equivalent to a unitary group. We consider therefore a bounded and closed subgroup $\{A\}$ of the full linear group. The fact that $|A^*|=|A|$ forces $|A^*A|\leq|A^*|\,|A|\leq M^2$ so that the collection of positively definite matrices $P=A^*A$ is also bounded; furthermore it is closed. In fact if L is an accumulation point of the set $\{P\}$ it is the limit of a convergent sequence $\{P_m\}$ where $P_m=A^*_mA_m$. If K is an accumulation point of the sequence $\{A_m\}$ we have, as before, $L=A^*_{p_m}A_{p_m}+\Delta_m$, $K=A_{p_m}+D_m$ where both $|\Delta_m|$ and $|D_m|<\epsilon$ (an arbitrary positive number) if m is large enough. Hence $|L-K^*K|\to 0$ with ϵ and its independence of ϵ forces $|L-K^*K|=0$, i. e. $L=K^*K$ proving the closure of the set $\{P\}$ since K belongs to the closed (by hypothesis) set $\{A\}$.

Before finishing the proof of our theorem it is necessary to make some remarks concerning a bounded and a closed point set $\{P\}$ lying in a *real* rectangular Cartesian space. Let n denote the dimension of the linear subspace S of *lowest* dimension which contains the given bounded and closed point set and let $x = (x^1, \cdots, x^n)$ be a rectangular Cartesian coördinate system in S. The points of S which satisfy the equation $(x \mid c) \equiv \sum_{(a)} c^a x^a = p$, where $(c \mid c) = 1$, lie on a "hyperplane" possessing the orientation c and as p varies we obtain a family of parallel hyperplanes; the numbers x, c, p being all real. An application of Schwarz' inequality gives $| p | = |(x \mid c)| \leq | x | \; | c | = | x |$ so that all points of the hyperplane $(x \mid c) = p$ have a distance from the origin $\geq | p |$. Restricting our attention to those hyperplanes of the parallel family $(x \mid c) = p$ which contain points of our given bounded set $\{P\}$ it follows that the numbers p form a bounded set:

$$-M \leq p \leq M$$

where $| x | \leq M$, x any point of the given bounded set $\{P\}$. Denoting by $p_-(c)$, $p_+(c)$ the greatest lower and least upper bounds, respectively, of the bounded set of numbers $\{p\}$ we term the collection of points x for which

$$(x \mid c) = p; \quad p_-(c) \leq p \leq p_+(c)$$

the c-slice of our n-dimensional rectangular Cartesian space determined by the point set $\{P\}$. The very definition of the terms greatest lower (and least upper) bound is such that every point of $\{P\}$ is contained in each c-slice determined by $\{P\}$ whilst no narrower slice having the orientation c contains all of $\{P\}$ (the obvious definition of the term width of the slice between the parallel hyperplanes $(x \mid c) = p_1$, $(x \mid c) = p_2$ being $| p_2 - p_1 |$). Then the collection of points common to *all* c-slices determined by P is termed the convex of $\{P\}$ and denoted by $Co(P)$. It is an immediate consequence of the definition that $\{P\} \subset Co(P)$ (since $\{P\}$ is contained in each and every c-slice determined by $\{P\}$); and that $Co(P)$ is bounded (every c-slice determined by $\{P\}$ being contained in the slice $-M \leq (x \mid c) \leq M$ so that $Co(P)$ is a subset of the spherical region $| x | \leq M$). If x, y are any two points of a c-slice determined by $\{P\}$ all points of the line segment joining x and y (i. e. all points $\alpha x + \beta y$ where α, β are *non-negative* numbers whose sum is unity) lie also in the c-slice. In fact the inequalities $p_-(c) \leq (x \mid c) \leq p_+(c)$, $p_-(c) \leq (y \mid c) \leq p_+(c)$ force $p_-(c) \leq \alpha(x \mid c) + \beta(y \mid c) = (\alpha x + \beta y \mid c) \leq p_+(c)$. It follows, therefore, that if x, y are any two points of $Co(P)$, i. e. any two points each of which is contained in *all* c-slices determined by P, then all points of the line segment joining the points x, y are contained in $Co(P)$. In technical language $Co(P)$ is *convex* (this property being the reason for the name *convex of* P which is abbreviated by the symbol $Co(P)$). It is clear that $Co(P)$ is closed; simply because the points of each c-slice determined by P for which $|x| \leq M$ form a closed set. In fact $(x \mid c)$ is a continuous function of x: $|(y \mid c) - (x \mid c)| = |(y - x \mid c)| \leq |y - x|$ and so the set of points defined by $p_-(c) \leq (x \mid c) \leq p_+(c)$, $|x| \leq M$, is closed; in fact if $x_1, x_2, \cdots, x_j, \cdots$ is a convergent sequence of points of the c-slice determined by $\{P\}$ (for which $|x_j| \leq M$) their limit x belongs to this c-slice. Simply because $|x - x_j| < \epsilon$ implies $|(x \mid c) - (x_j \mid c)| < \epsilon$ so that $p_-(c) - \epsilon < (x \mid c) < p_+(c) + \epsilon$ and the arbitrary nature of the non-negative number ϵ forces $p_-(c) \leq (x \mid c) \leq p_+(c)$.

It is important to notice that the continuity of $(x \mid c)$ coupled with the assumed closure of $\{P\}$ assures us that each of the boundary planes $(x \mid c) = p_-(c)$ and $(x \mid c) = p_+(c)$ of any c-slice determined by $\{P\}$ contains at least one point of $\{P\}$; for the continuous functions $(x \mid c) - p_-(c)$, $p_+(c) - (x \mid c)$, of the variable x, defined over the *closed* set $\{P\}$, must each assume at some point x of $\{P\}$ its greatest lower bound zero. We term these boundary planes of c-slices determined by $\{P\}$ *planes of support* of P. These planes of support constitute a closed set; i. e. if $(c_m, p_+(c_m))$, $m = 1, 2, 3, \cdots$ is a convergent sequence with limit (c, p) then $p = p_+(c)$. In fact let x_m be any point of $\{P\}$ in the plane of support $(x \mid c_m) = p_+(c_m)$ of $\{P\}$ and let x be an accumulation point of the bounded point set x_m, $m = 1, 2, \cdots$ so that x is a point of the *closed* set $\{P\}$. We may assume the sequence x_m *convergent* since if it were not we would merely select from it a convergent subsequence $x_{p_1}, x_{p_2}, \cdots, x_{p_m}, \cdots$ with limit x and consider, instead of the convergent sequence $(c_m, p_+(c_m))$, its convergent subsequence $(c_{p_m}, p_+(c_{p_m}))$. Then the continuity of $(x \mid c)$, regarded as a function of *both* its arguments (which continuity is a direct consequence of the Schwarz' inequality $|(x \mid y)| \leq |x| \; |y|$) tells us that, for arbitrary positive ϵ, $|(x \mid c) - (x_m \mid c_m)| < \epsilon$, m sufficiently large. The definition of x_m implies $(x_m \mid c_m) = p_+(c_m)$ and so $(x \mid c) = p$ forcing $p \leq p_+(c)$. But if y is any point of $\{P\}$ on the plane of support $(x \mid c) = p_+(c)$ of $\{P\}$ we have $(y \mid c) = p_+(c)$ and hence $|p_+(c) - (y \mid c_m)| < \epsilon$, m sufficiently large; if p were $< p_+(c)$ we would have $p_+(c_m) < p_+(c)$, m sufficiently large, and hence $(y \mid c_m) < p_+(c)$. Thus $p_+(c) - (y \mid c_m) < \epsilon$ implying $p_+(c) - p_+(c_m) < \epsilon$, m sufficiently large, i. e. $p_+(c) = p$.

If, now, x is any point of $Co(P)$ which does not lie on any plane of support of $\{P\}$ we have $p_+(c) - (x \mid c) > 0$ every c. This *continuous* function of the plane of support $(c, p_+(c))$ must (since the planes of support form a closed set) have a greatest lower bound b which is > 0. The entire spherical neighborhood of x consisting of points y for which $\mid y - x \mid < b$ belongs, accordingly, to *every* c-slice determined by P and hence to $Co(P)$; in other words x is an *interior* point of $Co(P)$. *Hence each boundary point of $Co(P)$ lies on at least one plane of support of P.* We use this to prove a result which is essential for us: *every point of $Co(P)$ is a linear combination, with non-negative coefficients whose sum is unity, of $n+1$ points of $\{P\}$.* The theorem is evidently true if P is a point set lying on a straight line ($n = 1$) since then $Co(P)$ is the line segment joining the points p_-, p_+ which points belong themselves to P, owing to the *closed* nature of $\{P\}$. In order to prove our theorem by the method of induction we assume it true for all bounded closed sets $\{P\}$ lying in a rectangular Cartesian space of $n - 1$ dimensions and derive from this assumption its validity for all bounded closed sets $\{P\}$ lying in a rectangular Cartesian space of n dimensions. Let, then, $\{P\}$ be a bounded, closed set in a rectangular Cartesian space of n dimensions (it being understood that it does not lie in a rectangular Cartesian space of $n - 1$ dimensions) and let Q be an arbitrary point of $Co(P)$. Denoting by R an arbitrary point of $\{P\}$ $(R \neq Q)$ we construct the line segment RQ all of whose points belong to $Co(P)$; producing this line segment, if necessary (in the sense $(R \rightarrow Q)$, it will strike the boundary of $Co(P)$ in a point T, say. T being a boundary point of $Co(P)$ must lie in a plane of support of $\{P\}$ and the convex of those points of P which lie in this plane of support contains T (this convex being the intersection of $Co(P)$ with the plane of support). The plane of support being of dimension $n - 1$ we know, by the hypothesis of the induction proof, that T is a linear combination with non-negative coefficients whose sum is unity of n points of $\{P\}$. But Q is a linear combination with non-negative coefficients, whose sum is unity, of the points R and T; in other words Q is a linear combination, with non-negative coefficients whose sum is unity, of $n + 1$ points of P, so that the proof by induction is complete.

We relegate to an appendix to this chapter the proof of the somewhat plausible theorem that the convex $Co(P)$ of every bounded, closed point set $\{P\}$ possesses a mean center which belongs to the convex. If, then, $\{A\}$ is a bounded, closed subgroup of the full linear group we construct the set (also bounded and closed) of positively definite matrices $P = A^*A$. Each point of the convex $Co(P)$ of this set, being a linear combination with non-negative coefficients (whose sum is unity) of points of $\{P\}$, is a positively definite matrix. In particular the mean center C of $Co(P)$ is a positively definite matrix. If B is any fixed element of the group $\{A\}$ the set $\{AB\}$ is the same as the set $\{A\}$; and hence the set $\{(AB)^*AB\} = \{B^*A^*AB\} = \{B^*PB\}$ is the same as the set $\{P\}$. The $2n^2$ coördinates of the representative point of B^*PB are homogeneous linear functions of the $2n^2$ coördinates of the representative point of P. To see what the $2n^2 \times 2n^2$ matrix of this linear transformation is we argue as follows: treating the elements $p_s{}^r$ of P as the components of a (complex) vector in an n^2-dimensional space the $n^2 \times n^2$ matrix T of the transformation $P \to B^*PB$ has for its (rs, jk) element

$$T^{rs}_{jk} = b^*{}_j{}^r b_s{}^k.$$

If D denotes the matrix reciprocal to B (so that D^* is reciprocal to B^*) the matrix S whose (rs, jk) element is $d^*{}_j{}^r d_s{}^k$ is inverse to T: $(TS)^{rs}_{jk} = b^*{}_a{}^r b_s{}^\beta d^*{}_j{}^a d_\beta{}^k = 0$ unless $(r, s) = (j, k)$ in which case it $= 1$. Hence T is non-singular. Splitting the complex vector $p_s{}^r$ and T into their real and imaginary parts, i. e. writing $p_s{}^r = l_s{}^r + im_s{}^r$, $T = J + iK$, where $l = (l_s{}^r)$ and $m = (m_s{}^r)$ are real as are also J and K the transformation $p \to Tp = (J + iK)(l + im)$ induces the transformation whose matrix is

$$F = \begin{pmatrix} J & -K \\ K & J \end{pmatrix}$$

on the $2n^2$-dimensional real vector (l, m). It is readily seen that the non-singularity of the $n^2 \times n^2$ complex matrix $T = J + iK$ implies the non-singularity of the $2n^2 \times 2n^2$ real matrix F. In fact the transformation on the $2n^2$ real variables (l, m) becomes, when presented in the basis obtained by setting $p = l + im$, $\bar{p} = l - im$, a transformation on the $2n^2$ complex variables $(p, \bar{p})$ whose matrix is

$$\begin{pmatrix} T & 0 \\ 0 & \bar{T} \end{pmatrix}.$$

The determinant of this matrix is $\det T \det \bar{T} = |\det T|^2$ and so $\det F = |\det T|^2$ since the determinant of any matrix is unaffected by a transformation of the matrix by any element of the full linear group (here of dimension $2n^2$). Hence if x is any point of the c-slice determined by (P), $\xi = Fx$ is a point of the Fc-slice determined by (B^*PB), i. e. is a point of the Fc-slice determined by (P). In other words $B^*Co(P)B$ belongs to $Co(P)$ every B, but this implies that B^{*-1} $B^*Co(P)B \cdot B^{-1}$, i. e. $Co(P)$ belongs to $B^{*-1}Co(P)B^{-1}$ every B and hence (on replacing B by B^{-1}) to $B^*Co(P)B$ every B. Hence $B^*Co(P)B = Co(P)$. If C is the mean center of $Co(P)$, B^*CB is the mean center of $B^*Co(P)B$; in fact the mean center x of any region S is furnished by a quotient of two integrals: $\bar{x} = \int_S x dv \div \int_S dv$ and if x is subjected to a non-singular linear homogeneous transformation F we have

$$F\bar{x} = \int_S Fxdv \div \int_S dv = \int_S Fx \mid \det F \mid dv \div \int_S \mid \det F \mid dv$$

$$= \int_{F(S)} F(x)\, dv' \div \int_{F(S)} dv'; \quad (dv' = \text{volume element of } F(S))$$

$$= \int_{F(S)} \xi dv' \div \int_{F(S)} dv'$$

$$= \text{mean center of } F(S).$$

Hence $B^*CB = C$, every B; and C being positively definite we may write it in the form T^*T, T non-singular. Thus $B^*T^*TB = T^*T$ so that TBT^{-1} *is unitary,* every B, T independent of B. *In other words the subgroup* $\{B\}$ *of the linear group is equivalent to a unitary group.*

When our subgroup $\{A\}$ is *finite* we may prove its equivalence to a unitary group without having recourse to the convex of $\{P\}$ where $P = A^*A$. We merely *average* $P = A^*A$ over the collection constructing the matrix

$$C = \frac{1}{r} \sum_A A^*A; \; r \text{ the order of } \{A\},$$

it being trivially evident that, then, $B^*CB = C$, every B. The rest of the argument is the same as before. When $\{A\} = \{D(s)\}$ is a representation of a *finite* group G, with elements $s, t, \cdots$, we may, instead of averaging over the *representation,* average over the *group,* i. e. construct the matrix

$$C = \frac{1}{g} \sum_s D^*(s)D(s); \; g \text{ the order of } G,$$

and it is again evident that $D^*(t)CD(t) = C$, every t, so that the rest of the argument is the same as before. For *some* infinite groups it is possible to define an averaging process over the *group,* in which integration replaces finite summation, and again prove the fundamental theorem without having recourse to the convex of (P). This *group averaging* has other important uses beyond the proof of the *unitary equivalence* theorem and we shall discuss it in a later chapter.

Appendix to Chapter Two

The volume and mean center of a convex point set.

We understand by a convex point set a bounded, closed point set having the property that it contains the entire line segment joining *any* two of its points; (so that, for instance, the convex of a bounded closed set is a convex point set); and we regard the points as points of a real n-dimensional rectangular Cartesian space where n is the dimension of the set (i. e. the set contains $n+1$ and not more than $n+1$ linearly independent points). Since the point set contains the entire simplex (analogue of segment of a line ($n=1$); triangle in a plane ($n=2$); tetrahedron in space ($n=3$)) determined by any $n+1$ linearly independent points of it, it certainly contains interior points (i. e. points of the set such that not only the points themselves but entire spherical neighborhoods of them belong to the set) and we place the origin of our rectangular Cartesian coördinate system at one of these interior points. If a is any unit vector: $(a \mid a)=1$, the line segment through the origin having the direction of a (i. e. the collection of points $\rho a, \rho \geqq 0$) has one and only one point in common with the boundary of our convex set; namely the point $x_0=\rho_0 a (\rho_0>0)$ such that ρa belongs to the convex set if $\rho \leqq \rho_0$ whilst ρa does not belong to the convex set if $\rho>\rho_0$. If $x=\rho a$ is any point on the join of the origin and x_0 (produced if necessary) the ratio ρ/ρ_0 is a non-negative function of x which is positively homogeneous of degree one: i. e. if $f(x)$ denotes ρ/ρ_0, $f \geqq 0$ and $f(kx)=kf(x)$, $k \geqq 0$ (it being evident that $f(0)=0$). The non-negative function $f(x)$ has the important property $f(x)+f(y) \geqq f(x+y)$, this being an immediate consequence of the fact that $f(x) \leqq 1$ if and only if x belongs to our convex point set. In fact on writing $x/f(x)=\xi$, $y/f(y)=\eta$, $(x \neq 0,\ y \neq 0)$, $f(\xi)=1$, $f(\eta)=1$ (owing to the positive homogeneity of f) and so ξ, η belong to our convex point set. On writing $f(x)/[f(x)+f(y)]=\alpha$; $f(y)/[f(x)+f(y)]=\beta$ the point $\alpha\xi+\beta\eta$ belongs to the line segment joining x, y and hence to our convex point set. Hence $f\left(\dfrac{x+y}{f(x)+f(y)}\right) \leqq 1$ or, equivalently, $f(x+y) \leqq f(x)+f(y)$. This *convex* property of $f(x)$ forces its *continuity*. In fact, if $e_1=(1,0,0,\cdots),\cdots, e_n=(0,0,\cdots,1)$ and M dominates the $2n$ numbers $f(\pm e_k)$, $k=1,\cdots,n$,

$$f(x) \leqq f(x^1 e_1)+\cdots+f(x^n e_n) \leqq M\{|x^1|+|x^2|+\cdots+|x^n|\}$$

where $x=(x^1,\cdots,x^n)$ (so that the points for which $|x^k| \leqq \dfrac{1}{nM}$,

$k = 1, \cdots, n$, all belong to our convex set). Observing that the basic convexity property $f(x+y) \leq f(x) + f(y)$ implies $-f(y) \leq f(x) - f(x+y)$, every x, y, or, equivalently, (on writing $-y$ for y, and $x+y$ for x) $-f(-y) \leq f(x+y) - f(x) \leq f(y)$, every (x, y), we have $|f(x+y) - f(x)|$ dominated by the greater of $|f(y)|$, $|f(-y)|$ and, à fortiori, by M $(|y^1| + \cdots + |y^n|)$ proving, incidentally, the continuity of $f(x)$ every x. If x is a unit vector, $|x| = 1$, the continuous function $f(x)$ defined over the closed set $|x| = 1$ assumes its least upper and greatest lower bounds (both positive) as x wanders over the unit sphere $|x| = 1$. Denoting these by $\frac{1}{r}$ and $\frac{1}{R}$ respectively we have, for arbitrary x (owing to the positive homogeneity of $f(x)$)

$$\frac{|x|}{r} \geq f(x) \geq \frac{|x|}{R}.$$

Hence the spherical region defined by $|x| \leq R$ contains all points of our convex set (these being characterised by $f \leq 1$) and has one point in common with the boundary of the set (so that it is, in fact, the *smallest* spherical region centered at the origin which contains all the points of the convex set); and the spherical region defined by $|x| \leq r$ belongs entirely to our convex set and has one point in common with the boundary of the set (so that it is, in fact, the largest spherical region centered at the origin which is entirely contained in the convex set). The fact that our convex set lies entirely in the spherical region $|x| \leq R$ implies, à fortiori, that it lies entirely in the "cube" (centered at the origin) $|x^k| \leq R$, $k = 1, \cdots, n$; and the fact that the spherical region $|x| \leq r$ belongs entirely to our convex set implies, à fortiori, that the "cube" (centered at the origin) $|x^k| \leq \frac{r}{\sqrt{n}}$, $k = 1, \cdots, n$, lies entirely in the point set. If we have an arbitrary "cubical grid" of mesh δ and if N denotes the number of elementary cubes of the grid which contain *only* points of our convex set, it follows that $N(\delta)^n \leq (2R)^n$; if we have a second cubical grid of mesh δ' and if Q denotes the number of elementary cubes of this grid which contain *at least one* point of our convex set, it follows that $Q(\delta')^n \geq \left(\frac{2r}{\sqrt{n}}\right)^n$. The fact that the Q cubes, of mesh δ' completely cover our set and hence completely cover the N cubes of mesh δ forces $0 \leq Q(\delta')^n - N(\delta)^n$. We now show that the *non-negative* number $Q(\delta')^n - N(\delta)^n$ is dominated by a number which tends to zero as δ, δ' tend, independently of each other, to zero. The bounded set of numbers $N(\delta)^n$

possesses an accumulation point V as $\delta \to 0$; this number V is, then, the limit of $Q(\delta')^n$ as $\delta' \to 0$ (and hence not merely an accumulation point but the *limit*, i.e. the *unique* accumulation point, of $N(\delta)^n$ as $\delta \to 0$). It is the *volume*, in the usual sense, of the convex set. To prove this statement let ϵ be an arbitrarily small positive proper fraction: $0 < \epsilon < 1$ and consider the collection of points of our set for which $f(x) \leq 1 - \epsilon$. Owing to the continuity of $f(x)$ we may make the mesh δ so small that each and every point of those elementary cubes which contain a point of our set for which $f \leq 1 - \epsilon$ is such that $f < 1 - \frac{\epsilon}{2}$, say. In other words the mesh δ can be made so small that if a cube contains a point for which $f \leq 1 - \epsilon$ the entire cube lies in the point set; similarly the mesh δ' can be made so small that if an elementary cube contains a point of the convex set every point of this elementary cube is such that $f(x) \leq 1 + \epsilon$. If N is the number of cubes of edge δ which contain a point of the set for which $f \leq 1 - \epsilon$ and we move each point x of these N cubes out from the origin to the point $\frac{1+\epsilon}{1-\epsilon} x$ we get a set of points of total volume $N\left(\frac{1+\epsilon}{1-\epsilon}\delta\right)^n$ which covers all the points x for which $f(x) \leq 1 + \epsilon$ and hence $N\left(\frac{1+\epsilon}{1-\epsilon}\delta\right)^n \geq Q(\delta')^n$. This implies

$$Q(\delta')^n - N(\delta)^n \leq N(\delta)^n \left\{ \left(\frac{1+\epsilon}{1-\epsilon}\right)^n - 1 \right\} \leq (2R)^n \left\{ \left(\frac{1+\epsilon}{1-\epsilon}\right)^n - 1 \right\} \to 0$$

with ϵ. This proves the existence of a volume or, equivalently, the multiple integral of unity:

$$V = \int dv$$

for any convex set.

The existence of the mean center of a convex set follows at once. We integrate the vector x over the region occupied by the N cubes of our mesh (obtaining $N(\delta)^n x_N$, say) and also over the Q cubes of our δ' mesh (obtaining $Q(\delta')^n x_Q$, say). The Q cubes of the δ' mesh cover the convex set which, in turn, covers the N cubes of the δ mesh so that the difference of our two integrals is the integral of x over a region whose volume $= Q(\delta')^n - N(\delta)^n$. Considering any component x^j of the vector x and observing that $|x^j| \leq (1+\epsilon)R$ over the Q cubes of the δ' mesh we obtain

$$|Q(\delta')^n x_Q{}^j - N(\delta)^n x_N{}^j| \leq (1+\epsilon)R\,|Q(\delta')^n - N(\delta)^n|.$$

Hence $N(\delta^n)x_N{}^j$, $Q(\delta')^n x_Q{}^j$ converge as $\delta, \delta' \to 0$ their common limit being, when divided by V, the j component of the mean center $\bar{x}$:

$$\bar{x} = \int xdv \div \int dv$$

of the convex set. When our convex set is the convex of a given bounded closed set (P) it is clear that $\bar{x}$ is itself a point of $Co(P)$; in fact the inequalities

$$p_-(c) \leq (x \mid c) \leq p_+(c)$$

which define a c-slice determined by (P) force

$$p_-(c) \leq (\bar{x} \mid c) \leq p_+(c)$$

so that $\bar{x}$ belongs to each c-slice determined by (P). In other words $\bar{x}$ is a point of $Co(P)$.

CHAPTER THREE

GROUP CHARACTERS

In this chapter we propose to discuss a method of multiplication of representations of a given group which enables us to derive new representations of the group from one or more given representations; and to apply our results to the determination of the number of non-equivalent irreducible representations of any *finite* group.

1. The Kronecker product.

Let A be any $m \times m$ matrix of which the element in the j-th row and k-th column is $a_k{}^j$ and let B be any $n \times n$ matrix of which the element in the p-th row and q-th column is $b_q{}^p$. Then the $mn \times mn$ products $a_k{}^j b_q{}^p$ constitute an $mn \times mn$ matrix C of which the element in the (j, p) row and (k, q) column is $a_k{}^j b_q{}^p$; C is termed the Kronecker product of B by A and is denoted by $A \times B$. It is convenient to arrange the row (and column) index-pairs (j, p) (and (k, q)) in dictionary order: so that (j, p), for example, precedes (j', p') if $j < j'$ or if $j = j'$, $p < p'$. When this is done $A \times B$ may be conveniently presented in the block form

$$(3.1) \qquad A \times B = \begin{pmatrix} a_1{}^1 B & a_2{}^1 B & \cdot & \cdot \\ a_1{}^2 B & \cdot & & \cdot \\ \cdot & & \cdot & \end{pmatrix}$$

$$\text{In particular } E_m \times B = \begin{pmatrix} B & 0 & 0 & \\ 0 & B & \cdot & \cdot \\ \cdot & \cdot & \cdot & \end{pmatrix} = B \dotplus B \dotplus \cdots \dotplus B \ (m \text{ terms})$$

so that $E_m \times E_n = E_{mn}$. It is clear that $B \times A$ is in general different from $A \times B$:

$$B \times A = \begin{pmatrix} b_1{}^1 A & b_2{}^1 A & \cdot & \cdot \\ b_1{}^2 A & \cdot & & \cdot \\ \cdot & & & \end{pmatrix}$$

Nevertheless $B \times A$ is obtainable from $A \times B$ by applying the *same* permutation to the rows and columns of the latter. Let us denote by $(j, p)^*$ the position of (p, j) when the ordering is dictionary-like, the label with the range n coming first; e. g., if $m = 2$, $n = 3$ the dictionary order where the label with the range 2 comes first is $(1, 1)$, $(1, 2)$, $(1, 3)$, $(2, 1)$, $(2, 2)$, $(2, 3)$ whilst the dictionary order when the label with the range 3 comes first is $(1,1)$, $(1,2)$, $(2,1)$, $(2,2)$, $(3,1)$, $(3,2)$. Hence $(1,1)^* = (1,1)$, $(1,2)^* = (1,3)$, $(1,3)^* = (2,2)$, $(2,1)^* = (1,2)$, $(2,2)^* = (2,1)$, $(2,3)^* = (2,3)$. Then if the (j,p) column of $A \times B$ is transferred to the $(j,p)^*$ position and the (k,q)row to the $(k,q)^*$ position we obtain $B \times A$. In other words

$$(B \times A) = P(A \times B)P^{-1} \tag{3.2}$$

where P is the permutation matrix associated with $\uparrow\begin{pmatrix}(j,p)^* \\ (j,p)\end{pmatrix}$.

Notice that P is quite independent of the elements of A and B being completely determined by their dimensions.

The Kronecker product $A \times B$ has several evident but important properties. In the first place it is *associative*. In other words if A, B, C are any three square matrices of dimensions m, n, p respectively then

$$A \times (B \times C) = (A \times B) \times C,$$

each side of this equation being the matrix of dimension mnp of which the element in the (j_1, j_2, j_3) row and (k_1, k_2, k_3) column is $a_{k_1}{}^{j_1} b_{k_2}{}^{j_2} c_{k_3}{}^{j_3}$. Owing to this associative property we may omit the parentheses and denote either side of our equation by $A \times B \times C$. If we multiply a given matrix A, of dimension n, by itself in this way m times we obtain the Kronecker m-th power

$$[A]_m = \underbrace{A \times A \times \cdots \times A}_{m \text{ terms}}$$

This is a matrix of dimension n^m of which the element in the $(j_1, j_2, \cdots, j_m)$-th row and $(k_1, k_2, \cdots, k_m)$-th column is $a_{k_1}{}^{j_1} a_{k_2}{}^{j_2} \cdots a_{k_m}{}^{j_m}$. The second important property to which we wish to call attention concerns the ordinary matrix product of two Kronecker products. Let A_1, A_2 be two $m \times m$ matrices and B_1, B_2 be two $n \times n$ matrices and consider the matrix product of the $mn \times mn$ matrix $A_2 \times B_2$ by the $mn \times mn$ matrix $A_1 \times B_1$: $(A_1 \times B_1)(A_2 \times B_2)$. This is an $mn \times mn$ matrix of which the element in the (j,p)-th row and (k,q)-th column is $(a_1)_\alpha{}^j (b_1)_\beta{}^p (a_2)_k{}^\alpha (b_2)_q{}^\beta$ where the summation labels α, β have the ranges $1, \cdots, m$ and $1, \cdots, n$, respectively. On summing first with respect to α and then with respect to β we obtain the product of the (j,k) element of A_1A_2 by the (p,q) element of B_1B_2. Hence

$$(A_1 \times B_1)(A_2 \times B_2) = A_1A_2 \times B_1B_2. \tag{3.3}$$

If A and B are *non-singular* square matrices, of dimensions m and n, respectively, it follows that

$$(A \times B)(A^{-1} \times B^{-1}) = E_m \times E_n = E_{mn}$$

so that $(A \times B)$ is itself non-singular, its inverse being $A^{-1} \times B^{-1}$. Since $A \times B = (A \times E_n)(E_m \times B)$ we have $\det(A \times B) = \det(A \times E_n) \det(E_m \times B)$. But $\det(E_m \times B) = (\det B)^m$ and $\det(A \times E_n) = \det(E_n \times A) = (\det A)^n$ since $A \times E_n$ and $E_n \times A$ are similar. Hence $\det(A \times B) = (\det A)^n \det(B)^m$. If, in particular, A and B have the same dimension n we have

$$\det(A \times B) = (\det A)^n \ (\det B)^n = \det(AB)^n.$$

Finally $(A \times B)^* = (A^* \times B^*)$; in fact the (jp, kq) element of $(A \times B)^* = \bar{a}_j{}^k \, \bar{b}_p{}^q = a^*{}_k{}^j \, b^*{}_q{}^p$ which is the (jp, kq) element of $(A^* \times B^*)$. In particular if A and B are both unitary matrices, U, V say, we have

$$(U \times V)^*(U \times V) = (U^* \times V^*)(U \times V) = (U^*U \times V^*V)$$
$$= (E_m \times E_n) = E_{mn}$$

so that $(U \times V)$ is itself unitary.

Let now Γ_1, Γ_2 be representations by matrices $D_1(s)$, $D_2(s)$, of dimensions m, n, respectively, of a given group G with elements $s, t, \cdots$; then the matrices $D_1(s) \times D_2(s)$ furnish a representation, of dimension mn, of G. In fact $D_1(s) \times D_2(s)$ is non-singular, every s, since $D_1(s)$, $D_2(s)$ are non-singular, every s; and

$$(D_1(t) \times D_2(t))(D_1(s) \times D_2(s))$$
$$= (D_1(t)D_1(s) \times D_2(t)D_2(s)) = D_1(ts) \times D_2(ts).$$

We term this mn-dimensional representation the Kronecker product of Γ_2 by Γ_1 and denote it by $\Gamma_1 \times \Gamma_2$. The product $\Gamma_2 \times \Gamma_1$ is a representation by the matrices $D_2(s) \times D_1(s)$ but $D_2(s) \times D_1(s) = P(D_1(s) \times D_2(s))P^{-1}$ where P is a non-singular (permutation) matrix which is independent of s. In other words the Kronecker product $\Gamma_2 \times \Gamma_1$ of Γ_1 by Γ_2 is the same as the Kronecker product $\Gamma_1 \times \Gamma_2$ of Γ_2 by Γ_1: *Kronecker multiplication of representations of a given group is commutative.* We may, in particular, form the Kronecker product $\Gamma \times \Gamma$ of a representation Γ of a given group G by itself; and, continuing, we may form the Kronecker m-th power of Γ

$$[\Gamma]_m = \underbrace{\Gamma \times \Gamma \times \cdots \times \Gamma}_{m \text{ factors}}.$$

If Γ is of dimension n, $[\Gamma]_m$ is of dimension n^m. For instance the elements $s, t, u, \cdots$ of the full linear group on n letters constitute an n-dimensional representation Γ of the full linear group. The Kronecker m-th power of Γ furnishes a representation, of dimension n^m, by matrices

$D(s)$, of the full linear group; it is a homogeneous rational integral representation of degree m since the $(j_1, j_2, \cdots, j_m; k_1, k_2, \cdots, k_m)$ element of $D(s)$ is $s_{k_1}{}^{j_1} s_{k_2}{}^{j_2} \cdots s_{k_m}{}^{j_m}$.

We may give a convenient geometrical picture of the Kronecker product $A \times B \times C \times \cdots$ as follows. Let $x, y, z, \cdots$ be arbitrary vectors in the carrier spaces of $A, B, C, \cdots$, respectively and write $\xi = Ax$, $\eta = By, \zeta = Cz, \cdots$. Then $\xi^{j_1} = a_{\alpha_1}{}^{j_1} x^{\alpha_1}$; $\eta^{j_2} = b_{\alpha_2}{}^{j_2} y^{\alpha_2}$; $\zeta^{j_3} = c_{\alpha_3}{}^{j_3} z^{\alpha_3}; \cdots$ so that $\xi^{j_1}\eta^{j_2}\zeta^{j_3} \cdots = a_{\alpha_1}{}^{j_1} b_{\alpha_2}{}^{j_2} c_{\alpha_3}{}^{j_3} \cdots x^{\alpha_1} y^{\alpha_2} z^{\alpha_3} \cdots$. Hence $A \times B \times C \cdots$ is the matrix of the transformation induced on the $mnp \cdots$ products $x^{k_1}y^{k_2}z^{k_3} \cdots$ by the transformations $x \rightarrow Ax$, $y \rightarrow By$, $z \rightarrow Cz, \cdots$ of the vectors $x, y, z, \cdots$. The products $x^{k_1}y^{k_2}z^{k_3} \cdots$ may be regarded as the components of a vector in a linear space—the carrier space of $A \times B \times C \cdots$. In particular the Kronecker m-th power $A \times A \times A \cdots \times A$ (m factors) is the matrix of the transformation induced on the n^m products $x_1{}^{k_1} \cdots x_m{}^{k_m}$ (where $x_1, \cdots, x_m$ are m arbitrary vectors of an n-dimensional carrier space) by the transformation $x \rightarrow Ax$ of this carrier space. For example let $n = 2$, $A = \begin{pmatrix} 1 & 0 \\ t & 1 \end{pmatrix}$ and let us calculate the Kronecker square of A. We have $\xi^1 = x^1$, $\xi^2 = tx^1 + x^2$; $\eta^1 = y^1$; $\eta^2 = ty^1 + y^2$ so that $\xi^1\eta^1 = x^1y^1$; $\xi^1\eta^2 = tx^1y^1 + x^1y^2$; $\xi^2\eta^1 = tx^1y^1 + x^2y^1$; $\xi^2\eta^2 = t^2x^1y^1 + tx^1y^2 + tx^2y^1 + x^2y^2$. Hence

$$[A]_2 = \begin{pmatrix} 1 & 0 & 0 & 0 \\ t & 1 & 0 & 0 \\ t & 0 & 1 & 0 \\ t^2 & t & t & 1 \end{pmatrix}.$$

Let v denote the vector of the carrier space S of $[A]_m = A \times A \times \cdots \times A$ (m factors) whose $(j_1, j_2, \cdots, j_m)$ component is $x_1{}^{j_1}x_2{}^{j_2} \cdots x_m{}^{j_m}$ where $x_1, x_2, \cdots, x_m$ are arbitrary vectors of the carrier space of A. If $p = \uparrow\begin{pmatrix} p_j \\ j \end{pmatrix}$ is *any* permutation on the m symbols $(1, \cdots, m)$ we denote by $p(v)$ the vector, in the carrier space S of $[A]_m$ whose $(j_1, \cdots, j_m)$ component is $x_1{}^{j_{p_1}} \cdots x_m{}^{j_{p_m}}$; and, generally, if $v^{j_1, \cdots, j_m}$ denote the components of *any* vector v of S we denote by $p(v)$ the vector of S whose $(j_1, \cdots, j_m)$ component is $v^{j_{p_1}, \cdots, j_{p_m}}$. The $m!$ equations $v - p(v) = 0$, every p, define a linear subspace R of S *and* R *is an invariant space of the operator* $[A]_m = A \times A \times \cdots \times A$ (m factors). In fact if $v^{j_1, \cdots, j_m}$ denote the components of an arbitrary vector v of R we have, by definition of R, $v^{j_1, \cdots, j_m} = v^{j_{p_1}, \cdots, j_{p_m}}$; every $p = \uparrow\begin{pmatrix} p_j \\ j \end{pmatrix}$. Hence, if $[A]_m v = w$,

$$w^{j_{p_1},\cdots,j_{p_m}} = a^{j_{p_1}}_{a_1}\cdots a^{j_{p_m}}_{a_m} v^{a_1,\cdots,a_m} = a^{j_{p_1}}_{a_{p_1}}\cdots a^{j_{p_m}}_{a_{p_m}} v^{a_{p_1},\cdots,a_{p_m}}$$
$$= a^{j_1}_{a_1}\cdots a^{j_m}_{a_m} v^{a_{p_1},\cdots,a_{p_m}} = a^{j_1}_{a_1}\cdots a^{j_m}_{a_m} v^{a_1,\cdots,a_m} = w^{j_1,\cdots,j_m}$$

proving the invariance of R under $[A]_m$. If Γ is a representation by matrices $D(s)$, of dimension n, of a group G with elements $s, t, \cdots$ it follows that the representation $[\Gamma]_m$ by matrices $[D(s)]_m$, of dimension n^m, of G has R as an invariant subspace and, hence, induces in R a representation of G of dimension equal to the dimension of R. This representation is termed the symmetrized Kronecker m-th power and we shall denote it by $[\Gamma]_{(m)}$.

It is clear that the carrier space S of $[A]_m$ is the complete n^m dimensional space obtained by assigning arbitrary values to each of the components $v^{j_1,\cdots,j_m}$. For, if not, the aggregate of vectors of the type $x_1^{j_1}x_2^{j_2}\cdots x_m^{j_m}$, where $x_1, x_2, \cdots, x_m$ are arbitrary vectors of the carrier space of A, would span a proper linear subspace of the complete n^m dimensional space; there would, therefore, exist one or more non-trivial equations of the type $c_{a_1a_2,\ldots,a_m}x_1^{a_1}\cdots x_m^{a_m} = 0$. But the validity of such an equation for all vectors $x_1, \cdots, x_m$ from the carrier space of A forces all the coefficients $c_{j_1,\ldots,j_m}$ to vanish. In fact on setting $x_m = e_k$, $k = 1, \cdots, n$, in turn, we find $c_{a_1,\ldots,a_{m-1}k}x_1^{a_1}\cdots x_{m-1}^{a_{m-1}} = 0$, every k, and an argument by induction with respect to m justifies our statement (it being clearly true for $m = 1$: $c_a x^a = 0$, every x, forces $c_j = 0$, every j). It is similarly clear that the space R is spanned by the collection of vectors $v^{j_1,\cdots,j_m} = x^{j_1}\cdots x^{j_m}$ where x is an arbitrary vector from the carrier space of A (which vectors obviously belong to R). In fact if this were not the case each vector $v^{j_1,\cdots,j_m} = x^{j_1}\cdots x^{j_m}$ would lie in a linear subspace of R; i. e. *in addition* to the linear equations $v = q(v)$: $v^{j_1,\cdots,j_m} - v^{j_{q_1}\cdots j_{q_m}} = 0$; $q = \uparrow\binom{q_j}{j}$; defining R there would have to be at least one non-trivial equation $c_{a_1,\ldots,a_m}v^{a_1,\cdots,a_m} = 0$. We use the equations $v = q(v)$ to secure the symmetry of the coefficients $c_{j_1\ldots j_m}$ (with respect to permutations of the labels $1, 2, \cdots, m$) and then we have the identical vanishing of the m-th degree polynomial in the n variables $(x^1, \cdots, x^n)$:

$$c_{a_1,\ldots,a_m}x^{a_1}\cdots x^{a_m} = \sum_{p_1,\ldots,p_n} \frac{m!\,d_{p_1,\ldots,p_n}}{p_1!\cdots p_n!}(x^1)^{p_1}\cdots(x^n)^{p_n};$$
$$p_1 + p_2 + \cdots + p_n = m$$

where $d_{p_1,\ldots,p_n}$ denotes $c_{j_1,\ldots,j_m}$ if the set $j_1, \cdots, j_m$ contains p_1 ones, p_2 twos, $\cdots$, p_n n's; (the numerical factor $\dfrac{m!}{p_1!\cdots p_n!}$ being the number of permutations of m things of which p_1 are alike, p_2 alike and so on).

But the identical vanishing of this polynomial forces the vanishing of all its coefficients, i. e. of all $c_{j_1,\ldots,j_m}$ and this proves that the vectors $v = x^{j_1} \cdots x^{j_m}$ span, as x wanders over the carrier space of A, the entire subspace R.

The matrices of the symmetrized Kronecker m-th power may be found by using the following principle. Let Γ be any reducible representation of a given group and let an invariant subspace R (of dimension m) of its carrier space be defined by a set of $n - m$ linearly independent homogeneous equations

$$\xi^{m+k} \equiv c_a{}^{m+k} x^a = 0; \qquad (k = 1, \cdots, n - m).$$

We introduce a new basis in which the last $n - m$ components of a vector x are ξ^{m+k} the other m being obtained by eliminating $n - m$ of the x's by means of the equations $\xi^{m+k} = c_a{}^{m+k} x^a$. In this basis Γ is reduced since any vector for which $\xi^{m+k} = 0$, $k = 1, \cdots, n - m$, goes over, by hypothesis, into a vector whose last $n - m$ components are zero. The representation induced in R by Γ is obtained by considering the transformation of the remaining m coördinates. Thus, to be specific, suppose we have eliminated $(x^{m+1}, \cdots, x^n)$ so that our new components of any vector x are $(x^1, \cdots, x^m, \xi^{m+1}, \cdots, \xi^n)$. We find the representation induced in R by eliminating $x^{m+1}, \cdots, x^n$ from $x \rightarrow Ax$ and since we need *only the coefficients* of $x^1, \cdots, x^m$ we may write *at the beginning* $\xi^{m+1} = 0, \cdots, \xi^n = 0$. For example if Γ is the Kronecker square $[A]_2$ our $\dfrac{n(n-1)}{2}$ equations $\xi = 0$ are $\xi^{r,s} \equiv v^{r,s} - v^{s,r} = 0$. We introduce as our first $\dfrac{n(n+1)}{2}$ coördinates the quantities $v^{r,s}$, $r \leq s$, and eliminate the remaining quantities $v^{r,s}$, $r > s$, by means of the equations $\xi^{r,s} = 0$, i. e. we replace $v^{r,s}$, $r > s$, by $v^{s,r}$. In other words $[A]_{(2)}$ is the matrix of the transformation on the $\dfrac{n(n+1)}{2}$ products $x^r x^s$, $r \leq s$, induced by the transformation $x \rightarrow Ax$ of any vector x of the carrier spaces of A. Similarly $[A]_{(m)}$ is the matrix of the transformation on the distinct products $x^{j_1} x^{j_2} \cdots x^{j_m}$ induced by the transformation $x \rightarrow Ax$ of any vector x of the carrier space of A; and the dimension of the carrier space of $[A]_{(m)}$ is the number of such distinct products. Thus if we consider the representation Γ, of dimension 2, by the matrices

$$D(s) = \begin{pmatrix} 1 & 0 \\ s & 1 \end{pmatrix}$$

of the (Abelian) group of complex numbers under addition the matrices of the symmetrized square are

$$[D(s)]_{(2)} = \begin{pmatrix} 1 & 0 & 0 \\ s & 1 & 0 \\ s^2 & 2s & 1 \end{pmatrix},$$

the representation being three-dimensional. To get the symmetrized m-th power we write $\xi^1 = x^1$, $\xi^2 = sx^1 + x^2$ and consider $(\xi^1)^j(\xi^2)^{m-j} = (x^1)^j(sx^1 + x^2)^{m-j}$. The representation is of dimension $m+1$ and if the components of v, i. e. $x^{j_1}x^{j_2}\cdots x^{j_m}$ are written in the order $(x^1)^m$, $(x^1)^{m-1}x^2$, $(x^1)^{m-2}(x^2)^2, \cdots, (x^2)^m$ the matrices of the symmetrized Kronecker m-th power appear as

$$(3.4) \qquad [D(s)]_{(m)} = \begin{pmatrix} 1 & 0 & 0 & 0 & \cdot & \cdot \\ s & 1 & 0 & 0 & \cdot & \cdot \\ s^2 & 2s & 1 & 0 & \cdot & \cdot \\ \cdot & \cdot & \cdot & \cdot & & \\ s^m & \binom{m}{1} s^{m-1} & & & \cdot & \cdot \end{pmatrix}$$

where $\binom{m}{r}$ denotes the binomial coefficient $m! \div r!\; m-r!$.

In general the dimension of the symmetrized Kronecker product is the number of combinations of m letters $(k_1, \cdots, k_m)$ each of which can take n values (repetitions being allowed). It is, therefore, the number of terms in the expansion of $(z_1 + z_2 + \cdots + z_n)^m$; in fact if there are p_1 1's, p_2 2's, $\cdots p_n$ n's in the set $k_1, \cdots, k_m$ we have $p_1 + p_2 + \cdots + p_n = m$ and we may associate each component $x^{k_1} \cdots x^{k_m}$ of a vector v of R with a term in the expansion of $(z_1 + z_2 + \cdots + z_n)^m$. Denoting the desired dimension of R by $N(n, m)$ it is clear, on expanding $(z_1 + z_2 + \cdots + z_n)^m$ by the *binomial* theorem (writing $z_1 + z_2 + \cdots + z_n$ in the form $z_1 + (z_2 + \cdots + z_n)$) that

$$(3.5) \qquad N(n, m) = N(n, m-1) + N(n-1, m)$$

(the first term on the right being the number of terms that have z_1 as a factor and the second being the number of terms free of z_1). Now $N(1, m) = 1$, every m, $N(n, 1) = n$ every n; setting $n = 2$ in the difference equation (3. 5) we find $N(2, m) - N(2, m-1) = N(1, m) = 1$ so that $N(2, m) = m + \text{constant} = m + 1$ since $N(2, 1) = 2$. Then $N(3, m) - N(3, m-1) = N(2, m) = m + 1$ so that $N(3, m) = \frac{1}{2}(m+1)(m+2)$ (the additive constant being zero since $N(3, 1) = 3$). Proceeding in this way we arrive at the general formula

$$(3.6) \qquad N(n, m) = \frac{(m + n - 1)!}{m!\; n - 1!}$$

which may readily be verified by induction (using the difference formula (3.5)).

The symmetrized Kronecker second power, or square, is of dimension $\frac{n(n+1)}{2}$ and may be regarded as the transformation on the $\frac{n(n+1)}{2}$ products $x^r x^s$ $(r \leq s)$ of the components of a vector x in the carrier space of A when x undergoes the transformation $x \rightarrow Ax$. If A is unitary and x is any vector in the carrier space of A the product x^*x is invariant under A and hence $Tr\bar{x}x^*xx'$ is invariant under A (which is merely another way of stating that the Kronecker square $[A]_2$ is unitary when A is unitary). If we write $z^{r,s} = \sqrt{2}\, x^r x^s$, $r < s$; $z^{r,r} = x^r x^r$ (which is merely a transformation of basis in the carrier space of $[A]_{(2)}$) it follows that z^*z is invariant when x undergoes the transformation $x \rightarrow Ax$. In other words $[A]_{(2)}$, *when presented in this new basis*, is unitary. If $a_s{}^r$ is the (r, s) element of A the (rs, pq) element of $[A]_{(2)}$, when presented in the new basis, is furnished by the formulae:

$$[A]_{(2)}{}^{r,r}_{p,p} = a_p{}^r a_p{}^r; \quad [A]_{(2)}{}^{r,r}_{p,q} = \sqrt{2}\, a_p{}^r a_q{}^r \qquad (p < q);$$
$$[A]_{(2)}{}^{r,s}_{p,p} = \sqrt{2}\, a_p{}^r a_p{}^s \ (r < s); \quad [A]_{(2)}{}^{r,s}_{p,q} = a_p{}^r a_q{}^s + a_q{}^r a_p{}^s \qquad (r < s, p < q).$$

These are obtained by writing $Ax = \xi$ and calculating $\xi^r\xi^r$, $\sqrt{2}\,\xi^r\xi^s$ $(r < s)$ in terms of $x^p x^p$, $\sqrt{2}\, x^p x^q$ $(p < q)$.

Another example of the symmetrized Kronecker power is the following. Let A be a unitary 2×2 matrix and consider the symmetrized Kronecker m-th power $[A]_{(m)}$. This will be of dimension $m + 1$ and may be obtained as the transformation induced on the products $(x^1)^k(x^2)^{m-k}$, $k = 0, 1, \cdots, m$, by the transformation $x \rightarrow Ax$ of the vector $x = (x^1, x^2)$. Since the non-symmetrized Kronecker m-th power of a unitary matrix is unitary it follows that if v is the vector $v^{j_1, \cdots, j_m} = x_1{}^{j_1} \cdots x_m{}^{j_m}$ (where each j has the range $(1, 2)$) v^*v is invariant under the non-symmetrized Kronecker m-th power. On setting $x_1 = x_2 = \cdots = x_m$, $v^{j_1, \cdots, j_m}$ becomes symmetric in the labels 1 to m; if k of the superscripts $j_1, \cdots, j_m$ assume the value 1 and $m - k$ the value 2 the term $v^{j_1, \cdots, j_m}$ furnishes, under permutations of the m superscripts $j_1, \cdots, j_m$, $\binom{m}{k} = \frac{m!}{k!\, m-k}$ terms all having the same value $(x^1)^k(x^2)^{m-k}$. If, then, we write $z^k = \sqrt{\binom{m}{k}}\, (x^1)^k(x^2)^{m-k}$, which amounts merely to a change of basis in the carrier space of $[A]_{(m)}$,

z^*z is invariant under $x \to Ax$ so that $[A]_{(m)}$ is, when presented in this basis, *unitary*. It is convenient to write $m = 2j$ (so that j takes the *half-integral* values $\frac{1}{2}, 1, 3/2, 2, \cdots$) and to denote $k - j$ by μ so that μ assumes the $m + 1 = 2j + 1$ values beginning with $-j$ and ending with $+j$. Then the transformation induced by $x \to Ax$ on the $2j + 1$ quantities

$$\xi^\mu = \frac{(x^1)^{j+\mu}(x^2)^{j-\mu}}{\sqrt{(j+\mu)!(j-\mu)!}};\ \mu = -j, -j+1, \cdots, \cdots j-1, j$$

(the constant factor $m!$ being omitted as unimportant) presents $[A]_{(m)}$ as a unitary matrix. As A runs over the 2×2 unitary group we obtain in this way a $2j + 1$-dimensional unitary representation Γ_j of this 2×2 unitary group. If this unitary representation were reducible, it would be completely reducible, i. e. each of its matrices could be presented in the form $T_1 \dotplus T_2$ where T_1 is of dimension p, say, and T_2 is of dimension $2j + 1 - p$. Then every matrix of the form $\alpha E_p + \beta E_{2j+1-p}$ (α, β arbitrary complex numbers) would be commutative with each matrix of Γ_j. If, then, we can show that the *only* matrices which are commutative with each and every matrix of Γ_j are scalar we shall know that the various representations Γ_j of the 2×2 unitary group are irreducible and this we proceed to show. We consider first the diagonal unitary (and unimodular) 2×2 matrices

$$A(\theta) = \begin{pmatrix} \exp(i\theta) & 0 \\ 0 & \exp(-i\theta) \end{pmatrix};\ \theta \text{ real.}$$

The corresponding matrices of $[A]_{(m)}$ are also diagonal since $x \to A(\theta)x$ forces $\xi^\mu \to \eta^\mu = \exp(2i\mu\theta)\xi^\mu$. Since the elements of these diagonal matrices are all different, the only matrices which commute with any one of them are diagonal: in fact if D is an n-dimensional diagonal matrix and T is any $n \times n$ matrix the (r, s) element of DT is $d_r t_s{}^r$ whilst the (r, s) element of TD is $t_s{}^r d_s$ so that if the diagonal elements $(d_1, d_2, \cdots d_n)$ of D are all different and $DT = TD$ then $t_s{}^r = 0$ if $r \neq s$, i. e. T is diagonal. Conversely if D is commutative with T and $t_s{}^r \neq 0$ then $d_r = d_s$. We next consider the non-diagonal (but still unimodular) unitary 2×2 matrices

$$A = \begin{pmatrix} a & b \\ -\bar{b} & \bar{a} \end{pmatrix};\ \bar{a}a + \bar{b}b = 1,\ a \neq 0,\ b \neq 0.$$

The last row of $[A]_{(2j)}$ is found by evaluating $\eta^j = \dfrac{(y^1)^{2j}}{\sqrt{2j!}}$ where $y = Ax$ so that $y^1 = (ax^1 + bx^2)$. We find

$$\eta^j = \frac{1}{\sqrt{2j!}} \sum_\mu \frac{2j!}{(j+\mu)!(j-\mu)!} a^{j+\mu} b^{j-\mu} (x^1)^{j+\mu} (x^2)^{j-\mu}$$
$$= \sum_\mu \sqrt{\frac{2j!}{(j+\mu)!(j-\mu)!}} a^{j+\mu} b^{j-\mu} \xi^\mu.$$

Hence the element in the j-th row and μ-th column of $[A]_{(2j)}$ is $\sqrt{\frac{2j!}{(j+\mu)!(j-\mu)!}} a^{j+\mu} b^{j-\mu}$. Since neither b nor a is zero none of these elements vanishes and hence any diagonal matrix which commutes with $[A]_{(2j)}$ must be scalar. This proves the irreducibility of the representation Γ_j of the 2×2 unitary subgroup of the two-dimensional full linear group and in fact more. The matrices of Γ_j which correspond to the *unimodular* 2×2 unitary matrices furnish a representation of this "smaller" subgroup of the two-dimensional full-linear group; and it might well be that whilst Γ_j is irreducible (i. e. possesses no proper invariant subspace of its $2j+1$-dimensional carrier space) yet the subgroup of it formed by the matrices which correspond to the *unimodular* 2×2 unitary matrices is reducible. But our argument shows that this is not the case; *the representations we have obtained of the unimodular 2×2 unitary group are irreducible.* We shall see later that there are no other continuous irreducible representations, i. e. unitary irreducible representations of this group (it being understood that the identity representation, in which every 2×2 unitary matrix is represented by the 1×1 unit matrix is cared for by setting $j = 0$).

The method described in the foregoing paragraph for 2×2 matrices is evidently applicable to the general case of $n \times n$ matrices. Here $[A]_{(m)}$ is the transformation induced on the $\frac{n+m-1!}{m!n-1!}$ products $(x^1)^{p_1} \cdots (x^n)^{p_n}$ where $p_1 + p_2 + \cdots + p_n = m$. On introducing the change of basis $z^{p_1, \cdots, p_n} = \sqrt{\frac{m!}{p_1! \cdots p_n!}} (x^1)^{p_1} \cdots (x^n)^{p_n}$ in the carrier space of $[A]_{(m)}$ this symmetrized Kronecker m-th power appears as a unitary matrix when A is unitary. $[A]_{(m)}$ is diagonal, with diagonal elements $\exp i(p_1\theta_1 + p_2\theta_2 + \cdots + p_n\theta_n)$ when A is diagonal with diagonal elements $\exp i\theta_k$. Hence the only matrices commutative with all those diagonal matrices (of this type) of $[A]_{(m)}$ for which $\theta_1 + \theta_2 + \cdots + \theta_m = 0$ are diagonal and as before they are seen to be scalar if they also commute with all those matrices of $[A]_{(m)}$ which correspond to unimodular unitary matrices A. Hence the representations (rational, integral of degree m) of the unitary subgroup of the full linear group (or of its unimodular subgroup) obtained in this way, i. e. by means of the symmetrized Kronecker m-th power, are *irreducible.*

2. The orthogonality relations for a finite group.

If X is any $m \times n$ matrix it may be regarded as a vector in the carrier space of $A \times B$ where A is any $m \times m$ matrix and B is any $n \times n$ matrix. If $x_s{}^r$, the element in the r-th row and s-th column of X, is regarded as the (r, s) component of the *vector* X the result of operating on the vector X by $A \times B$ is the vector whose (r, s) component is $a_\alpha{}^r\, b_\beta{}^s\, x_\beta{}^\alpha$, i. e. $X \rightarrow Y = AXB'$ where B' denotes the transpose of B (the matrix obtained from B by interchanging its rows and columns). If $\bar{B}$ is the conjugate complex of B an equivalent form of statement of this fact is the following:

Under the transformation $A \times \bar{B}$ *the vector* $X \rightarrow Y = AXB^*$. We say that the vector X is an invariant vector of $A \times \bar{B}$ when $Y = X$, i. e. when $X = AXB^*$ (it being trivially evident that if X is an invariant vector so also is αX, α any complex number).

Let us now consider two representations Γ_1, Γ_2, of dimensions m, n, respectively, by matrices $D_1(s), D_2(s)$ of a given group G with elements $s, t, \cdots$. From Γ_2 we obtain the representation $\bar{\Gamma}_2$, of dimension n, by matrices $\bar{D}_2(s)$ and from $\Gamma_1, \bar{\Gamma}_2$ the representation $\Gamma_1 \times \bar{\Gamma}_2$ of dimension mn, by matrices $D_1(s) \times \bar{D}_2(s)$. Writing any *vector* v of the carrier space of $\Gamma_1 \times \bar{\Gamma}_2$ as an $m \times n$ matrix X, the (r, s) component $v^{r,s}$ of the vector being the element $x_s{}^r$ in the r-th row and s-th column of the matrix X, we say that X is an invariant vector of $\Gamma_1 \times \bar{\Gamma}_2$ if it is an invariant vector of $D_1(s) \times \bar{D}_2(s)$, every s;

$$X = D_1(s) X D^*{}_2(s)\,; \text{ every } s$$

or, equivalently,

$$X(D^*{}_2(s))^{-1} = D_1(s)X; \text{ every } s.$$

The matrices $(D^*{}_2(s))^{-1}$ furnish a representation $\Gamma^*{}_2$, of dimension n, of G which is known as the adjoint of Γ_2. In fact both the star and reciprocal of a product reverse the order of the factors: $(AB)^* = B^*A^*$; $(AB)^{-1} = B^{-1}A^{-1}$ and so $\{(AB)^*\}^{-1} = (B^*A^*)^{-1} = (A^*)^{-1}(B^*)^{-1}$. Hence $\{D^*{}_2(st)\}^{-1} = [\{(D_2(s)D_2(t))\}^*]^{-1} = (D^*{}_2(s))^{-1}(D^*{}_2(t))^{-1}$ so that the collection $(D^*{}_2(s))^{-1}$ furnishes a representation of G (since it contains the unit matrix $(D^*{}_2(e))^{-1} = (E^*{}_n)^{-1} = (E_n)^{-1} = E_n$ and the inverse $(D^*{}_2(s^{-1}))^{-1}$ of each of its elements $(D^*{}_2(s))^{-1}$). If both Γ_1 and $\Gamma^*{}_2$ *are irreducible* it follows from Schur's lemma that either

1) $X = 0$, i. e. $\Gamma_1 \times \bar{\Gamma}_2$ possesses no non-trivial invariant vector (i. e. no invariant vector other than the zero vector)

or 2) $m = n$ and $\Gamma^*{}_2$ is equivalent to Γ_1.

For a *finite* group G it is very easy to formulate a rule for obtaining invariant vectors of *any* representation Γ of G. In fact if x is any vector of the carrier space of Γ we simply average $D(s)x$ over G obtaining the vector

$$v = \frac{1}{g}\sum_s D(s)x; \; g \text{ the order of } G.$$

It follows at once that $D(t)v = \frac{1}{g}\sum_{(s)} D(t)D(s)x = \frac{1}{g}\sum_{(s)} D(ts)x = \frac{1}{g}\sum_s D(s)x = v$, every t, since G is sent into itself by the *left-translation* t, i. e. the set of elements $\{ts\}$ is the same as the set $\{s\}$. It is clear that *all* invariant vectors are obtained in this way; in fact if v is any invariant vector the average, over G, of $D(s)v$ is v itself. Furthermore it is an immediate consequence of the definition of invariant vector that each invariant vector v of Γ spans a one-dimensional invariant subspace of the carrier subspace of Γ in which Γ induces the identity representation (i. e. the representation Γ_1 in which $D_1(s) = 1$). The invariant vectors of Γ span an invariant subspace of the carrier space of Γ and each vector of this invariant subspace is itself an invariant vector (it being trivially evident that the sum of any two invariant vectors of Γ is itself an invariant vector of Γ). All invariant vectors of Γ are secured by taking for x, in turn, the vectors e_k, $k = 1, \cdots, n$, of a basis in the carrier space of Γ and then the corresponding invariant vectors are

$$v_k = \frac{1}{g}\sum_s D(s)e_k.$$

v_k is, accordingly, obtained by averaging over G the k-th columns of the matrices of the representation Γ.

As an example of the construction of all invariant vectors of any representation Γ of a finite group G of order g let us consider the *regular representation* of G. This is a representation of dimension g obtained as follows. Denoting the elements of G by s_1 $(= e)$, $s_2, \cdots, s_g$ the left translation $s_p s_j = s_{p_j}$, p fixed, $j = 1, \cdots, g$, effects a permutation $p = \uparrow\begin{pmatrix} p_j \\ j \end{pmatrix}$ on the subscripts of the elements s; and it is clear that if $s_p \rightarrow p$, $s_q \rightarrow q$ then $s_q s_p \rightarrow qp$. If P is the permutation matrix associated with p (i. e. the matrix all of whose elements in the j-th column are zero save the one in the p_j-th row, which is unity, $j = 1, \cdots, g$) the matrices $P = D(s_p)$ furnish a g-dimensional representation of G which is known as the *regular representation* of G. Since for any given j a given p_j occurs once and only once (as s_p runs over G) the average over G of the j-th columns of $P = D(s_p)$ has all its elements equal to $1/g$

and, hence, does not vary with j. In other words the space of invariant vectors of the regular representation of G is one-dimensional so that the *regular representation of any finite group G contains the identity representation once and only once.*

Returning now to the representation $\Gamma_1 \times \bar{\Gamma}_2$ of any finite group G let us consider the space spanned by its invariant vectors. We have seen that if Γ_1 and Γ^*_2 are irreducible and not equivalent the space spanned by its invariant vectors must be the zero space. In other words the average over the group of $D_1(s) \times \bar{D}_2(s)$ must be the zero $mn \times mn$ matrix. Written out in full this gives

$$(3.7) \qquad \begin{aligned} &\sum_s (D_1(s))_k{}^j(\bar{D}_2(s))_q{}^p = 0, \text{ or equivalently,} \\ &\sum_s (D^*{}_2(s))_p{}^q(D_1(s))_k{}^j = 0 \end{aligned}$$

provided the representations Γ_1, Γ^*_2 by matrices $D_1(s)$ and $\{D^*{}_2(s)\}^{-1}$ are irreducible and non-equivalent. We may omit the star (since any representation Γ is the adjoint of its adjoint Γ^*) and write

$$(3.7^{\text{bis}}) \qquad \sum_s D_2(s^{-1})_p{}^q D_1(s)_k{}^j = 0,$$

provided the representations Γ_1, Γ_2 by matrices $D_1(s)$ and $D_2(s)$ are irreducible and non-equivalent.

On the other hand if Γ_1 and Γ^*_2 are equivalent we introduce appropriate bases so that $\{D^*{}_2(s)\}^{-1} = D_1(s)$ and then we see that any invariant vector X of $\Gamma_1 \times \bar{\Gamma}_2$ is such that $D_1(s)X = XD_1(s)$. If Γ_1 is irreducible it follows that X is a scalar matrix. Hence the average over G of the (k, q)-th columns of $D_1(s) \times \bar{D}_2(s)$ is a scalar matrix; in other words the average over G of $D_1(s)_k{}^j\bar{D}_2(s)_q{}^p$ is zero unless $p = j$ in which case its value is independent of j. To see what this value is we average over j and observe that $\sum_{(a)} D_1(s)_k{}^a\bar{D}_2(s)_q{}^a = D^*{}_2(s)_a{}^q D_1(s)_k{}^a$ $= (D^*{}_2(s)D_1(s))_k{}^q = \delta_k{}^q$. Hence if Γ is an irreducible representation of dimension n, by matrices $D(s)$, of a given finite group G we have

$$(3.8) \qquad \sum_s (D(s^{-1}))_p{}^q(D(s))_k{}^j = \frac{g}{n}\,\delta_k{}^q\delta_p{}^j$$

where $\delta_p{}^j$ is the Kronecker symbol: $\delta_p{}^j = 0$ if $j \neq p$; $\delta_j{}^j = 1$. When the representation Γ is unitary (which is no restriction since every representation of a finite group, being bounded, is equivalent to a unitary representation) our result takes the following form:

$$(3.9) \qquad \sum_s (D^*(s))_p{}^q\, D(s)_k{}^j = \frac{g}{n}\,\delta_k{}^q\,\delta_p{}^j.$$

The equations (3, 7) and (3, 8), or, equivalently, (3, 9) when Γ is presented in unitary form, are known as the orthogonality relations connecting *irreducible* representations of any given finite group.

3. The characters of any representation of a finite group.

If Γ is any representation, by matrices $D(s)$, of a group G, with elements $s, t, \cdots$ we term the collection of numbers $\chi(s) = TrD(s)$ the *characters* of Γ. Since the trace of a matrix is unaltered by a transformation of the matrix by any element of the full linear group two facts are evident: 1) the characters are unaffected by any change of basis; for under a change of basis $D(s) \to T^{-1}D(s)T$ and $TrD(s) = Tr(T^{-1}D(s)T)$. In other words the characters of a representation depend only on the representation and not upon the basis used to present it. Since every representation of a finite group is unitary we may suppose, when discussing the characters of a representation of a finite group, that the matrices of the representation are unitary and we shall do this. Since $U^*(s) = U^{-1}(s) = U(s^{-1})$ it follows that for *any* representation of a *finite* group $\chi(s^{-1}) = \bar{\chi}(s)$. 2) The characters $\chi(s)$ are unaffected by a transformation of s by any element t of G:

$$\chi(s) = \chi(t^{-1}st); \text{ every } t.$$

In fact $D(t^{-1}st) = D(t^{-1})D(s)D(t)$ so that $TrD(t^{-1}st) = TrD(s)$. The collection of elements $t^{-1}st$, s fixed, t variable over G, are said to form a *class*; and the class is said to be *determined by s*. It is clear that a class is determined by *any* one of its elements: $u^{-1}su = (t^{-1}u)^{-1}t^{-1}st(t^{-1}u)$, so that the class determined by s is contained in the class determined by $t^{-1}st$, s and t arbitrary in g. Hence the class determined by $t^{-1}st$ is contained in the class determined by $t \cdot t^{-1}st \cdot t^{-1} = s$. Thus the class determined by $t^{-1}st$ coincides with the class determined by s. We shall suppose that there are p $(\leq g)$ classes $C_1, \cdots, C_p$ in G and shall denote the character of the k-th class by χ^k: $\chi(s) = \chi^k$ when $s \subset C_k$, $k = 1, \cdots, p$. This property of the characters of any representation Γ of a group G; namely, that the characters of all elements of G which belong to the same class are the same, is described by the statement that the *characters* of a representation Γ constitute a *class-function* which is termed the *character* of Γ.

On writing $k = j$, $p = q$, and summing with respect to j and q, in the relations (3. 7) and (3. 9) we find first

$$\sum_s \bar{\chi}_2(s)\chi_1(s) = 0 \tag{3.10}$$

if Γ_1, Γ_2 are non-equivalent irreducible representations of the same finite group G. And, secondly,

(3.11) $$\sum_s \bar{\chi}(s)\chi(s) = g$$

if Γ is an irreducible representation of G. These relations are known as the *orthogonality relations* connecting the characters of irreducible representations of any finite group G. If n_k denotes the number of elements of G lying in the class C_k, $k = 1, \cdots, p$, the orthogonality relations may be written in the equivalent form

$$\sum_k n_k \bar{\chi}_2{}^k \chi_1{}^k = 0; \qquad \sum_k n_k \bar{\chi}^k \chi^k = g.$$

On writing $\sqrt{\frac{n_k}{g}}\chi^k = v^k$, $k = 1, \cdots, p$ and regarding v^k, $k = 1, \cdots, p$, as the coordinates of a vector v (named the *vector character* of Γ) in a p-dimensional space the orthogonality relations connecting the characters of irreducible representations of any given finite group appear in the convenient form

(3.12) $$(v_1 \mid v_2) = 0; \qquad (v \mid v) = 1.$$

Hence the vector-characters of non-equivalent irreducible representations form a unitary set; and, in consequence, the vector-characters of non-equivalent irreducible representations are linearly independent. In fact a hypothecated relation $c^a v_a = 0$ forces $(c^a v_a \mid v_j) = 0$, $j = 1, \cdots$ and hence $c^j = 0$, $j = 1, 2, \cdots$. An important consequence of this result is the following: *the number of non-equivalent irreducible representations of a finite group is limited, being not more than the number p of classes of the group.* For there cannot be more than p linearly independent vectors in a p-dimensional space.

The orthogonality relations amongst the characters of the irreducible representations of a finite group imply that non-equivalent irreducible representations cannot have the same character vector (or, equivalently, the same characters). For if they did we would have to have the contradictory relations $(v \mid v) = 0$, $(v \mid v) = 1$. Furthermore if we have a reducible representation Γ and resolve it into its irreducible components

$$\Gamma = c^a \Gamma_a$$

the coefficients c^k are uniquely determined. In fact the stated analysis of Γ implies

$$v = c^a v_a$$

and this forces $c^k = (v \mid v_k)$. Hence any representation, irreducible or not, is uniquely determined by its characters (this being the reason for the name). *Two representations are identical when and only when their character vectors (or, equivalently) their characters, are the same; equivalent representations being treated as identical.*

4. The number of non-equivalent irreducible representations of any finite group.

We have seen that the number of non-equivalent irreducible representations of any finite group G is not more than p, the number of classes of G. We now proceed to prove that it is precisely equal to p by showing that it is not less than p. Denoting by $\Gamma_1, \Gamma_2, \cdots, \Gamma_q$ the $q \leq p$ non-equivalent irreducible representations of G we consider the *regular representation*, of dimension g, of G. If s is any element of G other than the unit element e every diagonal element of $D(s) = 0$; whilst, since $D(e) = E_g$, every diagonal element of $D(e) = 1$. Denoting by C_1 the class consisting of the single element e of G we have, as the vector-character of the regular representation, $v = (v^1, \cdots, v^p)$ where $v^1 = \sqrt{g}$, $v^2 = v^3 = \cdots = v^p = 0$ and so, on writing $\Gamma = c^a \Gamma_a$ we have

$$c^k = (v | v_k) = \bar{v}_k{}^1 \sqrt{g}.$$

But $\bar{v}_k{}^1$ is the trace of $D^*{}_k(e) = D_k(e)$ (i. e. of the unit matrix of the representation Γ_k) divided by $\sqrt{g}$; hence c^k is the dimension of Γ_k. Thus we have the result that the *regular representation of G contains each and every irreducible representation of G a number of times equal to the dimension of the irreducible representation.* In other words *all* irreducible representations of G will be found in the regular representation. On denoting by d_k the dimension of Γ_k we have, for the regular representation

$$\Gamma = \sum_k d_k \Gamma_k \qquad (3.13)$$

and, on taking the character corresponding to the unit class, we obtain

$$g = \sum_k d_k{}^2. \qquad (3.14)$$

In words, *the sum of the squared dimensions of the various irreducible representations of G equals the order of G.* On taking the character of any other class C_j we find

$$\sum_k d_k \chi_k{}^j = 0, \qquad (j = 2, \cdots, p). \qquad (3.15)$$

Before completing the argument which proves $q \geq p$ (and hence that $q = p$) it is necessary to say a few words about class multiplication. We consider two classes C_j, C_k of G and form all products st where $s \subset C_j$, $t \subset C_k$ and we denote this collection of elements of G by $C_j C_k$. Since $u^{-1}stu = u^{-1}su \cdot u^{-1}tu$ the whole class determined by st occurs with st in the collection $C_j C_k$. If the element st occurs more than once in $C_j C_k$ (i. e. if $st = s't'$, $s \neq s'$, $t \neq t'$) every element in its class occurs equally as often as it. For $st = s't'$ implies $u^{-1}su \cdot u^{-1}tu = u^{-1}s'u \cdot u^{-1}t'u$ and

$s \neq s'$, $t \neq t'$ forces $u^{-1}su \neq u^{-1}s'u$, $u^{-1}tu \neq u^{-1}t'u$. Hence $u^{-1}stu$ occurs in C_jC_k *at least* as often as st (every u). Replacing s by usu^{-1} and t by utu^{-1} we see that st appears in C_jC_k at least as often as $ustu^{-1}$, every u, and hence (replacing u by u^{-1}) at least as often as $u^{-1}stu$, every u. Hence $u^{-1}stu$ occurs in C_jC_k exactly as often as st and the *class product* C_jC_k may be analysed into a collection of classes:

$$C_jC_k = c_{jk}{}^{a}C_a.$$

Since $st = sts^{-1}s$ it follows that $C_jC_k \subset C_kC_j$ and, interchanging j, k, $C_kC_j \subset C_jC_k$. Hence $C_kC_j = C_jC_k$: *class multiplication is commutative.* Expressing this in terms of the *class constants* $c_{jk}{}^{l}$ we have $c_{jk}{}^{l} = c_{kj}{}^{l}$. If C_1 is the unit class, which consists of the single element e, it is evident that $C_1C_k = C_k$ so that $c_{1k}{}^{l} = 0$ unless $l = k$ and $c_{1k}{}^{k} = 1$: $c_{1k}{}^{l} = c_{k1}{}^{l} = \delta_k{}^{l}$. Finally we observe that the class determined by s^{-1} consists of the inverses of the elements of the class determined by s; in fact $u^{-1}s^{-1}u = (u^{-1}su)^{-1}$. Hence C_jC_k does not contain the unit class at all unless C_k is the class consisting of the inverses of the elements of C_j and when this is the case C_jC_k contains the unit class exactly $n_j = n_k$ times. It is convenient to denote the class whose elements are the inverses of the elements of C_j by C_{-j} (it being clearly understood that C_j and C_{-j} may well coincide) and we then have

$$c_{j,k}{}^{1} = 0 \text{ unless } k = -j; \quad c_{j,-j}{}^{1} = n_j.$$

We now consider any representation Γ of our group and denote by S_j the sum of the matrices $D(s)$ of Γ which correspond to those elements s of G which lie in C_j. If t is any element of G, $t^{-1}st$ lies with s in C_j and as s runs over C_j so does $t^{-1}st$, it being clear that $s \neq s'$ forces $t^{-1}st \neq t^{-1}s't$ and conversely. Hence $D(t^{-1})S_jD(t) = S_j$ or, equivalently, $D(t)S_j = S_jD(t)$. In other words S_j is commutative with every matrix $D(t)$ of Γ. If Γ is *irreducible* and of dimension d it follows that S_j is a scalar matrix λ_jE_d, say; $j = 1, 2, \cdots, p$. Since the trace of each matrix of Γ which corresponds to an element s of G which lies in C_j is the same it follows that $Tr(S_j) = n_j\chi^j$ i.e. $d\lambda_j = n_j\chi^j$. From the relation $C_jC_k = c_{jk}{}^{a}C_a$ follows, on adding the matrices of Γ which correspond to the elements of G in C_jC_k, $S_jS_k = c_{jk}{}^{a}S_a$ and hence $\lambda_j\lambda_k = c_{jk}{}^{a}\lambda_a$. This implies $n_jn_k\chi^j\chi^k = \sum_a dc_{jk}{}^{a}n_a\chi^a$ and on summing this over the q irreducible representations Γ_h of G we find

$$n_jn_k \sum_h \chi_h{}^{j}\chi_h{}^{k} = \sum_a c_{jk}{}^{a}n_a \sum_h d_h\chi_h{}^{a} = c_{jk}{}^{1}g \text{ (by (3.14) and (3.15))}.$$

It follows that $\sum_h \chi_h{}^{j}\chi_h{}^{k} = 0$ unless $k = -j$, in which case it $= g/n_j$. Regarding, for a moment, the q quantities $\chi_h{}^{j}$, $h = 1, \cdots, q$, as the coordinates of a vector $v(j)$ in a linear vector space of q dimensions these equations imply that the p vectors $v(j)$, $j = 1, \cdots, p$ are linearly independent. In fact a hypothecated relation $c^{\alpha}v(\alpha) = 0$ implies $\sum_a c^a \chi_h{}^a = 0$ every h. On multiplying this by $\chi_h{}^j$ and summing with respect to h we obtain $c^{-j} = 0$ every j. Hence $p \leq q$ which is what we wished to prove. Summing up the results of this section we have:

Any finite group possesses as many non-equivalent irreducible representations $\Gamma_1, \cdots, \Gamma_p$ as the group has classes. The various vector characters v_j, $j = 1, \cdots, p$, of these representations form a unitary set: $(v_j|v_k) = 0, j \neq k$; $(v_j|v_j) = 1$. Written out in full these give, on using the relation $\chi^{-j} = \bar{\chi}^j$ which holds for *any* representation of any finite group, the two equivalent sets of orthogonality relations

$$(3.16) \qquad \sum_a n_a \chi_j{}^a \bar{\chi}_j{}^a = g; \qquad \sum_a n_a \chi_j{}^a \bar{\chi}_k{}^a = 0; \qquad j \neq k$$

$$(3.17) \qquad \sum_h \chi_h{}^j \bar{\chi}_h{}^j = \frac{g}{n_j}; \qquad \sum_h \chi_h{}^j \bar{\chi}_h{}^k = 0; \qquad j \neq k$$

(the first of the latter set being $\sum_h d_h{}^2 = g$). The analysis of *any* representation Γ is $c^a\Gamma_a$; $c^j = (v|v_j)$ where v is the vector-character of Γ. From $v = c^a v_a$ follows $(v|v) = \sum_a (c^a)^2$ so that the minimum value of $(v|v)$ is unity, this occurring *when and only when* Γ *is irreducible.* This criterion for irreducibility may be stated in the following equivalent form: *a representation* Γ *of a given finite group is irreducible when and only when the average over the group of* $|\chi(s)|^2$ *is equal to unity.*

5. Symmetric linear operators.

We close this chapter with a discussion of certain questions arising naturally from a consideration of the Kronecker m-th power $[A]_m$ of a linear operator A. The carrier space of this Kronecker m-th power is of dimension n^m and its vectors v have coordinates which may be conveniently designated by $v^{j_1, \cdots, j_m}$. All linear operators in this carrier space are presented, once a basis is selected, by $n^m \times n^m$ matrices whose $(j_1, \cdots, j_m; k_1, \cdots, k_m)$ elements may be designated by $a^{j_1, \cdots, j_m}_{k_1, \ldots, k_m}$; a special such linear operator is the Kronecker m-th power $[A]_m$ for which $a^{j_1, \cdots, j_m}_{k_1, \ldots, k_m}$ has the special form $a_{k_1}{}^{j_1} \cdots a_{k_m}{}^{j_m}$. A particularly noteworthy feature of the Kronecker m-th power is its symmetry in the labels $(1, \cdots, m)$: if $p = \uparrow\binom{p_j}{j}$ is any permutation on the m letters $(1, \cdots, m)$ then

$$(3.18) \qquad a^{j_{p_1}, \cdots, j_{p_m}}_{k_{p_1}, \ldots, k_{p_m}} = a^{j_1, \cdots, j_m}_{k_1, \ldots, k_m}$$

the obvious and simple reason being the commutativity of ordinary multiplication of complex numbers. In general we term *any* linear operator in the n^m dimensional carrier space of $[A]_m$ *symmetric* when it possesses the symmetry, with respect to all permutations of the labels $1, \cdots, m$, described by the equations (3.18); and we shall term those particular symmetric operators which are Kronecker m-th powers of linear operators in the underlying n-dimensional space *special symmetric operators.* It is clear from the very definition that the collection of all symmetric linear operators in the n^m dimensional carrier space of $[A]_m$ constitute a linear vector space of dimension n^{2m}; in fact if $a^{(j)}_{(k)} \equiv a^{j_1, \cdots, j_m}_{k_1, \ldots, k_m}$ is a symmetric linear operator in this space so also is $\alpha a^{(j)}_{(k)} = \alpha a^{j_1, \cdots, j_m}_{k_1, \ldots, k_m}$ where α is any complex number. And if $b^{(j)}_{(k)} = b^{j_1, \cdots, j_m}_{k_1, \ldots, k_m}$ is any second symmetric linear operator in the carrier space of $[A]_m$ then $a^{(j)}_{(k)} + b^{(j)}_{(k)} \equiv a^{j_1, \cdots, j_m}_{k_1, \ldots, k_m} + b^{j_1, \cdots, j_m}_{k_1, \ldots, k_m}$ is also a symmetric linear operator in this space. Since each symmetric operator has n^{2m} components the dimension of the linear space constituted by them $\leq n^{2m}$. We shall show that it is not less than n^{2m} by constructing n^{2m} linearly independent symmetric operators; these will be special symmetric operators so that we shall be able to state the theorem that *the linear space of all symmetric linear operators is spanned by special symmetric linear operators.* In fact they will not only be special symmetric linear operators (i. e. Kronecker m-th powers) but *special unitary symmetric linear operators* (i. e. Kronecker m-th powers of unitary linear operators).

Denote, then, by $u_s{}^r$ the element in the r-th row and s-th column of an $n \times n$ unitary matrix. Its Kronecker m-th power has as its $(r_1, \cdots, r_m; s_1, \cdots, s_m)$ element the quantity $u_{s_1}{}^{r_1} \cdots u_{s_m}{}^{r_m}$. Regarding this as a vector in the n^{2m} dimensional linear space which contains all symmetric linear operators we are faced with the following alternative: either the special unitary symmetric linear operators span the entire n^{2m} dimensional space or they span a proper linear subspace of it. In the latter case there must exist one or more linear homogeneous relations of the type $c^{\alpha_1, \cdots, \alpha_m}_{\beta_1, \ldots, \beta_m} u^{\beta_1}_{\alpha_1} \cdots u^{\beta_m}_{\alpha_m} = 0$ where the $c^{j_1, \cdots, j_m}_{k_1, \ldots, k_m}$ are constant coefficients which may, without loss of generality be assumed symmetric in the labels $(1, \cdots, m) : c^{j_{p_1}, \cdots, j_{p_m}}_{k_{p_1}, \ldots, k_{p_m}} = c^{j_1, \cdots, j_m}_{k_1, \ldots, k_m}$ where p is *any* permutation $\uparrow \begin{pmatrix} p_j \\ j \end{pmatrix}$.

Each of these relations is an identity in the $u_s{}^r$ where these are not independent but are subjected to the relations $u^*{}_a{}^r u_s{}^a = \delta_s{}^r$. On taking the differential of $c^{\alpha_1, \cdots, \alpha_m}_{\beta_1, \ldots, \beta_m} u^{\beta_1}_{\alpha_1} \cdots u^{\beta_m}_{\alpha_m}$ we obtain m terms (each an m-ple summation) which all have the same value owing to the symmetry of the coefficients $c^{j_1, \cdots, j_m}_{k_1, \ldots, k_m}$. Hence we must have $c^{\alpha_1, \cdots, \alpha_m}_{\beta_1, \ldots, \beta_m} u^{\beta_1}_{\alpha_1} \cdots u^{\beta_{m-1}}_{\alpha_{m-1}} du^{\beta_m}_{\alpha_m} = 0$

subject to the conditions $u^{*}{}_{a}{}^{r} du_{s}{}^{a} + du^{*}{}_{a}{}^{r} u_{s}{}^{a} = 0$. Applying the method of Lagrangian multipliers to these linear homogeneous equations connecting the $2n^2$ differentials $du_s{}^r$, $du^*{}_s{}^r$ we obtain, on denoting, for a moment,

$$c^{a_1, \ldots, a_{m-1}, j}_{\beta_1, \ldots, \beta_{m-1}, k} u^{\beta_1}_{a_1} \cdots u^{\beta_{m-1}}_{a_{m-1}} \text{ by } m_k{}^j, \quad m_k{}^j + \lambda_a{}^j u^*{}_k{}^a = 0; \quad \lambda_k{}^a u_a{}^j = 0$$

where the n^2 quantities $\lambda_s{}^r$ are the undetermined multipliers. Written in matrix notation these equations are

$$M + \Lambda U^* = 0; \quad U\Lambda = 0.$$

The second set imply $\Lambda = 0$, on multiplication on the left by U^*, and then the first that $M = 0$, i. e.

$$c^{a_1, \ldots, a_{m-1}, j_m}_{\beta_1, \ldots, \beta_{m-1}, k_m} u^{\beta_1}_{a_1} \cdots u^{\beta_{m-1}}_{a_{m-1}} = 0; \text{ every } j_m, k_m,$$

for every unitary matrix $U = (u_s{}^r)$. Repeating the argument, for a fixed, but arbitrary, j_m, k_m we find

$$c^{a_1, \ldots, a_{m-2}, j_{m-1}, j_m}_{\beta_1, \ldots, \beta_{m-2}, k_{m-1}, k_m} u^{\beta_1}_{a_1} \cdots u^{\beta_{m-2}}_{a_{m-2}} = 0; \text{ every } j_{m-1}, j_m, k_{m-1}, k_m$$

and so on till we finally obtain $c^{j_1, \ldots, j_m}_{k_1, \ldots, k_m} = 0$ proving our theorem that the special-unitary symmetrical linear operators span the complete n^{2m}-dimensional space of symmetric linear operators. In particular $(m = 1)$ we see that unitary $n \times n$ matrices span the entire n^2-dimensional space whose elements are $n \times n$ matrices. E. g., $n = 2$, the four unitary 2×2 matrices

$$\begin{pmatrix} 1 & 0 \\ 0 & 1 \end{pmatrix} \begin{pmatrix} 1 & 0 \\ 0 & -1 \end{pmatrix} \begin{pmatrix} 0 & 1 \\ 1 & 0 \end{pmatrix} \begin{pmatrix} 0 & -1 \\ 1 & 0 \end{pmatrix}$$

constitute a basis for all 2×2 matrices.

Let now R be a subspace of the n^m-dimensional carrier space of $[A]_m$ which is invariant under all special unitary symmetric operators. It follows from the theorem just proven that R is invariant under all symmetric operators. If R is irreducible with respect to the collection of all symmetric operators (i. e. if no proper subspace of R is invariant under all symmetric operators) it remains irreducible with respect to the (smaller) collection of all special unitary symmetric operators and, à fortiori, irreducible with respect to the collection of all special symmetric operators. In particular if R is irreducible with respect to the collection of special symmetric transformations it is irreducible with respect to the collection of special unitary transformations. For instance we know that $[A]_m$ furnishes a homogeneous rational integral representation, of degree m, of the full linear group (whose elements are $n \times n$

matrices). It induces a homogeneous rational integral representation, of degree m, of the unitary subgroup $\{U\}$ of the full linear group (by merely selecting from $[A]_m$ the subset $[U]_m$). We shall see later that $[A]_m$ is completely reducible; *then each of its irreducible components induces an irreducible homogeneous rational integral representation of the unitary subgroup of the full linear group.*

If $a \equiv a_{(s)}^{(r)} \equiv a_{s_1, \ldots, s_m}^{r_1, \ldots, r_m}$ is any symmetric linear operator in the n^m-dimensional carrier space of $[A]_m$ and $p = \uparrow \binom{p_j}{j}$ is any permutation on the m letters $(1, \cdots, m)$ we denote by $p(a)$ the symmetric linear operator whose $((r), (s))$ element is $a_{(s)}^{(r)} = a_{s_1, \ldots, s_m}^{r_{p_1}, \ldots, r_{p_m}}$. Since the definition of symmetric linear operator is contained in the formula

$$a_{(s)}^{(r)} = a_{(s_p)}^{(r_p)}$$

it is clear that $p(a)$ may be defined in either of two equivalent ways: we may apply the permutation p to the superscripts r of $a_{(s)}^{(r)}$ *or* the permutation p^{-1} to the subscripts s of $a_{(s)}^{(r)}$. Furthermore it is clear that the collection of symmetric linear operators is not merely a linear vector space but an *algebra*; i. e. it possesses the group property relative to a law of combination other than addition (and distributive with respect to the latter). This law of combination is defined by mere sequential performance. Thus if v is any vector of the carrier space of $[A]_m$ av is the vector w whose $(j_1, \cdots, j_m)$ component is $w^{j_1, \ldots, j_m} = a_{(a)}^{(j)} v^{(a)}$ $= a_{a_1, \ldots, a_m}^{j_1, \ldots, j_m} v^{a_1, \ldots, a_m}$ and then bw is the vector whose $(j_1, \cdots, j_m)$ component is $b_{(a)}^{(j)} w^{(a)} = b_{(a)}^{(j)} a_{(\beta)}^{(a)} v^{(\beta)}$. In other words ba is the symmetric linear operator $(ba)_{(k)}^{(j)} = b_{(a)}^{(j)} a_{(k)}^{(a)} = b_{a_1, \ldots, a_m}^{j_1, \ldots, j_m} a_{k_1, \ldots, k_m}^{a_1, \ldots, a_m}$.

If, in particular, a, b are both special symmetric linear operators, i. e. Kronecker m-th powers, we have

(3. 19) $[B]_m [A]_m = [BA]_m.$

Furthermore if q, p are any two permutations from the symmetric group on m letters we have

$$q(b)p(a) = qp(ba).$$

In fact the $(j), (k)$ element of the left-hand side is

$$b_{(a)}^{(j_q)} a_{(k)}^{(a_p)} = b_{(a_p)}^{(j_{qp})} a_{(k)}^{(a_p)} = (ba)_{(k)}^{(j_{qp})} = qp(ba)_{(k)}^{(j)}$$

(note that qp means: first p then q). When a, b are *special* we have

(3.20) $$q([B]_m)p([A]_m) = qp([BA]_m)$$

and in particular $q([E]_m)p([E]_m) = qp([E]_m)$ so that *the matrices* $p([E]_m)$ *furnish a representation, of dimension* n^m, *of the symmetric group on m letters.*

The Kronecker m-th power $[A]_m$ furnishes a representation of dimension n^m of the full linear group and it is easy to calculate the characters of this representation. In fact the $((r),(s))$ element of $[A]_m$ is $a_{s_1}{}^{r_1} a_{s_2}{}^{r_2} \cdots a_{s_m}{}^{r_m}$ and so the trace of $[A]_m$ is $a_{\alpha_1}{}^{\alpha_1} a_{\alpha_2}{}^{\alpha_2} \cdots a_{\alpha_m}{}^{\alpha_m} = (TrA)^m$. It is convenient to denote TrA by s_1, TrA^2 by s_2, TrA^3 by s_3, and so on, so that

(3.21) $$s_1 = a_{\alpha_1}{}^{\alpha_1}; \qquad s_2 = a_{\alpha_2}{}^{\alpha_1} a_{\alpha_1}{}^{\alpha_2}; \qquad s_3 = a_{\alpha_2}{}^{\alpha_1} a_{\alpha_3}{}^{\alpha_2} a_{\alpha_1}{}^{\alpha_3};$$

and so on. Then the characters of $[A]_m$ are $s_1{}^m$. In order to calculate the characters of the representation of the full linear group which is furnished by the symmetrized Kronecker power $[A]_{(m)}$ it is convenient to first calculate the trace of $p^{-1}([A]_m)$; this is $a_{\beta_{p_1}}{}^{\beta_1} a_{\beta_{p_2}}{}^{\beta_2} \cdots a_{\beta_{p_m}}{}^{\beta_m}$. If p is in the class (α), i.e. if p contains α_1 unary cycles, α_2 binary cycles, $\cdots$ this expression is at once seen to be

(3.22) $$s^{(\alpha)} = s_1{}^{\alpha_1} s_2{}^{\alpha_2} \cdots s_m{}^{\alpha_m}.$$

In fact let us suppose that p contains the ternary cycle $(1, j, k)$; then the trace of $p^{-1}([A]_m)$ contains the factor $a_{\beta_j}{}^{\beta_1} a_{\beta_k}{}^{\beta_j} a_1{}^{\beta_k} = s_3$ and so on.

The symmetrized Kronecker power is furnished by the transformation induced by $x \to Ax$ on the $\binom{n+m-1}{m}$ products $(x^1)^{p_1} \cdots (x^n)^{p_n}$, $p_1 + p_2 + \cdots + p_n = m$, and the $((r),(s))$ element is $\sum_q a_{(s_q)}^{(r)}$ the summation being over all permutations q which effect a rearrangement of $(s_1, s_2, \cdots, s_m)$. The diagonal elements are accordingly $\sum_q a_{(r_q)}^{(r)}$. If there are k_1 1's, k_2 2's, $\cdots$ in (r) there are $k_1!\, k_2! \cdots k_n!$ permutations which do not change each (r_q). Hence we may write the $((r),(r))$ diagonal element of $[A]_{(m)}$ as $\frac{1}{k_1! \cdots k_n!} \sum_p a_{(r_p)}^{(r)}$ where the summation is now over *all* permutations p of the symmetric group on m letters. There are $m! \div (k_1! \cdots k_n!)$ permutations which change the arrangement (r) and since none of these affects $a_{(r_p)}^{(r)}$ we may write the $((r),(r))$ diagonal element of $[A]_{(m)}$ as $\frac{1}{m!} \sum_p' a_{(r_p)}^{(r)}$ where $\sum_p' a_{(r_p)}^{(r)}$ means that the set (r) is rearranged in all possible ways and the results added. Hence the trace of $[A]_{(m)} = \frac{1}{m!} \sum_p a_{(\rho_p)}^{(\rho)}$ i.e. the average over the symmetric group of the trace of $p^{-1}([A]_m)$ i. e. $s^{(a)} = s_1^{a_1} \cdots s_n^{a_n}$. In other words the characters of the symmetrized Kronecker power representation $[A]_{(m)}$ of the full linear group are the functions $q_m(s)$ defined by

$$(3.23)\quad q_m(s) = \frac{1}{m!} \sum_{(a)} n_{(a)} s^{(a)} = \sum_{(a)} \frac{1}{\alpha_1 !\, \alpha_2 ! \cdots \alpha_m !} \left(\frac{s_1}{1}\right)^{\alpha_1} \cdots \left(\frac{s_m}{m}\right)^{\alpha_m}$$

(the summation being over all classes (α) of the symmetric group on m letters). These functions are of fundamental importance in the theory of the representations of the symmetric group on m letters which will be discussed in the next chapter.

CHAPTER FOUR

THE SYMMETRIC GROUP

In this chapter we shall obtain all irreducible representations of the symmetric group on m letters, i. e. the group of $m!$ different permutations of m different objects and shall use these to determine all homogeneous rational integral representations of the full linear group.

1. Cosets of a subgroup.

If G is any group, with elements $s, t, u, \cdots$, and H is any subset $h, j, k, \cdots$ of these which constitutes a group (with respect to the same law of combination as G) we term H a subgroup of G. Every group G possesses at least two subgroups: 1) $H = G$; i. e. G is a subgroup of itself; when we wish to rule out this subgroup we insist that the subgroup be *proper*, i. e. that there is at least one element of G not contained in it; 2) $H = e$, the unit element of G; we refer to this subgroup as the *identity* subgroup. In any event H, being a group, must contain the unit element e of G. If H coincides with G the collections sH, Ht, i. e. the collections sh, ht, where h is an arbitrary element of H, coincide with H; s, t, arbitrary elements of G. In fact $sH = sG$ is merely the left translation of G induced by s and so is merely a rearrangement of $G = H$; and similarly for Ht. If, on the other hand, H is a proper subgroup of G the set sH (whilst still coinciding with H if s is any element of G which also lies in H) will have no element in common with H if s does not lie in H. In fact $sh = j$ would force $s = jh^{-1}$ to lie in H if j were an element of H. We term sH the left coset of H determined by s and it is clear that $s = se$ is in the left coset of H determined by it. Moreover any element sh in this left coset determines the same coset as s. In fact any element $sh \cdot j$ of the left coset determined by an arbitrary element sh belonging to the coset determined by s lies in the left coset determined by s ($sh \cdot j = s \cdot hj$) so that the left coset determined by sh is contained in the left coset determined by s. But $s = sh \cdot h^{-1}$ belongs to the left coset determined by sh so that the left coset determined by s is contained in the left coset determined by sh. Combining both statements we see that the left coset determined by sh is the same as the left coset determined by s. Since s is not in H, s^{-1} is not in H and by the same reasoning as above the set Hs^{-1} (which consists of the inverses of the elements of the left coset sH) has no element in common with H. We term it the right coset of H determined by s^{-1} and we see that it is the same as the right coset of H which is determined by any element hs^{-1} belonging to it. If G is exhausted by H and sH, i. e. if every element of G belongs either to H or to sH we say that H possesses exactly two left cosets in G; it being convenient to regard H as a left coset of itself, namely, the left coset determined by any of its own elements. In this case G is exhausted by H and Hs^{-1} (since G is exhausted by the inverses of its elements) so that H has exactly two right cosets and $sH = Hs^{-1}$. Since s lies in Hs^{-1} (not lying in H) we have $Hs^{-1} = Hs$ so that we may write $sH = Hs$. Since this relation is trivially evident when s is an element of H it is true for any element of G; and we may write it in the convenient form $s^{-1}Hs = H$, every s in G. In general it is clear that if H is a subgroup of G so also is $s^{-1}Hs$, every s in G; we term this subgroup the *transform* of H by s. And when H coincides with its transform *for every s in G* we term H an invariant subgroup of G. We see, then, that, if H possesses exactly two left cosets in G, H is an invariant subgroup of G. As examples we cite: 1) G the group of $n!$ permutations on n letters; H the subgroup consisting of all even permutations on n letters; 2) G the group of all orthogonal (or real orthogonal) $n \times n$ matrices; H the subgroup consisting of all *proper* orthogonal (or real orthogonal) $n \times n$ matrices (a proper orthogonal matrix being one whose determinant is unity).

Returning to a consideration of any proper subgroup H of G let us suppose that G is not exhausted by H and sH (s not in H) and let t be an element of G belonging *neither* to H *nor* sH. Then the collection tH has (as we have already seen) no element in common with H; nor has it any element in common with sH. For $sh = tj$, where j is an element of H, would force $t = s \cdot hj^{-1}$ to lie in sH. If G is not exhausted by H, sH, tH we take an element u of G which lies in none of the collections H, sH, tH and we see at once that none of the elements in the entire collection uH lies in any one of the three collections H, sH, tH. Proceeding in this way G must finally be exhausted *if it is finite*; for each of the collections $H, sH, tH, \cdots$ contains exactly the same number of elements, say k, as H. If g is the order of G, H cannot have more left cosets than the quotient of g by k. Hence G is finally exhausted showing that the order of H is a divisor of the order of G, the quotient d being the number of left cosets. We shall suppose, if G is infinite, that it is exhausted by α left cosets of H and we shall denote these cosets by $H_1 = H$; $H_2 = s_2H$; $\cdots$ $H_a = s_aH$. Then it is clear that the right cosets H, $Hs_2^{-1}, \cdots, Hs_a^{-1}$ are all distinct (since each consists of the inverses of the elements in the corresponding left coset) and exhaust G (since G is exhausted by the reciprocals of its elements). Hence if H

possesses exactly d left cosets in G it possesses exactly d right cosets in G each right coset consisting of the inverses of a left coset.

Let us now examine what happens to the left cosets $(H_1, \cdots, H_d)$ when G is subjected to the left translation $s \rightarrow ts$ induced by an arbitrary element t of G. The coset $H_p = s_pH$, $p = 1, \cdots, d$, is translated into the coset determined by ts_p; and *different* cosets are translated into *different* cosets. In fact $ts_pH = ts_qH$ would force $ts_ph = ts_qj$ i. e. $s_ph = s_qj$ which is impossible when H_p and H_q are distinct. Hence the arbitrary element t of G induces (through the left translation of G caused by it) a permutation $p(t)$ of the d cosets $(H_1, \cdots, H_d)$ of H in G. If we follow the left translation of G caused by t by the left translation caused by u (an arbitrary element of G) we obtain the left translation caused by ut and so $p(ut) = p(u)p(t)$. Let $P(t)$ be the $d \times d$ permutation matrix defined by $p(t)$ so that $P(ut) = P(u)P(t)$; these permutation matrices furnish, therefore, a representation, of dimension d, of G. *Thus any subgroup of G which possesses exactly d left* (and, hence, exactly d right) *cosets in G furnishes us, by means of the permutations induced on these left cosets by the left translations of G, a d-dimensional unitary representation of G* (all permutation matrices being unitary); *and, in particular, any subgroup of a finite group G furnishes, in this way, a unitary representation of G.* As particular, but somewhat trivial, instances we may cite: 1) the case where $H = G$ in which case the representation obtained is the (one-dimensional) identity representation and 2) the case where $H = e$, G being finite; in this case the representation of dimension g, the order of G, is the regular representation.

The characters of the representation of G which is furnished by the permutations of the d left cosets of H in G (which characters are all non-negative integers since the matrices of the representation are *permutation matrices*) may be obtained as follows. Since $p(t)$ is the permutation $\uparrow \begin{pmatrix} tH_j \\ H_j \end{pmatrix}$, $P(t)$ will have as many units in its main diagonal as there are cosets H_j for which $tH_j = H_j$ (the remaining diagonal elements of $P(t)$ being zero). The relation $tH_j = H_j$ is equivalent to $ts_jh = s_jh'$ i. e. to the statement that t is in the transform $s_jHs_j^{-1}$ of H by s_j^{-1}. *Hence $\chi(t)$ is the number of these transforms of H in which t lies.* For instance if H is an invariant subgroup $\chi(t) = d$ if $t \subset H$ (all of the d transforms of H coinciding with H: note that the transform of H by s_j^{-1} is always the same as the transform of H by hs_j^{-1}) whilst $\chi(t) = 0$ if t is not in H. The average of $\chi(t)$ as t runs over G follows readily (when G is finite) from the fact that $tH_j = H_j$, for a given j, exactly k times where k is the order of H (since k is equally the order of $s_jHs_j^{-1}$). Hence this average is $kd \div g$ i. e. 1. But this average gives the number of times the representation contains the identity representation; *hence the representation of a finite group G which is furnished by the permutations of the left cosets of any subgroup of G is always reducible and contains the identity representation exactly once.*

The expression given above for $\chi(t)$ can be put in a slightly different and more convenient form. Let G contain p classes $C_1 = e, C_2, \cdots, C_p$. If t is an element of any one of these classes, C_j say, the entire class C_j consists of the elements $s^{-1}ts$, s variable over G. Two elements s, u of G yield the same element of C_j when $s^{-1}ts = u^{-1}tu$ i. e. when $us^{-1} \cdot t = t \cdot us^{-1}$. The elements of G which commute with t evidently form a subgroup of G; for $tv = vt$ implies $v^{-1}t = tv^{-1}$; and $tv = vt$, $tw = wt$ imply $twv = wtv = wvt$. Finally $te = et = t$. Denoting by K the subgroup of G consisting of the elements which commute with t let us assume that K is finite and of order r. Then each element of C_j will be repeated r times, (since $u^{-1}tu = s^{-1}ts$ if and only if $u = ks$, $k \subset K$), so that the number of elements n_j in C_j is a divisor of the order g of G if G is finite:

$$n_j r = g.$$

Now our condition $t \subset s_j H s_j^{-1}$ is equivalent to $s_j^{-1} t s_j \subset H$ and $\chi(t)$ is the number of times this happens. Since if it happens for any s_j it happens for any element of the coset $s_j H$ we can find $\chi(t)$ by calculating how often $s^{-1}ts \subset H$, s variable over G, and dividing the result by the order of H (which we shall now denote by h). As s wanders over G each member of the class C_j to which t belongs occurs r times; suppose then m_j members of C_j belong to H so that

$$\chi^j = \chi(t) = rm_j \div h = gm_j \div hn_j. \tag{4.1}$$

Here g is the order of G; h the order of its subgroup H; n_j the number of elements in the class C_j of G and m_j the number of these which lie in H.

If x is an arbitrary vector of the d-dimensional carrier space of the representation of G which is furnished by its subgroup H the (permutation) matrix $P(s)$ of the representation, s arbitrary in G, sends $x = (x^1, \cdots, x^d)$ into $sx = (x^{s_1}, \cdots, x^{s_d})$ where $P(s)$ is associated with the permutation $\uparrow \begin{pmatrix} s_j \\ j \end{pmatrix}$. In particular $se_k = e_{s_k}$ showing that $e_1 + \cdots + e_d$ is an invariant vector of the representation; this (with its multiples) is the only invariant vector since the representation contains the identity representation exactly once. Let now J be a subgroup of H (and, à fortiori, a subgroup of G) possessing exactly f left cosets in H

$$H = J_1(=J) + J_2 + \cdots + J_f; \quad J_k = h_k J,\ k = 1, \cdots, f.$$

If $H_q = s_q H$, $q = 1, \cdots, d$, are the left cosets of H in G the fd sets, of elements of G, $J_{qk} = s_q h_k J$ are all left cosets of J in G and exhaust G (since the sets $s_q H$ exhaust G). Furthermore they are all distinct; in fact $s_q h_k J$ is different from $s_p h_m J$ if $p \neq q$, (simply because $s_p H$ has no element in common with $s_q H$) and $s_p h_k J$ is different from $s_p h_m J$ if $m \neq k$ simply because $h_k J = J_k$ and $h_m J = J_m$ are different. Hence J possesses exactly fd left cosets in G and, therefore, furnishes a representation of dimension fd of G. *This representation is reducible and contains the representation, of dimension d, of G which is furnished by H.* In fact let us denote the vectors of a basis in the carrier space of the representation of G which is furnished by J by e_{pk}; $p = 1, \cdots, d$; $k = 1, \cdots, f$; and the linear subspaces of this carrier space each of which is spanned by f vectors $(e_{p1}, \cdots, e_{pf})$, $p = 1, \cdots, d$, by S_p. Then under the left translation of G induced by t: $s \to ts$, each space S_p is sent into another of these spaces S_{t_p}. In fact $tH_p = H_{t_p}$ so that tJ_{pk} is one of the sets $J_{t_p m}$, $m = 1, \cdots, f$. Hence e_{pk} is sent into $e_{t_p m}$, every k, proving the statement. Moreover as k varies from 1 to f so does m since no two cosets J_{pk} are translated by t into the same coset $J_{t_p m}$. Hence if we denote the vector $\sum_k e_{pk}$ by ϵ_p we have $t\epsilon_p = \epsilon_{t_p}$; $p = 1, \cdots, d$.

As p varies from 1 to d so also does t_p since no two different cosets H_p of H are translated by t into the same coset of H. Hence the d-dimensional subspace (of the carrier space of the representation of G furnished by J) spanned by the vectors $(\epsilon_1, \cdots, \epsilon_d)$ is an invariant space of this representation; and the representation induced in it is the representation furnished by H. Since the identity subgroup $J = e$ is a subgroup of every subgroup H of G it follows that the regular representation of G contains the representation of G furnished by *any* subgroup H. Since the regular representation contains each irreducible representation Γ_k, of dimension d_k, d_k times the representation of G which is furnished by H contains Γ_k a number of times $\leq d_k$.

2. The characteristics of a finite group.

Let G be any finite group, with elements $s, t, u, \cdots$, and let $f(s)$, $\theta(s)$ be any two complex valued functions defined over G. We denote by $(f \mid \theta)$ the average over G of the product $\bar{\theta}(s)f(s)$ and we term $(f \mid \theta)$ the scalar product over G of f by θ:

$$(f \mid \theta) = \frac{1}{g} \sum_s \bar{\theta}(s) f(s). \tag{4.2}$$

We shall be concerned only with the case where $f(s)$ and $\theta(s)$ are both *class functions*, i. e. $f(s)$ and $\theta(s)$ have the same values, f^j and θ^j respectively, for all elements s which belong to the same class C_j of G. In this case we can write $(f \mid \theta)$ in the form

$$(4.3) \qquad (f \mid \theta) = \frac{1}{g} \sum_j n_j \bar{\theta}^j f^j,$$

the summation being over the p-classes $C_1, \cdots, C_p$ of G; and if we introduce the vectors u, v in the p-dimensional class space

$$u^j = \sqrt{\frac{n_j}{g}} f^j; \quad v^j = \sqrt{\frac{n_j}{g}} \theta^j; \qquad j = 1, \cdots, p,$$

$(f \mid \theta)$ appears as the ordinary scalar product of u by v:

$$(4.4) \qquad (f \mid \theta) = \sum_j \bar{v}^j u^j = (u \mid v).$$

We know that G has exactly p irreducible representations, Γ_1 (the identity representation), $\Gamma_2, \cdots, \Gamma_p$, and the character $\chi_j(s)$ of any one, Γ_j, of these is a class function. Treating the p quantities $f^1, \cdots, f^p$ as indeterminates we term the p linear expressions in these indeterminates

$$(4.5) \qquad \phi_j(f) = (f \mid \chi_j) = \frac{1}{g} \sum_s f(s) \bar{\chi}_j(s) = (u \mid v_j); \quad j = 1, \cdots, p$$

(where v_j is the vector character of Γ_j) the *simple characteristics* of G; of these $\phi_1(f) = (u \mid v_1) = \frac{1}{g} \sum_s f(s)$ is the *principal characteristic* of G. The coefficient of any one of the indeterminates, f^k say, in $\phi_j(f)$ yields, when multiplied by g and divided by n_k, the conjugate complex of the character, of the irreducible representation Γ_j, which is associated with the class C_k. If $\Gamma = c^a \Gamma_a$ is *any* representation of G, so that the coefficients c^k are non-negative integers (i. e. positive integers, including zero) the expression $\phi(f) = c^a \phi_a(f)$ has a similar property: the coefficient of any one of the indeterminates, f^k say, in $\phi(f) = c^a \phi_a(f)$ yields, when multiplied by g and divided by n_k the conjugate complex $\bar{\chi}^k$ of the character of the representation Γ (which is reducible save when all c^j but one are zero, that one being unity) associated with the class C_k. The expression $\phi(f) = c^a \phi_a(f)$ is termed a *compound characteristic* of G when Γ is reducible; and the unqualified term characteristic includes both simple and compound characteristics. It is occasionally convenient to allow the integral coefficients c^j, which occur in the definition of $\phi(f)$, to assume negative as well as positive or zero values and in this case we term $\phi(f)$ a *generalized characteristic* of G; but in making this generalization we have sacrificed the basic property of simple or compound characteristics. When one of the coefficients c^j is negative the coefficient of f^k in $\phi(f)$ will not yield the character, associated with C_k, of a representation of G $(k=1,\cdots,p)$.

We know that the p vectors v_j form a unitary set and so any vector, in particular u, of the class space is expressible as a linear combination of them: $u=c^a v_a$ where $c^j=(u \mid v_j)=\phi_j(f)$, i. e.

$$(4.6) \qquad u=\sum_j \phi_j(f) v_j.$$

Since the k-th components of u and v_j are $\sqrt{\frac{n_k}{g}}\, f^k$ and $\sqrt{\frac{n_k}{g}}\, \chi_j{}^k$, respectively, we may express the content of (4.6) more explicitly in the form

$$(4.7) \qquad f^k=\sum_j \phi_j(f) \chi_j{}^k; \qquad k=1,2,\cdots,p;$$

an equation which expresses the p indeterminates f^k in terms of the simple characteristics $\phi_j(f)$ of G.

If H is any subgroup of G the class of elements of H determined by any element h belonging to H is, by the very definition of class, contained in the class of elements of G determined by h (regarded as an element of G). But the converse is evidently not true; not all elements of a given class C_j will, in general, belong to H nor will all those of its elements which belong to H necessarily belong to the same class of H. For two elements which are transformable into one another by an element of G are not necessarily transformable into one another by an element of H. We say that the subgroup H of G effects a *refinement* of the classes of G. Now any class function $f(s)$ defined over G *induces* a class function $f^*(j)$ defined over H by merely setting $f^*(j)=f(j)$; j in H. But a class function defined over H in this way is not the general class function defined over H; for it must assume the same value for all those classes of H which belong to the same class of G. Similarly each of the p irreducible representations $\Gamma_1, \Gamma_2, \cdots, \Gamma_p$ of G induces, by merely selecting from it those matrices which correspond to elements of H, a representation of H; but the representation of H obtained in this way is not, in general, irreducible. For there may well exist a proper subspace of the carrier space which is invariant under all the operators *selected* from Γ_j whilst there does not exist a proper subspace of this carrier space which is invariant under *all* the operators of Γ_j. On denoting by $\xi_r(j)$, $r=1,2,\cdots,q$, j variable over H, the characters of the irreducible representations of H, $\chi_m(j)$, $m=1,\cdots,p$, being the character of a reducible representation of H may be written in the form $\chi_m(j) = c_m{}^\alpha \xi_\alpha(j)$ whence $\frac{1}{h}\sum_j \chi_m(j)\bar{\xi}_k(j)=c_m{}^k$. If now $d^1,\cdots,d^q$ are any integers, positive, negative, or zero, the expression

$$\frac{1}{h}\sum_j f(j)\,d^\beta \bar{\xi}_\beta(j)$$

is a generalized characteristic of H (the expressions $\frac{1}{h}\sum_j f(j)\bar{\xi}_k(j)$ being simple characteristics of H); we regard the indeterminates in this generalized characteristic of H as not arbitrary but as conditioned by the fact that $f(j)$ takes the same value for all elements j of H which belong to the same class of G. From (4.7) we read

$$f(j) = \sum_a \phi_a(f)\chi_a(j)$$

so that

$$\frac{1}{h}\sum_j f(j)\bar{\xi}_k(j) = \sum_a \{\phi_a(f)\frac{1}{h}\sum_j \chi_a(j)\bar{\xi}_k(j)\} = \sum_a c_a{}^k\phi_a(f).$$

Hence our generalized characteristic of H appears in the form

$$\sum_a(\sum_\beta d^\beta c_a{}^\beta)\,\phi_a(f).$$

Since the d^k, $c_m{}^k$ are integers, positive negative or zero, $\sum_\beta d^\beta c_j{}^\beta$ is an integer, positive, negative or zero *and hence the generalized characteristic of H is also a generalized characteristic of G*. In other words we can construct from *any* generalized characteristic of H, by merely identifying the indeterminates associated with all those elements of H which belong to the same class of G, a generalized characteristic of G. In particular any compound (or simple) characteristic of H furnishes in this way a compound (possibly simple) characteristic of G. In other terms a knowledge of any representation, reducible or irreducible, of H enables us to construct the characters of a representation of G. This representation will be irreducible if and only if $(\chi|\chi) = \frac{1}{g}\sum_s \bar{\chi}(s)\chi(s)$ is unity. More generally let us consider the generalized characteristic of G derived, as described above, from a quite arbitrary generalized characteristic of H. It furnishes us a class function $\psi(s)$ of the type $c^a\chi_a(s)$ where the c^j are integers positive, negative, or zero. Owing to the orthogonality relations (3.10) and (3.11) we have

$$(4.8) \qquad (\psi|\psi) = \frac{1}{g}\sum_s \bar{\psi}(s)\psi(s) = \sum_a \bar{c}^a c^a$$

and so the generalized characteristic will be a simple characteristic if and only if $(\psi|\psi) = 1$ and, in addition $\psi(e) > 0$. If the generalized characteristic is not simple the coefficients c^j in the expression $\psi(s) = c^a\chi_a(s)$ are given by

$$(4.9) \qquad c^j = (\psi|\chi_j) = \frac{1}{g}\sum_s \bar{\chi}_j(s)\psi(s).$$

Examples.

As a quite trivial example let G be the symmetric group on two letters and H the identity subgroup. The principal (and only simple) characteristic of H is f^1 and this is also a characteristic (compound) of G. The characters of the corresponding reducible representation of G (which has two classes) are 2, 0. This representation contains the identity representation once since

$$c^1 = \tfrac{1}{2}(2 + 1.0) = 1.$$

The characters of the remainder of the representation are $(1, -1)$ and this representation is simple since $\frac{1}{2}(1^2 + (-1)^2) = 1$. Hence the characters of the two irreducible representations of the symmetric group on two letters are given by the table

	χ_1	χ_2
$C_1 = 1$	1	1
$C_2 = (12)$	1	-1

As a less trivial example we consider the case where G is the symmetric group, of order 6, on three letters and H is the subgroup consisting of those permutations leaving one letter, 3 say, fixed: $H = \{1, (12)\}$. G contains three classes:

$$C_1 = 1; \quad C_2 = (23), (31), (12); \quad C_3 = (123), (132).$$

The principal characteristic of H is $\frac{1}{2}(f^1 + f^2)$ and this is a compound characteristic of G; in fact the compound characteristic associated with the reducible representation of G whose characters are 3, 1, 0 (since $g = 6$, $n_1 = 1$, $n_2 = 3$, $n_3 = 2$). This contains the identity representation once since

$$c^1 = \tfrac{1}{6}(1.3 + 3.1 + 2.0) = 1$$

and the characters of the remaining representation are $(2, 0, -1)$. This representation is irreducible since $\frac{1}{6}(2^2 + 3.0^2 + 2(-1)^2) = 1$. Thus the principal characteristic of H furnishes us with two irreducible representations Γ_1, Γ_2 of G. The second simple characteristic of H is $\frac{1}{2}(f^1 - f^2)$ and, regarded as a compound characteristic of G, this yields the characters $(3, -1, 0)$ of a reducible representation of G. This representation does not contain the identity representation at all since $c^1 = \frac{1}{6}(1.3 + 3. -1 + 2.0) = 0$ but it contains Γ_2 once since $c^2 = \frac{1}{6}(2.3 + 0. -1 + (-1).0) = 1$. The remaining representation has characters $(1, -1, 1)$ and is, accordingly, irreducible since $\frac{1}{6}[(1)^2 + 3(-1)^2 + 2(1)^2] = 1$. Hence the characters of the three irreducible representations of the symmetric group on three letters are furnished by the table

	χ_1	χ_2	χ_3
C_1	1	2	1
C_2	1	0	-1
C_3	1	-1	1

In general the principal characteristic of H is $\frac{1}{h}\sum_h f(h)$ and, regarded as a compound characteristic of G, (which necessitates the identification of all $f(h)$ for those elements h of H which belong to the same class of G), we obtain a reducible representation of G whose characters are $\chi^j = \frac{g}{h}\frac{m_j}{n_j}$, m_j denoting the number of the n_j elements of C_j which belong to H. Since two representations of G with the same characters are identical it follows from (4.1) that this reducible representation is the representation furnished by the permutations of the left cosets of H in G which are induced by the left translations of G. The r-th simple characteristic of H furnishes, when regarded as a compound characteristic of G, the characters of a reducible representation of G:

$$\chi^j = \frac{g}{hn_j}\sum_k \xi_r(k)$$

the summation on the right being over all elements k of H which happen to lie in the class C_j of G. To find out how often this reducible representation contains Γ_m, $m = 1, \cdots, p$, we have to calculate $\frac{1}{g}\sum_j n_j\chi^j\bar{\chi}_m{}^j$, i. e. since this is a real number, $\frac{1}{g}\sum_j n_j\bar{\chi}^j\chi_m{}^j = \frac{1}{h}\sum_{k,j}\bar{\xi}_r(k)\chi_m{}^j$ where the summation on the right is over all classes C_j which contain elements of H (and over all elements k of H which lie in one of these classes). This is precisely the number of times that the reducible representation of H which is furnished by the irreducible representation Γ_m of G contains the r-th irreducible representation of H. Hence the theorem: *The compound representation of G which is furnished by the r-th irreducible representation of H contains the irreducible representation Γ_m of G precisely as often as does the reducible representation of H which is furnished by the irreducible representation Γ_m of G contain the r-th irreducible representation of H (Frobenius' Reciprocity Theorem).*

3. The direct product of two or more groups.

Let G be an arbitrary group with elements $s, t, \cdots$ and let K be a second arbitrary group with elements $\sigma, \tau, \cdots$. Then the pairs (s, σ), one element s from G and the other σ from K, constitute a group (as s runs over G and σ over K) under the law of combination

$$(t, \tau)(s, \sigma) = (ts, \tau\sigma).$$

In fact this law of combination assures the possession of the group property by the collection (s, σ); the collection contains the unit (e, ϵ) where e is the unit element of G and ϵ the unit element of K; and (s^{-1}, σ^{-1}) is inverse to (s, σ). We term the group whose elements are (s, σ) the direct product of K by G and we denote it by $G \times K$. Similarly if we have any finite collection of groups $G_1, G_2, \cdots, G_r$ the ordered sets $(s_1, s_2, \cdots, s_r)$, where s_j is an arbitrary element of G_j, constitute a group under the law of combination

$$(t_1, t_2, \cdots, t_r)(s_1, s_2, \cdots, s_r) = (t_1s_1, t_2s_2, \cdots, t_rs_r).$$

We term this group the direct product of the groups $G_1, G_2, \cdots, G_r$, taken in this order, and we denote it by $G_1 \times G_2 \times \cdots \times G_r$. If the groups $G_1, G_2, \cdots, G_r$ are finite their direct product $G = G_1 \times G_2 \times \cdots \times G_r$ is finite and of order equal to the product of the orders of the component groups $G_1, G_2, \cdots, G_r$:

$$g = g_1g_2 \cdots g_r.$$

It is clear also that the number of classes in g is the product of the various numbers of classes in the component groups; for if C_j is an arbitrary class of G_j, $j = 1, 2, \cdots, r$, $(C_1, C_2, \cdots, C_r)$ is a class of G. Hence the number of non-equivalent irreducible representations of G is the product of the numbers of non-equivalent irreducible representations of the various component groups $G_1, \cdots, G_r$.

If Γ_1 is an n_1-dimensional representation of G_1 and Γ_2 is an n_2-dimensional representation of G_2 then the Kronecker product $\Gamma_1 \times \Gamma_2$ is an n_1n_2-dimensional representation of $G_1 \times G_2$. A typical matrix of $\Gamma_1 \times \Gamma_2$ is $D_1(s_1) \times D_2(s_2)$ where s_1 is an arbitrary element of G_1 and s_2 is an arbitrary element of G_2 and the relation $\{D_1(t_1) \times D_2(t_2)\} \cdot \{D_1(s_1) \times D_2(s_2)\} = D_1(t_1)\, D_1(s_1) \times D_2(t_2)\, D_2(s_2) = D_1(t_1s_1) \times D_2(t_2s_2)$ proves the theorem stated (the unit matrix $E_{n_1n_2}$ being $D_1(e_1) \times D_2(e_2) = E_{n_1} \times E_{n_2}$ and the inverse of $D_1(s_1) \times D_2(s_2)$ being $D_1(s_1^{-1}) \times D_2(s_2^{-1})$. If ${}_1\chi(s_1)$ are the characters of Γ_1 and ${}_2\chi(s_2)$ the characters of Γ_2 the characters of the representation $\Gamma_1 \times \Gamma_2$ are ${}_1\chi(s_1)\, {}_2\chi(s_2)$. If f_1, f_2 are class functions defined over G_1 and G_2 respectively the function f defined by $f(s_1, s_2) = f_1(s_1)f_2(s_2)$ is a class function defined over $G_1 \times G_2$. It follows that the product of any generalized characteristic of G_1 by any generalized characteristic of G_2 is a generalized characteristic of $G_1 \times G_2$; in fact if ${}_1\chi_j(s_1)$, ${}_2\chi_k(s_2)$ are the characters of the irreducible representations of G_1 and G_2, respectively, an arbitrary generalized characteristic of G_1 is $\frac{1}{g_1}\sum_{s_1} c_1{}^a \, {}_1\bar{\chi}_a(s_1) f_1(s_1)$ whilst an arbitrary generalized characteristic of G_2 is $\frac{1}{g_2}\sum_{s_2} c_2{}^\beta \, {}_2\bar{\chi}_\beta(s_2) f_2(s_2)$ (the $c_1{}^j, c_2{}^k$ being integers, positive, negative or zero) so that their product is

$$\frac{1}{g_1 g_2}\sum_{s_1, s_2} c_1{}^a c_2{}^\beta \, {}_1\bar{\chi}_a(s_1) \, {}_2\bar{\chi}_\beta(s_2) f_1(s_1) f_2(s_2)$$
$$= \frac{1}{g}\sum_{s_1, s_2} c_1{}^a c_2{}^\beta \, \bar{\chi}_{a,\beta}(s_1, s_2) f(s_1, s_2)$$

where the $\chi_{j,k}(s_1, s_2)$ are the characters of the representation ${}_1\Gamma_j \times {}_2\Gamma_k$ of $G_1 \times G_2$. These are the irreducible representations, $p_1 p_2$ in number, of $G_1 \times G_2$. In fact the average of $\bar{\chi}_{j,k}(s_1, s_2)\chi_{j,k}(s_1, s_2)$ over $G_1 \times G_2$ is unity:

$$\frac{1}{g}\sum_{s_1, s_2} \bar{\chi}_{j,k}(s_1, s_2)\chi_{j,k}(s_1, s_2) = \frac{1}{g_1 g_2}\sum_{s_1, s_2} {}_1\bar{\chi}_j(s_1) \, {}_2\bar{\chi}_k(s_2) \, {}_1\chi_j(s_1) \, {}_2\chi_k(s_2)$$
$$= \frac{1}{g_1}\sum_{s_1} {}_1\bar{\chi}_j(s_1) \, {}_1\chi_j(s_1) \cdot \frac{1}{g_2}\sum_{s_2} {}_2\bar{\chi}_k(s_2) \, {}_2\chi_k(s_2) = 1$$

since the representations ${}_1\Gamma_j$, ${}_2\Gamma_k$ of G_1 and G_2, respectively, are irreducible. Similarly the average of $\bar{\chi}_{j_2,k_2}(s_1, s_2)\chi_{j_1,k_1}(s_1, s_2)$ over $G_1 \times G_2$ is zero unless $j_2 = j_1$, $k_2 = k_1$ when, as we have just seen, it is unity. Hence no two of the $p_1 p_2$ irreducible representations of $G_1 \times G_2$, whose characters are $\chi_{j,k}(s_1, s_2)$, are equivalent. When the integral coefficients $c_1{}^j, c_2{}^k$ are restricted to be non-negative so are their products $c_1{}^j c_2{}^k$ and we see that the product of two compound characteristics, one of G_1 and the other of G_2, is a compound characteristic of $G_1 \times G_2$. Furthermore the product of a simple characteristic of G_1 by a simple characteristic of G_2 is a simple characteristic of $G_1 \times G_2$, all simple characteristics of $G_1 \times G_2$ being obtained in this way; and, in particular, the product of the principal characteristic of G_1 by the principal characteristic of G_2 is the principal characteristic of $G_1 \times G_2$. These results are evidently at once extensible to the direct product $G_1 \times G_2 \times \cdots \times G_r$ of r finite groups. If ${}_j\Gamma$ is an irreducible representation of G_j then ${}_1\Gamma \times {}_2\Gamma \times \cdots \times {}_r\Gamma$ is an irreducible representation of $G_1 \times G_2 \times \cdots \times G_r$ and all irreducible representations of this direct product may be obtained in this way. If ${}_j\phi(f_j)$ is a simple characteristic of G_j then the product ${}_1\phi(f_1) \cdots {}_r\phi(f_r)$ is a simple characteristic of $G_1 \times \cdots \times G_r$ and all simple characteristics of this direct product are obtainable in this way. In particular the product of the principal characteristics of $G_1, \cdots, G_r$ is the principal characteristic of $G_1 \times G_2 \times \cdots \times G_r$.

Example. The subgroup $\{1, (12), (34), (12)(34)\}$ (known as the four-group) of the symmetric group on four letters may be regarded as the direct product of the group $G = \{1, (12)\}$ by the group $K = \{1, (34)\}$; in fact the groups $\{1, (12), (34), (12)(34)\}$ and $\{(1,1), ((12),1), (1, (34)), ((12), (34))\}$ are abstractly identical. The simple characteristics of G are

$$ {}_1\phi_1(f_1) = \tfrac{1}{2}(f_1{}^1 + f_1{}^2); \quad {}_1\phi_2(f_1) = \tfrac{1}{2}(f_1{}^1 - f_1{}^2) $$

whilst the simple characteristics of K are

$$ {}_2\phi_1(f_2) = \tfrac{1}{2}(f_2{}^1 + f_2{}^2); \quad {}_2\phi_2(f_2) = \tfrac{1}{2}(f_2{}^1 - f_2{}^2). $$

Hence the four simple characteristics of the Abelian group $G \times K$ are

$$ \phi_{1,1}(f) = \tfrac{1}{4}(f^{11} + f^{12} + f^{21} + f^{22}); \quad \phi_{1,2}(f) = \tfrac{1}{4}(f^{11} - f^{12} + f^{21} - f^{22}) $$
$$ \phi_{2,1}(f) = \tfrac{1}{4}(f^{11} + f^{12} - f^{21} - f^{22}); \quad \phi_{2,2}(f) = \tfrac{1}{4}(f^{11} - f^{12} - f^{21} + f^{22}) $$

so that the characters of the irreducible (hence one-dimensional) representations of the four-group are furnished by the table

	$\chi_{1,1}$	$\chi_{1,2}$	$\chi_{2,1}$	$\chi_{2,2}$
$C_{1,1} = 1$	1	1	1	1
$C_{1,2} = (34)$	1	-1	1	-1
$C_{2,1} = (12)$	1	1	-1	-1
$C_{2,2} = (12)(34)$	1	-1	-1	1

4. The principal characteristic of the symmetric group on *m* letters.

We have seen (p. 89) that the matrices $p([E]_m)$ furnish a representation, of dimension n^m, of the symmetric group on m letters. On setting $A = E$ and $q = e$ (the unit permutation) in (3.20) we obtain

$$ [B]_m p([E]_m) = p[B]_m, \text{ every } B, $$

or, equivalently

(4.10) $$ [A]_m p([E]_m) = p[A]_m, \text{ every } A. $$

Similarly on setting $B = E$, $p = e$ and replacing q by p in (3.20) we find $p([E]_m)[A]_m = p[A]_m$. Hence the matrix $[A]_m$ is commutative with every matrix of the representation $p([E]_m)$ of the symmetric group on m letters. This symmetric group possesses p non-equivalent irreducible representations (p, the number of classes in the group, being the number of partitions of m) $\Gamma_1, \cdots, \Gamma_p$, and the representation Γ furnished by $D(q) = q([E]_m)$ is of the form $\Gamma = c^a\Gamma_a$. When presented in the basis in which it is reduced $D(q)$ appears as

$$c^1D_1(q) \dotplus c^2D_2(q) \dotplus \cdots \dotplus c^pD_p(q) \quad \text{where } c^jD_j(q)$$

stands for $D_j(q) \dotplus \cdots \dotplus D_j(q)$ (c^j terms) $= E_{c_j} \times D_j(q)$. It follows at once, by an application of Schur's lemma, that the matrix $[A]_m$, being commutative with all the matrices $D(q)$, must be of the form

$$[A]_m = \sum_j (M_j(A) \times E_{d_j}) \tag{4.11}$$

where d_j is the dimension of Γ_j and $M_j(A)$ is of dimension c_j. The reason for this will be sufficiently clear by considering the case where $D(q)$ is

$$D(q) = \begin{pmatrix} D_j(q) & 0 & 0 \\ 0 & D_j(q) & 0 \\ 0 & 0 & D_k(q) \end{pmatrix}.$$

Let any matrix T commutative with $D(q)$ be displayed in the block form furnished by $D(q)$:

$$T = \begin{pmatrix} T_1^1 & T_2^1 & T_3^1 \\ T_1^2 & T_2^2 & T_3^2 \\ T_1^3 & T_2^3 & T_3^3 \end{pmatrix}.$$

Then $D(q)T = \begin{pmatrix} D_j(q)T_1^1 & D_j(q)T_2^1 & D_j(q)T_3^1 \\ D_j(q)T_1^2 & D_j(q)T_2^2 & D_j(q)T_3^2 \\ D_k(q)T_1^3 & D_k(q)T_2^3 & D_k(q)T_3^3 \end{pmatrix}$

whilst

$$TD(q) = \begin{pmatrix} T_1^1D_j(q) & T_2^1D_j(q) & T_3^1D_k(q) \\ T_1^2D_j(q) & T_2^2D_j(q) & T_3^2D_k(q) \\ T_1^3D_j(q) & T_2^3D_j(q) & T_3^3D_k(q) \end{pmatrix}.$$

Equating these we find equations such as $D_j(q)T_3^1 = T_3^1D_k(q)$ forcing $T_3^1 = 0$ since Γ_j, Γ_k are non-equivalent irreducible representations (of the symmetric group on m letters). Similarly $T_3^2 = 0$, $T_1^3 = 0$, $T_2^3 = 0$. The other equations such as $T_1^1D_j(q) = D_j(q)T_1^1$ force T_1^1 to be a scalar matrix (since the only matrices commutative with all the matrices of an irreducible representation of a group are scalar). Hence

$$T = \begin{pmatrix} m_1^1E_{d_j} & m_2^1E_{d_j} & 0 \\ m_1^2E_{d_j} & m_2^2E_{d_j} & 0 \\ 0 & 0 & m_3^3E_{d_k} \end{pmatrix} = (M_j \times E_{d_j}) \dotplus (M_k \times E_{d_k})$$

where, here, M_j is two-dimensional and M_k one-dimensional. The fact that $[A]_m$ appears, when the basis is properly chosen, in the form $\sum_j (M_j(A) \times E_{d_j})$ implies that $[A]_m$ may be presented (by merely permuting in an appropriate manner the vectors of the previous basis—see (3.2)) in the form $\sum_j (E_{d_j} \times M_j(A))$. In other words the representation $[A]_m$ (homogeneous and of degree m) of the full linear group is reducible, containing the representation $M_j(A)$ (also homogeneous of degree m) d_j times. We shall see, at the end of the present chapter, that the representations $M_j(A)$ of the full linear group are irreducible and exhaust the homogeneous representations of degree m of the full linear group but we do not need this precise result for the time being.

Since, when the basis is properly chosen,

$$q([E]_m) = \sum_j \{E_{c_j} \times D_j(q)\}; \quad [A]_m = \sum_j \{M_j(A) \times E_{d_j}\}$$

and since

$$q([A]_m) = q([E]_m)[A]_m$$

it follows that

$$q([A]_m) = \sum_j \{E_{c_j} \times D_j(q)\}\{M_j(A) \times E_{d_j}\},$$

i. e.

$$q([A]_m) = \sum_j \{M_j(A) \times D_j(q)\}. \tag{4.12}$$

On taking the traces of both sides of this matrix equation and denoting by $(\alpha) = (\alpha_1, \alpha_2, \cdots, \alpha_m)$ the class of the symmetric group on m letters to which q belongs we obtain (on using (3.22))

$$s^{(\alpha)} = \sum_j a^j \chi_j^{(\alpha)}; \qquad a^j = Tr M_j(A)$$

or, equivalently, on using (3.16),

$$a^k = \frac{1}{g} \sum_{(\alpha)} n_{(\alpha)} \bar{\chi}_k^{(\alpha)} s^{(\alpha)} = \sum_{(\alpha)} \frac{\bar{\chi}_k^{(\alpha)}}{\alpha_1! \cdots \alpha_m!} \left(\frac{s_1}{1}\right)^{\alpha_1} \cdots \left(\frac{s_m}{m}\right)^{\alpha_m}. \tag{4.13}$$

When $k = 1$, so that $\Gamma_k = \Gamma_1$ is the identity representation, we obtain

$$a^1 = \sum_{(\alpha)} \frac{1}{\alpha_1! \cdots \alpha_m!} \left(\frac{s_1}{1}\right)^{\alpha_1} \cdots \left(\frac{s_m}{m}\right)^{\alpha_m} = q_m(s)$$

so that the characters of $M_1(A)$ are the same as those of the symmetrized Kronecker m-th power $[A]_{(m)}$—see (3.23). In general the expression (4.13) may be simplified by noting that the characters of any representation of the symmetric group on m letters are real. In fact any representation of this group is equivalent to a unitary representation (simply because the representation is bounded, the group being finite) and hence $\bar{\chi}(s) = \chi(s^{-1})$ since $U^* = U^{-1}$. But s^{-1} is in the same class as s since the inverse of a cycle $(m_1, m_2, \cdots, m_j)$ is the same cycle written in reversed order i. e. $(m_j, m_{j-1}, \cdots, m_1)$. Hence $\bar{\chi}(s) = \chi(s)$ i. e. $\chi(s)$ is real. We may, therefore, write instead of (4. 13)

$$(4.14) \qquad a^k = \sum_{(a)} \frac{\chi_k^{(a)}}{\alpha_1! \cdots \alpha_m!} \left(\frac{s_1}{1}\right)^{\alpha_1} \cdots \left(\frac{s_m}{m}\right)^{\alpha_m}.$$

The function $s^{(a)} = s_1^{\alpha_1} \cdots s_m^{\alpha_m}$ is a class function defined over the symmetric group and we term the expressions occurring in (4. 14) the simple characteristics of the symmetric group on m letters. In other words we use instead of the indeterminates f^k which occurred in the definition of the simple characteristics of any finite group the quantities $s^{(a)} = s_1^{\alpha_1} \cdots s_m^{\alpha_m}$ where $(\alpha) = (\alpha_1, \alpha_2, \cdots, \alpha_m)$ is the cycle structure of the particular permutation for which the indeterminate class function is being evaluated. We shall denote a^k by $\phi_k(\mathbf{s})$:

$$(4.15) \qquad \phi_k(\mathbf{s}) = \sum_{(a)} \frac{\chi_k^{(a)}}{\alpha_1! \cdots \alpha_m!} \left(\frac{s_1}{1}\right)^{\alpha_1} \cdots \left(\frac{s_m}{m}\right)^{\alpha_m}.$$

The indeterminates $s_1, \cdots, s_m$ are the traces of $A, A^2, \cdots, A^m$, respectively, where A is an arbitrary element of the full linear group of dimension n. Denoting the characteristic numbers of A by $(\mathbf{z}) = (z_1, \cdots, z_n)$ it follows that

$$(4.16) \qquad s_k = z_1^k + z_2^k + \cdots + z_n^k; \qquad k = 1, 2, 3, \cdots.$$

When we are discussing merely the symmetric group on m letters and are not concerned with the connection between it and the full linear group (of given dimension) n is at our free choice subject only to the provision $n \geq m$ necessary to ensure the independence of the m indeterminates $(s_1, s_2, \cdots, s_m)$.

Of particular importance for us are the principal characteristics $q_m(\mathbf{s})$ (one for each value of m)

$$(4.17) \qquad q_m(\mathbf{s}) = \sum_{(a)} \frac{1}{\alpha_1! \cdots \alpha_m!} \left(\frac{s_1}{1}\right)^{\alpha_1} \cdots \left(\frac{s_m}{m}\right)^{\alpha_m}$$

and we call attention here to a few remarkable properties of this set of polynomials in the m variables $(s_1, \cdots, s_m)$ the first seven of which we write out explicitly.

$$q_1(\mathbf{s}) = s_1; \quad q_2(\mathbf{s}) = \tfrac{1}{2}(s_1^2 + s_2); \quad q_3(\mathbf{s}) = \frac{1}{3!}(s_1^3 + 3s_1s_2 + 2s_3);$$

$$q_4(\mathbf{s}) = \frac{1}{4!}(s_1^4 + 6s_1^2s_2 + 8s_1s_3 + 3s_2^2 + 6s_4);$$

$$q_5(\mathbf{s}) = \frac{1}{5!}(s_1^5 + 10s_1^3s_2 + 20s_1^2s_3 + 15s_1s_2^2 + 30s_1s_4 + 20s_2s_3 + 24s_5);$$

$$q_6(s) = \frac{1}{6!}(s_1^6 + 15s_1^4s_2 + 40s_1^3s_3 + 45s_1^2s_2^2 + 90s_1^2s_4 + 120s_1s_2s_3 + 144s_1s_5 + 15s_2^3 + 90s_2s_4 + 40s_3^2 + 120s_6);$$

$$q_7(s) = \frac{1}{7!}(s_1^7 + 21s_1^5s_2 + 70s_1^4s_3 + 105s_1^3s_2^2 + 210s_1^3s_4 + 420s_1^2s_2s_3 + 504s_1^2s_5 + 105s_1s_2^3 + 630s_1s_2s_4 + 280s_1s_3^2 + 840s_1s_6 + 210s_2^2s_3 + 504s_2s_5 + 420s_3s_4 + 720s_7).$$

The terms are arranged so that $s_1^{m_1}s_2^{m_2}\cdots$ comes before $s_1^{n_1}s_2^{n_2}\cdots$ if the first non-vanishing number of the set $m_1 - n_1, m_2 - n_2, \cdots$ is positive. The polynomials $q_m(s)$ furnish at a glance the structure of the corresponding symmetric group. Thus from $q_6(s)$ we see that the $6! = 720$ permutations of the symmetric group on 6 letters divide into 11 classes there being 45 elements, for example, in the class $(\alpha) = (2, 2, 0, 0, 0, 0)$.

Remembering that the numbers $(\alpha_1, \alpha_2, \cdots, \alpha_m)$ are subjected to the relation $\alpha_1 + 2\alpha_2 + \cdots + m\alpha_m = m$ it follows that $\alpha'_1 + 2\alpha_2 + \cdots + m\alpha_m = m - 1$ where $\alpha'_1 = \alpha_1 - 1$. On differentiating $q_m(s)$ with respect to s_1 we find

$$\frac{\partial q_m}{\partial s_1} = \sum_{(\alpha')} \frac{1}{\alpha'_1!\,\alpha_2!\cdots\alpha_m!}\left(\frac{s_1}{1}\right)^{\alpha'_1}\left(\frac{s_2}{2}\right)^{\alpha_2}\cdots\left(\frac{s_m}{m}\right)^{\alpha_m}$$

where $(\alpha') = (\alpha'_1, \alpha_2, \cdots, \alpha_m)$ so that $\partial q_m/\partial s_1 = q_{m-1}$, $m = 1, 2, \cdots$ ($q_0(s)$ being defined by $q_0(s) = 1$). Similarly on differentiating $q_m(s)$ with respect to s_2 and writing $\alpha'_2 = \alpha_2 - 1$ we find

$$2\frac{\partial q_m}{\partial s_2} = \sum_{(\alpha')} \frac{1}{\alpha_1!\,\alpha'_2!\,\alpha_3!\cdots\alpha_m!}\left(\frac{s_1}{1}\right)^{\alpha_1}\left(\frac{s_2}{2}\right)^{\alpha'_2}\cdots\left(\frac{s_m}{m}\right)^{\alpha_m}$$

where $(\alpha') = (\alpha_1, \alpha'_2, \cdots, \alpha_m)$. Since $\alpha_1 + 2\alpha'_2 + 3\alpha_3 + \cdots + m\alpha_m = m - 2$ it follows that

$$2\frac{\partial q_m}{\partial s_2} = q_{m-2}; \qquad m = 1, 2, \cdots$$

where $q_{-1}(s)$ is defined by $q_{-1}(s) = 0$. Reasoning in this way we obtain the general result

$$(4.18) \qquad k\frac{\partial q_m}{\partial s_k} = q_{m-k}(s); \qquad m = 0, 1, 2, \cdots; \; k = 1, \cdots, m.$$

(the q's carrying negative subscripts all being assigned the value zero).

It is important for us to have the explicit expression for the principal characteristics $q_m(s)$ in terms of the variables $(z) = (z_1, z_2, \cdots, z_n)$ of which the s_k are the power sums (see (4.16)). To obtain this consider the reciprocal of the polynomial $f(t) = (1 - z_1 t) \cdots (1 - z_n t)$ in the indeterminate t:

(4.19) $$\{f(t)\}^{-1} = \frac{1}{(1 - z_1 t) \cdots (1 - z_n t)} = \sum_0^\infty p_k(z) t^k.$$

On writing $(1 - z_j t)^{-1} = \sum_{\beta_j = 0}^{\infty} (z_j)^{\beta_j} t^{\beta_j}$ it becomes clear that

$$p_k(z) = \sum_{(\beta)} z_1^{\beta_1} \cdots z_n^{\beta_n}; \qquad \beta_1 + \beta_2 + \cdots + \beta_n = k$$

(the summation being over all partitions of k) is the complete homogeneous symmetric function of degree k in the n variables z. Since

$$\log \frac{1}{1 - z_j t} = \sum_{\beta_j = 1}^{\infty} \frac{1}{\beta_j} z_j^{\beta_j} t^{\beta_j}$$

we have

$$\log \{f(t)\}^{-1} = \sum_{j=1}^{n} \log \frac{1}{(1 - z_j t)} = \sum_1^\infty \left(\frac{s_{\beta_j}}{\beta_j}\right) t^{\beta_j}$$

so that

$$\begin{aligned} \{f(t)\}^{-1} &= e^{(s_1/1)t + (s_2/2)t^2 + \cdots} = e^{s_1 t/1} e^{s_2 t^2/2} \cdots \\ &= \sum_{\alpha_1 = 0}^{\infty} \frac{1}{\alpha_1!} \left(\frac{s_1}{1}\right)^{\alpha_1} t^{\alpha_1} \cdot \sum_{\alpha_2 = 0}^{\infty} \frac{1}{\alpha_2!} \left(\frac{s_2}{2}\right)^{\alpha_2} t^{2\alpha_2} \cdots \\ &= \sum_{k=0}^{\infty} \left\{ \sum_{(\alpha)} \frac{1}{\alpha_1! \cdots \alpha_k!} \left(\frac{s_1}{1}\right)^{\alpha_1} \cdots \left(\frac{s_k}{k}\right)^{\alpha_k} \right\} t^k \end{aligned}$$

where the summation is over all (α) for which $\alpha_1 + 2\alpha_2 + \cdots + k\alpha_k = k$. Hence $\{f(t)\}^{-1} = \sum_{k=0}^{\infty} q_k(s) t^k$ so that

(4.20) $$q_k(s) = p_k(z); \qquad k = 0, 1, 2, \cdots.$$

This relation remains valid for negative integral values of k if we define, as we shall do, $p_k(z) = 0$, $k = -1, -2, \cdots$.

A similar argument may be applied to the polynomial $g(t)$ in the indeterminate t:

(4.21) $$g(t) = (1 + z_1 t)(1 + z_2 t) \cdots (1 + z_n t) = \sum_0^n \sigma_k(z) t^k$$

where σ_k is the elementary symmetric function $\sigma_k = \Sigma z_1 z_2 \cdots z_k$ of degree k in the variables z. We find

$$\log g(t) = \frac{s_1}{1} t - \frac{s_2}{2} t^2 + \frac{s_3}{3} t^3 - \cdots$$

implying

(4.22) $$q_k(s^*) = \sigma_k(z)$$

where $\mathbf{s}^*$ is obtained from $\mathbf{s}$ by changing the signs of those s_j *which carry even subscripts*

$$(\mathbf{s}^*) = (s_1, -s_2, s_3, -s_4, \cdots).$$

We shall denote $q_k(\mathbf{s}^*)$ by $\pi_k(\mathbf{s})$ so that

$$\sigma_k(\mathbf{z}) = \pi_k(\mathbf{s}). \tag{4.23}$$

The polynomial $\pi_k(\mathbf{s})$ in the k variables $(s_1, \cdots, s_k)$, being obtained from $q_k(\mathbf{s})$ by changing the signs of $s_2, s_4, \cdots$ has the explicit expression

$$\pi_k(\mathbf{s}) = \sum_{(a)} \frac{(-1)^{\alpha_2+\alpha_4+\alpha_6+\cdots}}{\alpha_1! \cdots \alpha_k!} \left(\frac{s_1}{1}\right)^{\alpha_1} \cdots \left(\frac{s_k}{k}\right)^{\alpha_k}; \; k = 1, 2, \cdots. \tag{4.24}$$

Since every permutation of the symmetric group on m letters is either even or odd (being even or odd with $\alpha_2 + \alpha_4 + \alpha_6 + \cdots$) it is clear that, in addition to the identity representation, the symmetric group on m letters possesses a second one-dimensional representation (known as the *alternating* representation); namely, the representation which associates with each even permutation the number ($= 1 \times 1$ matrix) 1 and with each odd permutation the number ($= 1 \times 1$ matrix) -1. The polynomial $\pi_m(\mathbf{s})$ defined by (4.24) is the simple characteristic of the alternating representation. If Γ is any representation of the symmetric group on m letters the Kronecker product of Γ by the alternating representation is a representation of the same dimension as Γ and this representation will not be equivalent to Γ unless the characters of all odd permutations in Γ are zero (in which case it will be equivalent to Γ). If Γ is irreducible so also is the derived representation obtained by taking the Kronecker product of Γ and the alternating representation; in fact $|\chi(s)|^2$ is the same for Γ and for the derived representation, so that if the average of $|\chi(s)|^2$ (over the symmetric group) is unity for Γ it is also unity for the derived representation. This average is unity if and only if the representation is irreducible. Associated, then, with each irreducible representation Γ of the symmetric group is an irreducible representation Γ^* and the relation is reflexive: $(\Gamma^*)^* = \Gamma$. If $\Gamma^* = \Gamma$ we term Γ *self-associated*; otherwise we term the two distinct representations Γ, Γ^* *associated*. The identity and alternating representations are *associated*; and, generally, the simple characteristic of the symmetric group corresponding to Γ^* is obtained from the simple characteristic corresponding to Γ by changing the signs of $s_2, s_4 \cdots$.

5. The simple characteristics of the symmetric group.

Let us imagine the m letters whose permutations are the elements of our symmetric group placed in k compartments or boxes containing, respectively, $\lambda_1, \lambda_2, \cdots, \lambda_k$ letters; $\lambda_1 + \lambda_2 + \cdots + \lambda_k = m$. Those permutations which leave fixed all letters not in the j-th compartment or box form a subgroup G_j of the symmetric group on m letters, namely, the group of $\lambda_j!$ permutations on λ_j letters, $j = 1, 2, \cdots, k$. The direct product $G_1 \times G_2 \times \cdots \times G_k$ of the k groups $G_1, G_2, \cdots, G_j$ is also a subgroup, of order $\lambda_1! \lambda_2! \cdots \lambda_k!$ of the symmetric group on m letters; in fact, the subgroup consisting of those permutations of the m letters which do not send any letter out of its box. The principal characteristic of G_j being $q_{\lambda_j}(\mathbf{s})$ the principal characteristic of the direct product $G_1 \times G_2 \times \cdots \times G_k$ is $q_{\lambda_1}(\mathbf{s}) q_{\lambda_2}(\mathbf{s}) \cdots q_{\lambda_k}(\mathbf{s})$ and, regarded as a characteristic of our symmetric group G on n letters, this corresponds to a (generally reducible) representation of G; namely, the representation of dimension $m! \div \lambda_1! \lambda_2! \cdots \lambda_k!$ furnished by the permutations of the left cosets of $G_1 \times G_2 \times \cdots \times G_k$ in G which are induced by the left translations of G. We have, therefore, associated with each partition $(\lambda) = (\lambda_1, \lambda_2, \cdots, \lambda_k)$ of m a representation (in general reducible) of G which we shall denote by $\Delta(\lambda)$; its characteristic is $q_{\lambda_1}(\mathbf{s}) \cdots q_{\lambda_k}(\mathbf{s})$:

$$(4.25) \qquad \Delta(\lambda) \rightleftarrows q_{\lambda_1}(\mathbf{s}) q_{\lambda_2}(\mathbf{s}) \cdots q_{\lambda_k}(\mathbf{s}) = p_{\lambda_1}(\mathbf{z}) \cdots p_{\lambda_k}(\mathbf{z}).$$

We shall suppose $\lambda_1 \geqq \lambda_2 \geqq \cdots \geqq \lambda_k > 0$ and shall arrange the partitions (λ) in dictionary order as explained in Chapter One p. 8. Thus for $m = 4$ the five representations (all but the first of which are reducible) are denoted by

$$\Delta(4), \quad \Delta(3,1), \quad \Delta(2^2), \quad \Delta(2,1^2), \quad \Delta(1^4)$$

and their characteristics are

$$\Delta(4) \to q_4(\mathbf{s}) = \frac{1}{4!}(s_1^4 + 6s_1^2 s_2 + 8s_1 s_3 + 3s_2^2 + 6s_4)$$

$$\Delta(3,1) \to q_3(\mathbf{s}) q_1(\mathbf{s}) = \frac{1}{3!}(s_1^4 + 3s_1^2 s_2 + 2s_1 s_3)$$

$$\Delta(2^2) \to q_2(\mathbf{s}) q_2(\mathbf{s}) = \frac{1}{4}(s_1^4 + 2s_1^2 s_2 + s_2^2)$$

$$\Delta(2,1^2) \to q_2(\mathbf{s}) q_1(\mathbf{s}) q_1(\mathbf{s}) = \tfrac{1}{2}(s_1^4 + s_1^2 s_2)$$

$$\Delta(1^4) \to q_1(\mathbf{s})^4 = s_1^4.$$

It is clear that $\Delta(m) \to q_m(\mathbf{s})$ so that when $\lambda_1 = m$ the representation obtained is the irreducible identity representation; in all other cases $G_1 \times G_2 \times \cdots \times G_k$ is a *proper* subgroup of G and the representation is reducible containing the identity representation exactly once (see page 94).

The significance for us of the result expressed by (4.25) is the following. We shall readily show that every homogeneous symmetric polynomial of degree m, with integral coefficients, in the n variables $z_1, \cdots, z_n$ may be expressed in the form $\sum c_{(\lambda)} p_{\lambda_1}(z) \cdots p_{\lambda_k}(z)$ where the coefficients $c_{(\lambda)}$ are integers positive, negative or zero and the summation is over all partitions (λ) of m. Hence *any homogeneous symmetric function of degree m in the n variables $(z) = (z_1, \cdots, z_n)$, with integral coefficients, yields, when expressed in terms of the power sums $s_k = z_1^k + \cdots + z_n^k$, $k = 1, \cdots, m$, a generalized characteristic of the symmetric group on m letters.* There will remain only the task of finding those particular homogeneous symmetric polynomials of degree m in the n variables (z), with integral coefficients, which yield the simple characteristics of the symmetric group on m letters. To prove our statement we have merely to observe that any homogeneous symmetric polynomial (with integral coefficients) of degree m in the n variables (z) is expressible in the form $\sum_{(\alpha)} k_{(\alpha)} \sigma_1^{\alpha_1}(z) \cdots \sigma_n^{\alpha_n}(z)$ (where the $\sigma_j(z)$ are the elementary symmetric functions) and the $k_{(\alpha)}$ are integers (the summation being over all classes (α) of the symmetric group on m letters). This is simply the fundamental theorem of the theory of symmetric functions and may be expressed by the statement that the elementary symmetric functions $\sigma(z)$ constitute a basis for all symmetric polynomials. Its proof by the method of mathematical induction is immediate. We first observe that any homogeneous symmetric polynomial, with integral coefficients, of degree m in the n variables $(z) = (z_1, \cdots, z_n)$ is a linear combination with integral coefficients of the particular polynomials of this type:

$$T_{(\lambda)}(z) = \sum z_1^{\lambda_1} \cdots z_n^{\lambda_n} \tag{4.26}$$

where $\lambda_1 \geq \lambda_2 \geq \cdots \geq \lambda_n \geq 0$ is a partition of m: $\lambda_1 + \lambda_2 + \cdots + \lambda_n = m$. We suppose these $T_{(\lambda)}(z)$ arranged, for a given value of m, in dictionary order (with respect to (λ)) and observe that the $\sigma_m(z)$ are the last: $T_{(1^m)}(z)$, for each value of m. Evidently

$$T_{(\lambda)}(z) - \{\sigma_1(z)\}^{\lambda_1 - \lambda_2} \{\sigma_2(z)\}^{\lambda_2 - \lambda_3} \cdots \{\sigma_n(z)\}^{\lambda_n}$$

is a linear combination (with integral coefficients) of the $T_{(\lambda')}(z)$ where the partition (λ') follows (λ); simply because it is symmetric and the product of the σ's starts out with $T_{(\lambda)}(z)$. Assuming our theorem true for all partitions (λ') of m which follow (λ) its validity for (λ) follows. Since it is trivially true for $(\lambda') = (1^m)$ the induction proof is complete. What we have to prove is that this fundamental theorem of symmetric function theory implies that the complete homogeneous symmetric functions of degree m: $p_j(z) = \sum_{(\lambda)} T_{(\lambda)}(z)$ (the summation being over all partitions of j) may be used as a basis for all symmetric polynomials. To do this we observe that the *generating functions* $\{f(t)\}^{-1}$ and $g(t)$ of (4.19) and (4.21), respectively, are connected by the relation $g(t)\{f(-t)\}^{-1} = 1$ so that

$$\{\sum_0^n \sigma_j t^j\}\{\sum_0^\infty (-1)^k p_k t^k\} = 1$$

and this yields the series of relations

$$\sigma_0 p_0 = 1; \quad \sigma_0 p_1 - \sigma_1 p_0 = 0; \quad \sigma_0 p_2 - \sigma_1 p_1 + \sigma_2 p_0 = 0; \cdots$$

(it being understood that $\sigma_{n+1} = \sigma_{n+2} = \cdots = 0$). These relations may be conveniently expressed by the statement that the two matrices

$$P_k = \begin{pmatrix} p_0 & p_1 & \cdots & p_{k-1} \\ & p_0 & \cdots & p_{k-2} \\ & & & \\ & & & p_0 \end{pmatrix}; \quad \Sigma_k = \begin{pmatrix} \sigma_0 & -\sigma_1 & \sigma_2 & \cdots \\ & \sigma_0 & -\sigma_1 & \cdots \\ & & & \\ & & & \sigma_0 \end{pmatrix}$$

are reciprocal for every value of k; $k = 1, 2, \cdots$ (the elements below the main diagonal in each matrix being zero). Since $p_0 = \sigma_0 = 1$ the determinant of either matrix is unity so that each element of either is a cofactor of the other. In particular on taking the cofactors of the elements in the first column of P_k we read

$$(4.27) \quad \sigma_1 = p_1; \quad \sigma_2 = \begin{vmatrix} p_1 & p_2 \\ p_0 & p_1 \end{vmatrix} \quad \sigma_3 = \begin{vmatrix} p_1 & p_2 & p_3 \\ p_0 & p_1 & p_2 \\ 0 & p_0 & p_1 \end{vmatrix}; \cdots$$

showing that the p_j constitute a basis for the elementary symmetric functions σ_k and hence, by the fundamental theorem, for all symmetric polynomials. And if the coefficients in a given symmetric polynomial of degree m are *integral* it is expressible as a linear combination of the products $p_{\lambda_1}(z) \cdots p_{\lambda_k}(z)$ with integral coefficients; that $(\lambda) = (\lambda_1, \cdots, \lambda_k)$ is a partition of m is clear since each p_{λ_j} is homogeneous of degree λ_j in the n variables (z). If there occurred in the expression for our symmetric polynomial of degree m terms other than those for which $\lambda_1 + \lambda_2 + \cdots + \lambda_k = m$ we would collect together all expressions for which $\lambda_1 + \lambda_2 + \cdots + \lambda_k$ had the same value and then we would have a sum of homogeneous polynomials of different degrees which vanishes forcing the vanishing of each of the polynomials. Hence our given symmetric polynomial of degree m is expressible as a linear combination (with integral coefficients) of those products $p_{\lambda_1}(z) \cdots p_{\lambda_k}(z)$ for which (λ) is a partition of m.

Knowing now that *any* homogeneous symmetric polynomial of degree m in the n variables $(z) = (z_1, \cdots, z_n)$, with integral coefficients, furnishes, when expressed in terms of the power sums $s_k = z_1^k + \cdots + z_n^k$ a generalized characteristic of the symmetric group G on m letters what we need is a criterion which will tell us when a given set of generalized characteristics are, each and every one, simple. This criterion is furnished, for *any* finite group G, as follows. Let $\phi_j(f)$ be the simple characteristics of G and let f_1 and f_2 be any sets of values of the indeterminate function f defined over G; then $\phi_j(f_1) = \frac{1}{g}\sum_s \bar{\chi}_j(s)f_1(s)$; $\phi_j(f_2) = \frac{1}{g}\sum_t \bar{\chi}_j(t)f_2(t)$ the summations being over all elements s, t, respectively of G. On denoting by $\bar{\phi}_j(f_2)$ the expression $\frac{1}{g}\sum_t \chi(t)f_2(t)$ (so that the *coefficients* of $\bar{\phi}_j(f_2)$ are the conjugates of those of $\phi_j(f_2)$ whilst the indeterminate argument f_2 is the same) we derive, on multiplication, the formula

$$\phi_j(f_1)\bar{\phi}_j(f_2) = \frac{1}{(g)^2}\sum_{s,t} \bar{\chi}_j(s)\chi_j(t)f_1(s)f_2(t)$$

and on summing over the p simple characteristics $\phi_j(f)$, i. e. letting j run from 1 to p and adding, we obtain, after using the orthogonality relations (3.17)

$$\sum_{j=1}^{p} \phi_j(f_1)\bar{\phi}_j(f_2) = \frac{1}{g}\sum_s f_1(s)f_2(s) = \phi_1(f_1f_2) \tag{4.29}$$

the right-hand side being the principal characteristic of G when the indeterminate f has the value f_1f_2 defined by $f^k = f_1^kf_2^k$. The force of this relation is that its converse is true in the following sense. Suppose we have a set of p generalized characteristics:

$$F_j(f) = c_j^{\alpha}\phi_{\alpha}(f); \qquad j = 1, 2, \cdots, p,$$

which possess the property $\sum_{j=1}^{p} F_j(f_1)\bar{F}_j(f_2) = \phi_1(f_1f_2)$ then each and every one of the p generalized characteristics $F_j(f)$ is either simple or the negative of a simple characteristic and all simple characteristics of G are obtained from the set $F_j(f)$ in this way. In fact we are given that

$$\sum_{j=1}^{p} c_j^{\alpha}c_j^{\beta}\bar{\phi}_{\beta}(f_2)\phi_{\alpha}(f_1) = \phi_1(f_1f_2) = \sum_{j=1}^{p} \bar{\phi}_j(f_2)\phi_j(f_1)$$

and this implies $\sum_{j=1}^{p} c_j^{\beta}c_j^{k}\bar{\phi}_{\beta}(f_2) = \bar{\phi}_k(f_2)$ since the p simple characteristics $\phi_j(f_1)$ are linearly independent. Indeed an hypothecated relation

$a^a\phi_a(f_1) = 0$ would imply $a^a\bar{\chi}_a^k = 0$; on multiplication by $n_k\chi_j^k$ and summation with respect to k this yields $a^j = 0$, every j. Similarly the linear independence of the expressions $\bar{\phi}_j(f_2)$ tells us that the equation $\sum_{j=1}^{p} c_j^\beta c_j^k \bar{\phi}_\beta(f_2) = \bar{\phi}_k(f_2)$ implies

$$\sum_{j=1}^{p} c_j^r c_j^k = \delta_r^k.$$

In other words the $p \times p$ matrix whose elements are c_j^k is orthogonal; since its elements are integers (positive negative or zero) it follows that the elements in any row are all zero save one which is ± 1 and that the elements in any column are all zero save one which is ± 1. *Hence each of the p generalized characteristics $F_j(f)$ is either a simple characteristic or the negative of one* (it will be simple if the coefficient of f^1 is positive and the negative of a simple characteristic if this coefficient is negative); *and all of the p simple characteristics of G are obtained in this way.* In other words the generalized characteristics $F_j(f)$ are merely a rearrangement of the simple characteristics $\phi_j(f)$ followed, possibly, by a change of sign of some of them. In the particular case of the symmetric group on m letters our criterion for simple characteristics takes the form

$$(4.30) \qquad \sum_{j=1}^{p} F_j(\mathbf{s})\bar{F}_j(\mathbf{r}) = q_m(\mathbf{sr}) = p_m(\mathbf{zy})$$

where $\mathbf{sr}$ is the set of m quantities $(s_1r_1, \cdots, s_mr_m)$ and $\mathbf{zy}$ is the set of n^2 quantities z_jy_k (the symbols r being the power sums of the symbols y just as the symbols s are the power sums of the symbols z: $r_k = y_1^k + \cdots + y_n^k$). In fact $s^{(a)} = s_1^{a_1} \cdots s_m^{a_m}$ so that

$$(sr)^{(a)} = s_1^{a_1} \cdots s_m^{a_m} r_1^{a_1} \cdots r_m^{a_m} = (s_1r_1)^{a_1} \cdots (s_mr_m)^{a_m};$$

and

$$s_q r_q = \left(\sum_{j=1}^{n} z_j^q\right)\left(\sum_{k=1}^{n} y_k^q\right) = \sum_{j,k} (z_j y_k)^q.$$

We now proceed to the determination of the simple characteristics of the symmetric group on m letters. We denote by $A(l_1, \cdots, l_n)$ the n-th order determinant whose j-th row consists of the l_j-th powers of the n indeterminates $z_1, z_2, \cdots, z_n$, the symbols $l_1, \cdots, l_n$ being non-negative integers (no two of which are equal) which we may suppose arranged in descending order of magnitude: $l_1 > l_2 > \cdots > l_n \geq 0$. When the set $(l) = (l_1, \cdots, l_n)$ is the set $(n-1, n-2, \cdots, 1, 0)$ we obtain the Vandermonde determinant whose value is the difference product $\Delta = \Delta(\mathbf{z}) = \prod_{j<k} (z_j - z_k)$. It is clear that an interchange of any two

of the variables (z) changes the sign of each of the functions $A(l)$ and $\Delta(z)$, i. e. that both $A(l)$ and $\Delta(z)$ are alternating functions of the variables (z). Furthermore $A(l)$ contains $\Delta(z)$ as a factor and so the quotient $A(l) \div \Delta(z)$ is a symmetric polynomial (with integral coefficients) in the variables (z) of degree $(l_1 + \cdots + l_n) - ((n-1)(n-2) + \cdots + 1 + 0)$. If then, $(\lambda) = (\lambda_1, \lambda_2, \cdots, \lambda_n)$ is any partition of m with $\lambda_1 \geqq \lambda_2 \geqq \cdots \geqq \lambda_n \geqq 0$ and we set $l_1 = \lambda_1 + (n-1)$, $l_2 = \lambda_2 + (n-2), \cdots, l_n = \lambda_n$ we have $l_1 > l_2 > \cdots > l_n \geqq 0$ and the quotient $A(l) \div \Delta(z)$ is a symmetric polynomial (of degree m) with integral coefficients in the n variables (z). It furnishes, therefore, when expressed in terms of the power sums $(s) = (s_1, \cdots, s_m)$ a generalized characteristic of the symmetric group on m letters. We have, then, a rule for associating with each partition (λ) of m a generalized characteristic of the symmetric group on m letters and we propose to show that these generalized characteristics are all simple and are, in fact, the complete set of p simple characteristics of the symmetric group. We denote the generalized characteristic $A(l) \div \Delta(z)$, where $l_1 = \lambda_1 + (n-1), \cdots, l_n = \lambda_n$ by $\{\lambda\}(z)$ and we shall show that $\sum_{(\lambda)}\{\lambda\}(z)\{\lambda\}(y) = q_m(sr) = p_m(zy)$ and then that the coefficient of $s_1{}^m$ in $\{\lambda\}(z)$ is positive, every (λ). In view of the general theorem of the preceding paragraph this suffices to prove that the characteristics $A(l) \div \Delta(z)$ are all simple and exhaust the simple characteristics of the symmetric group.

To do this we first consider a determinant of order n of which the element in the i-th row and j-th column is $(a_i + b_j)^{-1}$. On subtracting the first *column* from each of the others and removing the common factors

$$(b_1 - b_2)(b_1 - b_3) \cdots (b_1 - b_n) \div (b_1 + a_1)(b_1 + a_2) \cdots (b_1 + a_n)$$

we obtain a determinant of which the elements in the i-th row are 1, $(a_i + b_2)^{-1}, \cdots, (a_i + b_n)^{-1}$. On subtracting the first row of this determinant from each of the others and removing the common factors $(a_1 - a_2)(a_1 - a_3) \cdots (a_1 - a_n) \div (a_1 + b_2)(a_1 + b_3) \cdots (a_1 + b_n)$ we obtain a determinant of order $n-1$ of which the element in the i-th row and j-th column is again $(a_i + b_j)^{-1}$ where now i, j run from 2 to n instead of from 1 to n as before. It follows at once that the n-th order determinant, of which the element in the i-th row and j-th column is $(a_i + b_j)^{-1}$, has the value $\Delta(a)\Delta(b) \div \Pi(a_i + b_j)$; $(i = 1, \cdots, n, j = 1, 2, \cdots, n)$, where $\Delta(a)$ denotes the difference product $(a_1 - a_2) \cdots (a_{n-1} - a_n)$ (a result due to Cauchy). On writing $a_i = \alpha_i{}^{-1}, b_j = -\beta_j$ this result of Cauchy appears in the following equivalent form: the determinant of order n of which the element in the i-th row and j-th column is $(1-\alpha_i\beta_j)^{-1}$ has the value

$$\Delta(\boldsymbol{\alpha})\Delta(\boldsymbol{\beta}) \div \Pi(1-\alpha_i\beta_j).$$

But if A denotes the $n \times \infty$ matrix of which the elements in the i-th *row* are $(1, \alpha_i, \alpha_i^2, \cdots)$ and B the $\infty \times n$ matrix of which the elements in the j-th column are $(1, \beta_j, \beta_j^2, \cdots)$ the product $A \cdot B$ is an $n \times n$ matrix of which the element in the i-th row and j-th column is $1 + \alpha_i\beta_j + \alpha_i^2\beta_j^2 + \cdots$ or $(1-\alpha_i\beta_j)^{-1}$. The determinant of the product AB may be found by selecting *any* n-th order matrix from A, multiplying its determinant by the determinant of the corresponding matrix from B and adding all products so obtained; that the number of products is infinite need cause no concern since $\boldsymbol{\alpha}$ and $\boldsymbol{\beta}$ are indeterminates and we may regard them so chosen that the components α_i, β_j are all < 1 in numerical magnitude so that the infinite series which appear are all absolutely convergent. All determinants of order n selected from the matrices A and B are of the type $A(l_1, \cdots, l_n)$ where we may, without lack of generality, agree that $l_1 > l_2 > \cdots > l_n \geq 0$. Hence we have

$$\sum_{(l)} A(l_1, \cdots, l_n)(\boldsymbol{\alpha})A(l_1, \cdots, l_n)(\boldsymbol{\beta}) = \Delta(\boldsymbol{\alpha})\Delta(\boldsymbol{\beta}) \div \prod(1-\alpha_i\beta_j).$$

On setting $\boldsymbol{\beta} = \boldsymbol{\delta}t$, i. e. $\beta_1 = \delta_1 t, \beta_2 = \delta_2 t, \cdots, \beta_n = \delta_n t$ where t is an indeterminate, we have $A(l_1, \cdots, l_n)(\boldsymbol{\beta}) = A(l_1, \cdots, l_n)(\boldsymbol{\delta})t^{l_1+l_2+\cdots+l_n}$, $\Delta(\boldsymbol{\beta}) = \Delta(\boldsymbol{\delta})t^{(n-1)+(n-2)\cdots+1+0}$, and on writing

$$l_1 - (n-1) = \lambda_1;\ l_2 - (n-2) = \lambda_2;\ \cdots;\ l_n = \lambda_n$$

we find

$$\sum_{(\lambda)} \{\lambda\}(\boldsymbol{\alpha})\{\lambda\}(\boldsymbol{\delta})t^{\lambda_1+\cdots+\lambda_n} = \{\Pi(1-\alpha_i\delta_j t)\}^{-1}.$$

On equating coefficients of t^m we obtain

$$\sum_{(\lambda)} \{\lambda\}(\boldsymbol{\alpha})\{\lambda\}(\boldsymbol{\delta}) = p_m(\boldsymbol{\alpha\delta})$$

where the summation is over all partitions $\{\lambda\}$ of m. This proves that the symmetric polynomials $\{\lambda\}(\boldsymbol{z})$, furnish, when expressed in terms of the power sums $(s_1, \cdots, s_m)$, either simple characteristics or the negatives of these; all simple characteristics being obtained in this way. To show that we have actually the simple characteristics, and not the negatives of any of them, we must show that the coefficient of $s_1{}^m$ in $\{\lambda\}(\boldsymbol{z}) > 0$. Before doing this we remark that Frobenius stated the result of this section in a slightly different form. From

$$\{\lambda\}(\boldsymbol{z}) = \phi_{(\lambda)}(\boldsymbol{s}) = A(l_1, \cdots, l_n) \div \Delta(\boldsymbol{z})$$

and (4. 7) we have

$$s^{(a)} = \sum_{(\lambda)} \chi_{(\lambda)}^{(a)} A(l, \cdots, l_n) \div \Delta(\boldsymbol{z})$$

so that $\chi^{(a)}_{(\lambda)}$ is the coefficient of $A(l_1, l_2, \cdots, l_n)$ in the development of

$$(4.31) \qquad \Delta(z)s^{(a)} = \prod_{p<q} (z_p - z_q)s_1^{a_1}s_2^{a_2} \cdots s_m^{a_m}.$$

In order to show that the coefficient of s_1^m in $\{\lambda\}(z)$ is positive we shall derive an expression, due to Jacobi, for $\{\lambda\}(z)$ as a determinant whose elements are members of the set $p_j(z) = q_j(s)$, $j = 0, 1, \cdots, m$. On denoting by f_j the polynomial:

$$f_j = (1 - z_1 t_j)(1 - z_2 t_j) \cdots (1 - z_n t_j)$$

in the indeterminate t_j, $j = 1, 2, \cdots, m$, we have

$$f_j^{-1} = \sum_0^\infty p_{k_j} t_j^{k_j}$$

so that

$$(4.32) \qquad (f_1 f_2 \cdots f_m)^{-1} = \sum_{(k)=0}^\infty p_{k_1} \cdots p_{k_m} t_1^{k_1} \cdots t_m^{k_m}.$$

The difference product $\Delta(t) = (t_1 - t_2) \cdots (t_{m-1} - t_m)$ is equivalent to the Vandermonde determinant, of order m, of which the elements in the p-th row are $(t_p^{m-1}, t_p^{m-2}, \cdots, t_p, 1)$, $p = 1, 2, \cdots, m$, and on multiplying both sides of (4.32) by $\Delta(t)$ we see that $\Delta(t)(f_1, \cdots, f_m)^{-1}$ is equivalent to a determinant of order m of which the elements in the p-th row are $(\sum_0^\infty p_{k_p} t_p^{k_p+m-1}, \sum_0^\infty p_{k_p} t_p^{k_p+m-2}, \cdots, \sum_0^\infty p_{k_p} t_p^{k_p})$. This determinant is the product of an $m \times \infty$ matrix A by an $\infty \times m$ matrix B where the p-th row of A is $(1, t_p, t_p^2, \cdots)$ whilst the q-th column of B is $(p_{-(m-q)}, p_{-(m-q)+1}, \cdots, p_0, p_1, \cdots)$; it may, accordingly, be written as the sum of products of an m-th order determinant from A by the corresponding m-th order determinant from B. A typical m-th order determinant from A has $(t_p^{l_1}, t_p^{l_2}, \cdots, t_p^{l_m})$ as the elements of its p-th row where $l_1 > l_2 > \cdots > l_m \geq 0$ and the corresponding determinant of B has, as the elements of its p-th row,

$$(p_{l_p-(m-1)}, p_{l_p-(m-2)}, \cdots, p_{l_p}), \qquad p = 1, \cdots, m.$$

On writing $\lambda_p = l_p - (m - p)$, $p = 1, 2, \cdots, m$, this m-th order determinant from B has $(p_{\lambda_1}, p_{\lambda_2}, \cdots, p_{\lambda_m})$ as its diagonal elements and the remaining elements are obtained from these diagonal elements by methodically increasing (decreasing) by unity the subscript attached to each $p(z)$ as we move from each column to its neighbor on the right (left). We propose to show that this determinant of order m is precisely $\{\lambda\}(z)$; we denote it, for the moment, by $\{\Lambda\}(z)$. On observing that the quotient of the m-th order determinant from A by $\Delta(\boldsymbol{t})$ is $\{\lambda\}(\boldsymbol{t})$ we see that

(4.33) $$(f_1 \cdots f_m)^{-1} = \sum_{(\lambda)} \{\Lambda\}(\boldsymbol{z})\{\lambda\}(\boldsymbol{t})$$

where the summation is over all sets of m numbers $(\lambda_1, \cdots, \lambda_m)$ for which $\lambda_1 \geqq \lambda_2 \geqq \cdots \geqq \lambda_m \geqq 0$. Since, however,

$$f_1 \cdots f_m = \prod_{p,q}^{m} (1 - z_p t_q)$$

we obtain, on writing $t_q = ty_q$,

$$(f_1 \cdots f_m)^{-1} = \sum_{0}^{\infty} p_k(\boldsymbol{zy})\, t^k$$

and, since $\{\lambda\}(\boldsymbol{t}) = \{\lambda\}(\boldsymbol{y})\, t^k$ where $\lambda_1 + \lambda_2 + \cdots + \lambda_m = k$ we have

$$\sum_{0}^{\infty} p_k(\boldsymbol{zy})\, t^k = \sum_{k=0}^{\infty} [\sum_{(\lambda)} \{\Lambda\}(\boldsymbol{z})\{\lambda\}(\boldsymbol{y})]\, t^k$$

where the summation with respect to (λ) is over all partitions of k. Hence

$$p_k(\boldsymbol{zy}) = \sum_{(\lambda)} \{\Lambda\}(\boldsymbol{z})\{\lambda\}(\boldsymbol{y}), \qquad k = 0, 1, 2, \cdots$$

and since we have already proved that $p_m(\boldsymbol{zy}) = \sum_{(\lambda)} \{\lambda\}(\boldsymbol{z})\{\lambda\}(\boldsymbol{y})$ we have

$$\sum_{(\lambda)} \{\lambda\}(\boldsymbol{z})\{\lambda\}(\boldsymbol{y}) = \sum_{(\lambda)} \{\Lambda\}(\boldsymbol{z})\{\lambda\}(\boldsymbol{y}),$$

the summations in each case being over all partitions $\{\lambda\}$ of m. The linear independence of the quantities $\{\lambda\}(\boldsymbol{y})$ is guaranteed by the fact that these quantities are (so far as we yet know) either the simple characteristics of the symmetric group on m letters or negatives of these; all simple characteristics being obtained in this way. Hence $\{\lambda\}(\boldsymbol{z}) = \{\Lambda\}(\boldsymbol{z})$, (λ) any partition of m. This proves the desired result: namely, that $\{\lambda\}(\boldsymbol{z}) \equiv A(l_1, \cdots, l_n) \div \Delta(\boldsymbol{z})$ may be expressed as an m-th order determinant of which the element in the i-th row and j-th column is $p_{l_i-(m-j)}(\boldsymbol{z}) = q_{l_i-(m-j)}(\boldsymbol{s})$. The diagonal elements are $p_{\lambda_i}(\boldsymbol{z}) = q_{\lambda_i}(\boldsymbol{s})$ the other elements in any row being obtained by methodically increasing (decreasing) the suffix carried by $p(\boldsymbol{z}) = q(\boldsymbol{s})$ as we move from any column to its neighbor on the right (left). If k is such that $\lambda_k > 0$ whilst $\lambda_{k+1} = \lambda_{k+2} = \cdots = \lambda_n = 0$ the last $n - k$ rows of our determinant have unity in the diagonal and zero's preceding the diagonal. Hence, and this is the essential simplification, $\{\lambda\}(\boldsymbol{z})$ may be expressed as a determinant of order k of the type described above.

It is now easy to calculate the coefficient of $s_1{}^m$ in $\{\lambda\}(\boldsymbol{z}) = \phi_{(\lambda)}(\boldsymbol{s})$ and to check our statement that it is positive. It is important to have its actual value as this yields, when multiplied by $m!$ the character of the unit permutation, i. e. the *dimension* of the representation (irreducible) of the symmetric group on m letters whose characteristic is $\phi_{(\lambda)}(\boldsymbol{s})$. To obtain this coefficient of $s_1{}^m$ we merely set $s_1 = 1$, $s_2 = s_3 = \cdots = s_m = 0$. Then $p_j(\boldsymbol{z}) = q_j(\boldsymbol{s}) = \frac{1}{j!}$ and the value of $\phi_{(\lambda)}(\boldsymbol{s})$, for this value of $\boldsymbol{s}$, may be calculated as follows. Set $\lambda_1 + k - 1 = l_1$, $\lambda_2 + k - 2 = l_2, \cdots, \lambda_k = l_k$ and multiply the j-th row of our k-th order determinant which furnishes $\phi_{(\lambda)}(\boldsymbol{s})$ (for the particular value of $\boldsymbol{s}$ mentioned above) by $l_j!$ We obtain a k-th order determinant of which the element in the j-th row and q-th column is $l_j(l_j - 1) \cdots (l_j + q + 1 - k)$ $(q = 1, 2, \cdots, k - 1)$ the elements in the k-th column being all unity. Since the element in the j-th row and q-th column is a polynomial of degree $k - q$ in l_j (the coefficients of which are independent of the row number j and the coefficient of the highest power being unity) it is at once clear, on subtracting from each column an appropriate linear combination of the succeeding columns, that the determinant we are seeking to evaluate is equivalent to the Vandermonde determinant whose j-th row is $(l_j{}^{k-1}, l_j{}^{k-2}, \cdots, l_j, 1)$. Hence its value is $\Delta(l) = \prod_{j<q} (l_j - l_q)$ and this > 0 since $l_1 > l_2 > \cdots > l_k > 0$.

Hence the dimension of the irreducible representation $D(\lambda)$ of the symmetric group whose characteristic is $\phi_{(\lambda)}(\boldsymbol{s})$ is given by the formula

$$(4.34)\quad d_{(\lambda)} = \frac{m!\ \Delta(l)}{l_1! \cdots l_k!};\ l_i = \lambda_i + k - i, i = 1, \cdots, k;\ \Delta(l) = \prod_{j<q} (l_j - l_q).$$

It is clear that (λ) may be written as an $n > k$ element partition of m by adding $(n - k)$ zeros $\lambda_{k+1} = \lambda_{k+2} = \cdots = \lambda_n$; and that then $d_{(\lambda)}$ appears in the form:

$$(4.34^{\text{bis}})\quad d_{(\lambda)} = m! \prod_{p<q}^{n} (l_p - l_q) \div l_1! \cdots l_n!;\ l_i = \lambda_i + n - i;\quad i = 1, 2, \cdots, n.$$

We resume the essential result (Frobenius-Schur) of this somewhat long section: Attached to each partition $\lambda_1 \geqq \lambda_2 \geqq \cdots \geqq \lambda_k > 0$, of m: $\lambda_1 + \lambda_2 + \cdots + \lambda_k = m$, is an irreducible representation $D(\lambda)$ of the symmetric group on m letters, *all* irreducible representations of this group being obtained in this way. Its characteristic is the k-th order determinant

$$(4.35)\quad \{\lambda\}(\boldsymbol{z}) = \phi_{(\lambda)}(\boldsymbol{s}) = \begin{vmatrix} q_{\lambda_1}(\boldsymbol{s}) & & & \\ & q_{\lambda_2}(\boldsymbol{s}) & & \\ & & \cdot & \\ & & & \cdot \\ & & & & q_{\lambda_k}(\boldsymbol{s}) \end{vmatrix}$$

(where the remaining elements of any row are obtained from the diagonal element by methodically increasing (decreasing) by unity the suffix carried by $q(\mathbf{s})$ as we move from any column to its neighbor on the right (left); it being understood that each q carrying a negative suffix is zero). The dimension of $D(\lambda)$ is given by (4. 34).

6. Associated irreducible representations of the symmetric group.

We have already seen that with each irreducible representation $D(\lambda)$ of the symmetric group on m letters there is associated a second (possibly the same) irreducible representation of the same dimension as $D(\lambda)$; namely the Kronecker product of $D(\lambda)$ by the one-dimensional alternating representation.. We now show that the representation associated with $D(\lambda)$ is the representation attached to the partition (μ) of m which is obtained from the partition (λ) as follows. We first represent (λ) by a diagram of horizontal rows of dots (all beginning on the same vertical line) the first row containing λ_1 dots, the second λ_2 dots, $\cdots$ and the last λ_k dots. Thus the partition $(3, 2^2, 1^3)$ of 10 is represented by the diagram

· · ·
· ·
· ·
·
·
·

By simply interchanging the rows and columns we obtain a second diagram (which is termed the *associate* of the original diagram) and the partition which defines this new diagram is the partition (μ) which is termed the *associate* of the partition (λ). It is clear that $\mu_1 = k$ and that the number j of non-zero parts in $(\mu) = (\mu_1, \cdots, \mu_j)$ is λ_1. Thus the associate of $(3, 2^2, 1^3)$ is $(6, 3, 1)$. When a diagram (or its defining partition) coincides with its associate it is termed *self-associated.* E. g., $(3, 2, 1)$ is a self-associated partition of $m = 6$. What we propose to prove is that associated representations are attached to associated partitions. Since the characteristic of the representation which is associated with $D(\lambda)$ is obtained from the characteristic of $D(\lambda)$ by changing the signs of $s_2, s_4, \cdots$ and since (see (4. 22), (4. 23))

$$q_j(s_1, -s_2, s_3, \cdots) = \pi_j(\mathbf{s}) = \sigma_j(\mathbf{z})$$

we have to show that

$$\{\mu\}(z) = \phi_{(\mu)}(s) = \begin{vmatrix} q_{\mu_1}(s) & & & \\ & q_{\mu_2}(s) & & \\ & & \cdot & \\ & & & \cdot \\ & & & & q_{\mu_j}(s) \end{vmatrix} = \begin{vmatrix} \pi_{\lambda_1}(s) & & & \\ & \pi_{\lambda_2}(s) & & \\ & & \cdot & \\ & & & \cdot \\ & & & & \pi_{\lambda_k}(s) \end{vmatrix}$$

$$= \begin{vmatrix} \sigma_{\lambda_1}(z) & & & \\ & \cdot & & \\ & & \cdot & \\ & & & \sigma_{\lambda_k}(z) \end{vmatrix}$$

(it being always understood that the non-diagonal elements are obtained by a methodical increase (decrease) by unity of the subscript as we pass from each column to its neighbor on the right (left)). This fact merely reflects the fact that the matrices

$$P_k = \begin{pmatrix} p_0 & p_1 \cdots p_{k-1} \\ & p_0 \cdot \cdot \quad p_{k-2} \\ \\ & \quad p_0 \end{pmatrix}; \quad \Sigma_k = \begin{pmatrix} \sigma_0 & -\sigma_1 & \sigma_2 & \cdot \\ & \sigma_0 & -\sigma_1 & \cdot \\ \\ & & & \sigma_0 \end{pmatrix}$$

are reciprocal for each $k = 1, 2, 3, \cdots$ (see p. 112). In fact the j-rowed determinant

$$\{\mu\}(z) = \begin{vmatrix} p_{\mu_1}(z) & & & \\ & \cdot & & \\ & & \cdot & \\ & & & \cdot \\ & & & & p_{\mu_j}(z) \end{vmatrix}$$

is a certain j-rowed minor of P_{μ_1+j}; namely, the minor obtained by *erasing* the first μ_1 *columns* and *retaining* the first, the $(\mu_1 - \mu_2 + 2)$-nd, the $(\mu_1 - \mu_3 + 3)$-rd, $\cdots$ and the $(\mu_1 - \mu_j + j)$-th *rows*. Save for a question of sign which can be readily settled later $\{\mu\}(z)$ is, therefore, equal to that minor of the reciprocal matrix $\sum\limits_{\mu_1+j}$ which is obtained by *retaining* the first μ_1 *rows* and *erasing* the first, the $(\mu_1 - \mu_2 + 2)$-nd, $\cdots$ and the $(\mu_1 - \mu_j + j)$-th columns. Since $\mu_j > 0$ the last column is kept and the suffix attached to the $\sigma(z)$ in the lower right-hand corner is j (for the minor has μ_1 rows and the subscripts diminish methodically by one as we step from each row to its neighbor below whilst the σ at the top of the last column has the subscript $\mu_1 + j - 1$). Counting from the last column the first column omitted is the $(\mu_j + 1)$-st and so the suffixes of the last μ_j diagonal elements of the minor of $\sum\limits_{\mu_1+j}$ in question all equal j; the second column omitted, counting from the last is the

$(\mu_{j-1}+2)$-nd and so on, so that the next diagonal suffix, counting upwards to the left, is less than j by the number of μ's that equal μ_j. Reasoning in this way, we see that the diagonal suffixes of the minor of $\sum\limits_{\mu_1+j}$ reading upwards to the left, constitute the partition (λ) of m which is associated with (μ). For instance if $m=4$ and $\mu=(2,1^2)$, so that $(\lambda)=(3,1)$, we have proved that

$$\{2,1^2\}(z)\equiv\begin{vmatrix} p_2 & p_3 & p_4 \\ p_0 & p_1 & p_2 \\ 0 & p_0 & p_1 \end{vmatrix}=\pm\begin{vmatrix} -\sigma_1 & \sigma_4 \\ \sigma_0 & -\sigma_3 \end{vmatrix}.$$

The negative signs may be removed from the σ's carrying odd subscripts by changing the signs of all columns having a σ with an odd subscript at the bottom and following this by a change of sign of all rows having a σ with an even subscript at the end. On reflecting the σ-minor about its secondary diagonal, an operation which does not affect its value, we have proved that

$$\mu(z)\equiv\begin{vmatrix} p_{\mu_1}(z) & & \\ & \cdot & \\ & & \cdot \\ & & & p_{\mu_j}(z) \end{vmatrix}=\pm\begin{vmatrix} \sigma_{\lambda_1}(z) & & \\ & \cdot & \\ & & \cdot \\ & & & \sigma_{\lambda_k}(z) \end{vmatrix};\ \lambda_1=j,\ k=\mu_1$$

or, equivalently,

$$\phi_{(\mu)}(s)\equiv\begin{vmatrix} q_{\mu_1}(s) & & \\ & \cdot & \\ & & \cdot \\ & & & q_{\mu_j}(s) \end{vmatrix}=\pm\begin{vmatrix} \pi_{\lambda_1}(s) & & \\ & \cdot & \\ & & \cdot \\ & & & \pi_{\lambda_k}(s) \end{vmatrix}$$

Since $\pi_r(s)$ and $q_r(s)$ take the same value $\dfrac{1}{r!}$ when $s_1=1$, $s_2=s_3=\cdots=s_m=0$ and since the value of $\phi_{(\mu)}(s)$ is positive, for all partitions (μ), when the (s) are assigned these values (being, in fact, the dimension of $D(\mu)$ divided by $m!$) it follows that the connecting sign is positive. Hence

$$\phi_{(\mu)}(s)=\phi_{(\lambda)}(s^*)\quad\text{where}\quad s^*=(s_1,-s_2,s_3,\cdots)$$

showing that $D(\mu)$ is the representation associated with $D(\lambda)$. It may be observed that when (λ) is self-associated the sum of the number of dots in the first row and first column of the representative diagram $=2\lambda_1-1$; when this first row and first column are erased the sum of the number of dots in the new first row and column $=2\lambda_2-3$ and so on. Thus every self-associated partition of m yields a partition of m into unequal odd numbers and vice versa. E. g., when $m = 8$ we have the two self-associated partitions $(4, 2, 1^2)$, $(3^2, 2)$ corresponding to the partitions $(7, 1)$, $(5, 3)$ of 8 into unequal odd numbers.

7. The homogeneous rational integral representations of the full linear group.

We have seen, (4. 10), that the matrices $[A]_m$ of the Kronecker m-th powers of the $n \times n$ matrices A of the full linear group are all commutative with the matrices $p([E]_m)$ of an n^m-dimensional representation of the symmetric group on m letters, and (p. 105) that this implies the existence of a basis in which the matrices $[A]_m$ appear in reduced form:

$$(4.36) \qquad [A]_m = \sum_j \{E_{d_j} \times M_j(A)\}.$$

The summation on the right is over the irreducible representations of the symmetric group which occur in the reduction of the representation $\Gamma = p([E]_m)$ and the dimension δ_j of $M_j(A)$ is equal to the number of times Γ_j, whose dimension is d_j, occurs in Γ: $\Gamma = \sum_j \delta_j \Gamma_j$. The matrices $M_j(A)$ furnish a homogeneous rational integral representation of the full linear group on n letters (since they are derived from $[A]_m$ by the mere introduction of a suitable basis). The identity representation Γ_1 certainly occurs in the reduction of $p([E]_m)$ and the number of times it occurs is $\dfrac{n + m - 1!}{(n-1)!\,m!}$. In fact the trace of $p([A]_m)$ is $s^{(a)} = s_1^{\alpha_1} \cdots s_m^{\alpha_m}$ (see (3. 22)) and so the trace of $p([E]_m)$ is the value of $s^{(a)}$ when $A = E$, i. e. when $s_1 = s_2 = \cdots = s_m = n$. The number of times $p([E]_m)$ contains Γ_1 is the average of the trace of $p([E]_m)$ over the symmetric group, i. e. $\delta_1 = q_m(\boldsymbol{s}) = p_m(\boldsymbol{z})$ when $s_1 = s_2 = \cdots = s_m = n$; or, equivalently, when $z_1 = z_2 = \cdots = z_n = 1$. Turning to the equation (4. 19) we see that δ_1 is the coefficient of t^m in the expansion $(1 - t)^{-n}$, i. e.

$$\delta_1 = \frac{n + m - 1!}{(n-1)!\,m!} = \binom{n + m - 1}{m}.$$

Included, therefore, in the analysis (4. 36) of $[A]_m$ is the representation $M_1(A)$, of dimension $\binom{n + m - 1}{m}$, of the full linear group. It follows from (4. 14) that the characters of the representation $M_1(A)$ of the full linear group are given by

$$\phi_1(\boldsymbol{s}) = q_m(\boldsymbol{s}) = \sum_{(a)} \frac{1}{\alpha_1! \cdots \alpha_m!} \left(\frac{s_1}{1}\right)^{\alpha_1} \cdots \left(\frac{s_m}{m}\right)^{\alpha_m}$$

where $s_1 = Tr(A)$; $s_2 = Tr(A^2)$; $\cdots$ $s_m = Tr(A^m)$. Similarly the characters of any of the representations $M_j(A)$ which occur in (4.36) are furnished by the corresponding simple characteristic of the symmetric group on m letters on setting $s_1 = Tr(A), \cdots, s_m = Tr(A^m)$; *thus if* $\Gamma_j = D(\lambda)$ *the characters of* M_j *are furnished by* $\phi_{(\lambda)}(s)$.

We now proceed to show 1) that the homogeneous rational integral representations of the full linear group which are obtained in this way (i. e. by the reduction of $[A]_m$) are all irreducible; 2) that no two of them are equivalent and; 3) that they exhaust the homogeneous rational integral representations of the full linear group. To do this we first calculate the sum of the squared dimensions $\Sigma(\delta_j)^2$ of the various representations $M_j(A)$. Since $\Gamma = \Sigma\delta_j\Gamma_j$ the desired sum is the average over the symmetric group on m letters of the squared characters of $\Gamma = p([E]_m)$ (p. 85); in other words it is the value of $q_m(s) = p_m(z)$ when $s_1 = s_2 = \cdots = s_m = n^2$ (*not* n) or, equivalently, when the n^2 (*not* n) variables (z) all equal unity. Hence it is the coefficient of t^m in the expansion of $(1-t)^{-n^2}$:

$$(4.37) \quad \Sigma(\delta_j)^2 = \binom{n^2+m-1}{m} = \frac{(n^2+m-1)!}{(n^2-1)!\,m!} = q, \text{ say.}$$

In other words the sum of the squared dimensions of the various representations $M_j(A)$ of the full linear group on n letters equals the number of terms in the expansion of $(z_1 + z_2 + \cdots + z_{n^2})^m$. On identifying the n^2 indeterminates (z) with the n^2 elements (a_s^r) of A we see that $\Sigma(\delta_j)^2$ equals the number of power products of degree m in the elements (a_s^r) of A. Let us denote, for a moment, these q power products by $v^1, \cdots, v^q$; then each v^k is an element of $[A]_m$ and each element of $[A]_m$ is one of the v's. The various elements of the matrices $M_j(A)$ number $\Sigma(\delta_j^2) = q$ and we denote them, arranged in any order, by $(w^1, \cdots, w^q)$. Then the fact that $[A]_m$ and $\sum_j \{E_{d_j} \times M_j(A)\}$ are merely different presentations of the same matrix tells us that the $(v) = (v^1, \cdots, v^q)$ are homogeneous linear functions of the $(w) = (w^1, \cdots, w^q)$ and that, conversely, the (w) are homogeneous linear functions of the (v). But this prevents the reducibility of any one of the representations $M_j(A)$ or the equivalence of any two of them. For in either event we would have

$$[A]_m = \sum_j \{E_{d_j} \times M_j(A)\} = \Sigma \{E_k \times N_k(A)\}$$

where the sum of the squared dimensions of the representations $N_k(A) < q$. But this is impossible since it would imply the possibility of expressing the q *linearly independent* variables v as homogeneous linear functions of a lesser number of variables (namely, the elements of the various matrices $N_k(A)$); that the variables v are linearly independent is a consequence of the fact that the identical vanishing of a homogeneous polynomial of degree m in n^2 variables implies the vanishing of each and every one of its coefficients. Similarly there are no other irreducible homogeneous rational integral representations of the full linear group than those furnished by the $M_j(A)$; for if there existed a single such representation $D(A)$ of dimension d the $q + d^2$ elements of the non-equivalent irreducible representations $M_j(A), D(A)$ of the full linear group would be linearly independent (by the Frobenius-Schur extension of Burnside's Theorem (p. 51)). But this is impossible since they are, each and every one, homogeneous linear functions of the q variables (v).

We have seen, then, that the Kronecker m-th power $[A]_m$ is a source in which may be found all irreducible homogeneous, rational integral representations, of degree m, of the full linear group; and that the number of these is precisely the number of irreducible representations of the symmetric group on m letters which occur in the reduction of $p([E]_m)$. It remains only to find which representations $D(\lambda)$ of the symmetric group on m letters appear in $p([E]_m)$. The number of times $D(\lambda)$ occurs in $p([E]_m)$ is found by averaging, over the symmetric group, the product $s^{(a)}\chi^{(a)}_{(\lambda)}$ where $s_1 = s_2 = \cdots = s_m = n$; in other words it is the value of $\phi_{(\lambda)}(\boldsymbol{s})$ for this value of $\boldsymbol{s}$. Since each $q_k(\boldsymbol{s})$ has, for this value of $\boldsymbol{s}$, the value $\binom{n+k-1}{k}$ we have to evaluate a k-th order determinant (where (λ) is a k element partition of m) with these numbers as its elements. It will be convenient to write (λ) as an m element partition of m (whose last $m - k$ elements are zero) and to calculate the m-th order determinant

$$(4.38) \qquad \phi_{(\lambda)}(\boldsymbol{s}) = \begin{vmatrix} q_{\lambda_1}(\boldsymbol{s}) & & & \\ & \cdot & & \\ & & \cdot & \\ & & & \cdot \\ & & & q_{\lambda_m}(\boldsymbol{s}) \end{vmatrix}$$

for the stated value of $(\boldsymbol{s})$. Since $\binom{n+k-1}{k} = \dfrac{(n+k-1)!}{k!\,(n-1)!}$ we may remove the common factor $\dfrac{1}{(n-1)!}$ from each row and we are, then, confronted by a determinant of order m whose first row is

$$\left(\frac{(n+\lambda_1-1)!}{\lambda_1!}, \frac{(n+\lambda_1)!}{(\lambda_1+1)!}, \cdots, \frac{(n+\lambda_1+m-2)!}{(\lambda_1+m-1)!}\right)$$

On making the substitution $\lambda_j + m - j = l_j$, $j = 1, 2, \cdots, m$, the j-th row of our determinant is

$$\left(\frac{(n+l_j-m)!}{(l_j+1-m)!}, \frac{(n+l_j+1-m)!}{(l_j+2-m)!}, \cdots, \frac{(n+l_j-1)!}{l_j!}\right)$$

(it being understood that any term in which the factorial of a negative number appears in the denominator is to be assigned the value *zero*) and on subtracting the $(m-1)$-st column from the m-th the element in the j-th row and m-th column changes into $(n-1)(n+l_j-2)! \div l_j!$ so that the common factor $(n-1)$ may be removed from the last column. Subtracting now the $(m-2)$-nd column from the $(m-1)$-st and so on we see that the factor $(n-1)^{m-1}$ may be removed leaving us with a determinant whose j-th row is

$$(4.39) \quad \left(\frac{(n+l_j-m)!}{(l_j+1-m)!}, \frac{(n+l_j-m)!}{(l_j+2-m)!}, \frac{(n+l_j+1-m)!}{(l_j+3-m)!}, \cdots, \frac{(n+l_j-2)!}{l_j!}\right).$$

Of course this does not mean that our original determinant vanishes when $n = 1$ because we have multiplied it by $\{(n-1)!\}^m$. If $n = 1$, $\binom{n+k-1}{k} = 1$ so that we have to evaluate the determinant $\phi_{(\lambda)}(\mathbf{s})$ of (4.38) where each $q_j(\mathbf{s})$ *which has a non-negative subscript* is unity, the $q_j(\mathbf{s})$ for which j is negative having the value zero. Hence if $\lambda_2 > 0$ our determinant is zero since both its first and second rows consist entirely of ones. In other words: when $n = 1$ the only irreducible representation $D(\lambda)$ which appears in the reduction of $p([E]_m)$ is $D(m)$, i.e. the unit representation, this one occurring once. We explicitly mention this trivially evident fact (trivial because $p([E]_m)$ is of dimension n^m which is unity when $n = 1$) because it directs attention to the general situation. Conversely if $\lambda_1 = m$ so that $\lambda_2 = \lambda_3 = \cdots = \lambda_m = 0$, whilst n is arbitrary, the unit representation $D(m)$ occurs $q_m(\mathbf{s})$ or $\binom{n+m-1}{m}$ times in $p([E]_m)$ so that $M_{(m)}(A)$, of dimension $\binom{n+m-1}{m}$ occurs once in the reduction of $[A]_m$. We turn now first to the case $n = 2$ and assume $\lambda_2 > 0$; then the first row of our modified form of our m-th order determinant is $(\lambda_1 + 1, 1, 1, \cdots, 1)$ whilst the second is $(\lambda_2, 1, 1, \cdots, 1)$. On subtracting the second row from the first we see that we can remove the factor $(\lambda_1 - \lambda_2 + 1)$ and have then merely to evaluate a determinant of order $m-1$ whose first row is $(1, 1, \cdots, 1)$

and whose second row is $(1, 1, \cdots, 1)$ or $(0, 1, 1, \cdots, 1)$ according as $\lambda_3 \geqq 0$. Hence if $n = 2$ no partition for which there are more than two non-zero elements will appear in the reduction of $p([E]_m)$. Conversely if we have a partition with only two non-zero elements: $(\lambda) = (\lambda_1, \lambda_2)$, $\lambda_1 + \lambda_2 = m$; and $n \geqq 2$ is arbitrary the number of times the corresponding representation $D(\lambda)$ occurs in the reduction of $p([E]_m)$ is the value of the determinant (second order)

$$\begin{vmatrix} q_{\lambda_1}(s) & q_{\lambda_1+1}(s) \\ q_{\lambda_2-1}(s) & q_{\lambda_2}(s) \end{vmatrix} \text{ when } s_1 = s_2 = \cdots = s_m = n.$$

By the same argument as that given above for the m-th order determinant (i. e. by subtracting the first column from the second) this works out to be

$$\frac{(n + \lambda_1 - 1)!\,(n + \lambda_2 - 2)!}{(n-1)\{(n-2)!\}^2} \begin{vmatrix} \dfrac{1}{\lambda_1!} & \dfrac{1}{(\lambda_1+1)!} \\ \dfrac{1}{(\lambda_2-1)!} & \dfrac{1}{\lambda_2!} \end{vmatrix},$$

i. e. $\dfrac{(n + \lambda_1 - 1)!\,(n + \lambda_2 - 2)!}{(n-1)\{(n-2)!\}^2} \dfrac{d_{(\lambda)}}{m!} = \delta_{(\lambda)}$. In other words when $n = 2$ no $D(\lambda)$ occurs in the reduction of $p([E]_m)$ for which (λ) contains more than two elements; and every $D(\lambda)$, for which $(\lambda) = (\lambda_1, \lambda_2)$ is a two element partition, occurs in the reduction of $p([E]_m)$, provided $n \geqq 2$, $\delta_{(\lambda)}$ times so that the dimension of the corresponding representation $M_{(\lambda)}(A)$ of the full linear group is $\delta_{(\lambda)}$. If $n \geqq 3$, $\lambda_3 > 0$, we simplify (4. 39) by subtracting each column (starting with the $(m-1)$-st) from its successor and note that we can remove the factor $(n-2)^{m-2}$; we are confronted with an m-th order determinant of which the j-th row is

$$\left(\frac{(n + l_j - m)!}{(l_j + 1 - m)!}, \frac{(n + l_j - m)!}{(l_j + 2 - m)!}, \frac{(n + l_j - m)!}{(l_j + 3 - m)!}, \right.$$
$$\left. \frac{(n + l_j + 1 - m)!}{(l_j + 4 - m)!}, \cdots, \frac{(n + l_j - 3)!}{l_j!}\right).$$

For the case $n = 3$ we find on subtracting the second row from the first, the third from the second, removing the common factors $(\lambda_1 - \lambda_2 + 1)$, $(\lambda_2 - \lambda_3 + 1)$, then subtracting the new second row from the first and removing the common factor $(\lambda_1 - \lambda_3 + 2)$, that we are left with the evaluation of a determinant of order $m - 2$ whose first row is $(1, 1, \cdots)$ and whose second row is $(1, 1, \cdots, 1)$ or $(0\,1, 1, \cdots)$ according as $\lambda_4 \geqq 0$. Hence if $n = 3$ no $D(\lambda)$ for which the number of non-zero elements > 3 will appear in the reduction of $p([E]_m)$ whilst if we have a three-element partition and $n \geqq 3$, $D(\lambda)$ will certainly occur with the multiplicity

$$\delta_{(\lambda)} = \frac{(n+\lambda_1-1)!\,(n+\lambda_2-2)!\,(n+\lambda_3-3)!}{(n-1)(n-2)^2\{(n-3)!\}^3}\frac{d_{(\lambda)}}{m!}.$$

The argument is quite general: if $m > n$ no partition for which the number of non-zero elements $> n$ will appear in the reduction of $p([E]_m)$ so that for such partitions (λ) there are no irreducible representations $M_{(\lambda)}(A)$ of the full linear group. In fact the relation $\{\sum_0^n \sigma_j t^j\}\{\sum_0^\infty (-1)^k p_k t^k\} = 1$ of p. 112 gives us, on comparing the coefficients of $(-1)^{\lambda_1} t^{n+\lambda_1}$, the relation

$$\sigma_n p_{\lambda_1} - \sigma_{n-1} p_{\lambda_1+1} + \cdots + (-1)^n \sigma_0 p_{\lambda_1+n} = 0.$$

Similarly on comparing the coefficients of $(-1)^{\lambda_2-1} t^{n+\lambda_2-1}$ we find

$$\sigma_n p_{\lambda_2-1} - \sigma_{n-1} p_{\lambda_2} + \cdots + (-1)^n \sigma_0 p_{\lambda_2+n-1} = 0$$

and so on; the last equation (obtained by comparing the coefficients of $(-1)^{\lambda_{n+1}-n} t^{\lambda_{n+1}}$) being

$$\sigma_n p_{\lambda_{n+1}-n} - \cdots + (-1)^n \sigma_0 p_{\lambda_{n+1}} = 0.$$

Since these $n+1$ homogeneous relations between the $n+1$ quantities $\sigma_n, -\sigma_{n-1}, \cdots, (-1)^n\sigma_0$, are consistent (with $\sigma_0 = 1$) the determinant of their coefficients must vanish (not only for the special values $s_1 = s_2 = \cdots = s_m = n$ but identically in $\boldsymbol{s}$). For any k element partition of m ($k \leqq n$) there will be an attached representation of the full linear group and its dimension $\delta_{(\lambda)}$ is furnished by the formula

$$(4.40)\quad \delta_{(\lambda)} = \frac{(n+\lambda_1-1)!\,(n+\lambda_2-2)!\cdots(n+\lambda_k-k)!}{(n-1)(n-2)^2(n-3)^3\cdots(n-k+1)^{k-1}\{(n-k)!\}^k}\frac{d_{(\lambda)}}{m!}$$

where $d_{(\lambda)}$ is furnished by the formula (4.34); $M_{(\lambda)}(A)$ appearing $d_{(\lambda)}$ times in the reduction of $p([E]_m)$. The expression (4.40) can be given a more convenient form by evaluating, if $n > k$, an n-th order determinant rather than a k-th order determinant. In other words we add the $n-k$ zero elements $\lambda_{k+1} = \lambda_{k+2} = \cdots = \lambda_n = 0$ to (λ) which then appears in the form $(\lambda) = (\lambda_1, \lambda_2, \cdots, \lambda_n)$. On setting $k = n$ in (4.40) we find

$$\delta_{(\lambda)} = \frac{l_1!\,l_2!\cdots l_n!}{(n-1)(n-2)^2(n-3)^3\cdots 2^{n-2}1^{n-1}}\frac{d_{(\lambda)}}{m!}$$

where

$$l_j = \lambda_j + n - j;\ j = 1, 2, \cdots, n.$$

But $\frac{d_{(\lambda)}}{m!} = \frac{\Delta(l)}{l_1! \cdots l_n!}$ (4.34^{bis}) so that

$$(4.41)\quad \delta_{(\lambda)} = \frac{\Delta(l)}{(n-1)!\,(n-2)!\cdots 2!\,1!};$$

$$l_j = \lambda_j + n - j;\ j = 1, 2, \cdots, n.$$

We have, accordingly, determined all irreducible homogeneous rational integral representations of degree m of the full linear group on n letters. There is one of these, $M_{(\lambda)}(A)$ attached to each partition of m which contains not more than n non-zero elements and its dimension is furnished by (4.41). Any two irreducible representations of the full linear group (which are homogeneous rational integral representations of degree m) which are equivalent to one another must be equivalent to one and only one of these. In fact the argument of pp. 124–25 shows that no two of the $M_j(A)$ have the same characters. In other words two irreducible homogeneous rational integral representations of degree m of the full linear group are equivalent if they have the same characters.

The results of the preceding paragraphs were derived for *irreducible* homogeneous rational integral representations of the full linear group. We now complete the theory of rational representations of the full linear group by proving that *every reducible homogeneous rational integral representation* Γ, *of degree* m, *of the full linear group is completely reducible* and, hence, expressible in the form $\Gamma = c^a\Gamma_a$ where the Γ_j are the irreducible representations $M_j(A)$ of the preceding paragraph and the c^j are positive integers or zero. Let $D(A)$ be the matrices of Γ, whose dimension is d, so that each of the d^2 elements of $D(A)$ is a homogeneous polynomial of degree m in the n^2 elements of A. The subset $D(U)$ of the collection of matrices $D(A)$, where U is an arbitrary unitary $n \times n$ matrix, constitute a group (this subset being, in fact, a d-dimensional representation of the unitary subgroup $\{U\}$ of the full linear group). Owing to the defining relation $U^*U = E_n$, i. e. $\sum_a \bar{u}_r{}^a u_s{}^a = \delta_s{}^r$ each element $u_s{}^r$ of U has its absolute value not greater than unity. If, then, the positive number B dominates the absolute value of each of the $d^2 \binom{n^2+m-1}{m}$ coefficients of the various polynomials which constitute the elements of $D(A)$ the absolute value of each element of $D(U)$ is dominated by $\binom{n^2+m-1}{m}$ B, every U. Hence the collection of $d \times d$ matrices $D(U)$ is a bounded subgroup of the d-dimensional full linear group. Hence, by the basic theorem of p. 57, it may be presented, by a proper choice of basis, as a collection of unitary matrices. The representation $\Gamma = \{D(A)\}$ being, by hypothesis, reducible, the subset $\{D(U)\}$ is à fortiori reducible and, hence, since each $D(U)$ is unitary we can find a transforming matrix T, with elements independent of U, such that $T^{-1}D(U)T = D_1(U) \dotplus D_2(U)$. Each of the d^2 equations implied by this matrix equation expresses the vanishing of a homogeneous polynomial of degree m in the n^2 variables u_s^r these variables being conditioned only by the fact that they are the elements of a unitary matrix. It follows, by the argument of pp. 86-87, that these polynomials must vanish identically; in other words $T^{-1}D(A)T = D_1(A) \dotplus D_2(A)$ where A is an arbitrary $d \times d$ matrix. Hence the reducible representation $\Gamma = \{D(A)\}$ is completely reducible; its irreducible parts $M_j(A)$ furnishing irreducible representations $M_j(U)$ of the unitary subgroup of the full linear group. Moreover *the coefficients c^j occurring in the reduction of Γ are uniquely determined by the characters $\chi(A)$ of Γ.* In fact the relation $\Gamma = c^a\Gamma_a$ implies $\chi(A) = c^a\chi_a(A)$ where the $\chi_j(A)$ are those simple characteristics of the symmetric group on m letters which correspond to partitions (λ) of m which contain *not more than n non-zero elements* (the variables (s) in these simple characteristics being assigned the values $s_1 = Tr(A)$, $s_2 = Tr(A^2), \cdots$). Hence if a reducible representation had two analyses $\Gamma = b^a\Gamma_a$, $\Gamma = c^a\Gamma_a$ we would have $b^a\chi_a(A) = c^a\chi_a(A)$ forcing $b^k = c^k$, every k, in view of the linear independence of the $\chi_k(A) = \phi_k(s)$. In other words *any homogeneous rational integral representation of degree m of the full linear group is determined up to an equivalence* (i.e. *a change of basis*) by its characters. Since any non-homogeneous rational integral representation is expressible as a sum of homogeneous rational integral representations of different degrees (p. 45) the characters of any non-homogeneous rational integral representation are furnished by a polynomial (non-homogeneous) in the n independent variables $(s_1, \cdots, s_n)$. If, then, we have two non-homogeneous rational integral representations Γ, Γ' with the same characters, their homogeneous parts (of corresponding degrees) must have the same characters and, hence, be equivalent; for if a non-homogeneous polynomial in n independent variables vanishes identically its homogeneous parts must vanish identically. *Hence every rational integral representation of the full linear group is completely reducible, the coefficients occurring in the reduction being uniquely determined by the characters of the representation.* Finally this implies, on using the theorem of p. 34, that every rational representation of the full linear group is completely reducible and is determined (up to an equivalence) by its characters. In fact let $\Gamma = \{R(A)\}$ and $\Gamma' = \{R'(A)\}$ be two rational representations which have the same characters. Then

$$R(A) = \frac{P(A)}{(\det A)^k}, \quad R'(A) = \frac{P'(A)}{(\det A)^{k'}} \quad \text{where} \quad \{P(A)\}, \{P'(A)\}$$

are rational integral representations. If $k' \neq k$ let $k > k'$ and write $R'(A)$ in the form $\dfrac{Q'(A)}{(\det A)^k}$ where $Q'(A) = \{(\det A)^{k-k'}P(A)\}$ is a rational integral representation. Then $\{P(A)\}, \{Q'(A)\}$ have the same characters and are, accordingly, equivalent; this equivalence implies, in turn, the equivalence of $\{R(A)\}$ and $\{R'(A)\}$.

CHAPTER FIVE

THE CHARACTERS OF THE SYMMETRIC GROUP

In this chapter we shall discuss in some detail the characters of the symmetric group and shall show how to analyse the reducible representations $\Delta(\lambda)$ of this group. We shall also analyse the reducible representation of the symmetric group on $m_1 + m_2$ letters which is furnished by the direct product of any irreducible representation of the symmetric group on m_1 letters by any irreducible representation of the symmetric group on m_2 letters.

1. The construction of the character tables for the symmetric groups.

It follows from (4.35) and (4.18) that $p \dfrac{\partial \phi_{(\lambda)}(s)}{\partial s_p}$ may be expressed as the sum of k determinants (where the partition (λ) of m consists of k non-zero parts) of which the j-th differs from the determinant which furnishes $\phi_{(\lambda)}(s)$ in the fact that the suffixes of the q's in the j-th row are all decreased by p $(j = 1, 2, \cdots, k)$. The suffixes of the diagonal elements of this j-th determinant, namely $(\lambda_1, \lambda_2, \cdots, \lambda_j - p, \cdots, \lambda_k)$ add up to $m - p$ but they will not, in general, constitute a partition of $m - p$ for $\lambda_j - p$ may well be negative and even if it is not the normal non-increasing order may well be destroyed. However, an interchange of two adjacent rows of our determinant, which amounts only to a change of its sign, changes two adjacent diagonal suffixes by interchanging them and at the same time decreasing the one which was originally on the right by unity and increasing the one which was originally on the left by unity. By doing this sufficiently often the sequence $(\lambda_1, \lambda_2, \cdots, \lambda_j - p, \cdots, \lambda_k)$ may be put in non-ascending order. If it then *ends* in a negative integer we discard the corresponding determinant, whose last row consists entirely of zeros; if it ends in one or more zeros we ignore *these* as the corresponding determinant has units in the diagonal places in the last one or more rows, all preceding elements in these rows being zero. We shall understand by $\{\lambda_1, \lambda_2, \cdots, \lambda_j - p, \cdots, \lambda_k\}$ the simple characteristic of the symmetric group on $m - p$ letters $(p = 1, 2, \cdots, m - 1)$ corresponding to the partition of $m - p$ obtained in this way *provided the number of necessary interchanges is even* and the negative of this simple characteristic if the number of interchanges is *odd*. Since $\{\cdots a, b \cdots\} = -\{\cdots b - 1, a + 1 \cdots\}$ it is clear that $\{\cdots a, b \cdots\} = 0$ if $b = a + 1$; similarly $\{\cdots a, b, c, d \cdots\}$

$=0$ if $c=a+2$ or if $d=a+3$ and so on. With this understanding of the symbol $\{\lambda_1, \lambda_2, \cdots, \lambda_j - p, \cdots, \lambda_k\}$ we have, then,

$$(5.1) \qquad p\frac{\partial \phi_{(\lambda)}(s)}{\partial s_p} = \sum_{j=1}^{k} \{\lambda_1, \lambda_2, \cdots, \lambda_j - p, \cdots, \lambda_k\}.$$

On writing out $\phi_{(\lambda)}(s)$ thus:

$$\phi_{(\lambda)}(s) = \sum_{(\alpha)} \frac{\chi_{(\lambda)}^{(\alpha)}}{\alpha_1! \cdots \alpha_m!} \left(\frac{s_1}{1}\right)^{\alpha_1} \cdots \left(\frac{s_m}{m}\right)^{\alpha_m}$$

we have

$$p\frac{\partial \phi_{(\lambda)}(s)}{\partial s_p} = \sum_{(\alpha')} \frac{\chi_{(\lambda)}^{(\alpha)}}{\alpha_1! \cdots \alpha'_p! \cdots \alpha_m!} \left(\frac{s_1}{1}\right)^{\alpha_1} \cdots \left(\frac{s_p}{p}\right)^{\alpha'_p} \cdots \left(\frac{s_m}{m}\right)^{\alpha_m}$$

where $\alpha'_p = \alpha_p - 1$ and $(\alpha') = (\alpha_1, \cdots, \alpha'_p, \cdots, \alpha_m)$ is that class of the symmetric group on $m-p$ letters which contains one less cycle on p letters than the class (α) of the symmetric group on m letters. On equating coefficients of $s_1^{\alpha_1} \cdots s_p^{\alpha'_p} \cdots s_m^{\alpha_m}$ on both sides of the equation (5.1) we find

$$\chi_{(\lambda)}^{(\alpha)} = \sum_{j=1}^{k} \chi_{(\lambda')_j}^{(\alpha')}; \text{ where } (\lambda')_j = (\lambda_1, \cdots, \lambda_j - p, \cdots, \lambda_k),$$

a relation which we find convenient to write in the form

$$(5.2) \qquad \{\lambda_1, \cdots, \lambda_k\}_{(\alpha)} = \sum_{j=1}^{k} \{\lambda_1, \lambda_2, \cdots, \lambda_j - p, \cdots, \lambda_k\}_{(\alpha')}.$$

This basic formula enables us to write down at once those characters of the symmetric group on m letters which correspond to a class containing at least one cycle on p letters when the characters of that class of the symmetric group on $m-p$ letters which contains one less cycle on p letters are known; $(p=1, \cdots, m-1)$. The same formula yields directly the characters of the class containing but one cycle on m letters; since $\lambda_k \geq 1, \lambda_2 \geq \lambda_3 \geq \cdots \geq \lambda_k \geq 1$ we have $\lambda_1 + k - 1 \leq m$ (the equality holding only when $\lambda_2 = \lambda_3 = \cdots = \lambda_k = 1$) and so $\lambda_1 - m + (k-1) \leq 0$ and this implies $\{\lambda_1 - m, \lambda_2, \cdots, \lambda_k\} = 0$ unless $\lambda_2 = \lambda_3 = \cdots = \lambda_k = 1$ since then the last term, when it is rearranged in non-increasing order, namely $\lambda_1 - m + k - 1 < 0$. The other terms $\{\lambda_1, \lambda_2 - m, \cdots, \lambda_k\}$ etc., are zero for *all* partitions (λ) since $\lambda_2 - m + (k-2) < \lambda_1 - m + k - 1 < 0$ and so on. Hence the characters of the class containing but one cycle on m letters are zero unless the partition (λ) is of the type $(m-k+1, 1^{k-1})$. On subtracting m from the first number $m-k+1$ of this partition of m we obtain $\{1-k, 1^{k-1}\}$

and $k-1$ arrangements are necessary to write this as $\{0^k\}$ which $=1$. Hence

$$(5.3) \qquad \{m-k+1, 1^{k-1}\}_{a_m=1} = (-1)^{k-1},\ k=1,2,\cdots,m;$$
$$\text{all other } \{\lambda\}_{a_m=1} = 0.$$

This formula has the definite advantage, over the recurrence formula (5.2) that it tells us explicitly, *without referring to data concerning the symmetric group on a lesser number of letters*, the characters attached to a *particular class* of the symmetric group on *m letters*, namely the class containing but one cycle on m letters. The formula (4.34) of Frobenius giving the dimension of $D(\lambda)$, or, equivalently, the character attached to the unit class, has a similar advantage. We may combine our recurrence formula with the dimension formula of Frobenius to determine *directly* characters of classes containing one or more unary cycles. E.g., suppose we wish to calculate the characters of the symmetric group on $m=20$ letters corresponding to the class containing $\alpha_1=12$ unary cycles and $\alpha_8=1$ cycle on 8 letters. We shall illustrate by considering the representation $D(9,6,3,2)$. Applying our recurrence formula with $p=8$ we obtain

$$\{9,6,3,2\}_{(a)} = \{1,6,3,2\}_{(a')} + \{9,-2,3,2\}_{(a')}$$
$$+ \{9,6,-5,2\}_{(a')} + \{9,6,3,-6\}_{(a')};$$

of the four terms on the right the first, third and fourth vanish; the first because $3=1+2$; the third because $-5+1<0$ and the fourth because $-6<0$. There remains $\{9,-2,3,2\}_{(a')} = -\{9,2,-1,2\}_{(a')} = \{9,2,1\}_{(a')}$ and since (α') is the unit class the dimension formula (4.34) yields, since

$$(l_1,l_2,l_3)=(11,3,1),\ \frac{12!}{11!\,3!\,1!}\,(8)(10)(2)=320.$$

Similar, although not quite such convenient, formulae may be found for the characters of a class containing only cycles of the same length. E.g., let $n=2m$ and consider the class containing m binary cycles. The characters of this class are found by setting $s_2=1$, $s_1=s_3=\cdots s_m=0$ in the expressions for the simple characteristics; it being clear that then $q_j=0$ if j is odd whilst $q_{2p}=1/2^p.\,p!$. Thus, when $m=12$, the character, for the class $\alpha_2=6$, of $D(5,4,2,1)$ is

$$2^6.\,6!\begin{vmatrix} 0 & (2^3.\,3!)^{-1} & 0 & (2^4.\,4!)^{-1} \\ 0 & (2^2.\,2!)^{-1} & 0 & (2^3.\,3!)^{-1} \\ 1 & 0 & 2^{-1} & 0 \\ 0 & 0 & 1 & 0 \end{vmatrix} = 6!\,\{(4!\,2!)^{-1}-(3!)^{-2}\} = -5.$$

Similarly the character for the class $\alpha_3 = 4$ of $D(6, 3^2)$ is

$$3^4.4! \begin{vmatrix} (3^2.2!)^{-1} & 0 & 0 \\ 0 & 3^{-1} & 0 \\ 0 & 0 & 3^{-1} \end{vmatrix} = 12,$$

whilst the character for the class $\alpha_4 = 3$ of $D(7, 2^2, 1)$ is

$$4^3.3! \begin{vmatrix} 0 & (4^2.2!)^{-1} & 0 & 0 \\ 0 & 0 & 0 & 4^{-1} \\ 1 & 0 & 0 & 0 \\ 0 & 0 & 1 & 0 \end{vmatrix} = -3.$$

Two more examples will suffice; suppose when $m = 15$ we wish the character, for the class $\alpha_5 = 3$, of the representation $D(5, 4, 3, 2, 1)$. On setting $s_5 = 1$, $s_1 = s_2 = \cdots = s_{15} = 0$ all the q_j vanish save those for which j is a multiple of 5 and q_{5p} takes the value $(5^p.p!)^{-1}$. Then the desired character is

$$5^3.3! \begin{vmatrix} 5^{-1} & 0 & 0 & 0 & 0 \\ 0 & 0 & 5^{-1} & 0 & 0 \\ 0 & 0 & 0 & 0 & 5^{-1} \\ 0 & 1 & 0 & 0 & 0 \\ 0 & 0 & 0 & 1 & 0 \end{vmatrix} = -6.$$

If we wish, as a final example, to obtain, when $m = 12$, the character, for the class $\alpha_1 = 1$, $\alpha_2 = 1$, $\alpha_3 = 3$, of the representation $D(7, 1^5)$ we may proceed as follows. On applying our recurrence formula twice, first with $p = 1$ and then with $p = 2$, we find

$$\begin{aligned} \{7, 1^5\}_{(\alpha)} &= \{6, 1^5\}_{(\alpha')} + \{7, 1^4\}_{(\alpha')} \\ &= \{4, 1^5\}_{(\alpha'')} - \{6, 1^3\}_{(\alpha'')} + \{5, 1^4\}_{(\alpha'')} - \{7, 1^2\}_{(\alpha'')} \end{aligned}$$

where (α'') is the class, of the symmetric group on 9 letters, consisting of permutations each of which has three ternary cycles. Since this class is positive $\{4, 1^5\}_{(\alpha'')} = \{6, 1^3\}_{(\alpha'')}$ and we have merely to calculate $\{5, 1^4\}_{(\alpha'')}$ and $\{7, 1^2\}_{(\alpha'')}$. We find

$$\{5, 1^4\}_{(\alpha'')} = 3^3.3! \begin{vmatrix} 0 & (3^2.2!)^{-1} & 0 & 0 & (3^3.3!)^{-1} \\ 1 & 0 & 0 & 3^{-1} & 0 \\ 0 & 1 & 0 & 0 & 3^{-1} \\ 0 & 0 & 1 & 0 & 0 \\ 0 & 0 & 0 & 1 & 0 \end{vmatrix} = -2$$

$$\{7, 1^2\}_{(\alpha'')} = 3^3.3! \begin{vmatrix} 0 & 0 & (3^3.3!)^{-1} \\ 1 & 0 & 0 \\ 0 & 1 & 0 \end{vmatrix} = 1$$

so that the desired character is -3.

The same method enables us to obtain readily an explicit formula for the characters of the class $\alpha_1 = 1$, $\alpha_{m-1} = 1$ of the symmetric group on m letters. First of all it is clear that the character is zero (provided $k > 2$) unless $\lambda_3 = \lambda_4 = \cdots = \lambda_k = 1$. In fact if this is not the case $\lambda_3 + \lambda_4 + \cdots + \lambda_k > k - 2$, $\lambda_2 \geq 2$ and so $m = \lambda_1 + \lambda_2 + \cdots + \lambda_k > \lambda_1 + k$ or, equivalently, $\lambda_1 - (m-1) < -k + 1$. Hence after $k - 1$ transpositions (which bring $\lambda_1 - (m-1)$ to the end rather than the beginning of the partition) it remains negative so that $\{\lambda_1 - m + 1, \lambda_2, \cdots, \lambda_k\} = 0$; the other terms $\{\lambda_1, \lambda_2 - m + 1, \lambda_3, \cdots, \lambda_k\}, \cdots, \{\lambda_1, \lambda_2, \cdots, \lambda_{k-1}, \lambda_k - m + 1\}$ vanish à fortiori. If $\lambda_3 = \lambda_4 = \cdots = \lambda_k = 1$ and $\lambda_2 > 2$ we have $\lambda_1 < m - k$ and the same argument shows that $\{\lambda\}_{\alpha_1=1, \alpha_{m-1}=1} = 0$. It remains only (provided $k > 2$) to discuss the cases $\lambda_2 = 1$, $\lambda_2 = 2$. In the first case $\lambda_1 = m - k + 1$ and $\{\lambda_1 - m + 1, 1^{k-1}\} = \{2 - k, 1^{k-1}\}$ and this vanishes since the last element, 1, equals the first, $2 - k$, plus $k - 1$. Also $\{\lambda_1, \lambda_2 - m + 1, 1^{k-2}\} = \{\lambda_1, 2 - m, 1^{k-2}\}$ and since $2 - m$ plus $k - 2 = k - m < 0$ (unless $k = m$, in which case we are dealing with the alternating representation whose characters are known, being $1(-1)$ for the even (odd) classes) $\{\lambda_1, \lambda_2 - m + 1, 1^{k-2}\} = 0$; the other terms $\{\lambda_1, \lambda_2, \lambda_3 - m + 1, \cdots, \lambda_k\}, \cdots, \{\lambda_1, \lambda_2, \cdots, \lambda_{k-1}, \lambda_k - m + 1\}$ vanish à fortiori. If $\lambda_2 = 2$, $\lambda_1 = m - k$ and we have to calculate $\{1 - k, 2, 1^{k-2}\} = (-1)^{k-1}$; the other terms vanish as before. Hence if $k > 2$ the characters, for the class $\alpha_1 = 1$, $\alpha_{m-1} = 1$, all vanish save those for which $k = m$, (the alternating representation) and those for which $\lambda_1 = m - k$, $\lambda_2 = 2$, $\lambda_3 = \lambda_4 = \cdots = \lambda_k = 1$. If $k = 2$ all $\{\lambda_1 - m + 1, \lambda_2\}$ vanish for which $\lambda_1 - m + 2 < 0$ and since $\lambda_2 > 0$ the only possibilities for λ_1 are $m - 1$, $m - 2$. Since $\{0, 1\}$ vanishes the character of $(m - 1, 1)$ for the class in question is zero whilst the character of $(m - 2, 2)$ is -1. Since $k = 1$ yields the identity representation we may resume our results as follows: outside the identity and alternating representations whose characters are known the only representations for which the characters for the class $\alpha_1 = 1$, $\alpha_{m-1} = 1$ differ from zero are those for which $(\lambda) = (m - k, 2, 1^{k-2})$ whose characters are $(-1)^{k-1}$ and those for which $(\lambda) = (m - 2, 2)$ whose characters are -1:

$$\{m - k, 2, 1^{k-2}\}_{\substack{\alpha_1=1\\ \alpha_{m-1}=1}} = (-1)^{k-1}; \quad \{m\}_{\substack{\alpha_1=1\\ \alpha_{m-1}}} = 1;$$

$$(5.4) \qquad \{m - 2, 2\}_{\substack{\alpha_1=1\\ \alpha_{m-1}=1}} = -1; \quad \begin{cases} \{1^m\}_{\substack{\alpha_1=1\\ \alpha_{m-1}=1}} = 1 \text{ if } m \text{ is even} \\ \qquad = -1 \text{ if } m \text{ is odd} \end{cases}$$

$$\text{All other } \{\lambda\}_{\substack{\alpha_1=1\\ \alpha_{m-1}=1}} = 0.$$

We may derive by the method just described explicit formulae for the characters of those classes of the symmetric group on m letters which consist of $\alpha_1 = m - p$ unary cycles and $\alpha_p = 1$ cycle on p letters; $(p = 2, 3, 4, \cdots)$. We first remark that a partition (λ) of m may be conveniently specified as follows: draw the principal diagonal of the diagram of the partition (i. e. the diagonal starting at the upper left-hand corner) and suppose it strikes s columns. Denote by $b_1 > b_2 > \cdots > b_s \geq 0$ the number of dots to the right of the diagonal in the rows $1, 2, \cdots, s$, respectively, and by $a_1 > a_2 > \cdots > a_s \geq 0$ the number of dots below the diagonal in the columns $1, \cdots, s$ respectively. Then the partition is described by $\boldsymbol{b} = (b_1, \cdots, b_s)$, $\boldsymbol{a} = (a_1, \cdots, a_s)$ it being clear that the partition is self-associated when and only when $\boldsymbol{a} = \boldsymbol{b}$. The number of dots in the first row and column together $= b_1 + a_1 + 1$; when these are deleted the number of dots in the new first row and column $= b_2 + a_2 + 1$. Proceeding in this way we have $m = \sum_{j=1}^{s} (b_j + a_j + 1)$. It is clear from the definition that $b_j = \lambda_j - j$ $(j = 1, \cdots, s)$, whilst the differences $p - \lambda_{p+1}$ $(p = s, \cdots, k-1)$, satisfy the inequalities

$$0 \leq s - \lambda_{s+1} < s + 1 - \lambda_{s+2} < \cdots < k - 1 - \lambda_k < k - 1.$$

Hence they are the complementary set to the set $a_1 > a_2 > \cdots > a_s$ in the set $0, 1, \cdots, k-1$. In fact $\lambda_k > 0$ shows that $a_1 = k - 1$ is not in the set; if $\lambda_k > 1$, $a_2 = k - 2$ is not in the set and so on. The following will serve as illustrations of the definitions of $\boldsymbol{b}$ and $\boldsymbol{a}$

$$\begin{array}{llll} (\lambda) = (3, 2^2, 1^2); & s = 2; & \boldsymbol{b} = (2, 0); & \boldsymbol{a} = (4, 1) \\ (\lambda) = (4, 2, 1^2); & s = 2; & \boldsymbol{b} = (3, 0); & \boldsymbol{a} = (3, 0) \\ (\lambda) = (4^3, 1); & s = 3; & \boldsymbol{b} = (3, 2, 1); & \boldsymbol{a} = (3, 1, 0). \end{array}$$

We denote, for convenience, by $\chi_{(\lambda)}(p)$ the characters of $D(\lambda)$ for the class $\alpha_1 = m - p$, $\alpha_p = 1$ so that, for instance, $\chi_{(\lambda)}(2)$ are the characters for the transposition class whilst $\chi_{(\lambda)}(1)$ are the characters for the unit class (i. e. the dimensions of the various irreducible representations). Our object is to obtain for $\chi_{(\lambda)}(p)$ $(p = 2, 3, 4, \cdots)$, an explicit formula analogous to (4. 34) which furnishes $\chi_{(\lambda)}(1)$. The recurrence formula (5. 2) tells us that $\chi_{(\lambda)}(p)$ is the sum of the dimensions of the irreducible representations

$$D(\lambda_1, \lambda_2, \cdots, \lambda_j - p, \cdots, \lambda_k); \qquad (j = 1, \cdots, k),$$

of the symmetric group on $m - p$ letters (where we follow the previously agreed on convention for the restoration of the normal non-increasing order of the $(\lambda_1, \lambda_2, \cdots)$ when this has been destroyed by the subtraction of p). Writing, as before

$$l_1 = \lambda_1 + (k-1),\ l_2 = \lambda_2 + (k-2), \cdots, l_k = \lambda_k$$

the dimension of $D(\lambda_1 - p, \lambda_2, \cdots, \lambda_k)$ is

$$(m-p)!\,(l_1-p-l_2)\cdots(l_1-p-l_k)(l_2-l_3)\cdots(l_{k-1}-l_k) \div (l_1-p)!\,l_2!\cdots l_k!$$

and there are similar expressions of the dimensions of the other irreducible representations. On dividing through by

$$\chi_{(\lambda)}(1) = m!\,(l_1-l_2)\cdots(l_{k-1}-l_k) \div l_1!\cdots l_k!$$

the quotient $\chi_{(\lambda)}(p) \div \chi_{(\lambda)}(1)$ appears as a sum of k terms of which the first is

$$l_1(l_1-1)\cdots(l_1-p+1)(l_1-p-l_2)\cdots(l_1-p-l_k) \div m(m-1)\cdots(m-p+1)(l_1-l_2)\cdots(l_1-l_k).$$

If we write $f(x) = (x-l_1)\cdots(x-l_k)$ this may be written as the quotient of $l_1(l_1-1)\cdots(l_1-p+1)f(l_1-p)$ by $-pm(m-1)\cdots(m-p+1)f'(l_1)$ where f' indicates the derivative of f; hence

$$\frac{\chi_{(\lambda)}(p)}{\chi_{(\lambda)}(1)} = \frac{-1}{pm(m-1)\cdots(m-p+1)} \sum_{j=1}^{k} \frac{l_j(l_j-1)\cdots(l_j-p+1)f(l_j-p)}{f'(l_j)}.$$

Now the analysis of the function $x(x-1)\cdots(x-p+1)f(x-p) \div f(x)$ into simple fractions yields a polynomial in x plus terms $A_j \div (x-l_j)$ where $A_j = l_j(l_j-1)\cdots(l_j-p+1)f(l_j-p) \div f'(l_j)$ so that

$$\chi_{(\lambda)}(p) \div \chi_{(\lambda)}(1) = -\left(\sum_{j=1}^{k} A_j\right) \div pm(m-1)\cdots(m-p+1).$$

On writing $(x-l_j)^{-1} = (1/x) + (l_j/x^2) + \cdots$ it is clear that $\sum_{j=1}^{k} A_j$ is the coefficient of $(1/x)$ in the development of

$$x(x-1)\cdots(x-p+1)f(x-p) \div f(x)$$

as a series of *descending* powers of x. The zeros of $f(x)$ are the k numbers $(l_1, \cdots, l_k)$ so that, if $y = x-k$, the zeros of $f(y+k)$ are the k numbers $l_1-k, \cdots, l_k-k$ i. e. the k numbers $\lambda_j - j$ $(j = 1, \cdots, k)$. Of these the first s are the numbers $(b_1, \cdots, b_s)$ whilst the remaining $k-s$ are the negatives of $\alpha_j + 1$ where the two sets $\boldsymbol{a} = (a_1, \cdots, a_s)$ and $\boldsymbol{\alpha} = (\alpha_{s+1}, \cdots, \alpha_k)$ together form the set $0, 1, \cdots, (k-1)$. Hence

$$f(y+k) = \prod_{j=1}^{s}(y-b_j) \cdot \prod_{s+1}^{k}(y+\alpha_k+1)$$
$$= \prod_{j=1}^{s}\{(y-b_j)/(y+a_j+1)\} \cdot (y+1)\cdots(y+k).$$

It will be convenient to denote the function

$$(y-b_1)\cdots(y-b_s)/(y+a_1+1)\cdots(y+a_s+1)$$

by $F(y)$ and then $f(x)=f(y+k)=F(y)(y+1)\cdots(y+k)$. The desired sum $\sum_{j=1}^{k} A_j$, being the coefficient of $1/x$ in the development of

$$x(x-1)\cdots(x-p+1)f(x-p)\div f(x)$$

in a series of descending powers of x, is, equivalently, the coefficient of $1/y$ in the development of this same function in a descending series of powers of y. But

$$\begin{aligned} &x(x-1)\cdots(x-p+1)f(x-p)\div f(x) \\ &\quad=(y+k)\cdots(y+k+1-p)\cdot(y+k-p)\cdots(y+1-p)F(y-p) \\ &\qquad\div(y+1)\cdots(y+k)F(y) \\ &\quad=y(y-1)\cdots(y-p+1)F(y-p)\div F(y)\end{aligned}$$

and we have merely to seek the coefficient of $(1/y)$ in the development of this function. An application of Taylor's expansion yields

$$\begin{aligned} F(y-p)\div F(y)=1-pF'(y)/F(y)&+p^2F''(y)/2!\,F(y) \\ &-p^3F'''(y)/3!\,F(y)+\cdots;\end{aligned}$$

and, on taking the logarithmic derivative of

$$F(y)=\prod_{j=1}^{s}\{(y-b_j)/(y+a_j+1)\}$$

we find

$$\begin{aligned} F'(y)/F(y)&=\sum_{j=1}^{s}\{[1/(y-b_j)]-[1/(y+a_j+1)]\} \\ &=(m/y^2)+c_3/y^3+(c_4/y^4)+\cdots\end{aligned}$$

where

$$c_3=\sum_{j=1}^{s}\{b_j^2-(a_j+1)^2\};\quad c_4=\sum_{j=1}^{s}\{b_j^3+(a_j+1)^3\};$$

$$c_5=\sum_{j=1}^{s}\{b_j^4-(a_j+1)^4\};\cdots$$

(we have availed ourselves of the relation $\sum_{j=1}^{s}\{b_j+(a_j+1)\}=m$). On successive differentiation of this relation we find

$$\begin{aligned} F''(y)/F(y)&=\{F'(y)/F(y)\}^2+\{F'(y)/F(y)\}'=(-2m/y^3) \\ &\qquad+(m^2-3c_3)/y^4+(2mc_3-4c_4)/y^5+\cdots \\ F'''(y)/F(y)&=\{F''(y)/F(y)\}\{F'(y)/F(y)\}+\{F''(y)/F(y)\}' \\ &=(6m/y^4)+(12c_3-6m^2)/y^5+\cdots\end{aligned}$$

$$F^{(''''')}(y)/F(y) = \{F'''(y)/F(y)\}\{F'(y)/F(y)\} + \{F'''(y)/F(y)\}'$$
$$= (-24m/y^5) + \cdots.$$

Hence

$$F(y-p) \div -pF(y) = -(1/p) + (m/y^2) + (pm + c_3)/y^3$$
$$+\tfrac{1}{2}(2c_4 + 3pc_3 + 2mp^2 - pm^2)/y^4$$
$$+\{c_5 + 2pc_4 + p(2p-m)c_3 + mp^2(p-m)\}/y^5 + \cdots.$$

This has to be multiplied by $y(y-1)\cdots(y-p+1)$ and the coefficient of y^{-1} in the product then determined; equivalently we may multiply by $(y-1)\cdots(y-p+1)$ and determine the coefficient of y^{-2}. This coefficient yields, when divided by $m(m-1)\cdots(m-p+1)$ the desired quantity $\chi_{(\lambda)}(p) \div \chi_{(\lambda)}(1)$. We carry out the calculation for $p = 2, 3, 4$.

$$p = 2; \quad \chi_{(\lambda)}(2) \div \chi_{(\lambda)}(1) = (m + c_3) \div m(m-1).$$

Since

$$c_3 = \sum_{j=1}^{s} \{b_j^2 - (a_j+1)^2\}; \quad m = \sum_{j=1}^{s} \{b_j + (a_j+1)\}$$
$$c_3 + m = \sum_{j=1}^{s} \{b_j(b_j+1) - a_j(a_j+1)\}$$

so that

$$(5.5) \quad \chi_{(\lambda)}(2) \div \chi_{(\lambda)}(1) = \sum_{j=1}^{s} \{b_j(b_j+1) - a_j(a_j+1)\} \div m(m-1).$$

The formula (5.5) may be readily transformed as follows. We have $b_j = \lambda_j - j$, $(j = 1, \cdots, s)$, $\alpha_j + 1 = j - \lambda_j$ $(j = s+1, \cdots, k)$ where $\boldsymbol{a} = (a_1, \cdots, a_s)$ and $\boldsymbol{\alpha} = (\alpha_{s+1}, \cdots, \alpha_k)$ together form the set $(0, \cdots, k-1)$; hence

$$\sum_{j=1}^{s} \{a_j(a_j+1)\} = \sum_{0}^{k-1} p(p+1) - \sum_{s+1}^{k} \alpha_j(\alpha_j+1)$$
$$= \sum_{1}^{k} p(p-1) - \sum_{s+1}^{k} (\lambda_j - j)(\lambda_j - j + 1).$$

Thus

$$\sum_{1}^{s} \{b_j(b_j+1) - a_j(a_j+1)\} = \sum_{1}^{k} (\lambda_j - j)(\lambda_j - j + 1) - \sum_{1}^{k} p(p-1)$$
$$= \sum_{1}^{k} \lambda_j(\lambda_j - 2j + 1)$$

so that

$$(5.6) \quad \chi_{(\lambda)}(2) \div \chi_{(\lambda)}(1) = \sum_{1}^{k} \lambda_j(\lambda_j - 2j + 1) \div m(m-1)$$

$p=3$; here we must multiply by $(y-1)(y-2)$ and the coefficient of y^{-2} is

$$(2c_4+3c_3-3m^2+4m)/2=\tfrac{1}{2}[\sum_{j=1}^{s}\{(2b_j^3+3b_j^2+b_j)$$
$$+2(a_j+1)^3-3(a_j+1)^2+(a_j+1)\}-3m(m-1)].$$

Hence

$$(5.7)\quad \chi_{(\lambda)}(3)\div\chi_{(\lambda)}(1)=[\sum_{j=1}^{s}\{b_j(b_j+1)(2b_j+1)$$
$$+a_j(a_j+1)(2a_j+1)\}-3m(m-1)]\div 2m(m-1)(m-2)$$

$p=4$; here we must multiply by

$$(y-1)(y-2)(y-3)=y^3-6y^2+11y-6$$

and the coefficient of y^{-2} is

$$c_5+2c_4+c_3-2(2m-3)(c_3+m)$$
$$=\sum_{j=1}^{s}[\{b_j^2(b_j+1)^2-a_j^2(a_j+1)^2\}$$
$$-2(2m-3)\{b_j(b_j+1)-a_j(a_j+1)\}]$$

so that

$$(5.8)\quad \chi_{(\lambda)}(4)\div\chi_{(\lambda)}(1)=\sum_{j=1}^{s}[\{b_j^2(b_j+1)^2-a_j^2(a_j+1)^2\}$$
$$-2(2m-3)\{b_j(b_j+1)-a_j(a_j+1)\}]\div m(m-1)(m-2)(m-3).$$

For higher values of p it is more serviceable to use the recurrence formula (5.2) as the expressions deduced by the manner described above become too complicated.

Examples:

As examples illustrating the use of the general results already obtained we shall construct the character tables of the symmetric groups on 4 and 5 letters; the tables for $m=2,3$ having been already determined (pp. 99, 100).

1. $m=4$.

Here there are 5 classes and we shall arrange these according to the following scheme; (α) precedes (α') if the first non-vanishing member of the set of differences $\alpha_1-\alpha'_1, \alpha_2-\alpha'_2, \cdots$ is positive. It is unnecessary to write down the characters of $D(2,1^2)$ and $D(1^4)$ since these representations are associated with $D(3,1)$ and $D(4)$, respectively. We shall denote the class (α) by the symbol $(1^{\alpha_1}, 2^{\alpha_2}, \cdots, m^{\alpha_m})$ (the terms with zero exponents being omitted.) For $\lambda=(3,1)$ we have $\boldsymbol{a}=1, \boldsymbol{b}=2$ and the character for the transposition class $(1^2,2)$ follows at once from (5.5). The character, for this class, of the self-associated representation $D(2^2)$, is zero, since the class is negative. The characters for the classes (4) and (1, 3) are furnished by (5.3) and (5.4), respectively. There remains only the class (2^2) (the characters for the class (1^4), i.e. the dimensions of the various irreducible representations being given by (4.34)). For this class we use the reduction formula (5.2) and find

$$\{3,1\}_{(2^2)} = \{1^2\}_{(2)} = -1;$$
$$\{2^2\}_{(2^2)} = \{0,2\}_{(2)} + \{2\}_{(2)} = \{2\}_{(2)} - \{1^2\}_{(2)} = 2.$$

Hence the character table for the symmetric group on 4 letters is (even (odd) classes being denoted by the attached sign +(—) and self-associated representations being denoted by a *)

	{4}	{3, 1}	$\{2^2\}^*$	
$(1^4)^+$	1	3	2	1
$(1^2,2)^-$	1	1	0	6
$(1,3)^+$	1	0	-1	8
$(2^2)^+$	1	-1	2	3
$(4)^-$	1	-1	0	6

The numbers at the right of the table indicate the number of elements in the corresponding class.

2. $m = 5$.

Here there are seven classes and the table is readily constructed (the characters for the class $(1^2, 3)$ being given by (5.7))

	{5}	{4, 1}	{3, 2}	$\{3,1^2\}^*$	
$(1^5)^+$	1	4	5	6	1
$(1^3,2)^-$	1	2	1	0	10
$(1^2,3)^+$	1	1	-1	0	20
$(1,2^2)^+$	1	0	1	-2	15
$(1,4)^-$	1	0	-1	0	30
$(2,3)^-$	1	-1	1	0	20
$(5)^+$	1	-1	0	1	24

It may be noticed that the characters of {3, 1} and {4, 1} are simply $\alpha_1 - 1$. This is but a special instance of a general formula which states that the characters of $D(m-1, 1)$ are given by $\alpha_1 - 1$. We proceed to the derivation of several formulae of this type.

2. Formulae giving those characters of the symmetric group which are attached to two and three element partitions of m in terms of the class numbers.

We first discuss the case of two element partitions: $(\lambda) = (\lambda_1, \lambda_2)$, $\lambda_1 + \lambda_2 = m$. On expanding the two-row determinant

$$\begin{vmatrix} q_{\lambda_1}(s) & q_{\lambda_1+1}(s) \\ q_{\lambda_2-1}(s) & q_{\lambda_2}(s) \end{vmatrix}$$

(which furnishes the simple characteristic $\{\lambda_1, \lambda_2\}$ of the symmetric group on m letters) in terms of the first row we obtain

$$\{\lambda_1, \lambda_2\} = q_{\lambda_1}(s) q_{\lambda_2}(s) - q_{\lambda_1+1}(s) q_{\lambda_2-1}(s).$$

Now a typical term of $q_{\lambda_1}(s)$ is $\dfrac{1}{\theta_1! \cdots \theta_m!}\left(\dfrac{s_1}{1}\right)^{\theta_1} \cdots \left(\dfrac{s_m}{m}\right)^{\theta_m}$ where $(\theta) = (\theta_1, \cdots, \theta_m)$ is a class of the symmetric group on λ_1 letters; since $\lambda_1 < m$ one or more of the elements $\theta_m, \theta_{m-1}, \cdots$ of (θ) are zero. Similarly a typical element of $q_{\lambda_2}(s)$ is $\dfrac{1}{\tau_1! \cdots \tau_m!}\left(\dfrac{s_1}{1}\right)^{\tau_1} \cdots \left(\dfrac{s_m}{m}\right)^{\tau_m}$ so that the product $q_{\lambda_1}(s) q_{\lambda_2}(s)$ is obtained by adding

$$\frac{1}{\theta_1! \cdots \theta_m!\, \tau_1! \cdots \tau_m!}\left(\frac{s_1}{1}\right)^{\theta_1+\tau_1} \cdots \left(\frac{s_m}{m}\right)^{\theta_m+\tau_m}$$

over all classes (θ) and (τ) of the symmetric groups on λ_1 and λ_2 letters, respectively. On writing $\alpha_1 = \theta_1 + \tau_1, \cdots, \alpha_m = \theta_m + \tau_m$ it is clear that $(\alpha) = (\alpha_1, \cdots, \alpha_m)$ is a class of the symmetric group on $\lambda_1 + \lambda_2 = m$ letters. Hence the coefficient of $\dfrac{1}{\alpha_1! \cdots \alpha_m!}\left(\dfrac{s_1}{1}\right)^{\alpha_1} \cdots \left(\dfrac{s_m}{m}\right)^{\alpha_m}$, (α) any class of the symmetric group on m letters, in the product $q_{\lambda_1}(s) q_{\lambda_2}(s)$ is the sum over all classes (τ) of the symmetric group on λ_2 letters of the product $\dbinom{\alpha_1}{\tau_1} \cdots \dbinom{\alpha_m}{\tau_m}$ where $\dbinom{\alpha_j}{\tau_j}$ denotes the binomial coefficient $\dfrac{\alpha_j!}{\tau_j!\, \alpha_j - \tau_j!}$ (it being understood that $\dbinom{\alpha_j}{\tau_j} = 0$ if $\tau_j > \alpha_j$). Similarly for the product $q_{\lambda_1+1}(s) q_{\lambda_2-1}(s)$; the coefficient of

$$\frac{1}{\alpha_1! \cdots \alpha_m!}\left(\frac{s_1}{1}\right)^{\alpha_1} \cdots \left(\frac{s_m}{m}\right)^{\alpha_m}$$

in this product is $\sum_{(\sigma)} \dbinom{\alpha_1}{\sigma_1} \cdots \dbinom{\alpha_m}{\sigma_m}$ where (σ) is any class of the symmetric group on $\lambda_2 - 1$ letters. Hence

$$\{\lambda_1, \lambda_2\}_{(\alpha)} = \sum_{(\tau)} \binom{\alpha_1}{\tau_1} \cdots \binom{\alpha_m}{\tau_m} - \sum_{(\sigma)} \binom{\alpha_1}{\sigma_1} \cdots \binom{\alpha_m}{\sigma_m}.$$

Since, when $\tau_1 \geqq 1$, $(\tau') = (\tau_1 - 1, \tau_2, \cdots, \tau_m)$ is a class (σ) of the symmetric group on $\lambda_2 - 1$ letters we may combine the terms

$$\binom{\alpha_1}{\sigma_1+1}\binom{\alpha_2}{\sigma_2}\cdots\binom{\alpha_m}{\sigma_m} - \binom{\alpha_1}{\sigma_1}\cdots\binom{\alpha_m}{\sigma_m}$$

getting $\sum_{(\sigma)} \frac{(\alpha_1 - 2\sigma_1 - 1)}{\sigma_1 + 1}\binom{\alpha_1}{\sigma_1}\cdots\binom{\alpha_m}{\sigma_m}$. Denoting by (β) an arbitrary class, of the symmetric group on λ_2 letters, which does not contain any fixed letter (= unary cycle) we have

$$(5.9)\quad \{\lambda_1, \lambda_2\}_{(\alpha)} = \sum_{(\sigma)} \frac{(\alpha_1 - 2\sigma_1 - 1)}{(\sigma_1 + 1)}\binom{\alpha_1}{\sigma_1}\cdots\binom{\alpha_m}{\sigma_m} + \sum_{(\beta)}\binom{\alpha_2}{\beta_2}\cdots\binom{\alpha_m}{\beta_m}$$

the first summation being over *all* classes (σ) of the symmetric group on $\lambda_2 - 1$ letters and the second over *those* classes (β) of the symmetric group on λ_2 letters for which $\beta_1 = 0$. The particular case for which $\lambda_2 = 1$ is a little special (since $\lambda_2 - 1 = 0$); but in this case we have merely to evaluate $\binom{\alpha_1}{1}\binom{\alpha_2}{0}\cdots\binom{\alpha_m}{0} - \binom{\alpha_1}{0}\cdots\binom{\alpha_m}{0} = \alpha_1 - 1.$

As examples of these results we cite:

$$\{m-1, 1\}_{(\alpha)} = \alpha_1 - 1$$
$$\{m-2, 2\}_{(\alpha)} = \tfrac{1}{2}\alpha_1(\alpha_1 - 3) + \alpha_2$$
$$\{m-3, 3\}_{(\alpha)} = \tfrac{1}{6}\alpha_1(\alpha_1 - 1)(\alpha_1 - 5) + (\alpha_1 - 1)\alpha_2 + \alpha_3$$
$$\{m-4, 4\}_{(\alpha)} = \tfrac{1}{24}\alpha_1(\alpha_1 - 1)(\alpha_1 - 2)(\alpha_1 - 7) + \tfrac{1}{2}\alpha_1(\alpha_1 - 3)\alpha_2 + (\alpha_1 - 1)\alpha_3 + \tfrac{1}{2}\alpha_2(\alpha_2 - 1) + \alpha_4.$$

To obtain a formula analogous to (5.9) for three element partitions $(\lambda) = (\lambda_1, \lambda_2, \lambda_3)$ we expand the third order determinant

$$\begin{vmatrix} q_{\lambda_1}(\boldsymbol{s}) & q_{\lambda_1+1}(\boldsymbol{s}) & q_{\lambda_1+2}(\boldsymbol{s}) \\ q_{\lambda_2-1}(\boldsymbol{s}) & q_{\lambda_2}(\boldsymbol{s}) & q_{\lambda_2+1}(\boldsymbol{s}) \\ q_{\lambda_3-2}(\boldsymbol{s}) & q_{\lambda_3-1}(\boldsymbol{s}) & q_{\lambda_3}(\boldsymbol{s}) \end{vmatrix}$$

which furnishes the simple characteristic $\{\lambda_1, \lambda_2, \lambda_3\}$, in terms of the first row. The coefficient of $q_{\lambda_1}(\boldsymbol{s})$ is $\{\lambda_2, \lambda_3\}$; that of $-q_{\lambda_1+1}(\boldsymbol{s})$ is $\begin{vmatrix} q_{\lambda_2-1}(\boldsymbol{s}) & q_{\lambda_2+1}(\boldsymbol{s}) \\ q_{\lambda_3-2}(\boldsymbol{s}) & q_{\lambda_3}(\boldsymbol{s}) \end{vmatrix} = \frac{\partial}{\partial s_1}\{\lambda_2, \lambda_3\}$ (the two-rowed determinant furnishing $\{\lambda_2, \lambda_3\}$ being differentiated with respect to s_1 by differentiating the columns one at a time); finally the coefficient of $q_{\lambda_1+2}(\boldsymbol{s})$ is $\{\lambda_2 - 1,$

$\lambda_3 - 1\}$. Since $\{\lambda_2, \lambda_3\} = \sum_{(\beta)} \frac{\{\lambda_2, \lambda_3\}_{(\beta)}}{\beta_1 ! \cdots \beta_m !} \left(\frac{s_1}{1}\right)^{\beta_1} \cdots \left(\frac{s_m}{m}\right)^{\beta_m}$ where $\beta = (\beta_1, \cdots, \beta_m)$ is an arbitrary class of the symmetric group on $\lambda_2 + \lambda_3$ letters, the coefficient of $\frac{1}{\alpha_1 ! \cdots \alpha_m !} \left(\frac{s_1}{1}\right)^{\alpha_1} \cdots \left(\frac{s_m}{m}\right)^{\alpha_m}$ in the product $q_{\lambda_1}(s)\{\lambda_2, \lambda_3\}$ is

$$\sum_{(\beta)} \{\lambda_2, \lambda_3\}_{(\beta)} \binom{\alpha_1}{\beta_1} \cdots \binom{\alpha_m}{\beta_m}.$$

Also
$$\frac{\partial}{\partial s_1}\{\lambda_2, \lambda_3\} = \sum_{(\beta')} \frac{\{\lambda_2, \lambda_3\}_{\beta}}{\beta'_1 ! \beta_2 ! \cdots \beta_m !} \left(\frac{s_1}{1}\right)^{\beta'_1} \cdots \left(\frac{s_m}{m}\right)^{\beta_m}$$

where $\beta'_1 = \beta_1 - 1$ so that $(\beta') = (\beta'_1, \beta_2, \cdots, \beta_m)$ is an arbitrary class of the symmetric group on $\lambda_2 + \lambda_3 - 1$ letters; hence the coefficient of

$$\frac{1}{\alpha_1 ! \cdots \alpha_m !} \left(\frac{s_1}{1}\right)^{\alpha_1} \cdots \left(\frac{s_m}{m}\right)^{\alpha_m} \text{ in } q_{\lambda_1+1}(s) \frac{\partial}{\partial s_1}\{\lambda_2, \lambda_3\}$$
$$= \sum_{(\beta')} \{\lambda_2, \lambda_3\}_{(\beta)} \binom{\alpha_1}{\beta'_1} \cdots \binom{\alpha_m}{\beta_m}$$

the summation being over all classes (β') of the symmetric group on $\lambda_2 + \lambda_3 - 1$ letters. Similarly the coefficient of $\frac{1}{\alpha_1 ! \cdots \alpha_m !} \left(\frac{s_1}{1}\right)^{\alpha_1} \cdots \left(\frac{s_m}{m}\right)^{\alpha_m}$ in the product $q_{\lambda_1+2}(s)\{\lambda_2 - 1, \lambda_3 - 1\}$ is

$$\sum_{(\gamma)} \{\lambda_2 - 1, \lambda_3 - 1\}_{(\gamma)} \binom{\alpha_1}{\gamma_1} \cdots \binom{\alpha_m}{\gamma_m}$$

the summation being over all classes (γ) of the symmetric group on $\lambda_2 + \lambda_3 - 2$ letters. Combining these results we obtain

$$\{\lambda_1, \lambda_2, \lambda_3\}_{(\alpha)} = \sum_{(\beta)} \{\lambda_2, \lambda_3\}_{(\beta)} \binom{\alpha_1}{\beta_1} \cdots \binom{\alpha_m}{\beta_m} - \sum_{(\beta')} \{\lambda_2, \lambda_3\}_{(\beta)} \binom{\alpha_1}{\beta'_1} \cdots \binom{\alpha_m}{\beta_m}$$
$$+ \sum_{(\gamma)} \{\lambda_2 - 1, \lambda_3 - 1\}_{(\gamma)} \binom{\alpha_1}{\gamma_1} \cdots \binom{\alpha_m}{\gamma_m}$$

the summations on the right being, respectively, over all classes (β) of the symmetric group on $\lambda_2 + \lambda_3$ letters, all classes (β') of the symmetric group on $\lambda_2 + \lambda_3 - 1$ and all classes (γ) of the symmetric group on $\lambda_2 + \lambda_3 - 2$ letters. On separating, in the first summation, those classes (β) which contain one or more unary cycles $(\beta_1 \geq 1)$ and writing $\beta_1 = \beta'_1 + 1$ we obtain

$$(5.10)\quad \{\lambda_1, \lambda_2, \lambda_3\}_{(\alpha)} = \sum_{(\beta')} \frac{\alpha_1 - 2\beta'_1 - 1}{\beta'_1 + 1} \{\lambda_2, \lambda_3\}_{(\beta)} \binom{\alpha_1}{\beta'_1} \cdots \binom{\alpha_m}{\beta_m} +$$

$$\sum_{(\delta)} \{\lambda_2, \lambda_3\}_{(\delta)} \binom{\alpha_2}{\delta_2} \cdots \binom{\alpha_m}{\delta_m} + \sum_{(\gamma)} \{\lambda_2 - 1, \lambda_3 - 1\}_{(\gamma)} \binom{\alpha_1}{\gamma_1} \cdots \binom{\alpha_m}{\gamma_m}$$

where (δ) is any class of the symmetric group on $\lambda_2 + \lambda_3$ letters for which $\delta_1 = 0$. Suppose, for instance, $\lambda_1 = m - 2$, $\lambda_2 = \lambda_3 = 1$. Then $\lambda_2 + \lambda_3 - 1 = 1$ and there is only one term in the first summation: that for which $\beta'_1 = 1$. There is also only one term in the second summation: that for which $\delta_2 = 1$. The third summation has only one term: that for which all $\gamma = 0$ and this yields unity since $\{0^2\} = 1$. Hence $\{m-2, 1^2\}_{(a)} = \frac{1}{2}\alpha_1(\alpha_1 - 3) - \alpha_2 + 1 = \frac{1}{2}(\alpha_1 - 1)(\alpha_1 - 2) - \alpha_2$; for $\beta_1 = \beta'_1 + 1 = 2$ and $\{1^2\}_{(1^2)} = 1$ whilst $\delta_2 = 1$ and $\{1^2\}_{(2)} = -1$. As examples of the use of (5.10) we cite the following:

$$\begin{aligned}
\{m-2, 1^2\}_{(a)} &= \tfrac{1}{2}(\alpha_1 - 1)(\alpha_1 - 2) - \alpha_2 \\
\{m-3, 2, 1\}_{(a)} &= \tfrac{1}{3}\alpha_1(\alpha_1 - 2)(\alpha_1 - 4) - \alpha_3 \\
\{m-4, 3, 1\}_{(a)} &= \tfrac{1}{8}\alpha_1(\alpha_1 - 1)(\alpha_1 - 3)(\alpha_1 - 6) + \tfrac{1}{2}\alpha_1(\alpha_1 - 3)\alpha_2 \\
&\quad - \tfrac{1}{2}\alpha_2(\alpha_2 - 3) - \alpha_4 \\
\{m-4, 2^2\}_{(a)} &= \tfrac{1}{12}\alpha_1(\alpha_1 - 1)(\alpha_1 - 4)(\alpha_1 - 5) - (\alpha_1 - 1)\alpha_3 \\
&\quad + \alpha_2(\alpha_2 - 2).
\end{aligned}$$

Using the results of this paragraph we may at once write down the character table for the symmetric group on 6 letters (which contains eleven classes). It is

$m = 6.$

	$\{6\}$	$\{5,1\}$	$\{4,2\}$	$\{4,1^2\}$	$\{3^2\}$	$\{3,2,1\}^*$	
$(1^6)^+$	1	5	9	10	5	16	1
$(1^4,2)^-$	1	3	3	2	1	0	15
$(1^3,3)^+$	1	2	0	1	−1	−2	40
$(1^2,2^2)^+$	1	1	1	−2	1	0	45
$(1^2,4)^-$	1	1	−1	0	−1	0	90
$(1,2,3)^-$	1	0	0	−1	1	0	120
$(1,5)^+$	1	0	−1	0	0	1	144
$(2^3)^-$	1	−1	3	−2	−3	0	15
$(2,4)^+$	1	−1	1	0	−1	0	90
$(3^2)^+$	1	−1	0	1	2	−2	40
$(6)^-$	1	−1	0	1	0	0	120

The formulae already given yield all characters of the symmetric group on seven letters save those of the self-associated representation $\{4, 1^3\}^*$; and all characters of the symmetric group on eight letters save those of the representations $\{5, 1^3\}$ and $\{4, 2, 1^2\}^*$. Formulae taking care of these may be readily derived. Thus if we expand the fourth order determinant which furnishes the simple characteristic $\{m-3, 1^3\}$ of the symmetric group on m letters in terms of the first column we obtain

$$\{m-3, 1^3\} = q_{m-3}(\mathbf{s})\{1^3\} - \{m-2, 1^2\}.$$

Since the characters of $\{1^3\}$ are $1, -1, 1$, we see that the coefficient of

$$\frac{1}{\alpha_1! \cdots \alpha_m!}\left(\frac{s_1}{1}\right)^{\alpha_1} \cdots \left(\frac{s_m}{m}\right)^{\alpha_m} \text{ in } q_{m-3}\{1^3\} = \binom{\alpha_1}{3} - \alpha_1\alpha_2 + \alpha_3$$

and so

$$\begin{aligned}\{m-3, 1^3\}_{(a)} &= \tfrac{1}{6}\alpha_1(\alpha_1-1)(\alpha_1-2) - \alpha_1\alpha_2 + \alpha_3 \\ &\quad -\tfrac{1}{2}(\alpha_1-1)(\alpha_1-2) + \alpha_2 \\ &= \tfrac{1}{6}(\alpha_1-1)(\alpha_1-2)(\alpha_1-3) - (\alpha_1-1)\alpha_2 + \alpha_3.\end{aligned}$$

The same argument furnishes a formula for $\{m-k, 1^k\}$. Thus

$$\begin{aligned}\{m-4, 1^4\}_{(a)} &= \binom{\alpha_1}{4} - \binom{\alpha_1}{2}\alpha_2 + \alpha_1\alpha_3 + \binom{\alpha_2}{2} - \alpha_4 \\ &\quad -\tfrac{1}{6}(\alpha_1-1)(\alpha_1-2)(\alpha_1-3) + (\alpha_1-1)\alpha_2 - \alpha_3 \\ &= 1/24\,(\alpha_1-1)(\alpha_1-2)(\alpha_1-3)(\alpha_1-4) \\ &\quad -\tfrac{1}{2}(\alpha_1-1)(\alpha_1-2)\alpha_2 + (\alpha_1-1)\alpha_3 \\ &\quad +\tfrac{1}{2}\alpha_2(\alpha_2-1) - \alpha_4.\end{aligned}$$

To obtain a formula for the characters of $\{m-4, 2, 1^2\}$ we expand the four-rowed determinant which furnishes $\{m-4, 2, 1^2\}$ in terms of the first column obtaining

$$\{m-4, 2, 1^2\} = q_{m-4}\{2, 1^2\} - \{m-3, 1^2\}\{1\}.$$

Since the characters of $\{2, 1^2\}$ are $(3, -1, 0, -1, 1)$ the coefficient of $\frac{1}{\alpha_1!\cdots\alpha_m!}\left(\frac{s_1}{1}\right)^{\alpha_1}\cdots\left(\frac{s_m}{m}\right)^{\alpha_m}$ in the product $q_{m-4}\{2, 1^2\}$ is $3\binom{\alpha_1}{4} - \binom{\alpha_1}{2}\alpha_2 - \binom{\alpha_2}{2} + \alpha_4$. If $(\alpha') = (\alpha_1 - 1, \cdots, \alpha_m)$ is any class of the symmetric group on $m-1$ letters the coefficient of $\frac{1}{\alpha'_1!\cdots\alpha_m!}\left(\frac{s_1}{1}\right)^{\alpha'_1}\cdots\left(\frac{s_m}{m}\right)^{\alpha_m}$ in $\{m-3, 1^2\}$ is

$$\tfrac{1}{2}(\alpha'_1-1)(\alpha'_1-2) - \alpha_2 = \tfrac{1}{2}(\alpha_1-2)(\alpha_1-3) - \alpha_2$$

and so the coefficient of $\frac{1}{\alpha_1!\cdots\alpha_m!}\left(\frac{s_1}{1}\right)^{\alpha_1}\cdots\left(\frac{s_m}{m}\right)^{\alpha_m}$ in the product

$\{m-3, 1^2\}\{1\}$ is $\frac{1}{2}\alpha_1(\alpha_1-2)(\alpha_1-3)-\alpha_1\alpha_2$. Hence

$$\begin{aligned}\{m-4, 2, 1^2\}_{(a)} &= 3\binom{\alpha_1}{4}-\binom{\alpha_1}{2}\alpha_2-\binom{\alpha_2}{2}+\alpha_4\\ &\quad -\tfrac{1}{2}\alpha_1(\alpha_1-2)(\alpha_1-3)+\alpha_1\alpha_2\\ &= \tfrac{1}{8}\alpha_1(\alpha_1-2)(\alpha_1-3)(\alpha_1-5)\\ &\quad -\tfrac{1}{2}\alpha_1(\alpha_1-3)\alpha_2-\tfrac{1}{2}\alpha_2(\alpha_2-1)+\alpha_4.\end{aligned}$$

With the aid of these formulae we may write down the character tables for the symmetric groups on seven and eight letters. They are

$m=7$.

	$\{7\}$	$\{6,1\}$	$\{5,2\}$	$\{5,1^2\}$	$\{4,3\}$	$\{4,2,1\}$	$\{4,1^3\}^*$	$\{3^2,1\}$	
$(1^7)^+$	1	6	14	15	14	35	20	21	1
$(1^5,2)^-$	1	4	6	5	4	5	0	1	21
$(1^4,3)^+$	1	3	2	3	-1	-1	2	-3	70
$(1^3,2^2)^+$	1	2	2	-1	2	-1	-4	1	105
$(1^3,4)^-$	1	2	0	1	-2	-1	0	-1	210
$(1^2,2,3)^-$	1	1	0	-1	1	-1	0	1	420
$(1^2,5)^+$	1	1	-1	0	-1	0	0	1	504
$(1,2^3)^-$	1	0	2	-3	0	1	0	-3	105
$(1,2,4)^+$	1	0	0	-1	0	1	0	-1	630
$(1,3^2)^+$	1	0	-1	0	2	-1	2	0	280
$(1,6)^-$	1	0	-1	0	0	1	0	0	840
$(2^2,3)^+$	1	-1	2	-1	-1	-1	2	1	210
$(2,5)^-$	1	-1	1	0	-1	0	0	1	504
$(3,4)^-$	1	-1	0	1	1	-1	0	-1	420
$(7)^+$	1	-1	0	1	0	0	-1	0	720

$m = 8.$

	$\{8\}$	$\{7,1\}$	$\{6,2\}$	$\{6,1^2\}$	$\{5,3\}$	$\{5,2,1\}$	$\{5,1^3\}$	$\{4^2\}$	$\{4,3,1\}$	$\{4,2^2\}$	$\{4,2,1^2\}^*$	$\{3^2,2\}^*$	
$(1^8)^+$	1	7	20	21	28	64	35	14	70	56	90	42	1
$(1^6,2)^-$	1	5	10	9	10	16	5	4	10	4	0	0	28
$(1^5,3)^+$	1	4	5	6	1	4	5	−1	−5	−4	0	−6	112
$(1^4,2^2)^+$	1	3	4	1	4	0	−5	2	2	0	−6	2	210
$(1^4,4)^-$	1	3	2	3	−2	0	1	−2	−4	0	0	0	420
$(1^3,2,3)^-$	1	2	1	0	1	−2	−1	1	1	−2	0	0	1120
$(1^3,5)^+$	1	2	0	1	−2	−1	0	−1	0	1	0	2	1344
$(1^2,2^3)^-$	1	1	2	−3	2	0	−3	0	−2	4	0	0	420
$(1^2,2,4)^+$	1	1	0	−1	0	0	−1	0	0	0	2	−2	2520
$(1^2,3^2)^+$	1	1	−1	0	1	−2	2	2	1	−1	0	0	1120
$(1^2,6)^-$	1	1	−1	0	−1	0	0	0	1	1	0	0	3360
$(1,2^2,3)^+$	1	0	1	−2	1	0	1	−1	−1	0	0	2	1680
$(1,2,5)^-$	1	0	0	−1	0	1	0	−1	0	−1	0	0	4032
$(1,3,4)^-$	1	0	−1	0	1	0	1	1	−1	0	0	0	3360
$(1,7)^+$	1	0	−1	0	0	1	0	0	0	0	−1	0	5760
$(2^4)^+$	1	−1	4	−3	−4	0	3	6	−2	8	−6	−6	105
$(2^2,4)^-$	1	−1	2	−1	−2	0	1	2	0	0	0	0	1260
$(2,3^2)^-$	1	−1	1	0	1	−2	2	−2	1	1	0	0	1120
$(2,6)^+$	1	−1	1	0	−1	0	0	0	1	−1	0	0	3360
$(3,5)^+$	1	−1	0	1	1	−1	0	−1	0	1	0	−1	2688
$(4^2)^+$	1	−1	0	1	0	0	−1	2	−2	0	2	2	1260
$(8)^-$	1	−1	0	1	0	0	−1	0	0	0	0	0	5040

3. The analysis of the reducible representations $\Delta(\lambda)$ of the symmetric group on m letters.

$$\text{Since } \{\lambda\} = \begin{vmatrix} q_{\lambda_1}(s) & & & \\ & q_{\lambda_2}(s) & & \\ & & \ddots & \\ & & & q_{\lambda_k}(s) \end{vmatrix}$$

the irreducible representation $D(\lambda)$ is a linear combination of the reducible representations $\Delta(\lambda')$; no (λ') which follows (λ) occurring in the linear combination; moreover the coefficient of $\Delta(\lambda)$ in the linear combination is unity. Hence the matrix transforming the $\Delta(\lambda)$ into the $D(\lambda)$ is a triangle matrix all of whose diagonal elements are unity (the elements above the diagonal being zero). The determinant of this matrix is unity and so the $\Delta(\lambda)$ may be expressed in terms of the $D(\lambda)$ by merely transposing terms from one side of a system of linear equations to another. Thus we have the equations:

$$\begin{aligned}
D(m) &= \Delta(m) \\
D(m-1,1) &= -\Delta(m) + \Delta(m-1,1) \\
D(m-2,2) &= -\Delta(m-1,1) + \Delta(m-2,2) \\
D(m-2,1^2) &= \Delta(m) - \Delta(m-1,1) - \Delta(m-2,2) \\
&\qquad + \Delta(m-2,1^2) \\
D(m-3,3) &= -\Delta(m-2,2) + \Delta(m-3,3) \\
D(m-3,2,1) &= \Delta(m-1,1) - \Delta(m-2,1^2) - \Delta(m-3,3) \\
&\qquad + \Delta(m-3,2,1) \\
D(m-3,1^3) &= -\Delta(m) + \Delta(m-1,1) + \Delta(m-2,2) \\
&\qquad - \Delta(m-2,1^2) + \Delta(m-3,3) \\
&\qquad - 2\Delta(m-3,2,1) + \Delta(m-3,1^3).
\end{aligned}$$

The last of these equations, if calculated directly, would require the expansion of the fourth order determinant which furnishes $\{m-3,1^3\}$. On expanding this determinant in terms of the first column we find $\{m-3,1^3\} = q_{m-3}(s)\{1^3\} - \{m-2,1^2\}$. On setting $m = 3$ in the formula already given for $\{m-2,1^2\}$ we find

$$\{1^3\} = (3) - (2,1) - (1,2) + (1^3)$$

where we denote by (λ) the *characteristic* $q_{\lambda_1}(s)q_{\lambda_2}(s)\cdots q_{\lambda_k}(s)$ of $\Delta(\lambda)$ so that, for example, $(1,2)=(2,1)$; hence

$$\{1^3\}=(3)-2(2,1)+(1^3)$$

so that $(m-3)\{1^3\}=(m-3,3)-2(m-3,2,1)+(m-3,1^3)$ it being evident, for example, that $(m-3)(2,1)=(m-3,2,1)$ both being $q_{m-3}(s)q_2(s)q_1(s)$. On using the equation already given for $D(m-2,1^2)$ we find

$$\{m-2,1^2\}=(m)-(m-1,1)-(m-2,2)+(m-2,1^2)$$

and the expression given for $\{m-3,1^3\}$ follows at once.

On solving for $\Delta(\lambda)$ the equations given above we find

$$\begin{aligned}
\Delta(m) &= D(m)\\
\Delta(m-1,1) &= D(m)+D(m-1,1)\\
\Delta(m-2,2) &= D(m)+D(m-1,1)+D(m-2,2)\\
\Delta(m-2,1^2) &= D(m)+2D(m-1,1)+D(m-2,2)\\
&\quad +D(m-2,1^2)\\
\Delta(m-3,3) &= D(m)+D(m-1,1)+D(m-2,2)\\
&\quad +D(m-3,3)\\
\Delta(m-3,2,1) &= D(m)+2D(m-1,1)+2D(m-2,2)\\
&\quad +D(m-2,1^2)+D(m-3,3)\\
&\quad +D(m-3,2,1)\\
\Delta(m-3,1^3) &= D(m)+3D(m-1,1)+3D(m-2,2)\\
&\quad +3D(m-2,1^2)+D(m-3,3)\\
&\quad +2D(m-3,2,1)+D(m-3,1^3).
\end{aligned}$$

It is understood that if the arrangement of (λ) in any of the $D(\lambda)$ on the right is not the normal non-increasing order this normal order is restored in the usual way (so that, for instance, if any of the $\lambda_j=\lambda_{j-1}+1$ the term $D(\lambda)$ is dropped). It will be convenient to drop the symbols D and Δ and to denote the irreducible representations $D(\lambda)$ by $\{\lambda\}$ and the reducible representations $\Delta(\lambda)$ by (λ). Thus we read from the few formulae already given:

$m=1$; $\quad\{1\}=(1)$; $(1)=\{1\}$

$m=2$; $\quad\{2\}=(2)$; $(2)=\{2\}$
$\quad\{1^2\}=-(2)+(1^2)$; $(1^2)=\{2\}+\{1^2\}$

$$m=3; \quad \{3\}=(3);\ (3)=\{3\}$$
$$\{2,1\}=-(3)+(2,1);\ (2,1)=\{3\}+\{2,1\}$$
$$\{1^3\}=(3)-2(2,1)+(1^3);\ (1^3)=\{3\}+2\{2,1\}+\{1^3\}$$
$$m=4; \quad \{4\}=(4);\ (4)=\{4\}$$
$$\{3,1\}=-(4)+(3,1);\ (3,1)=\{4\}+\{3,1\}$$
$$\{2^2\}=-(3,1)+(2^2);\ (2^2)=\{4\}+\{3,1\}+\{2^2\}$$
$$\{2,1^2\}=(4)-(3,1)-(2^2)+(2,1^2);$$
$$(2,1^2)=\{4\}+2\{3,1\}+\{2^2\}+\{2,1^2\}$$
$$\{1^4\}=-(4)+2(3,1)+(2^2)-3(2,1^2)+(1^4);$$
$$(1^4)=\{4\}+3\{3,1\}+2\{2^2\}+3\{2,1^2\}+\{1^4\}.$$

We give below two tables, one the reciprocal of the other, the first of which expresses the $D(\lambda)$ in terms of the $\Delta(\lambda)$ as far as $(m-6, 1^6)$ and the second of which expresses the $\Delta(\lambda)$ in terms of the $D(\lambda)$ again as far as $(m-6, 1^6)$. In reading these tables turn the page so that the left-hand side becomes the top of the page.

Table 1. Furnishing $D(\lambda)$ as linear combinations of the $\Delta(\lambda)$.

	(m)	$(m-1,1)$	$(m-2,2)$	$(m-2,1^2)$	$(m-3,3)$	$(m-3,2,1)$	$(m-3,1^3)$	$(m-4,4)$	$(m-4,3,1)$	$(m-4,2^2)$	$(m-4,2,1^2)$	$(m-4,1^4)$	$(m-5,5)$	$(m-5,4,1)$	$(m-5,3,2)$	$(m-5,3,1^2)$	$(m-5,2^2,1)$	$(m-5,2,1^3)$	$(m-5,1^5)$	$(m-6,6)$	$(m-6,5,1)$	$(m-6,4,2)$	$(m-6,4,1^2)$	$(m-6,3^2)$	$(m-6,3,2,1)$	$(m-6,3,1^3)$	$(m-6,2^3)$	$(m-6,2^2,1^2)$	$(m-6,2,1^4)$	$(m-6,1^6)$
$\{m\}$	1																													
$\{m-1,1\}$	−1	1																												
$\{m-2,2\}$	0	−1	1																											
$\{m-2,1^2\}$	1	−1	−1	1																										
$\{m-3,3\}$	0	0	−1	0	1																									
$\{m-3,2,1\}$	0	1	0	−1	−1	1																								
$\{m-3,1^3\}$	−1	1	1	−1	1	−2	1																							
$\{m-4,4\}$	0	0	0	0	−1	0	0	1																						
$\{m-4,3,1\}$	0	0	1	0	0	−1	0	−1	1																					
$\{m-4,2^2\}$	0	0	−1	1	1	−1	0	0	−1	1																				
$\{m-4,2,1^2\}$	0	−1	0	1	0	1	−1	1	−1	−1	1																			
$\{m-4,1^4\}$	1	−1	−1	1	−1	2	−1	−1	2	1	−3	1																		
$\{m-5,5\}$	0	0	0	0	0	0	0	−1	0	0	0	0	1																	
$\{m-5,4,1\}$	0	0	0	0	1	0	0	0	−1	0	0	0	−1	1																
$\{m-5,3,2\}$	0	0	0	0	−1	1	0	1	0	−1	0	0	0	−1	1															
$\{m-5,3,1^2\}$	0	0	−1	0	0	1	0	0	0	1	−1	0	1	−1	−1	1														
$\{m-5,2^2,1\}$	0	0	1	−1	0	−1	1	−1	2	0	−1	0	0	1	−1	−1	1													
$\{m-5,2,1^3\}$	0	1	0	−1	0	−1	1	0	−1	0	2	−1	−1	1	2	−1	−2	1												
$\{m-5,1^5\}$	−1	1	1	−1	1	−2	1	1	−2	−1	3	−1	1	−2	−2	3	3	−4	1											
$\{m-6,6\}$	0	0	0	0	0	0	0	0	0	0	0	0	−1	0	0	0	0	0	0	1										
$\{m-6,5,1\}$	0	0	0	0	0	0	0	1	0	0	0	0	0	−1	0	0	0	0	0	−1	1									
$\{m-6,4,2\}$	0	0	0	0	0	0	0	−1	1	0	0	0	1	0	−1	0	0	0	0	0	−1	1								
$\{m-6,4,1^2\}$	0	0	0	0	−1	0	0	0	1	0	0	0	0	0	1	−1	0	0	0	1	−1	−1	1							
$\{m-6,3^2\}$	0	0	0	0	0	0	0	0	−1	1	0	0	0	1	−1	0	0	0	0	0	0	−1	0	1						
$\{m-6,3,2,1\}$	0	0	0	0	1	−1	0	0	−1	0	1	0	−1	1	1	0	−1	0	0	0	1	0	−1	−1	1					
$\{m-6,3,1^3\}$	0	0	1	0	0	−1	0	0	0	−1	1	0	0	0	−1	0	2	−1	0	−1	1	1	−1	+1	−2	1				
$\{m-6,2^3\}$	0	0	0	0	−1	2	−1	1	−1	−1	1	0	0	−1	1	1	−1	0	0	0	0	−1	1	1	−2	0	1			
$\{m-6,2^2,1^2\}$	0	0	−1	1	0	1	−1	0	0	1	−2	1	1	−2	−1	2	1	−1	0	0	−1	1	1	0	0	−1	−1	1		
$\{m-6,2,1^4\}$	0	−1	0	1	0	1	−1	0	1	0	−2	1	0	1	0	−2	−1	3	−1	1	−1	−2	1	−1	4	−1	1	−3	1	
$\{m-6,1^6\}$	1	−1	−1	1	−1	2	−1	−1	2	1	−3	1	−1	2	2	−3	−3	4	−1	−1	2	2	−3	1	−6	4	−1	6	−5	1

Table 2. Furnishing $\Delta(\lambda)$ as linear combinations of the $D(\lambda)$.

	$\{m\}$	$\{m-1,1\}$	$\{m-2,2\}$	$\{m-2,1^2\}$	$\{m-3,3\}$	$\{m-3,2,1\}$	$\{m-3,1^3\}$	$\{m-4,4\}$	$\{m-4,3,1\}$	$\{m-4,2^2\}$	$\{m-4,2,1^2\}$	$\{m-4,1^4\}$	$\{m-5,5\}$	$\{m-5,4,1\}$	$\{m-5,3,2\}$	$\{m-5,3,1^2\}$	$\{m-5,2^2,1\}$	$\{m-5,2,1^3\}$	$\{m-5,1^5\}$	$\{m-6,6\}$	$\{m-6,5,1\}$	$\{m-6,4,2\}$	$\{m-6,4,1^2\}$	$\{m-6,3^2\}$	$\{m-6,3,2,1\}$	$\{m-6,3,1^3\}$	$\{m-6,2^3\}$	$\{m-6,2^2,1^2\}$	$\{m-6,2,1^4\}$	$\{m-6,1^6\}$
(m)	1																													
$(m-1,1)$	1	1																												
$(m-2,2)$	1	1	1																											
$(m-2,1^2)$	1	2	1	1																										
$(m-3,3)$	1	1	1	0	1																									
$(m-3,2,1)$	1	2	2	1	1	1																								
$(m-3,1^3)$	1	3	3	3	1	2	1																							
$(m-4,4)$	1	1	1	0	1	0	0	1																						
$(m-4,3,1)$	1	2	2	1	2	1	0	1	1																					
$(m-4,2^2)$	1	2	3	1	2	2	0	1	1	1																				
$(m-4,2,1^2)$	1	3	4	3	3	4	1	1	2	1	1																			
$(m-4,1^4)$	1	4	6	6	4	8	4	1	3	2	3	1																		
$(m-5,5)$	1	1	1	0	1	0	0	1	0	0	0	0	1																	
$(m-5,4,1)$	1	2	2	1	2	1	0	2	1	0	0	0	1	1																
$(m-5,3,2)$	1	2	3	1	3	2	0	2	2	1	0	0	1	1	1															
$(m-5,3,1^2)$	1	3	4	3	4	4	1	3	4	1	1	0	1	2	1	1														
$(m-5,2^2,1)$	1	3	5	3	5	6	1	3	5	3	2	0	1	2	2	1	1													
$(m-5,2,1^3)$	1	4	7	6	7	11	4	4	9	5	6	1	1	3	3	3	2	1												
$(m-5,1^5)$	1	5	10	10	10	20	10	5	15	10	15	5	1	4	5	6	5	4	1											
$(m-6,6)$	1	1	1	0	1	0	0	1	0	0	0	0	1	0	0	0	0	0	0	1										
$(m-6,5,1)$	1	2	2	1	2	1	0	2	1	0	0	0	2	1	0	0	0	0	0	1	1									
$(m-6,4,2)$	1	2	3	1	3	2	0	3	2	1	0	0	2	2	1	0	0	0	0	1	1	1								
$(m-6,4,1^2)$	1	3	4	3	4	4	1	4	4	1	1	0	3	4	1	1	0	0	0	1	2	1	1							
$(m-6,3^2)$	1	2	3	1	4	2	0	3	3	1	0	0	2	2	2	0	0	0	0	1	1	1	0	1						
$(m-6,3,2,1)$	1	3	5	3	6	6	1	5	7	3	2	0	3	5	4	2	1	0	0	1	2	2	1	1	1					
$(m-6,3,1^3)$	1	4	7	6	8	11	4	7	12	5	6	1	4	9	6	6	2	1	0	1	3	3	3	1	2	1				
$(m-6,2^3)$	1	3	6	3	7	8	1	6	9	6	3	0	3	6	6	3	3	0	0	1	2	3	1	1	2	0	1			
$(m-6,2^2,1^2)$	1	4	8	6	10	14	4	8	16	9	9	1	4	10	10	8	6	2	0	1	3	4	3	2	4	1	1	1		
$(m-6,2,1^4)$	1	5	11	10	14	24	10	11	27	16	21	5	5	16	17	18	13	8	1	1	4	6	6	3	8	4	2	3	1	
$(m-6,1^6)$	1	6	15	15	20	40	20	15	45	30	45	15	6	24	30	36	30	24	6	1	5	9	10	5	16	10	5	9	5	1

Table 2 furnishes the analysis of all $\Delta(\lambda)$ for the symmetric groups up to $m \leqq 8$ save for the single representation $\Delta(1^8)$. But this is the regular representation of the symmetric group on 8 letters so that its analysis is given by (3.13) the coefficients d_k being furnished by the top row of the table on page 149. The only representations of the symmetric group on 9 letters which are not cared for by Table 2 are $\Delta(2^4, 1)$, $\Delta(2^3, 1^3)$, $\Delta(2^2, 1^5)$, $\Delta(2, 1^7)$ and the regular representation $\Delta(1^9)$. We have given elsewhere (*American Journal of Mathematics*, **59**, pp. 475-477 (1937)) the complete tables furnishing the analysis of $\Delta(\lambda)$ for all $m \leqq 9$. However, the single Table 2 given above has the advantage over the various tables there given that it is a master table available for *all* values of m. In reading it one must remember the rule about rearranging disordered partitions and we treat an example, namely $\Delta(3, 2^3)$. Table 2 gives, on setting $m = 9$,

$$\begin{aligned}\Delta(3, 2^3) = {} & \{9\} + 3\{8,1\} + 6\{7,2\} + 3\{7,1^2\} + 7\{6,3\} + 8\{6,2,1\} \\ & + \{6,1^3\} + 6\{5,4\} + 9\{5,3,1\} + 6\{5,2^2\} + 3\{5,2,1^2\} \\ & + 3\{4,5\} + 6\{4^2,1\} + 6\{4,3,2\} + 3\{4,3,1^2\} + 3\{4,2^2,1\} \\ & + \{3,6\} + 2\{3,5,1\} + 3\{3,4,2\} + \{3,4,1^2\} + \{3^3\} \\ & + 2\{3^2,2,1\} + \{3,2^3\}.\end{aligned}$$

The terms $3\{4,5\}$, $3\{3,4,2\}$, $\{3,4,1^2\}$ on the right must be dropped whilst $\{3,6\}$ must be replaced by $-\{5,4\}$ and $2\{3,5,1\}$ by $-2\{4^2,1\}$. The final result is, therefore,

$$\begin{aligned}\Delta(3, 2^3) = {} & \{9\} + 3\{8,1\} + 6\{7,2\} + 3\{7,1^2\} + 7\{6,3\} + 8\{6,2,1\} \\ & + \{6,1^3\} + 5\{5,4\} + 9\{5,3,1\} + 6\{5,2^2\} + 3\{5,2,1^2\} \\ & + 4\{4^2,1\} + 6\{4,3,2\} + 3\{4,3,1^2\} + 3\{4,2^2,1\} + \{3^3\} \\ & + 2\{3^2,2,1\} + \{3,2^3\}.\end{aligned}$$

4. The analysis of the direct product of irreducible representations of the symmetric groups.

Let m', m'' be any two positive integers and let $(\lambda') = (\lambda'_1, \cdots, \lambda'_{m'})$, $(\lambda'') = (\lambda''_1, \cdots, \lambda''_{m''})$ be any partitions of m' and m'' respectively:

$$\begin{aligned}&\lambda'_1 \geqq \lambda'_2 \geqq \cdots \geqq \lambda'_{m'} \geqq 0; \quad \lambda'_1 + \lambda'_2 + \cdots + \lambda'_{m'} = m' \\ &\lambda''_1 \geqq \lambda''_2 \geqq \cdots \geqq \lambda''_{m''} \geqq 0; \quad \lambda''_1 + \lambda''_2 + \cdots + \lambda''_{m''} = m''.\end{aligned}$$

Then $D(\lambda')$ and $D(\lambda'')$ are irreducible representations of the symmetric groups on m' and m'' letters, respectively, and their Kronecker product $D(\lambda') \times D(\lambda'')$ is an irreducible representation of the direct product of these two groups (p. 101). This direct product of the two symmetric groups is a subgroup of the symmetric group on $m' + m''$ letters;

namely the subgroup consisting of those permutations which do not send any one of the m' letters into any one of the m'' letters (or, equivalently, the subgroup which consists of the permutations on m letters which permute the letters of each of the two sets, one consisting of m' and the other of m'' letters, amongst themselves). If (α'), (α'') are any classes of the symmetric groups on m' and m'' letters, respectively, $(\alpha) = (\alpha') + (\alpha'')$ is a class of the symmetric group on m letters; the equation $(\alpha) = (\alpha') + (\alpha'')$ meaning $\alpha_j = \alpha'_j + \alpha''_j$, $j = 1, 2, \cdots, m$, where $\alpha'_j = 0$ if $j > m'$ and $\alpha''_j = 0$ if $j > m''$. Furthermore $((\alpha'), (\alpha''))$ is a class of the direct product of the symmetric groups on m' and m'' letters and the character of the irreducible representation $D(\lambda') \times D(\lambda'')$ of this direct product which is attached to the class $((\alpha'), (\alpha''))$ of the direct product is $\{\lambda'\}_{(\alpha')}\{\lambda''\}_{(\alpha'')}$; hence the simple characteristic of the direct product is

$$\frac{1}{m'!\,m''!}\sum_{(\alpha')(\alpha'')} n_{(\alpha')}n_{(\alpha'')}\{\lambda'\}_{(\alpha')}\{\lambda''\}_{(\alpha'')}(s')^{(\alpha')}(s'')^{(\alpha'')}$$

where

$$n_{(\alpha')} = \frac{m'!}{1^{\alpha'_1}\alpha'_1!\cdots m'^{\alpha'_{m'}}\cdot\alpha'_{m'}!},\quad n_{(\alpha'')} = \frac{m''!}{1^{\alpha''_1}\alpha''_1!\cdots m''^{\alpha''_{m''}}\cdot\alpha''_{m''}!}$$

$$(s')^{(\alpha')} = (s'_1)^{\alpha'_1}\cdots(s'_{m'})^{\alpha'_{m'}};\qquad (s'')^{(\alpha'')} = (s''_1)^{\alpha''_1}\cdots(s''_{m''})^{\alpha''_{m''}}.$$

From this simple characteristic of the subgroup of the symmetric group on m letters, which is constituted by the direct product of the symmetric groups on m' and m'' letters, respectively, we may construct, by the method of p. 98, a characteristic, in general compound, of the symmetric group on m letters. To do this we have to identify the indeterminates $(s')^{(\alpha')}(s'')^{(\alpha'')}$ which are associated with the same class of the symmetric group on m letters; i. e. for which $(\alpha') + (\alpha'') = (\alpha)$. The character of the corresponding representation, in general reducible, of the symmetric group on m letters which is attached to the class (α) of this group is

$$\frac{m!}{m'!\,m''!}\sum_{(\alpha')+(\alpha'')=(\alpha)} n_{(\alpha')}n_{(\alpha'')}\{\lambda'\}_{(\alpha')}\{\lambda''\}_{(\alpha'')}$$

so that, in particular, the dimension of the representation, i. e. the character of the unit class, is

$$(5.11)\qquad d = \frac{m!}{m'!\,m''!}d'd''.$$

where d', d'' are the dimensions of $D(\lambda')$ and $D(\lambda'')$, respectively. Hence the characteristic of the representation in question (which we shall term the *direct product of* $D(\lambda')$ *and* $D(\lambda'')$) is

$$\frac{1}{m'!\,m''!}\sum_{(a)}\Big\{\sum_{(a')+(a'')=(a)} n_{(a')}n_{(a'')}\{\lambda'\}_{(a')}\{\lambda''\}_{(a'')}\Big\}s^{(a)}$$

$$(5.12)\qquad =\frac{1}{m'!\,m''!}\sum_{(a')(a'')} n_{(a')}n_{(a'')}\{\lambda'\}_{(a')}\{\lambda''\}_{(a'')}s^{(a')+(a'')}$$

where, as usual

$$s^{(a)} = s_1^{a_1}\cdots s_m^{a_m}$$

and the s_k are the power sums of n independent variables $(z) = (z_1, \cdots, z_n)$:

$$s_k = z_1^k + \cdots + z_n^k; \qquad k = 1, 2, \cdots, m;$$

the summation in (5.12) being over *all* classes (α') of the symmetric group on m' letters and *all* classes (α'') of the symmetric group on m'' letters. If we replace (s') and (s'') in the simple characteristics $\phi_{(\lambda')}(s')$, $\phi_{(\lambda'')}(s'')$ by (s) the expression (5.12) is the product $\phi_{(\lambda')}(s)\cdot\phi_{(\lambda'')}(s)$ or, as we shall write it, $\{\lambda'\}\cdot\{\lambda''\}$. Hence the product of a simple characteristic $\{\lambda'\}$ of the symmetric group on m' letters by a simple characteristic $\{\lambda''\}$ of the symmetric group on m'' letters is a characteristic, in general compound, of the symmetric group on $m = m' + m''$ letters; it being understood that the indeterminates (s) which appear in the simple characteristics $\{\lambda'\}$ and $\{\lambda''\}$ are power sums of m variables z. Our concern in the present section is the analysis of the representation of the symmetric group on m letters which is obtained in this way into its irreducible components. We know that $\{\lambda'\}(s)$ is the character $\chi'(A)$ of an irreducible homogeneous rational integral representation of degree m' of the full linear group on n variables (p. 106); the indeterminates (s) being defined by $s_k = Tr(A^k)$ so that the $(z) = (z_1, \cdots, z_n)$ are the characteristic numbers of A. The same remark may be made concerning $\{\lambda''\}(s)$ and so the product $\{\lambda'\}\cdot\{\lambda''\}$ is the character $\chi(A) = \chi'(A)\chi''(A)$ of the Kronecker product of the two irreducible representations in question; this Kronecker product being a homogeneous rational integral representation, in general reducible, of degree $m' + m'' = m$ of the full linear group on n variables. In other words the analysis of the direct product of $D(\lambda')$ and $D(\lambda'')$ is equally the analysis of the Kronecker product of the corresponding representations of the full linear group.

In order to obtain the desired analysis of the direct product of $D(\lambda')$ and $D(\lambda'')$ we shall first generalize the fundamental recurrence formula (5.2). Let ξ_j, $j = 1, \cdots, m$, be an operator which reduces by 1 the

j-th element λ_j of (λ); then $\xi_j{}^p$ reduces this element by p: $\xi_j{}^p\{\lambda\} = \{\lambda_1, \lambda_2, \cdots, \lambda_j - p, \cdots, \lambda_m\}$ and we may rewrite (5.2) in the form

$$\{\lambda\}_{(\alpha)} = [\sum_{j=1}^{m} \xi_j{}^p\{\lambda\}]_{(\alpha')} = [\sigma_p\{\lambda\}]_{(\alpha')}$$

where $\sigma_p = \xi_1{}^p + \cdots + \xi_m{}^p$, $p = 1, \cdots, m$. (α') is that class of the symmetric group on $m - p$ letters which contains one less cycle on p letters than does the class (α) of the symmetric group on m letters; we may express the result of (5.2) by the statement that *we have stripped off one cycle on p letters.* We may now strip off a further cycle on q letters from each of the $[\xi_j{}^p\{\lambda\}]_{(\alpha')}$ and we obtain

$$\{\lambda\}_{(\alpha)} = [\sigma_q\sigma_p\{\lambda\}]_{(\alpha')}$$

where, now, (α') is that class of the symmetric group on $m - p - q$ letters which contains one less cycle on p letters and one less cycle on q letters than does the class (α) of the symmetric group on m letters; we say that we have stripped off one cycle on p letters and one cycle on q letters (or two cycles on p letters if $q = p$). Continuing this process we may strip off α_1'' cycles on one letter, α_2'' cycles on two letters and so on and obtain

$$\{\lambda\}_{(\alpha)} = [\sigma^{(\alpha'')}\{\lambda\}]_{(\alpha')}; \quad \sigma^{(\alpha'')} = \sigma_1{}^{\alpha_1''} \cdots \sigma_{m''}{}^{\alpha''_{m''}}$$

where $(\alpha'') = (\alpha_1'', \alpha_2'', \cdots)$ is any class of the symmetric group on m'' letters (i.e. $\alpha_1'' + 2\alpha_2'' + \cdots + m''\alpha_{m''} = m''$) and (α') is that class of the symmetric group on $m' = m - m''$ letters which contains α_1'' less unary cycles, α_2'' less binary cycles and so on, than does the class (α) of the symmetric group on m letters. In other words

$$\{\lambda\}_{(\alpha)} = [\sigma^{(\alpha'')}\{\lambda\}]_{(\alpha')}; \quad (\alpha) = (\alpha'') + (\alpha'), \tag{5.13}$$

and we may say that we have stripped off a class (α'') of the symmetric group on m'' letters.

Since the quantities $s^{(\alpha)} = s_1{}^{\alpha_1} s_2{}^{\alpha_2} \cdots s_n{}^{\alpha_n}$ are the indeterminates $(f^1, \cdots, f^p)$ which occur in the definition of the simple characteristics of the symmetric group on m letters (p. 106) it follows from (4.7) that

$$s^{(\alpha)} = \sum_{(\lambda)} \chi^{(\alpha)}_{(\lambda)} \phi_{(\lambda)}(s) = \sum_{(\lambda)} \{\lambda\}_{(\alpha)} \phi_{(\lambda)}(s) \tag{5.14}$$

and so (5.13) may be written in the form

$$\{\lambda\}_{(\alpha)} = [\sum_{(\mu'')} (\{\mu''\}_{(\alpha'')} \phi_{(\mu'')}(\sigma)) \{\lambda\}]_{(\alpha')}, \tag{5.15}$$

the summation on the right being over *all* partitions (μ'') of m'' letters and (α''), (α') being *any* two classes of the symmetric groups on m'' and m' letters, respectively, whose sum $(\alpha'') + (\alpha')$ is the class (α) of the symmetric group on $m = m'' + m'$ letters. On substituting for $s^{(\alpha)}$ in (5.12) its value as given in (5.14) we find that the characteristic of the direct product of $D(\lambda')$ and $D(\lambda'')$ is

$$\frac{1}{m'!\,m''!} \sum_{(\alpha'),(\alpha'')} n_{(\alpha')} n_{(\alpha'')} \{\lambda'\}_{(\alpha')} \{\lambda''\}_{(\alpha'')} \sum_{(\lambda)} \{\lambda\}_{(\alpha')+(\alpha'')} \phi_{(\lambda)}(s)$$

$$= \frac{1}{m'!\,m''!} \sum_{(\alpha'),(\alpha'')} n_{(\alpha')} n_{(\alpha'')} \{\lambda'\}_{(\alpha')} \{\lambda''\}_{(\alpha'')} \times$$

$$\sum_{(\lambda)} [(\sum_{(\mu'')} \{\mu''\}_{(\alpha'')} \phi_{(\mu'')}(\sigma)) \{\lambda\}]_{(\alpha')} \phi_{(\lambda)}(s).$$

On summing with respect to (α''), over all classes of the symmetric group on m'' letters, we obtain (since $\frac{1}{m''!} \sum_{(\alpha'')} n_{(\alpha'')} \{\lambda''\}_{(\alpha'')} \{\mu''\}_{(\alpha'')} = 0$ save when $(\mu'') = (\lambda'')$, in which case it is unity, by (3.16))

$$\frac{1}{m'!} \sum_{(\alpha')} n_{(\alpha')} \{\lambda'\}_{(\alpha')} \{\sum_{(\lambda)} [\phi_{(\lambda'')}(\sigma) \{\lambda\}]_{(\alpha')} \phi_{(\lambda)}(s).$$

Now $\phi_{(\lambda'')}(\sigma)$ is a symmetric function of degree m'' in the m operators ξ_j, $j = 1, 2, \cdots, m$; let us write it $\Sigma c_{(\mu'')} T_{(\mu'')}(\xi)$ where

(5.16) $$T_{(\mu'')}(z) = \Sigma (z)^{(\mu'')} = \Sigma z_1^{\mu_1''} \cdots z_m^{\mu''_m};$$

then

$$\phi_{(\lambda'')}(\sigma) \{\lambda\} = \sum_{(\mu'')} c_{(\mu'')} \{[(\lambda) - (\mu'')]\}$$

where $[(\lambda) - (\mu'')]$ indicates the result of subtracting (μ''), in *all* possible arrangements, from *each* set of m'' of the m elements of (λ). To take the simplest example let $m'' = 1$ so that $(\lambda'') = (1)$; then $\phi_{(\lambda'')}(\sigma) = \sigma_1 = \xi_1 + \xi_2 + \cdots + \xi_m$ and $\phi_{(\lambda'')}(\sigma)\{\lambda\} = \{\lambda_1 - 1, \cdots, \lambda_m\} + \cdots + \{\lambda_1, \cdots, \lambda_{m-1}, \lambda_m - 1\}$. Each member of $[(\lambda) - (\mu'')]$, when rearranged in the usual way if disordered, is a partition of m'; let (μ') be a typical one of these partitions of m'. Then, since $\frac{1}{m'!} \sum_{(\alpha')} n_{(\alpha')} \{\lambda'\}_{(\alpha')} \{\mu'\}_{(\alpha')}$ is zero unless $(\mu') = (\lambda')$, in which case it is unity, it is clear that those, and only those $\phi_{(\lambda)}(s)$ will occur in the analysis of the direct product of $D(\lambda')$ and $D(\lambda'')$ for which (λ) is obtained from (λ') (supposed written with m elements by the addition of m'' zeros) by adding (μ''), in all possible arrangements to each set of m'' of the m elements of (λ'); (μ'') running over those partitions of m'' which appear when $\phi_{(\lambda'')}(\sigma)$ is written as a linear combination of symmetric functions, of degree m'', of the m variables $(\xi_1, \cdots, \xi_m)$. In adding (μ'') to (λ') in this way we may well obtain a disordered partition of m; this is supposed to be rearranged in the usual way.

We illustrate this general result by the simplest example. Suppose $m''=1$ so that $(\lambda'')=(1)$; then $\phi_{(\lambda'')}(\sigma)=\phi_{(1)}(\sigma)=\sigma_1=\xi_1+\cdots+\xi_m$ so that $(\mu'')=(1)$. Then (λ') when written with m elements is $(\lambda'_1,\cdots,\lambda'_{m'},0)$ and hence

$$\{\lambda'\}\cdot\{1\}=\{\lambda'_1+1,\cdots,\lambda'_{m'}\}+\cdots+\{\lambda'_1,\cdots,\lambda'_{m'}+1\}+\{\lambda'_1,\cdots,\lambda'_{m'},1\}.$$

If $(\lambda')=(\lambda'_1,\cdots,\lambda'_k)$ contains only $k<m'$ non-zero elements we drop any term on the right in which a 1 is preceded by a zero. Dropping also the attached primes, as of no further service, we have the general result

$$(5.17)\quad \{\lambda_1,\cdots,\lambda_k\}\cdot\{1\}=\{\lambda_1+1,\lambda_2,\cdots,\lambda_k\}+\{\lambda_1,\lambda_2+1,\cdots,\lambda_k\}+\cdots+\{\lambda_1,\cdots,\lambda_k+1\}+\{\lambda_1,\cdots,\lambda_k,1\}.$$

This furnishes the analysis of the direct product of $D(\lambda)$ by $D(1)$ where (λ) is any partition of the symmetric group on m' letters. Since (5.17) is an identity in the variables $(s)=(s_1,\cdots,s_m)$, $m=m'+1$, it remains true when $s_2,s_4,s_6\cdots$ are replaced by their negatives. Hence if (μ) is that partition of m' which is associated with (λ) the direct product of $D(\mu)$ and $D(1)$ follows at once from that of $D(\lambda)$ and $D(1)$ by taking the associates of all the representations which occur in the latter. It is not necessary, therefore, to analyse both products and it is convenient to analyse the one for which (λ) follows its associate (μ) when the partitions are arranged in dictionary order.

Examples.

$\{1\}\cdot\{1\}=\{2\}+\{1^2\}$;

$\{2\}\cdot\{1\}=\{3\}+\{2,1\}$; implying $\{1^2\}\cdot\{1\}=\{1^3\}+\{2,1\}$;

$\{3\}\cdot\{1\}=\{4\}+\{3,1\}$; implying $\{1^3\}\cdot\{1\}=\{1^4\}+\{2,1^2\}$;

$\{2,1\}\cdot\{1\}=\{3,1\}+\{2^2\}+\{2,1^2\}$.

For less trivial direct products we use the fact that the representations occurring in the direct product of $D(\lambda')$ and $D(\lambda'')$ are the associates of those occurring in the direct product of $D(\mu')$ and $D(\mu'')$ (where (λ'), (μ') are associated partitions of m' and (λ''), (μ'') associated partitions of m'') to arrange that (λ'') is preceded by (if it is not identical with) its associate (μ'') when the partitions of m'' are arranged in dictionary order. It is also convenient to arrange the notation so that m' is greater than, if it is not equal to, m''. A general recurrence method is available and the essential points of this may be illustrated by considering the next simplest case, namely, $m'' = 2$, $(\lambda'') = (1^2)$. Then $\phi_{(\lambda'')}(\sigma) = \Sigma\xi_1\xi_2 = \xi_1\sigma^*_1 + \Sigma^*\xi_2\xi_3$ where the attached * indicates that the summation runs from 2 to m and *not* from 1 to m. Hence the product $\{\lambda'_1, \lambda'_2, \cdots, \lambda'_{k'}\} \cdot \{1^2\}$ may be expressed as the sum of two parts:

1. A part, corresponding to the term $\xi_1\sigma^*_1$ in $\phi_{(1^2)}(\sigma)$ and consisting of those $\{\lambda\}$ for which $\lambda_1 = \lambda'_1 + 1$ and for which the $(\lambda_2, \cdots, \lambda_m)$ are given by

$$\{\lambda'_2, \cdots, \lambda'_{k'}\}\{1\} = \{\lambda'_2 + 1, \cdots, \lambda'_{k'}\} + \cdots + \{\lambda'_2, \cdots, \lambda'_{k'} + 1\} + \{\lambda'_2, \cdots, \lambda'_{k'}, 1\}.$$

We may describe this part of our result by saying that we prefix $\lambda'_1 + 1$ to the product $\{\lambda'_2, \cdots, \lambda'_{k'}\}\{1\}$.

2. A part, corresponding to the term $\Sigma^*\xi_2\xi_3$ in $\phi_{(1^2)}(\sigma)$ in which λ'_1 is prefixed to the product $\{\lambda'_2, \cdots, \lambda'_{k'}\} \cdot \{1^2\}$. Since $\{0\} = 1$ it follows that $\{\lambda_1\} \cdot \{1^2\} = \{\lambda_1 + 1, 1\} + \{\lambda_1, 1^2\}$. An immediate application of the principle of mathematical induction gives the formula for $\{\lambda_1, \cdots, \lambda_k\} \cdot \{1^2\}$: *write* $\{\lambda_1, \cdots, \lambda_k\}$ *in the form* $\{\lambda_1, \cdots, \lambda_k, 0, 0\}$ *and add the pair* $(1, 1)$ *in all possible ways.*

Examples.

$\{2\} \cdot \{1^2\} = \{3, 1\} + \{2, 1^2\}$;

$\{1^2\} \cdot \{1^2\} = \{2^2\} + \{2, 1^2\} + \{1^4\}$; implying $\{2\} \cdot \{2\} = \{4\} + \{3, 1\} + \{2^2\}$;

$\{3\} \cdot \{1^2\} = \{4, 1\} + \{3, 1^2\}$; implying $\{1^3\} \cdot \{2\} = \{3, 1^2\} + \{2, 1^3\}$;

$\{2, 1\} \cdot \{1^2\} = \{3, 2\} + \{3, 1^2\} + \{2^2, 1\} + \{2, 1^3\}$; implying $\{2, 1\} \cdot \{2\} = \{4, 1\} + \{3, 2\} + \{3, 1^2\} + \{2^2, 1\}$;

$\{1^3\} \cdot \{1^2\} = \{2^2, 1\} + \{2, 1^3\} + \{1^5\}$; implying $\{3\} \cdot \{2\} = \{5\} + \{4, 1\} + \{3, 2\}$.

It is clear from the examples given that the problem of analysing $\{\lambda'\} \cdot \{\lambda''\}$ may be solved in the following manner. First express $\phi_{(\lambda'')}(\sigma)$ as a symmetric function of degree m'' in the operators $\{\xi_1, \cdots, \xi_m\}$ and write the result as a polynomial of degree not greater than m'' in ξ_1; next express each coefficient of this polynomial as a linear combination of the simple characteristics of the appropriate symmetric group (the coefficient of ξ_1^p being expressible as a linear combination of the simple characteristics of the symmetric group on $m'' - p$ letters). Then prefix $\lambda'_1 + p$ to each term occurring in the products of each of these simple characteristics by $\{\lambda''\}$ and add the various terms obtained in this way for the various values of p. There are, then, two essential steps in the procedure outlined:

1. The expression of each simple characteristic $\phi_{(\lambda'')}(s)$ of the sym-

metric group on m'' letters as a linear combination of the various symmetric functions $T_{(\mu'')}(z) = \Sigma z_1^{\mu_1''} \cdots z_{m''}^{\mu''_{m''}}$ of degree m'' in the m variables (z);

2. The expression of the symmetric function, of degree θ, in n variables z:

$$T_{(\theta)}(z) = \Sigma z_1^{\theta_1} \cdots z_n^{\theta_n}; \quad \theta = \theta_1 + \theta_2 + \cdots + \theta_n$$

in terms of the simple characteristics $\phi_{(e)}(s)$ of the symmetric group on n letters.

Both problems are closely related and it will be convenient to first discuss the second. If we multiply $T_{(\theta)}(z)$ by the Vandermonde determinant $A(n-1, n-2, \cdots, 1, 0) = \prod_{p<q} (z_p - z_q)$ we obtain a sum of determinants $A(l_1, l_2, \cdots, l_n)$ where the element in the i-th row and j-th column of $A(l_1, \cdots, l_n)$ is $z_j^{l_i}$. On dividing through by $A(n-1, \cdots, 1, 0)$ we see that $T_{(\theta)}(z)$ is expressible as a linear combination of the simple characteristics $\{\tau\}$ of the symmetric group on n letters; only those simple characteristics $\{\tau\}$ occurring for which the partition (τ) of n increased by the set $(n-1, n-2, \cdots, 1, 0)$, arranged in any order, is the set $(e) = (e_1, \cdots, e_n)$ where $e_j = \theta_j + n - j$, $j = 1, \cdots, n$. For example let us consider $T_{(2,1)} = \Sigma z_1^2 z_2$; here $\theta = 3$ and $(\theta) = (2, 1, 0)$ so that $(e) = (4, 2, 0)$. From (e) we subtract the set $(2, 1, 0)$ arranged in all (six) orders, prefixing a negative sign when the order is an odd arrangement of the natural order; we obtain $(2, 1)$, $-(2, 2, -1)$, $-(3)$, $(4, 0, -1)$, $(3, 2, -2)$, $(4, 1, -2)$. Of these all but the first and third vanish since they end in a negative integer and we obtain $T_{(2,1)}(z) = \{2, 1\} - \{3\}$. The following simple remark, however, makes it unnecessary to go through this calculation. The determinant of order n which furnishes $\{\lambda\}$ is

$$\{\lambda\} = \begin{vmatrix} q_{\lambda_1}(s) & \cdots & q_{\lambda_1+n-1}(s) \\ & \cdot & \\ & \cdot & \\ & \cdot & \\ & & q_{\lambda_n}(s) \end{vmatrix}$$

and on writing, as usual, $l_1 = \lambda_1 + n - 1, \cdots, l_n = \lambda_n$ this is the same as the result of operating with the determinantal operator

$$\begin{vmatrix} \xi_1^{n-1} & \cdots & \xi_n^{n-1} \\ \xi_1^{n-2} & & \xi_n^{n-2} \\ \cdot & & \cdot \\ 1 & \cdots & 1 \end{vmatrix}$$

upon the product $q_{l_1}(s)\cdots q_{l_n}(s)$. If, therefore, we denote by $K_{(\mu)}(s)$ the characteristic $q_{\mu_1}(s)\cdots q_{\mu_n}(s)$ of the compound representation $\Delta(\mu)$ of the symmetric group on n letters it is clear that $\{\lambda\}$ is a linear combination of the $K_{(\mu)}$, only those $K_{(\mu)}$ occurring for which (μ) increased by the set $(n-1, n-2, \cdots, 1, 0)$, arranged in *any* order, is the set (l); the sign attached to $K_{(\mu)}$ being $+$ if the arrangement of the set $(n-1, \cdots, 1, 0)$ which is added to (μ) is even and $-$ if this arrangement is odd. For example let $(\lambda) = (3, 2, 1)$ so that $(l) = (5, 3, 1)$; we subtract $(2, 1, 0)$ in all orders obtaining the six possibilities for (μ): $(3, 2, 1), -(3^2), (5, 1, 0), -(5, 2, -1), (4, 3, -1), -(4, 1^2)$. Of these the fourth and fifth vanish since they contain a negative element (each $q_j(s)$ for which j is negative being zero). Hence $\{3, 2, 1\} = K_{(5,1)} - K_{(4,1^2)} - K_{(3^2)} + K_{(3,2,1)}$. The result of this discussion which is important for us is the following: *the coefficient of $K_{(\mu)}$ in the development of $\{\lambda\}$ is the same as the coefficient of $\{\lambda\}$ in the development of $T_{(\mu)}(z)$.* In other words the Table 1 of p. 153 serves to express any symmetric function of degree n in the n variables (z) in terms of the simple characteristics $\{\lambda\}$ of the symmetric group on n letters. But now we must enter the table from the top, the desired coefficients being obtained in a column (instead of, as before, in a row) of the table. For a given value of m it is better to first construct from the master table the table corresponding to that value of m. E. g. for $m = 4$ the table is

	(4)	(3, 1)	(2^2)	$(2, 1^2)$	(1^4)
{4}	1				
{3, 1}	-1	1			
$\{2^2\}$	0	-1	1		
$\{2, 1^2\}$	1	-1	-1	1	
$\{1^4\}$	-1	2	1	-3	1

and we read

$$
\begin{aligned}
T_{(4)}(z) &= \Sigma z_1{}^4 = \{4\} - \{3, 1\} + \{2, 1^2\} - \{1^4\}\\
T_{(3,1)}(z) &= \Sigma z_1{}^3 z_2 = \{3, 1\} - \{2^2\} - \{2, 1^2\} + 2\{1^4\}\\
T_{(2^2)}(z) &= \Sigma z_1{}^2 z_2{}^2 = \{2^2\} - \{2, 1^2\} + \{1^4\}\\
T_{(2,1^2)}(z) &= \Sigma z_1{}^2 z_2 z_3 = \{2, 1^2\} - 3\{1^4\}\\
T_{(1^4)}(z) &= \Sigma z_1 z_2 z_3 z_4 = \{1^4\}.
\end{aligned}
$$

If we denote by $c^{(\lambda)}_{(\mu)}$ the coefficient of $K_{(\mu)}$ in the development of $\{\lambda\}$:

$$\{\lambda\} = \sum_{(\mu)} c^{(\lambda)}_{(\mu)} K_{(\mu)}$$

the result of the preceding paragraph (which result we shall call Kostka's theorem) finds its expression in the formula

$$T_{(\mu)}(z) = \sum_{(\lambda)} c_{(\mu)}^{(\lambda)}\{\lambda\}.$$

In other words the matrix which transforms the $\{\lambda\}$ into the $T_{(\mu)}$ is the transpose of the matrix which transforms the $K_{(\mu)}$ into the $\{\lambda\}$. Since the reciprocal of the transpose of a matrix is the transpose of its reciprocal it follows that if we write

$$K_{(\mu)}(z) = \sum_{(\lambda)} d_{(\mu)}^{(\lambda)}\{\lambda\}$$

then

$$\{\lambda\} = \sum_{(\mu)} d_{(\mu)}^{(\lambda)} T_{(\mu)}(z).$$

In other words *the coefficient of $T_{(\mu)}(z)$ in the expression of $\{\lambda\}$ as a symmetric function of degree n in the variables (z) is the same as the coefficient of $\{\lambda\}$ in the analysis of $K_{(\mu)}(z)$ or, equivalently as the coefficient of $D(\lambda)$ in the analysis of the reducible representation $\Delta(\mu)$ of the symmetric group on n letters.* The desired coefficients are, accordingly, furnished by the Table 2 of p. 154. Again we must enter at the top of the table (instead of at the side) the desired coefficients being found in a column (instead of in a row) of the table. For a given value of m it is again convenient to first construct from the master table the table corresponding to that particular value of m. Thus for $m = 4$ the table is

	$\{4\}$	$\{3,1\}$	$\{2^2\}$	$\{2,1^2\}$	$\{1^4\}$
(4)	1				
$(3,1)$	1	1			
(2^2)	1	1	1		
$(2,1^2)$	1	2	1	1	
(1^4)	1	3	2	3	1

and we read

$$\begin{aligned}
\{4\} &= T_{(4)}(z) + T_{(3,1)}(z) + T_{(2^2)}(z) + T_{(2,1^2)}(z) + T_{(1^4)}(z)\\
\{3,1\} &= T_{(3,1)}(z) + T_{(2^2)}(z) + 2T_{(2,1^2)}(z) + 3T_{(1^4)}(z)\\
\{2^2\} &= T_{(2^2)}(z) + T_{(2,1^2)}(z) + 2T_{(1^4)}(z)\\
\{2,1^2\} &= T_{(2,1^2)}(z) + 3T_{(1^4)}(z)\\
\{1^4\} &= T_{(1^4)}(z).
\end{aligned}$$

The solution of the two essential steps described on p. 161 is accordingly contained in the master tables 1 and 2 of pp. 153-154. The procedure for analysing $\{\lambda'\} \cdot \{\lambda''\}$ which has been outlined on p. 161 may be formalised as follows:

A. Precede by λ'_1 each partition occurring in the, supposed known, analysis of the product of $\{\lambda'_2, \cdots, \lambda'_{m'}\}$ by $\{\lambda''\}$.

B. Precede by $\lambda'_1 + 1$ each partition of the, supposed known, analysis of the product of $\{\lambda'_2, \cdots, \lambda'_{m'}\}$ by a linear combination of simple characteristics of the symmetric group on $m'' - 1$ letters. This linear combination is obtained by first expressing $\{\lambda''\}$ as a linear combination of the symmetric functions $K_{(\mu'')}(z)$, of degree m'', of m letters (z) and then expressing the coefficient of z_1, which is a symmetric function, of degree $m'' - 1$, of $m - 1$ letters, in terms of the simple characteristics of the symmetric group on $m'' - 1$ letters. We shall denote this linear combination by B.

C. Precede by $\lambda'_1 + 2$ each partition of the, supposed known, analysis of the product $\{\lambda'_2, \cdots, \lambda'_{m'}\}$ by a linear combination of simple characteristics of the symmetric group on $m'' - 2$ letters. This linear combination is obtained from the coefficient of z_1^2 in the expression for $\{\lambda''\}$ in terms of the $K_{(\mu'')}(z)$; we denote it by C.

D. Same as in B save that $\lambda'_1 + 1$ is replaced by $\lambda'_1 + 3$ and $m'' - 1$ by $m'' - 3$. We denote the linear combination by D.

E. Same as in B save that $\lambda'_1 + 1$ is replaced by $\lambda'_1 + 4$ and $m'' - 1$ by $m'' - 4$. We denote the linear combination by E; and so on.

Example:

Let $m'' = 3$, $(\lambda'') = (2, 1)$. Then $\{\lambda''\} = T_{(2,1)}(z) + 2T_{(1^3)}(z)$; the coefficient of z_1 is $\Sigma^* z_2^2 + 2\Sigma^* z_2 z_3 = T_{(2)} + 2T_{(1^2)} = \{2\} + \{1^2\}$. Hence $B = \{2\} + \{1^2\}$. The coefficient of z_1^2 is $\Sigma^* z_2 = T_{(1)} = \{1\}$ so that $C = \{1\}$. There are no further terms. Suppose, then, we wish to analyse $\{2, 1\} \cdot \{2, 1\}$. The first step is the analysis of $\{1\} \cdot \{2, 1\} = \{2, 1\} \cdot \{1\} = \{3, 1\} + \{2^2\} + \{2, 1^2\}$; a 2 must be prefixed to each of these giving $\{2^3\} + \{2^2, 1^2\}$ (the first term $\{2, 3, 1\}$ vanishing). The next step is the analysis of $\{1\} \cdot [\{2\} + \{1^2\}] = \{2\} \cdot \{1\} + \{1^2\} \cdot \{1\} = \{3\} + 2\{2, 1\} + \{1^3\}$ and on prefixing a 3 we get $\{3^2\} + 2\{3, 2, 1\} + \{3, 1^3\}$. Finally we analyse $\{1\} \cdot \{1\} = \{2\} + \{1^2\}$ and prefixing a 4 we get $\{4, 2\} + \{4, 1^2\}$. Collecting our results we find

$$\{2, 1\} \cdot \{2, 1\} = \{4, 2\} + \{4, 1^2\} + \{3^2\} + 2\{3, 2, 1\} + \{3, 1^3\} + \{2^3\} + \{2^2, 1^2\}.$$

We give in the tables below the necessary expressions B, C, D, E for all $\{\lambda''\}$ for which $m'' \leq 8$; it being always understood that (λ'') is preceded by, if it is not identical with, its associate (μ'').

Tables furnishing the necessary linear combinations B, C, D, E.

1. $n = 2$.

	B
$\{1^2\}$	$\{1\}$

2. $n = 3$.

	B	C
$\{1^3\}$	$\{1^2\}$	
$\{2, 1\}$	$\{2\} + \{1^2\}$	$\{1\}$

3. $n = 4$.

	B	C
$\{1^4\}$	$\{1^3\}$	
$\{2, 1^2\}$	$\{2, 1\} + \{1^3\}$	$\{1^2\}$
$\{2^2\}$	$\{2, 1\}$	$\{2\}$

4. $n = 5$.

	B	C	D
$\{1^5\}$	$\{1^4\}$		
$\{2, 1^3\}$	$\{2, 1^2\} + \{1^4\}$	$\{1^3\}$	
$\{2^2, 1\}$	$\{2^2\} + \{2, 1^2\}$	$\{2, 1\}$	
$\{3, 1^2\}$	$\{3, 1\} + \{2, 1^2\}$	$\{2, 1\} + \{1^3\}$	$\{1^2\}$

5. $n = 6$.

	B	C	D
$\{1^6\}$	$\{1^5\}$		
$\{2, 1^4\}$	$\{2, 1^3\} + \{1^5\}$	$\{1^4\}$	
$\{2^2, 1^2\}$	$\{2^2, 1\} + \{2, 1^3\}$	$\{2, 1^2\}$	
$\{2^3\}$	$\{2^2, 1\}$	$\{2^2\}$	
$\{3, 1^3\}$	$\{3, 1^2\} + \{2, 1^3\}$	$\{2, 1^2\} + \{1^4\}$	$\{1^3\}$
$\{3, 2, 1\}$	$\{3, 2\} + \{3, 1^2\} + \{2^2, 1\}$	$\{3, 1\} + \{2^2\} + \{2, 1^2\}$	$\{2, 1\}$

6. $n = 7$.

	B	C	D	E
$\{1^7\}$	$\{1^6\}$			
$\{2, 1^5\}$	$\{2, 1^4\} + \{1^6\}$	$\{1^5\}$		
$\{2^2, 1^3\}$	$\{2^2, 1^2\} + \{2, 1^4\}$	$\{2, 1^3\}$		
$\{2^3, 1\}$	$\{2^3\} + \{2^2, 1^2\}$	$\{2^2, 1\}$		
$\{3, 1^4\}$	$\{3, 1^3\} + \{2, 1^4\}$	$\{2, 1^3\} + \{1^5\}$	$\{1^4\}$	
$\{3, 2, 1^2\}$	$\{3, 2, 1\} + \{3, 1^3\} + \{2^2, 1^2\}$	$\{3, 1^2\} + \{2^2, 1\} + \{2, 1^3\}$	$\{2, 1^2\}$	
$\{3, 2^2\}$	$\{3, 2, 1\} + \{2^3\}$	$\{3, 2\} + \{2^2, 1\}$	$\{2^2\}$	
$\{4, 1^3\}$	$\{4, 1^2\} + \{3, 1^3\}$	$\{3, 1^2\} + \{2, 1^3\}$	$\{2, 1^2\} + \{1^4\}$	$\{1^3\}$

7. $n = 8$.

	B	*C*	*D*	*E*
$\{1^8\}$	$\{1^7\}$			
$\{2, 1^6\}$	$\{2, 1^5\} + \{1^7\}$	$\{1^6\}$		
$\{2^2, 1^4\}$	$\{2^2, 1^3\} + \{2, 1^5\}$	$\{2, 1^4\}$		
$\{2^3, 1^2\}$	$\{2^3, 1\} + \{2^2, 1^3\}$	$\{2^2, 1^2\}$		
$\{2^4\}$	$\{2^3, 1\}$	$\{2^3\}$		
$\{3, 1^5\}$	$\{3, 1^4\} + \{2, 1^5\}$	$\{2, 1^4\} + \{1^6\}$	$\{1^5\}$	
$\{3, 2, 1^3\}$	$\{3, 2, 1^2\} + \{3, 1^4\} + \{2^2, 1^3\}$	$\{3, 1^3\} + \{2^2, 1^2\} + \{2, 1^4\}$	$\{2, 1^3\}$	
$\{3, 2^2, 1\}$	$\{3, 2^2\} + \{3, 2, 1^2\} + \{2^3, 1\}$	$\{3, 2, 1\} + \{2^3\} + \{2^2, 1^2\}$	$\{2^2, 1\}$	
$\{3^2, 1^2\}$	$\{3^2, 1\} + \{3, 2, 1\}$	$\{3, 2, 1\} + \{3, 1^3\}$	$\{3, 1^2\}$	
$\{3^2, 2\}$	$\{3^2, 1\} + \{3, 2^2\}$	$\{3^2\} + \{3, 2, 1\}$	$\{3, 2\}$	
$\{4, 1^4\}$	$\{4, 1^3\} + \{3, 1^4\}$	$\{3, 1^3\} + \{2, 1^4\}$	$\{2, 1^3\} + \{1^5\}$	$\{1^4\}$
$\{4, 2, 1^2\}$	$\{4, 2, 1\} + \{4, 1^3\} + \{3, 2, 1^2\}$	$\{4, 1^2\} + \{3, 2, 1\} + \{3, 1^3\} + \{2^2, 1^2\}$	$\{3, 1^2\} + \{2^2, 1\} + \{2, 1^3\}$	$\{2, 1^2\}$

We have given elsewhere the analysis of all direct products $\{\lambda'\} \cdot \{\lambda''\}$ for which $m' + m'' \leq 10$ (*American Journal of Mathematics* **59**, pp. 483-487 (1937) and **60**, pp. 44-65 (1938)). We have also given, as illustrative examples (in the second of the two papers referred to) the analysis of the products $\{4, 2^2\} \cdot \{2, 1\}$, $\{7, 2\} \cdot \{3, 1\}$, $\{4, 3, 1\} \cdot \{2^2, 1\}$ and $\{4^2\} \cdot \{2^4\}$. The direct product being analysed in the last of these examples is a representation of dimension 2,522,520 of the symmetric group on 16 letters.

CHAPTER SIX

THE ALTERNATING GROUP

In this chapter we shall show how the knowledge of the character table of the symmetric group on m letters enables us to construct the character table of its alternating subgroup, i.e. the group of $m!/2$ even permutations on m letters.

1. The classes of the alternating group.

Since a class (α) of the symmetric group, G, on m letters, is either even or odd, i. e. consists entirely of even or of odd permutations, this class will either lie entirely in the alternating subgroup, H, or have no element in common with it; the class (α) lying entirely in H if $\alpha_2 + \alpha_4 + \cdots$ is even. Assuming that (α) lies entirely in H it remains to see whether or not H refines (α), i. e. whether or not all elements of (α) belong to the same class of H. Two elements s and t of (α) belong to the same class of H if there exists an element h of H (i. e. an *even* permutation h) such that $h^{-1}sh = t$. Since, s, t belong to the same class (α) of G there exists a permutation p of G such that $p^{-1}sp = t$; if then there exists an *odd* permutation q which is commutative with s: $qs = sq$: we have $s = q^{-1}sq$ so that, in addition to $p^{-1}sp = t$ we have $p^{-1}q^{-1}sqp = t$, i. e. $(qp)^{-1}sqp = t$. Since q is odd, one or other of the two permutations p, qp is even so that we have the basic result: *a class* (α) *of the symmetric group on m letters is not refined by the alternating subgroup if any element of it is commutative with an odd permutation.* It is evident that if any one member s of (α) is commutative with an odd permutation any other member t of (α) has this property. For $s = hth^{-1}$ so that $s = q^{-1}sq$ implies $hth^{-1} = q^{-1}hth^{-1}q$, i. e. $h^{-1}qht = th^{-1}qh$ and $h^{-1}qh$ is odd when q is. Since any permutation s of (α) is commutative with each of its cycles and since a cycle on an even number of letters is an odd permutation it is clear that (α) is not refined by H if any of the numbers $\alpha_2, \alpha_4, \cdots > 0$. Furthermore (α) is not refined by H if any of the numbers $\alpha_1, \alpha_3, \alpha_5, \cdots > 1$; in fact let a permutation s of (α) contain two cycles $(1, 2, \cdots, 2p+1)(2p+2, \cdots, 4p+2)$ on $2p+1$ letters. Then s is commutative with $(1, 2p+2)(2, 2p+3)\cdots(2p+1, 4p+2)$ for

$$(1, 2, \cdots, 2p+1)(2p+2, \cdots, 4p+2)(1, 2p+2)\cdots(2p+1, 4p+2)$$
$$= (1, 2p+3, 3, 2p+5, \cdots)$$

(all the numbers in the second half of this cycle being reduced by $2p+1$) and

$$(1, 2p+2) \cdots (2p+1, 4p+2)(1, 2, \cdots, 2p+1)(2p+2, \cdots, 4p+2)$$

also $= (1, 2p+3, 3, 2p+5, \cdots)$. Since the product

$$(1, 2p+2)(2, 2p+3) \cdots (2p+1, 4p+2)$$

is odd it follows that (α) is not refined by H. The only case when (α) is (possibly) refined by H is that where $\alpha_1 = 1$ or 0; $\alpha_3 = 1$ or 0; $\cdots$ $\alpha_2 = \alpha_4 = \cdots = 0$. In this case any element s of (α) is not commutative with *any* odd permutation; in fact the elements in G which are commutative with any element s belonging to the class (α) of G form a subgroup of G of order $m! \div n_{(\alpha)}$ and when (α) contains only cycles of unequal length this is the product of the lengths of these cycles. This subgroup contains the subgroup consisting of the products of the various powers of the individual cycles of s; since the lowest power of a cycle on k letters which is the identity is the k-th the order of the subgroup consisting of the products of the various powers of the cycles of s is the product of the lengths of these cycles. Hence the group of all permutations commutative with s is exhausted by the group generated by its cycles; but every element of this group is even since each cycle, being of odd length, is even. Hence s is not commutative with any odd permutation of G. It follows that (α) is actually refined by H. In fact let p be any *odd* permutation and consider the two elements s and $t = p^{-1}sp$ of (α); there does not exist any even permutation h which transforms s into t since $t = h^{-1}sh$ would imply $p^{-1}sp = h^{-1}sh$, i.e. $s \cdot ph^{-1} = ph^{-1} \cdot s$ which is impossible since ph^{-1} is odd. The elements $h^{-1}sh$, h variable over H, form a class (α') of H and the elements $p^{-1}sp$; p odd, form a second class (α'') of H; for if p and q are both odd and we write $p^{-1}sp = t$, $q^{-1}sq = u$ we have $u = q^{-1}ptp^{-1}q$ where $q^{-1}p = h$ is even. The final result of the discussion is then the following:

All classes (α) of the symmetric group on m letters are unrefined by the alternating subgroup H save those for which the permutations contain only cycles of unequal odd length, and each of these classes is refined into exactly two classes of H. The number of elements $n_{(\alpha')}$ in the class (α') of H is the same as the number of elements $n_{(\alpha'')}$ in the class (α'') of H each being one-half the number of elements $n_{(\alpha)}$ in the class (α) of G. In fact the number of elements in (α') is the quotient of the order $m!/2$ of H by the order of the subgroup of H which consists of the elements of H which are commutative with a given element h' of

(α'); but all elements of G which are commutative with h' are even, and, hence lie in H. Hence the number of elements in (α') is

$$n_{(\alpha')} = (m!/2) \div (m!/n_{(\alpha)}) = n_{(\alpha)}/2$$

and, similarly, $n_{(\alpha'')} = n_{(\alpha)}/2$. Since a class (α) is refined by H when and only when $\alpha_1 = 1$ or 0; $\alpha_3 = 1$ or 0; $\cdots \alpha_2 = \alpha_4 = \cdots = 0$ the number of classes which are refined equals the number of partitions of m into unequal odd numbers, i. e. to the number of self-associated partitions of m. This number is the coefficient of x^m in the continued product $(1+x)(1+x^3)(1+x^5)\cdots$ and this is the same as the coefficient of x^m in the development of $\dfrac{1}{(1-x)(1+x^2)(1-x^3)\cdots}$.
In fact this fraction

$$= \frac{1+x}{(1-x^2)(1+x^2)(1-x^3)\cdots} = \frac{1+x}{(1-x^3)(1-x^4)(1+x^4)(1-x^5)\cdots}$$
$$= \frac{(1+x)(1+x^3)}{(1-x^5)(1-x^6)(1+x^6)\cdots} = \frac{(1+x)(1+x^3)(1+x^5)}{(1-x^7)\cdots}$$

and so on. On writing out the expansions

$$\frac{1}{1-x} = \sum_0^\infty x^{\alpha_1}; \quad \frac{1}{1+x^2} = \sum_0^\infty (-1)^{\alpha_2} x^{2\alpha_2}; \quad \frac{1}{1-x^3} = \sum_0^\infty x^{3\alpha_3} \cdots$$

the coefficient of x^m in the product $\dfrac{1}{(1-x)(1+x^2)(1-x^3)\cdots}$ is seen to be the difference between the number of solutions of $\alpha_1 + 2\alpha_2 + \cdots + m\alpha_m = m$ for which $\alpha_2 + \alpha_4 + \cdots$ is even and the number for which it is odd. In other words if u denotes the number of odd classes of the symmetric group on m letters and if v denotes the number of (even) classes of this symmetric group G which are refined by its alternating subgroup H (each into two classes, containing the same number of elements, of H) the number of even classes of $G = u + v$ so that the number of classes p of $G = 2u + v$ whilst the number of classes p' of H is $u + 2v$. Each of the v classes consists of permutations containing unequal cycles of odd lengths; with any one of these we can associate an *odd* class formed by reducing the length of one of the cycles by 1 and adding a unary cycle. Hence $u \geqq v$ so that the number of classes p' of H is not greater than the number of classes p of G. The values of u, v, p, p' for the various symmetric groups up to $m = 10$ are given in the following table:

m	u	v	p	p'
2	1	0	2	1
3	1	1	3	3
4	2	1	5	4
5	3	1	7	5
6	5	1	11	7
7	7	1	15	9
8	10	2	22	14
9	14	2	30	18
10	20	2	42	24

Since v is the number of self-associated irreducible representations of the symmetric group G on m letters and since the total number of distinct irreducible representations of G is $p = 2u + v$, u is also the number of pairs of associated representations of G. The number of distinct irreducible representations of the alternating subgroup of H is $p' = u + 2v$. We shall see in the next section that each pair of associated irreducible representations of G furnishes an irreducible representation of H and that each self-associated irreducible representation of G furnishes two irreducible representations of H, the irreducible representations of H obtained in this way being all distinct.

2. The simple characteristics of the alternating group on *m* letters.

Let $D(\lambda)$ be an irreducible representation of the symmetric group, G, on m letters with characters $\chi_{(\lambda)}(s)$. Then $\sum_s \{\chi_{(\lambda)}(s)\}^2 = m!$ the summation being over all permutations s of G. If h is an arbitrary element of the alternating subgroup H and p is any odd permutation we may write this equation in the form

$$\sum_h \{\chi_{(\lambda)}(h)\}^2 + \sum_h \{\chi_{(\lambda)}(ph)\}^2 = m!$$

the summations being over all elements h of H. If $D(\mu)$ is the associated representation of G ($D(\lambda)$ being supposed *not* self-associated) $\chi_{(\mu)}(h) = \chi_{(\lambda)}(h)$; $\chi_{(\mu)}(ph) = -\chi_{(\lambda)}(ph)$ and the relation $\sum_s \chi_{(\lambda)}(s)\chi_{(\mu)}(s) = 0$ yields $\sum_h \{\chi_{(\lambda)}(h)\}^2 = \sum_h \{\chi_{(\lambda)}(ph)\}^2$ so that

$$\sum_{(h)} \chi_{(\lambda)}(h)^2 = m! \div 2. \qquad (6.1)$$

The numbers $\chi_{(\lambda)}(h)$ are the characters of a representation of H and the equation (6.1) tells us that this representation is irreducible (since the order of $H = m! \div 2$). Hence each *pair* of associated simple characteristics of G furnishes a simple characteristic of H. These simple characteristics are all distinct; in fact if $D(\lambda')$, $D(\mu')$ is a second pair of associated irreducible representations of G we have

$$\sum_h \chi_{(\lambda)}(h)\chi_{(\lambda')}(h) + \sum_h \chi_{(\lambda)}(ph)\chi_{(\lambda')}(ph) = 0$$

and also

$$\sum_h \chi_{(\lambda)}(h)\chi_{(\mu')}(h) + \sum_h \chi_{(\lambda)}(ph)\chi_{(\mu')}(ph) = 0.$$

Since $\chi_{(\mu')}(h) = \chi_{(\lambda')}(h)$, $\chi_{(\mu')}(ph) = -\chi_{(\lambda')}(ph)$ we obtain, on adding the two equations just written,

$$\sum_h \chi_{(\lambda)}(h)\chi_{(\lambda')}(h) = 0$$

showing that the two irreducible representations of H, whose characters are $\chi_{(\lambda)}(h)$ and $\chi_{(\lambda')}(h)$, respectively, are non-equivalent. We obtain, therefore, the characters of u non-equivalent irreducible representations of H by merely writing down those characters of either one of a pair of associated irreducible representations of G which are attached to the even classes of G. These characters take the same value over each of the two classes into which H divides each of the v classes of G whose elements consist of cycles of unequal odd lengths.

To obtain the remaining $2v$ simple characteristics of H we consider the v self-associated representations of G. Let $D(\lambda)$ be one of these; then $\chi_{(\lambda)}(h)$ are the characters of a representation of H which is, however, reducible. In fact $\chi_{(\lambda)}(ph) = 0$ so that

$$\sum_h \{\chi_{(\lambda)}(h)\}^2 = \sum_s \{\chi_{(\lambda)}(s)\}^2 = m! = \frac{m!}{2}\cdot 2.$$

Hence the representation of H whose characters are $\chi_{(\lambda)}(h)$ contains two irreducible representations of H each one once. We denote these two representations of H by $D'(\lambda)$, $D''(\lambda)$ so that $\chi_{(\lambda)}(h) = \chi'_{(\lambda)}(h) + \chi''_{(\lambda)}(h)$. Now the characters of the representation $D'(\lambda)$ of H furnish a simple characteristic of H and this enables us to construct by the method of p. 98 a characteristic of G; the characters of the corresponding representation Γ of G are found by averaging the characters of $D'(\lambda)$ over the classes of H which constitute a refinement, by H, of a class of G and by then multiplying this average by 2 (the ratio of the order of G to that of H). Denoting the characters of this representation of G by χ we have

$$\left.\begin{array}{l}\chi(h) = \chi'_{(\lambda)}(h) + \chi'_{\lambda}(p^{-1}hp)\\ \chi(p) = 0\end{array}\right\}\text{; } p \text{ any odd permutation of } G.$$

If h belongs to a class of G which is not refined by H $\chi'_{(\lambda)}(p^{-1}hp) = \chi'_{(\lambda)}(h)$ so that $\chi(h) = 2\chi'_{(\lambda)}(h)$.

The numbers $\chi'_{(\lambda)}(p^{-1}hp)$ are the characters $\psi(h)$ of a second representation of H which is said to be *conjugate* to the representation $D'(\lambda)$ and which is obtained as follows. Let $A(h)$ denote the matrices of $D'(\lambda)$ and define the matrices $B(h)$ thus:

$$B(h) = A(p^{-1}hp).$$

Then the matrices $B(h)$ furnish a representation of H: in fact

$$\begin{aligned} B(h')B(h) &= A(p^{-1}h'p)A(p^{-1}hp) = A(p^{-1}h'p \cdot p^{-1}hp) \\ &= A(p^{-1}h'hp) = B(h'h). \end{aligned}$$

Also $B(e) = A(e) = E_{d'_{(\lambda)}}$ where e is the unit permutation and $d'_{(\lambda)}$ is the dimension of $D'(\lambda)$; finally $B(h^{-1})B(h) = B(e) = E_{d'_{(\lambda)}}$. Denoting this conjugate representation of $D'(\lambda)$ by $\tilde{D}'(\lambda)$ it is clear from the definition that the conjugate of $\tilde{D}'(\lambda)$ is $D'(\lambda)$; and we have seen that both representations have the same dimension $d'_{(\lambda)}$. If p were an even, and not an odd, permutation the characters $\tilde{\chi}'_{(\lambda)}(h)$ of $\tilde{D}'(\lambda)$ would be the same as those of $D'(\lambda)$ so that the two conjugate representations would coincide. But this cannot happen when p is an odd permutation; for if $D'(\lambda)$ and $\tilde{D}'(\lambda)$ were equivalent the characters $\chi(h)$ of the representation Γ of G which are attached to elements of H would be twice those of $D'(\lambda)$, the remaining characters of Γ being zero. Hence Γ would contain two irreducible representations of G. One of these is $D(\lambda)$ (by the theorem of p. 100) and the other would have to be self-associated since all its characters which are attached to odd permutations p vanish. Denoting it by $D(\mu)$ we have $\chi_{(\lambda)}(h) + \chi_{(\mu)}(h) = 2\chi'_{(\lambda)}(h)$ i.e.

$$\chi'_{(\lambda)}(h) + \chi''_{(\lambda)}(h) + \chi'_{(\mu)}(h) + \chi''_{(\mu)}(h) = 2\chi'_{(\lambda)}(h)$$

or

$$\chi'_{(\lambda)}(h) = \chi''_{(\lambda)}(h) + \chi'_{(\mu)}(h) + \chi''_{(\mu)}(h)$$

implying $D'(\lambda) = D''(\lambda) + D'(\mu) + D''(\mu)$ which is absurd since $D'(\lambda)$ is irreducible.

It is clear that the characters of $\tilde{D}'(\lambda)$ are merely a rearrangement of the characters of $D'(\lambda)$, simply because $p^{-1}hp$ runs, with h, over H. Hence the irreducibility of $D'(\lambda)$ implies that of $\tilde{D}'(\lambda)$ (the criterion of irreducibility being that the average over H of the squared moduli of the characters be unity). It follows that the representation Γ of G whose characters are χ is irreducible:

$$\begin{aligned} \sum_s |\chi(s)|^2 = \sum_h |\chi(h)|^2 &= \sum_h |\chi'_{(\lambda)}(h) + \chi'_{(\lambda)}(p^{-1}hp)|^2 \\ &= \sum_h \{\chi'_{(\lambda)}(h) + \chi'_{(\lambda)}(p^{-1}hp)\}\{\chi'_{(\lambda)}(h^{-1}) + \chi'_{(\lambda)}(p^{-1}h^{-1}p)\} \\ &= \tfrac{1}{2}m! + 0 + \tfrac{1}{2}m! = m!. \end{aligned}$$

Since it must contain $D(\lambda)$ once it must coincide with $D(\lambda)$. Hence the second simple representation $D''(\lambda)$ of H is the same as the conjugate representation $\tilde{D}'(\lambda)$:

$$\chi_{(\lambda)}(h) = \chi'_{(\lambda)}(h) + \chi'_{(\lambda)}(p^{-1}hp). \tag{6.2}$$

We have, then, obtained from the u pairs of associated representations and from the v self-associated representations of the symmetric group G on m letters $u + 2v$ irreducible representations of its alternating subgroup H; and we have seen that no two of the first u of these are equivalent. No one of the last $2v$ irreducible representations of H is equivalent to any one of the first u; in fact if $\chi_{(\mu)}(h)$ are the characters of one of these u representations the non-equivalence of the representations $D(\lambda), D(\mu)$ of G yields $\sum_s \chi_{(\lambda)}(s)\chi_{(\mu)}(s) = 0$ or, equivalently, $\sum_h \chi_{(\lambda)}(h)\chi_{(\mu)}(h) = 0$. Hence $\sum_h \{\chi'_{(\lambda)}(h) + \tilde{\chi}'_{(\lambda)}(h)\}\chi_{(\mu)}(h) = 0$; and since the representations $D'(\lambda), \tilde{D}'(\lambda)$ of H are non-equivalent one or other (and hence both) of the two sums $\sum_h \chi'_{(\lambda)}(h)\chi_{(\mu)}(h)$, $\sum_h \tilde{\chi}'_{(\lambda)}(h)\chi_{(\mu)}(h)$ must vanish. This proves that neither $D'(\lambda)$ nor $\tilde{D}'(\lambda)$ is equivalent to any one of the first u irreducible representations of H. Finally, if $D(\lambda), D(\mu)$ are *any* two self-associated representations of G, neither of the two irreducible representations $D'(\mu), \tilde{D}'(\mu)$ of H is equivalent to either of the two irreducible representations $D'(\lambda)$, $\tilde{D}'(\lambda)$ of H. In fact the non-equivalence of $D(\lambda)$ and $D(\mu)$ yields $\sum_h \{\chi'_{(\lambda)}(h) + \tilde{\chi}'_{(\lambda)}(h)\}\{\chi'_{(\mu)}(h^{-1}) + \tilde{\chi}'_{(\mu)}(h^{-1})\} = 0$. Since $D'(\mu)$, $\tilde{D}'(\mu)$ are non-equivalent one or other of the two sums $\sum_h \chi'_{(\lambda)}(h)\chi'_{(\mu)}(h^{-1})$, $\sum_h \chi'_{(\lambda)}(h)\tilde{\chi}'_{(\mu)}(h^{-1})$ must vanish. For the sake of definiteness suppose the first vanishes and observe that this implies the vanishing of $\sum_h \chi'_{(\lambda)}(p^{-1}hp)\chi'_{(\mu)}(p^{-1}h^{-1}p)$, i. e. of $\sum \tilde{\chi}'_{(\lambda)}(h)\tilde{\chi}'_{(\mu)}(h^{-1})$. Hence

$$\sum_h \chi'_{(\lambda)}(h)\tilde{\chi}'_{(\mu)}(h^{-1}) + \sum_h \tilde{\chi}'_{(\lambda)}(h)\chi'_{(\mu)}(h^{-1}) = 0;$$

on replacing h by $p^{-1}hp$ in the first of the two sums it becomes clear that the two sums are equivalent so that $\sum_h \chi'_{(\lambda)}(h)\tilde{\chi}'_{(\mu)}(h^{-1}) = 0$ implying the non-equivalence of $D'(\lambda)$ and $\tilde{D}'(\mu)$ (or, equivalently, the non-equivalence of $\tilde{D}'(\lambda)$ and $D'(\mu)$.) Hence no two of the $u + 2v$ irreducible representations of the alternating group whose characters have been found from those of the containing symmetric group, are equivalent and we are in possession of the complete character table of the alternating group.

Examples:

The cases $m = 2, 3$ are uninteresting. For $m = 2$, H is the group consisting of but one element and the only irreducible representation is the identical representation. For $m = 3$, H is the cyclic group of order three consisting of the permutations 1, (123), (132). Its character table is

	$\chi_{(3)}$	$\chi'_{(2,1)}$	$\tilde{\chi}'_{(2,1)}$	
$C_1 = (1^3)$	1	1	1	1
$C_2 = C'_3 = (123)$	1	ω	ω^2	1; $1 + \omega + \omega^2 = 0$.
$C_3 = C''_3 = (132)$	1	ω^2	ω	1

The case $m = 4$ is quite interesting, the corresponding group, of order 12, being known as the *tetrahedral group* (since it can be geometrically realised by the group of rotations sending a regular tetrahedron into itself). It has four classes: C_1, the identity; $C_2 = (2^2)$ the set of three rotations, through π, around a line joining the mid-points of opposite edges of the tetrahedron; $C_3 = (1, 3)'$ the set of four rotations, through $2\pi/3$, round an altitude of the tetrahedron; and $C_4 = (1, 3)''$, the set of four rotations through $-(2\pi/3)$ round an altitude of the tetrahedron. Remembering that $\chi'_{(\lambda)}(h) = \frac{1}{2}\chi_{(\lambda)}(h)$ if h belongs to a class of G which is not refined by H and that the characters $\tilde{\chi}'_{(\lambda)}$ are a rearrangement of $\chi'_{(\lambda)}$ (the sum $\chi'_{(\lambda)} + \tilde{\chi}'_{(\lambda)}$ being $\chi_{(\lambda)}$) we at once write down

	$\chi_{(4)}$	$\chi_{(3,1)}$	$\chi'_{(2^2)}$	$\tilde{\chi}'_{(2^2)}$	
$C_1 = (1^4)$	1	3	1	1	1
$C_2 = (2^2)$	1	-1	1	1	3
$C_3 = (1, 3)'$	1	0	x	y	4
$C_4 = (1, 3)''$	1	0	y	x	4

where $x + y = -1$. Since $\chi'_{(2^2)}$, $\tilde{\chi}'_{(2^2)}$ are one dimensional representations and all elements of the class C_3 and C_4 are of order 3 (i. e. have their cubes = the identical permutation) x and y must be cube roots of unity. Since their sum is -1 we have $x = \omega, y = \omega^2$ where $1 + \omega + \omega^2 = 0$ i. e. $\omega = (-1 + \sqrt{-3})/2$. Hence the character table for the tetrahedral group is

	$\chi_{(4)}$	$\chi_{(3,1)}$	$\chi'_{(2^2)}$	$\tilde{\chi}'_{(2^2)}$	
$C_1 = (1^4)$	1	3	1	1	1
$C_2 = (2^2)$	1	-1	1	1	3
$C_3 = (1, 3)'$	1	0	ω	ω^2	4
$C_4 = (1, 3)''$	1	0	ω^2	ω	4

When $m = 5$ the alternating group is of order 60 and is known as the group of the icosahedron. Its character table is

	$\chi_{(5)}$	$\chi_{(4,1)}$	$\chi_{(3,2)}$	$\chi_{(3,1^2)}$	$\tilde{\chi}'_{(3,1^2)}$	
$C_1 = (1^5)$	1	4	5	3	3	1
$C_2 = (1^2, 3)$	1	1	-1	0	0	20
$C_3 = (1, 2^2)$	1	0	1	-1	-1	15
$C_4 = (5)'$	1	-1	0	x	y	12
$C_5 = (5)''$	1	-1	0	y	x	12

The permutations of the class C_5 are the squares of those of C_4 and vice versa; for (12345) is sent into its square (13524) by the *odd* permutation (2453). Hence each of the classes C_4, C_5 contains the fourth power (i. e. the reciprocal) of each of its elements so that the numbers x and y are real; we have $x + y = 1$ and the orthogonality relation connecting the fourth and fifth rows of the table yields $xy + 1 = 0$ so that x, y are the roots of the quadratic equation $\theta^2 - \theta - 1 = 0$. Hence $x = (1 + \sqrt{5})/2$, $y = (1 - \sqrt{5})/2$.

CHAPTER SEVEN

LINEAR GROUPS

In this chapter we shall discuss the *continuous representations* of the unimodular subgroup of the full linear group and shall consider the *semi-rational* representations of the full linear group. The chapter closes with a description of *all* continuous representations of the full linear group.

1. The rational representations of the unimodular group.

The unimodular group of dimension n consists of all $n \times n$ matrices A of determinant 1. We denote the matrices of any rational representation of this group by $D(A)$ so that the elements of $D(A)$ are rational functions of the elements of A. Reducing these to a common denominator $\phi(A)$ the elements of $D(A)$ are all of the type $\psi_s{}^r(A)/\phi(A)$ where the $\psi_s{}^r(A)$, $\phi(A)$ are polynomials in the n^2 elements $a_q{}^p$ of A. If B is *any* non-singular $n \times n$ matrix the matrix $A = \alpha B$, where $\alpha^n = (\det B)^{-1}$, is an element of the unimodular group (α being chosen, for convenience, so that $\alpha = 1$ when $\det B = 1$). The n roots of the equation for α: $\alpha^n = (\det B)^{-1}$ being denoted by $\alpha_k = \alpha e^{2\pi ik/n}$, $k = 0, 1, \cdots, n-1$, the product $\prod_{k=0}^{n-1} \phi(\alpha e^{2\pi ik/n}B)$ is a polynomial in the elements of B whose coefficients are symmetric polynomial functions of the α_k. It is accordingly a polynomial in the elements of B and in $(\det B)^{-1}$; i. e. it is a rational function of the elements of B. Each element $\psi_s{}^r(A)/\phi(A) = \psi_s{}^r(\alpha B)/\phi(\alpha B)$ appears, accordingly, on multiplying both numerator and denominator by $\prod_{1}^{n-1} \phi(\alpha e^{2\pi ik/n}B)$ as a polynomial of degree $n-1$ in α whose coefficients are rational functions of the elements of B; in other words $D(A) = D(\alpha B)$ may be expressed as a polynomial of degree $n-1$ in α whose coefficients are matrices whose elements are rational functions of the elements of B:

$$D(A) = \sum_{k=0}^{n-1} R_k(B)\alpha^k.$$

Let B_1 be any other non-singular $n \times n$ matrix and let the unimodular matrix A_1 be derived from B_1 just as A was derived above from B, then the representation property $D(A_1A) = D(A_1)D(A)$ yields (since the α for B_1B is $\alpha_1\alpha$)

$$(7.1) \qquad \sum_{k=0}^{n-1} R_k(B_1B)(\alpha_1\alpha)^k = \left(\sum_{p=0}^{n-1} R_p(B_1)\alpha_1{}^p\right)\left(\sum_{q=0}^{n-1} R_q(B)\alpha^q\right).$$

Holding B_1 fixed and regarding B as variable this is an equation of degree $< n$ satisfied by α (the coefficients of the equation being rational functions of the elements of B). Since $\det B$ is an irreducible polynomial in its elements the equation $\alpha^n - (\det B)^{-1} = 0$ is irreducible i. e. no equation, with coefficients rational functions of the elements of B, of degree $< n$ is satisfied by α. Hence (7. 1) must be an identity in α so that

$$R_q(B_1B)\alpha_1{}^q = \sum_{p=0}^{n-1} R_p(B_1)R_q(B)\alpha_1{}^p; \qquad q = 0, 1, \cdots, n-1.$$

Repeating our previous argument (where now B_1 is variable and B fixed) we find

$$(7.2) \quad R_q(B_1B) = R_q(B_1)R_q(B); \quad R_p(B_1)R_q(B) = 0, \quad p \neq q.$$

This implies that $R(B) = \sum_{k=0}^{n-1} R_k(B)$ is a rational representation of the full linear group. When B is unimodular $\alpha = 1$, $A = B$ and $D(A) = R(A)$. In other words *any* rational representation of the unimodular subgroup may be imbedded in a rational representation of the full linear group. Since, by the theorem of p. 34, $R(B) = P(B)/(\det B)^k$ where k is a positive integer or zero and $P(B)$ is a rational integral (= polynomial) representation of the full linear group and since when B is unimodular $P(B) = R(B)$ we have the basic result:

Any rational representation of the unimodular subgroup of the full linear group may be imbedded in a rational integral representation of the full linear group. In other words we are in possession of all rational representations of the unimodular group when we know the rational integral representations of the full linear group. Since all rational integral representations of the full linear group are either irreducible or analysable (= completely reducible) it follows that all rational representations of the unimodular group are either irreducible or completely reducible. In fact it is clear from the construction of the imbedding representation $\{P(B)\}$ that when $\{D(A)\}$ is reducible so also is $\{P(B)\}$ (in fact each zero element of $D(A)$ yields a corresponding zero element of each and every $R_k(B)$, $k = 0, 1, \cdots, n-1$, and hence a zero element of $P(B)$). Hence the reducibility of $\{D(A)\}$ forces the reducibility of $\{P(B)\}$; this implies the analysability of $\{P(B)\}$ (by the basic theorem of p. 129) and hence, à fortiori, the analysability of $\{D(A)\}$ since the collection of matrices $\{D(A)\}$ is a subset of the collection $\{P(B)\}$. The irreducible representations (rational) of the unimodular group are to be sought for amongst the irreducible rational integral representations of the full linear group; and the converse is true: *each irreducible rational integral representation* $\{P(B)\}$ *of the full linear group furnishes by the selection principle, i. e. by setting* $D(A) = P(A)$, *an irreducible representation of the unimodular subgroup.* The proof of this statement is precisely the same as the proof of the corresponding theorem for the unitary subgroup (p. 130). We first prove that any homogeneous polynomial in the n^2 elements of an $n \times n$ matrix B which vanishes when these elements are the elements of a unimodular matrix A must vanish identically. Any such polynomial of degree m may be written in the form $c^{\alpha_1 \cdots \alpha_m}_{\beta_1 \cdots \beta_m} b^{\beta_1}_{\alpha_1} \cdots b^{\beta_m}_{\alpha_m}$ where the coefficients $c^{j_1 \cdots j_m}_{k_1 \cdots k_m}$ may, without any loss of generality, be taken as symmetric in the superscripts (j) and in the subscripts (k). We are given that $c^{\alpha_1 \cdots \alpha_m}_{\beta_1 \cdots \beta_m} a^{\beta_1}_{\alpha_1} \cdots a^{\beta_m}_{\alpha_m} = 0$ when the variables $(a_j{}^k)$ are conditioned by the single equation $\det A = 1$. On forming the differential of $c^{\alpha_1 \cdots \alpha_m}_{\beta_1 \cdots \beta_m} a^{\beta_1}_{\alpha_1} \cdots a^{\beta_m}_{\alpha_m}$ we obtain m terms (each of which is an emmuple summation) but, owing to the symmetry of the coefficients $c^{j_1 \cdots j_m}_{k_1 \cdots k_m}$ these are all the same. Hence, on writing for the moment $c^{\alpha_1 \cdots \alpha_{m-1} j_m}_{\beta_1 \cdots \beta_{m-1} k_m} a^{\beta_1}_{\alpha_1} \cdots a^{\beta_{m-1}}_{\alpha_{m-1}} = f^{j_m}_{k_m}$ we have $f^{\alpha_m}_{\beta_m} da^{\beta_m}_{\alpha_m} = 0$. The differential of $\det A$ is found by taking, in turn, the differential of each row and adding the results so that it is $A_\beta{}^\alpha \, da_\alpha{}^\beta$ where $A_s{}^r$ is the cofactor of $a_r{}^s$ in the expansion of $\det A$. Hence we must have $f_\beta{}^\alpha \, da_\alpha{}^\beta = 0$ where the differentials $da_j{}^k$ are connected by the *single* relation $A_\beta{}^\alpha \, da_\alpha{}^\beta = 0$. Hence $f_j{}^k = \lambda A_j{}^k$ where λ is an, as yet, undetermined multiplier. To determine it we substitute back in the original relation which now appears in the condensed form $f_\beta{}^\alpha a_\alpha{}^\beta = 0$ and find $\lambda \det A = 0$ i. e. $\lambda = 0$ (since $\det A = 1$). Hence $f_j{}^k = 0$ or $c^{\alpha_1 \cdots \alpha_{m-1} k_m}_{\beta_1 \cdots \beta_{m-1} j_m} a^{\beta_1}_{\alpha_1} \cdots a^{\beta_{m-1}}_{\alpha_{m-1}} = 0$. Proceeding with each of these homogeneous polynomials of degree $m - 1$ in precisely the same way (in other words, using the principle of mathematical induction) we are forced to the conclusion $c^{k_1 \cdots k_m}_{j_1 \cdots j_m} = 0$ so that $c^{\alpha_1 \cdots \alpha_m}_{\beta_1 \cdots \beta_m} b^{\beta_1}_{\alpha_1} \cdots b^{\beta_m}_{\alpha_m} = 0$. If then $\{D(A)\} = \{P(A)\}$ were reducible (hence completely reducible) the collection $\{P(B)\}$ would also be reducible, contrary to hypothesis; in fact the assumed analysability of $\{D(A)\}$ is expressed by the fact that there exists a transforming matrix T (with elements independent of A) such that

$$T^{-1} D(A) T = D_1(A) \dotplus D_2(A).$$

Each of the equations implied by this matrix equation expresses the vanishing of a homogeneous polynomial in the elements of A. Hence these polynomials must vanish identically so that

$$T^{-1} P(B) T = P_1(B) \dotplus P_2(B).$$

The results of the present section may be expressed concisely by the statement: *the rational representations of the unimodular subgroup furnish nothing new.* They are all completely reducible and the irreducible representations are obtained by the selection principle from the irreducible (hence homogeneous) rational integral representations of the full linear group. Their characters are $\phi_{(\lambda)}(\mathbf{s})$ where (λ) is a partition of m (the degree of the representation) containing not more than n non-zero elements (where n is the dimension of the unimodular group) and $s_k = Tr(A^k)$. No two of these irreducible representations can have the same characters if they are of the same degree m; for an assumed relation $\phi_{(\lambda')}(\mathbf{s}) = \phi_{(\lambda)}(\mathbf{s})$ valid when $s_k = Tr(A^k)$, $\det A = 1$ would imply $\phi_{(\lambda')}(\mathbf{s}) = \phi_{(\lambda)}(\mathbf{s})$ valid when $s_k = Tr(B^k)$, $\det B$ arbitrary (since the $\phi_{(\lambda)}(\mathbf{s})$, as polynomials in $(\mathbf{s})$, are polynomials, homogeneous of degree m, in the elements of B). But the characters of the irreducible representations $M_{(\lambda')}(B), M_{(\lambda)}(B)$ of the full linear group are different if $(\lambda) \neq (\lambda')$ (p. 129); hence the corresponding characters of the unimodular subgroup are different if $(\lambda) \neq (\lambda')$. In other words *two irreducible rational representations of the unimodular group are equivalent if they have the same characters.*

2. The rational representations of the extended unimodular group.

The extended unimodular group, of dimension n, consists of all $n \times n$ matrices whose determinants $= \pm 1$. It contains the unimodular group as a subgroup of index 2 (hence invariant). Denoting, as before, by A a typical element of the unimodular group *any* matrix C of the extended unimodular group whose determinant $= -1$ is of the form $C = JA$ where J is a *particular* such matrix. We shall take $J = \begin{pmatrix} -1 & 0 \\ 0 & E_{n-1} \end{pmatrix}$ so that $J^2 = E_n$; then the unimodular group $H = \{A\}$ possesses in the extended unimodular group H' the two cosets $H_1 = H$, $H_2 = \{JA\}$. Let Γ' be any non-analysable rational representation of H'; it induces, by the selection principle, a representation $\Gamma = \{D(A)\}$ of H. So far as we yet know Γ may be reducible; if it is it must be completely reducible (by the result of the preceding section) and a typical matrix of it may be presented in the form

$$D(A) = D_1(A) \dotplus \cdots \dotplus D_k(A) \tag{7.3}$$

where $\{D_j(A)\}$ is an irreducible rational representation of H, $j = 1, 2, \cdots, k$. Now J sends any element A of H into an element $\tilde{A}$ of H: $\tilde{A} = J^{-1}AJ$ and the collection $\{\tilde{D}_j(A)\}$ defined by $\tilde{D}_j(A) = D_j(\tilde{A}) = D_j(J^{-1}AJ)$ constitutes a representation of H (by the reasoning of p. 173) known as the conjugate of $\{D_j(A)\}$. Since $\{D_j(A)\}$

may be imbedded in a representation $\{P_j(B)\}$ of the full linear group we have

$$\tilde{D}_j(A) = D_j(\tilde{A}) = P_j(\tilde{A}) = P_j(J^{-1}AJ)$$
$$= P_j(J^{-1})P_j(A)P_j(J) = (P_j(J))^{-1}D_j(A)P_j(J)$$

so that $\{\tilde{D}_j(A)\}$ coincides with its conjugate $\{D_j(A)\}$. Denoting by K the matrix which corresponds to J in the representation Γ' of H' we have, since Γ is imbedded in Γ'

$$K\tilde{D}(A) = KD(J^{-1}AJ) = D(A)K, \tag{7.4}$$

and if K, when written as a block matrix of the type determined by (7.3) is

$$K = \begin{pmatrix} K_1^1 & \cdots & K_k^1 \\ \cdot & & \cdot \\ \cdot & & \cdot \\ K_1^k & \cdots & K_k^k \end{pmatrix}$$

(7.4) yields the equations (since $\tilde{D}(A) = \sum_{j=1}^{k} D_j(J^{-1}AJ) = \sum_{j=1}^{k} \tilde{D}_j(A)$)

$$K_p^q\tilde{D}_p(A) = D_q(A)K_p^q; \qquad p, q = 1, 2, \cdots, k. \tag{7.5}$$

If the irreducible representations $\{D_p(A)\}, \{D_q(A)\}$ are non-equivalent the irreducible representations $\{\tilde{D}_p(A)\}, \{D_q(A)\}$ are non-equivalent, since $\{\tilde{D}_p(A)\}$ and $\{D_p(A)\}$ are equivalent and so, by Schur's lemma, $K_p^q = 0$; an interchange of p and q yielding $K_q^p = 0$. If, then, $\{D_1(A)\}, \cdots, \{D_r(A)\}$ are equivalent whilst no one of the remaining representations $\{D_{r+1}(A)\}, \cdots, \{D_k(A)\}$ are equivalent to $\{D_1(A)\}$ all K_p^q, K_q^p vanish for which p belongs to the set $(1, \cdots, r)$ and q to the set $(r+1, \cdots, k)$; there being no lack of generality in denoting by $\{D_2(A)\}, \cdots, \{D_r(A)\}$ the representations in the set $\{D_j(A)\}$ which are equivalent to $\{D_1(A)\}$ since this can always be arranged, if necessary, by means of a transforming permutation matrix. Since the matrices of the representation Γ' of H are of the forms $D(A), KD(A)$ it follows (in order not to contradict the hypothecated non-analysability of Γ') that *no two of the irreducible representations* $\{D_j(A)\}$ *of* H *are non-equivalent.* We may, therefore, by a proper choice of basis, write

$$D(A) = E_k \times D_1(A) \tag{7.6}$$

and the equations (7.5) then appear in the form

$$K_p^q\tilde{D}_1(A) = D_1(A)K_p^q; \qquad p, q = 1, \cdots, k. \tag{7.7}$$

The equivalence of $\{\tilde{D}_1(A)\}$ and $\{D_1(A)\}$ is expressed by the formula $\tilde{D}_1(A) = T^{-1}D_1(A)T$ and so (7.7) implies $K_p^qT^{-1}D_1(A)T = D_1(A)K_p^q$

or, equivalently, $(K_p{}^qT^{-1})D_1(A) = D_1(A)(K_p{}^qT^{-1})$. Hence, by Schur's lemma, $K_p{}^qT^{-1}$ is a scalar matrix:

$$K_p{}^q = f_p{}^qT; \qquad K = F \times T \tag{7.8}$$

where F is a $k \times k$ matrix and T is the matrix $P_1(J)$ which transforms $\{D_1(A)\}$ into $\{\bar{D}_1(A)\}$. It should be observed that if we effect a change of basis for the representation Γ' of H' by means of a transforming matrix R of the type $S \times E_{d_1}$ (where S is a $k \times k$ matrix and d_1 is the dimension of $D_1(A)$) the matrices $D(A) = E_k \times D_1(A)$ are unaffected since

$$\begin{aligned}(S \times E_{d_1})^{-1}&(E_k \times D_1(A))(S \times E_{d_1})\\ &= (S^{-1} \times E_{d_1})(E_k \times D_1(A))(S \times E_{d_1}) = E_k \times D_1(A)\end{aligned}$$

whilst K undergoes the transformation

$$K \rightarrow (S \times E_{d_1})^{-1}(F \times T)(S \times E_{d_1}) = S^{-1}FS \times T$$

so that the change of basis for Γ' induces the transformation of F by S. Since K and $T = P_1(J)$ correspond to J in the representations Γ' and $\{P_1(B)\}$ of H' and the full linear group, respectively, and since $J^2 = E_n$ we have $K^2 = E_d$, $T^2 = E_{d_1}$ where d is the common dimension of Γ' and Γ and d_1 is the dimension of $\{D_1(A)\}$. Since $K^2 = (F \times T)(F \times T) = F^2 \times T^2$ we have $E_d = F^2 \times E_{d_1}$ so that $F^2 = E_k$. On introducing a new basis for Γ', if necessary, so that F is presented in its Schur canonical form (p. 25) we have, since $F^2 = E_k$,

$$F = \begin{pmatrix} E_{k'} & 0 \\ 0 & -E_{k''} \end{pmatrix}; \; k' + k'' = k.$$

But this apparently implies that $K = F \times T$ is analysable and, hence, the analysability, contrary to hypothesis, of Γ' whose matrices are $\{D(A)\} = \{E_k \times D_1(A)\}$ and $KD(A) = \{F \times TD_1(A)\}$. The only loophole for escape from this dilemma is that $k = 1$ in which case $F = \pm 1, K = \pm P_1(J)$. Hence the representation Γ of H which is obtained, by means of the selection principle, from any given non-analysable representation of H' is irreducible and Γ' is of the form $\{D(A), \pm P(J)D(A)\}$ where $P(J)$ is the matrix corresponding to J in the irreducible rational integral representation of the full linear group in which the irreducible representation $\{D(A)\}$ of the unimodular group is imbedded. When the positive sign is taken $\Gamma' = \{D(A) = P(A); P(J)D(A) = P(JA)\}$ is imbedded in the irreducible representation $P(B)$ of the full linear group. Whichever sign is taken Γ' is irreducible since the subset $\Gamma = \{D(A)\}$ is irreducible. Hence every non-analysable rational representation of the extended unimodular group is irreducible so that *reducibility* and *complete reducibility* are synonymous for rational representations of the extended unimodular group (just as they are for rational representations of the unimodular group, or of the full linear group). All irreducible representations of the extended unimodular group are found by taking an irreducible rational integral representation $\{P(B)\}$ of the full linear group and setting $\Gamma' = \{P(A); P(JA)\}$ or $\Gamma'' = \{P(A); -P(JA)\}$, A running over the unimodular group and $J^2 = E_n$, $\det J = -1$. If C denotes an arbitrary element of the extended unimodular group.

$$\Gamma' = \{P(C)\}; \quad \Gamma'' = \{\det CP(C)\}.$$

3. The continuous representations of the unimodular group.

If A is an arbitrary element of the n dimensional unimodular group H and if $\{D(A)\}$ is a representation Γ of H we say that Γ is continuous at a "point" A of H if the elements of $D(A)$ are, each and every one, continuous functions of the elements $(a_s{}^r)$ of A at the set of values $a_s{}^r$; this is equivalent (p. 54) to the statement

$$|D(A + \Delta A) - D(A)| \rightarrow 0 \text{ with } |\Delta A|.$$

If B is *any* point of H we have $D(B) = D(BA^{-1})D(A)$, and, ΔB being arbitrary we define $A + \Delta A$, and hence ΔA, by the equation

$$(7.9) \qquad (A + \Delta A) = AB^{-1}(B + \Delta B); \quad \Delta A = AB^{-1}\Delta B$$

so that as $\Delta B \rightarrow 0$, $\Delta A \rightarrow 0$. Then

$$D(B + \Delta B) = D(BA^{-1})D(A + \Delta A)$$

so that

$$D(B + \Delta B) - D(B) = D(BA^{-1})(D(A + \Delta A) - D(A))$$

implying $D(B + \Delta B) - D(B) \rightarrow 0$ with ΔB. In other words a representation Γ of H which is continuous at any *one given* point A of H is continuous at *each and every* point B of H. The only discontinuous representations of H are those which are everywhere discontinuous. In the derivation of this result no specific properties of H were used other than the fact that all $A + \Delta A$ defined by (7.9) belong to H if $|\Delta B|$ is sufficiently small. We understand in what follows that all representations referred to are *continuous*.

If s is any real number the matrix

$$A(s) = \left(\begin{array}{cc|c} 1 & 0 & 0 \\ s & 1 & \\ \hline 0 & & E_{n-2} \end{array}\right)$$

is a member of H and the collection $\{A(s)\}$ is an Abelian subgroup K

of H; it being evident that $A(s)A(t) = A(s+t) = A(t)A(s)$. The collection of 2×2 matrices $\tilde{A}(s) = \begin{pmatrix} 1 & 0 \\ s & 1 \end{pmatrix}$ is a representation of this subgroup and hence its symmetrized Kronecker m-th power (p. 74)

$$[\tilde{A}(s)]_{(m)} = \begin{bmatrix} 1 & 0 & 0 & \cdot & \cdot \\ s & 1 & 0 & \cdot & \cdot \\ s^2 & 2s & 1 & \cdot & \cdot \\ s^m & \binom{m}{1} s^{m-1} & \binom{m}{2} s^{m-2} & \cdot & \cdot & 1 \end{bmatrix}$$

is a representation of K. That this representation is non-analysable follows from the fact that the only matrices which commute with every matrix of $[\tilde{A}(s)]_{(m)}$ have all their characteristic numbers equal; it being at once clear, on developing the matrix equation

$$[\tilde{A}(s)]_{(m)} P = P[\tilde{A}(s)]_{(m)}$$

that P must be a triangle matrix (i. e. a matrix with all elements above the main diagonal zero) with all its diagonal elements equal. We now show that *any real continuous non-analysable* representation, of dimension $m+1$, of K is equivalent to $[\tilde{A}(s)]_{(m)} e^{\alpha s}$, α an arbitrary real constant. To do this we denote the matrices of any such representation of K by $F(s)$ so that $F(s)$ has, for every s, only one characteristic number $\lambda(s)$ (p. 39) (since the collection $\{F(t)\}$ is non-analysable and $F(s)$ commutes with every member of it). $\lambda(s)$ is a continuous function of the elements of $F(s)$ and, hence, of s since the representation $\{F(s)\}$ is assumed to be a continuous representation of K. Furthermore it satisfies the equation $\lambda(s+t) = \lambda(s)\lambda(t)$ since $\lambda(s)\lambda(t)$ is a characteristic number of $F(s)F(t)$ (p. 44) and this product being $= F(s+t)$ has only one characteristic number, namely, $\lambda(s+t)$. Hence, (p. 32) $\lambda(s) = e^{\alpha s}$ where α is a real constant ($\lambda(s) \neq 0$ since $F(s)$ is non-singular). The quotient $G(s) = F(s)/\lambda(s) = F(s)e^{-\alpha s}$ furnishes again a representation of K and all the characteristic numbers of $G(s)$ are unity, every s; hence $L(s) = G(s) - E_{m+1}$ has all its characteristic numbers zero so that $(L(s))^{m+1} = 0$. Denoting $L(1)$ by C we have $C^{m+1} = 0$ so that, if n is any positive integer, the matrix

$$(E_{m+1} + C)^n = E_{m+1} + \binom{n}{1} C + \cdot \cdot \cdot + \binom{n}{m} C^m = H(n), \text{ say.}$$

Hence $H(n)H(n') = H(n+n')$ if n, n' are any two positive integers. If s is any real number the matrix

$$H(s) = E_{m+1} + \binom{s}{1} C + \cdots + \binom{s}{m} C^m,$$

where

$$\binom{s}{j} = \frac{s(s-1)\cdots(s-j+1)}{j!},$$

has all its elements polynomials of degree $\leq m$ in s. Hence the equation $H(s)H(t) = H(s+t)$ being valid for *all* positive integral values of s, t must be an identity, i. e. valid for all real values of s, t. Continuing now with the argument of pp. 45-46, we find $G(s) = H(s)$, every real s; so that

$$F(s) = \{E_{m+1} + \binom{s}{1} C + \cdots + \binom{s}{m} C^m\} e^{\alpha s}.$$

If the constant matrix C were analysable the representation $F(s)$ would, accordingly, be analysable contrary to hypothesis. Hence C must have only one elementary divisor of degree $m+1$ (p. 37) or, equivalently, $C^m \neq 0$. Now a particular non-analysable representation of dimension $m+1$ of K is furnished by $\tilde{F}(s) = [\tilde{A}(s)]_{(m)}$; for this representation $\alpha = 0$ so that $\tilde{F}(s)$ is necessarily of the type

$$F(s) = E_{m+1} + \binom{s}{1} \tilde{C} + \cdots + \binom{s}{m} \tilde{C}^m$$

where $\tilde{C} = \tilde{F}(1) - E_{m+1}$ has but one elementary divisor i. e. $\tilde{C}^m \neq 0$. Hence $\tilde{C}$ is equivalent to C implying $F(s)$ equivalent to $\tilde{F}(s)e^{\alpha s}$. Any representation whatsoever of K, i. e. any collection of non-singular matrices $M(s)$ for which

$$M(s)M(t) = M(s+t),$$

being representable as a direct sum of non-analysable representations of K, it follows that, no matter what basis is chosen, the elements of $M(s)$ must all be of the form $\Sigma p_j(t)e^{\alpha_j t}$ where the $p_j(t)$ are polynomials in t and the α_j are constants.

Denoting by $\tilde{T}$ the 2×2 unimodular matrix $\begin{pmatrix} \alpha & 0 \\ 0 & \alpha^{-1} \end{pmatrix}$, $\alpha \neq 0$, the transform of $\tilde{A}(s)$ by $\tilde{T}$ is $A(\alpha^2 s)$:

$$\begin{pmatrix} \alpha^{-1} & 0 \\ 0 & \alpha \end{pmatrix}\begin{pmatrix} 1 & 0 \\ s & 1 \end{pmatrix}\begin{pmatrix} \alpha & 0 \\ 0 & \alpha^{-1} \end{pmatrix} = \begin{pmatrix} 1 & 0 \\ \alpha^2 s & 1 \end{pmatrix}.$$

If, then $T = \begin{pmatrix} \tilde{T} & 0 \\ 0 & E_{n-2} \end{pmatrix}$ (so that T is a member of H) we have

$$T^{-1}A(s)T = A(\alpha^2 s). \tag{7.10}$$

Let Γ be any representation of K and denote by $M(s)$ the matrix of Γ which corresponds to the element $A(s)$ of K. Then $M(s)M(t) = M(s+t)$ so that $M(s)$ is of the form $\sum_0^k R_j(s)e^{\alpha_j s}$ where the α_j are distinct constants and the elements of each of the matrices $R_j(s)$, $j=0,\cdots,k$ are polynomials in s. If one of the α_j is zero we separate it from the rest and write

$$(7.11) \qquad M(s) = R_0(s) + \sum_1^k R_j(s)e^{\alpha_j s}$$

where the α_j are distinct constants, none of which is zero, and where $R_0(s)$ is the zero matrix if none of the $(\alpha_0, \alpha_1, \cdots, \alpha_k)$ vanish. If N is the matrix of Γ which corresponds to the element T of H the equation (7.10) implies

$$N^{-1}M(s)N = M(\alpha^2 s)$$

and on writing $N^{-1}R_j(s)N = Q_j(s)$ this appears as

$$(7.12) \quad Q_0(s) + \sum_1^k Q_j(s)e^{\alpha_j(s)} = R_0(\alpha^2 s) + \sum_1^k R_j(\alpha^2 s)e^{\alpha^2\alpha_j s}.$$

On choosing α^2 distinct from any of the ratios α_p/α_q, $p, q = 1, \cdots, k$, the $2k$ numbers α_j, $\alpha^2\alpha_j$ are all distinct and no one of them is zero. Now it is clear that if $n_1 \neq n_2$ and if $P_1(s), P_2(s)$ are any two polynomials in s an assumed relation $P_1(s)e^{n_1 s} + P_2(s)e^{n_2 s} \equiv 0$ implies $P_1(s) \equiv 0$, $P_2(s) \equiv 0$ simply because e^s never vanishes. In fact if $P_1(s) \not\equiv 0$ our assumed relation yields $e^{(n_1-n_2)s} = -\dfrac{P_2(s)}{P_1(s)}$, $e^{(n_2-n_1)s} = -\dfrac{P_1(s)}{P_2(s)}$ forcing $P_2(s)$ and $P_1(s)$ to be numerical constants (since if either is not a value of s could be found which would make it vanish). But this would force $(n_1-n_2)s$ to be constant contrary to the hypothesis $n_1 \neq n_2$. It follows that if n_1, n_2, n_3 are three distinct numbers an assumed relation $P_1(s)e^{n_1 s} + P_2(s)e^{n_2 s} + P_3(s)e^{n_3 s} \equiv 0$, where the P_1, P_2, P_3 are polynomials in s, implies $P_1(s) \equiv 0$, $P_2(s) \equiv 0$, $P_3(s) \equiv 0$. In fact let k_1, k_2, k_3 be the degrees of $P_1(s), P_2(s), P_3(s)$, respectively, and set $n_2 - n_1 = \alpha$, $n_3 - n_1 = \beta$ so that $P_2(s)e^{\alpha s} + P_3(s)e^{\beta s} = -P_1(s)$. On differentiating this k_1+1 times we obtain $\{(D+\alpha)^{k_1+1}P_2(s)\}e^{\alpha s} + \{(D+\beta)^{k_1+1}P_3(s)\}e^{\beta s} = 0$, where $D = d/ds$, and the fact that $\alpha \neq \beta$ implies $\{(D+\alpha)^{k_1+1}P_2(s)\} \equiv 0$, $\{(D+\beta)^{k_1+1}P_3(s)\} \equiv 0$. But $(D+\alpha)^{k_1+1}P_2(s)$ is a polynomial of which the term of highest degree is α^{k_1+1} times the term of highest degree in $P_2(s)$; hence $P_2(s) \equiv 0$ (in which case $P_1(s) \equiv 0$, $P_3(s) \equiv 0$ since our assumed relation reduces to the two term relation $P_1(s)e^{n_1 s} + P_3(s)e^{n_3 s} = 0$) since $\alpha \neq 0$. Proceeding in this way it follows that if $n_1, n_2, \cdots, n_q$ are q numbers, no two of which are equal, an assumed relation of the type

$$P_1(s)e^{n_1 s} + \cdots + P_q(s)e^{n_q s} = 0$$

where the $P_1, \cdots, P_q$ are polynomials in s implies the identical vanishing of these polynomials. This means, further, that an assumed relation $R_1(s)e^{n_1 s} + \cdots + R_q(s)e^{n_q s} = 0$, where the $R_1, \cdots, R_q$ are *rational* functions of s implies the identical vanishing of each of these rational functions; for the rational functions can be written with a common denominator: $R_j(s) = P_j(s) \div \phi(s)$ and the identical vanishing of $P_j(s)$ forces that of $R_j(s)$, $j = 1, \cdots, q$. It follows, therefore, from (7.12) that $R_j(s) \equiv 0$, $j = 1, \cdots, k$, so that

$$M(s) = R_0(s).$$

Hence the matrices of any continuous representation Γ of the unimodular n-dimensional group H are such that the elements of those matrices of Γ which correspond to the matrices $A(s)$ of H, s real, are rational functions of s, i. e. of the elements of $A(s)$. Starting with the 2×2 matrix $\tilde{A}'(s) = \begin{pmatrix} 1 & s \\ 0 & 1 \end{pmatrix}$ we may repeat the argument verbatim and we find that the elements of those matrices $M^\dagger(s)$ of Γ which correspond to the matrices

$$A'(s) = \begin{pmatrix} \tilde{A}'(s) & 0 \\ 0 & E_{n-2} \end{pmatrix}$$

of H are rational functions of the elements of $A'(s)$. Let now P be any $n \times n$ permutation matrix; since $PP' = E_n$, $\det P = \pm 1$; we refer to those permutation matrices for which $\det P = 1$ as *proper* (those for which $\det P = -1$ being termed *improper*) and observe that $A'(s)$ is the transform of $A(s)$ by the improper permutation matrix

$$P = \begin{pmatrix} 0 & 1 & \\ 1 & 0 & 0 \\ & 0 & E_{n-2} \end{pmatrix}.$$

Hence the transform of $A(s)$ by any permutation matrix, proper or improper, is the transform of either $A(s)$ or $A'(s)$ by a proper permutation matrix, i. e. by an element of H. Let then $B(s)$ be the transform of $A(s)$ by any permutation matrix so that either $B(s) = P^{-1}A(s)P$ or $B(s) = P^{-1}A'(s)P$ where P is a proper permutation matrix. If T is the matrix of Γ which corresponds to P and $N(s)$ the matrix of Γ which corresponds to $B(s)$ we have either

$$N(s) = K^{-1}M(s)K \text{ or } N(s) = K^{-1}M^{\dagger}(s)K$$

so that, in either event, the elements of those matrices of Γ which correspond to the matrices $B(s)$ of H are rational functions of the elements of $B(s)$. We now show that any element A of H may be represented as the product of a number of matrices $B_1(s_1)\cdots B_q(s_q)$, where the $s_1, \cdots, s_q$ are rational real functions of the elements of A; it follows from this result that the elements of those matrices of Γ which correspond to real elements of H are rational functions of the elements of the matrices of H: i. e. *every continuous representation of the real unimodular n-dimensional group is rational.*

We begin the proof of the theorem that any n-dimensional unimodular matrix may be factored in the form $B_1(s_1)\cdots B_q(s_q)$ by remarking that this is almost evident when $n = 2$. In fact let $A = \begin{pmatrix} a & c \\ b & d \end{pmatrix}$, $ad - bc = 1$ be any 2×2 unimodular matrix; then either $a = 0$ or $a \neq 0$. If $a = 0$, $c = -b^{-1}$ and

$$A = \begin{pmatrix} 0 & -b^{-1} \\ b & d \end{pmatrix} = \begin{pmatrix} 1 & 0 \\ b(1-d) & 1 \end{pmatrix}\begin{pmatrix} 1 & -b^{-1} \\ 0 & 1 \end{pmatrix}\begin{pmatrix} 1 & 0 \\ b & 1 \end{pmatrix}$$

If $a \neq 0$

$$A = \begin{pmatrix} a & c \\ b & d \end{pmatrix} = \begin{pmatrix} 1 & 0 \\ ba^{-1} & 1 \end{pmatrix}\begin{pmatrix} a & 0 \\ 0 & a^{-1} \end{pmatrix}\begin{pmatrix} 1 & ca^{-1} \\ 0 & 1 \end{pmatrix}.$$

and

$$\begin{pmatrix} a & 0 \\ 0 & a^{-1} \end{pmatrix} = \begin{pmatrix} 1 & 0 \\ \alpha & 1 \end{pmatrix}\begin{pmatrix} 1 & -a\delta \\ 0 & 1 \end{pmatrix}\begin{pmatrix} 1 & 0 \\ -a\alpha & 1 \end{pmatrix}\begin{pmatrix} 1 & \delta \\ 0 & 1 \end{pmatrix}$$

where $\alpha\delta = (a-1)/a^2$, so that every 2×2 unimodular matrix may be presented as the product of matrices of the types $A(s) = \begin{pmatrix} 1 & 0 \\ s & 1 \end{pmatrix}$, $A'(s) = \begin{pmatrix} 1 & s \\ 0 & 1 \end{pmatrix}$, where each s is a rational function of the elements of A. For n-dimensional unimodular matrices ($n > 2$) we use the method of mathematical induction; we assume the theorem true for matrices of dimension $n-1$ and show that this assumption implies its validity for matrices of dimension n. Let, then, A be a unimodular matrix of dimension n and denote by $A_s{}^r$ the cofactor of $a_r{}^s$ in the expansion of $\det A$. There is no lack of generality in assuming that $A_n{}^n \neq 0$ since, in any neighborhood of a matrix A for which $A_n{}^n = 0$, there are matrices for which $A_n{}^n \neq 0$ so that, since the theorem we wish to prove expresses the vanishing of rational functions of the elements of A, it will be true for those matrices for which $A_n^{\ n} = 0$ if it is true for those matrices for which $A_n^{\ n} \neq 0$. Now the matrix $A(s)$ is the matrix of the transformation: $x \to x'$ where $x'_2 = sx_1 + x_2$; $x'_j = x_j$, $j \neq 2$ so that, for any fixed j, the matrix of the transformation $x \to x'$ where $x'_n = s_j x_j + x_n$; $x'_k = x_k$, $k \neq n$, is of the type $B(s)$. The product of the $n - 1$ matrices obtained in this way by giving j the values $1, 2, \cdots, n - 1$ is the matrix

$$\begin{pmatrix} E_{n-1} & 0 \\ x^* & 1 \end{pmatrix}$$

where x^* is the $1 \times n - 1$ matrix $(s_1, \cdots, s_{n-1})$. Similarly the unimodular matrix $\begin{pmatrix} E_{n-1} & y \\ 0 & 1 \end{pmatrix}$ where y is any real $n - 1 \times 1$ matrix is a product of factors of the type $B(s)$ (the s being, again, rational functions of the matrix which is being factored). Since the reciprocal of any $B(s)$ is also a $B(s)$ (being in fact $B(-s)$) the reciprocals of the matrices $\begin{pmatrix} E_{n-1} & 0 \\ x^* & 1 \end{pmatrix}$, $\begin{pmatrix} E_{n-1} & y \\ 0 & 1 \end{pmatrix}$ are also factorable as products of matrices $B(s)$. If we set $y^j = A_n^{\ j}/A_n^{\ n}$ it is at once seen that

$$A \cdot \begin{pmatrix} E_{n-1} & y \\ 0 & 1 \end{pmatrix} = \begin{pmatrix} A_{n-1} & 0 \\ x^* & 1/A_n^{\ n} \end{pmatrix}$$

where A_{n-1} is the matrix obtained from A by erasing its last row and column and x^* is the $1 \times n - 1$ matrix formed by the first $n - 1$ elements of the n-th row of A. If we set $(z^*) = (z_1, \cdots, z_{n-1})$ where $z_j = A_j^{\ n}/A_n^{\ n}$, $j = 1, \cdots, n - 1$ the product

$$\begin{pmatrix} E_{n-1} & 0 \\ z^* & 1 \end{pmatrix} A \begin{pmatrix} E_{n-1} & y \\ 0 & 1 \end{pmatrix} = \begin{pmatrix} E_{n-1} & 0 \\ z^* & 1 \end{pmatrix} \begin{pmatrix} A_{n-1} & 0 \\ x^* & 1/A_n^{\ n} \end{pmatrix}$$

$$= \begin{pmatrix} A_{n-1} & 0 \\ 0 & 1/A_n^{\ n} \end{pmatrix} = \begin{pmatrix} A_n^{\ n} & & 0 \\ & E_{n-2} & \\ 0 & & 1/A_n^{\ n} \end{pmatrix} \begin{pmatrix} B_{n-1} & 0 \\ 0 & 1 \end{pmatrix}$$

where B_{n-1} is the $n - 1 \times n - 1$ matrix obtained from A_{n-1} by dividing its first row by $A_n^{\ n}$. We have already seen that the 2×2 matrix $\begin{pmatrix} a & 0 \\ 0 & 1/a \end{pmatrix}$ is the product of a set of factors $A(s)$ and this implies that the $n \times n$ matrix $\begin{pmatrix} A_n^{\ n} & & 0 \\ & E_{n-2} & \\ 0 & & 1/A_n^{\ n} \end{pmatrix}$ is the product of a set of factors $B(s)$. Also our induction hypothesis tells us that B_{n-1} is the product of a set of factors $B(s)$ (of dimension $n - 1$). By adding to each of these a last row and column all of whose elements are zero save the diagonal element which is unity we obtain a set of factors $B(s)$, of dimension n, whose product $=\begin{pmatrix} B_{n-1} & 0 \\ 0 & 1 \end{pmatrix}$. Hence A is a product of a set of factors $B(s)$ the s of each factor being a rational function of the elements of A.

Having proven that every continuous representation of the *real* unimodular n-dimensional group is rational we pass to a consideration of the continuous representations of the full unimodular group H. If Γ is any continuous representation of this group the matrices $M(s)$ of Γ which correspond to the matrices $A(s)$ (s now complex) of H satisfy, as before, the equation $M(s)M(t) = M(s+t)$. On setting $s = s_1 + is_2$, s_1, s_2 real, $M(s) = M(s_1)M(is_2) = M(s_1)N(s_2)$ where $N(s_2) = M(is_2)$. Both $M(s_1)$ and $N(s_2)$ satisfy the basic underlying equation $F(s)F(t) = F(s+t)$ and every $M(s_1)$ commutes with every $N(s_2)$. Hence (7.11)

$$M(s_1) = R_0(s_1) + \Sigma R_j(s_1) e^{\alpha_j s_1}$$
$$N(s_2) = S_0(s_2) + \Sigma S_j(s_2) e^{\beta_j s_2}$$

from which it follows that

$$M(s) = M(s_1)N(s_2) = T_0(s_1, s_2) + \Sigma T_j(s_1, s_2) e^{\alpha_j s_1 + \beta_j s_2}.$$

where the elements of the matrices T_0, T_j are rational functions of the real and imaginary parts s_1, s_2 of s. We obtain in precisely the same way as (7.12) was obtained

$$Q_0(s_1, s_2) + \Sigma Q_j(s_1, s_2) e^{\alpha_j s_1 + \beta_j s_2} = T_0(\alpha^2 s_1, \alpha^2 s_2) + \Sigma T_j(\alpha^2 s_1, \alpha^2 s_2) e^{\alpha^2(\alpha_j s_1 + \beta_j s_2)}.$$

But the relation $\sum_j P_j(s_1, s_2) e^{\alpha_j s_1 + \beta_j s_2} = 0$, where no two of the numbers α_j or of the numbers β_j are equal, and the $P_j(s_1, s_2)$ are polynomials, implies each $P_j(s_1, s_2) \equiv 0$; in fact on fixing s_2 we have (p. 187) each $P_j(s_1, s_2) e^{\beta_j s_2} = 0$, every s_1 and this forces $P_j(s_1, s_2) = 0$ every s_1 and every s_2 since $e^{\beta_j s_2} \neq 0$. Hence $T_j(s_1, s_2) = 0$, $j = 1, 2, \cdots$ and

$$M(s) = T_0(s_1, s_2).$$

Hence every continuous representation Γ of the full unimodular group H is such that the elements of those matrices of Γ which correspond to the elements $A(s)$ of H are rational functions of the real and imaginary parts of s. This implies, since each matrix A of H is factorable as a product of matrices $B(s)$ where each s is a rational function of the elements of A, that the elements of each matrix of Γ are rational functions of the real and imaginary parts of the elements of A. Such representations are termed semi-rational so that the principal theorem concerning continuous representations of the unimodular group may be stated as follows: *all continuous representations of the unimodular group are semi-rational.*

Let $x = (x_s^r), y = (y_s^r)$ be the real and imaginary parts of the elements $a = (a_s^r)$ of any matrix A of the n-dimensional unimodular group H. Then the elements of the matrix $D(A)$ which correspond to A in a semi-rational representation Γ of H are rational functions of x and y so that the basic representation property

$$D(A_1)D(A) = D(A_1A)$$

is expressed (on regarding A_1 as fixed) by the vanishing of a set of polynomials in x, y. Let $\phi(x, y)$ be one of these polynomials so that $\phi(x, y) = 0$ for all real values of x, y for which $\det A = 1$. Since $\det A \neq 0$ not all its cofactors vanish; let A_j^k be one of the non-vanishing cofactors so that x_k^j, y_k^j may be expressed as rational functions of the remaining variables x, y (since the equation $\det A = 1$ may be written in the form $a_\alpha^j A_j^\alpha = 1$ giving $a_k^j = (1 - \sum_\alpha' a_\alpha^j A_j^\alpha)/A_j^k$ where $\sum_\alpha'$ means that the value $\alpha = k$ is omitted). On substituting these values for x_k^j, y_k^j in the polynomial $\phi(x, y)$ we obtain a polynomial $\psi(x', y')$ (where x' means the $n^2 - 1$ variables obtained from the n^2 variables x by omitting x_k^j and y' means the $n^2 - 1$ variables obtained from the n^2 variables y by omitting y_k^j) which must vanish for *all real* x', y'. Hence it must vanish identically, i. e. for *all complex* x', y'. In other words $\phi(x, y)$ must vanish for all those complex x, y for which $\det A = 1$. When x, y are complex the numbers $a_s^r = x_s^r + iy_s^r$, $b_s^r = x_s^r - iy_s^r$ are independent (and not one the conjugate of the other as is the case when x, y are real); in fact when a_s^r, b_s^r are arbitrarily given $x_s^r = \frac{1}{2}(a_s^r + b_s^r)$; $y_s^r = \frac{1}{2i}(a_s^r - b_s^r)$. The statement $\det A = 1$ is equivalent to $a_k^j = R(x', y')$, where R is a rational function of the $2n^2 - 2$ variables x', y' obtained by omitting x_k^j, y_k^j, i. e. to $x_k^j = \frac{1}{2}\{R(x', y') + R(x', -y')\}$; $y_k^j = \frac{1}{2i}\{R(x', y') - R(x', -y')\}$, since a_k^j is a rational function, *with real coefficients*, of the remaining elements a_q^p of A. A change in the sign of y' leaves x_k^j unaffected and changes the sign of y_k^j; when x, y are real this merely says that $\det A = 1$ implies $\det \bar{A} = 1$. But when x, y are arbitrary complex numbers and we set $a_s^r = x_s^r + iy_s^r$, $b_s^r = x_s^r - iy_s^r$ we see that $\det A = 1$ implies

$\det B = 1$. The elements of $D(A)$, being rational functions of x, y (x, y real), are rational functions of $a_s{}^r$ and $\bar{a}_s{}^r$ and we indicate this by writing $R(A, \bar{A})$ for $D(A)$. We have seen, then, that the equation $R(A_1, \bar{A}_1)R(A, \bar{A}) = R(A_1A, \overline{A_1A})$, assumed valid for all matrices A, A_1 for which $\det A = 1$, $\det A_1 = 1$ implies

$$(7.13) \qquad R(A_1, B_1)R(A, B) = R(A_1A, B_1B)$$

for all matrices A, A_1, B, B_1 for which $\det A = 1$, $\det A_1 = 1$, $\det B = 1$, $\det B_1 = 1$. It follows by the reasoning given on pp. 177-178 that the semi-rational representation $R(A, \bar{A})$ of the unimodular group may be imbedded in a semi-rational integral representation of the full linear group. In fact any element of $R(A, B)$ is of the type $\psi_s{}^r(A, B)/\phi(A, B)$ where the $\psi_s{}^r(A, B), \phi(A, B)$ are polynomial functions of the elements of A and B. If F, G are any two non-singular matrices we set $A = \alpha F$, $B = \beta G$ where $\alpha^n = (\det F)^{-1}$, $\beta^n = (\det F)^{-1}$, α and β being so chosen that $\alpha = 1$, $\beta = 1$ when $\det F = 1$, $\det G = 1$. On multiplying both numerator and denominator of the fraction $\dfrac{\psi_s{}^r(A, B)}{\phi(A, B)} = \dfrac{\psi_s{}^r(\alpha F, \beta G)}{\phi(\alpha F, \beta G)}$ by $\prod_{j=1}^{n-1}\prod_{k=1}^{n-1} \phi(\alpha e^{2\pi i j/n}F, \beta e^{2\pi i k/n}G)$ the denominator appears as a rational function of the elements of F and G so that $R(A, B) = R(\alpha F, \beta G)$ is of the form

$$R(A, B) = \sum_{j=0}^{n-1} \sum_{k=0}^{n-1} T_{jk}(F, G)\alpha^j\beta^k,$$

the elements of the matrices T_{jk} being rational functions of the elements of F, G. On substituting this expression in (7.13) we obtain

$$\sum_{j=0}^{n-1} \sum_{k=0}^{n-1} T_{jk}(F_1F, G_1G)(\alpha_1\alpha)^j(\beta_1\beta)^k$$
$$= \{\sum_{j=0}^{n-1} \sum_{k=0}^{n-1} T_{jk}(F_1, G_1)\alpha_1{}^j\beta_1{}^k\}\{\sum_{p=0}^{n-1} \sum_{q=0}^{n-1} T_{pq}(F, G)\alpha^p\beta^q\}.$$

On holding F_1, G_1, G fixed we find as on p. 178 that this must be an identity in α:

$$\sum_{k=0}^{n-1} T_{pk}(F_1F, G_1G)\alpha_1{}^p(\beta_1\beta)^k$$
$$= \{\sum_{j=0}^{n-1} \sum_{k=0}^{n-1} T_{jk}(F_1, G_1)\alpha_1{}^j\beta_1{}^k\}\{\sum_{q=0}^{n-1} T_{pq}(F, G)\beta^q\}.$$

Holding F_1, G_1 fixed this must be an identity, for each p, in β:

$$T_{pq}(F_1F, G_1G)\alpha_1{}^p\beta_1{}^q = \{\sum_{j=0}^{n-1} \sum_{k=0}^{n-1} T_{jk}(F_1, G_1)\alpha_1{}^j\beta_1{}^k\}T_{pq}(F, G).$$

From this we derive

$$T_{pq}(F_1F, G_1G) = T_{pq}(F_1, G_1)T_{pq}(F, G)$$
$$0 = T_{jk}(F_1, G_1)T_{pq}(F, G) \text{ if either } j \neq p \text{ or } q \neq k$$

and these imply that $T(F, G) = \sum_{j=0}^{n-1} \sum_{k=0}^{n-1} T_{jk}(F, G)$ satisfies the equation

$$(7.14) \qquad T(F_1F, G_1G) = T(F_1, G_1)T(F, G)$$

so that $T(F, \bar{F})$ is a semi-rational representation of the full linear group in which the representation Γ of the unimodular group is imbedded. For when $\det F = 1$, $\alpha = 1$ and $R(A, \bar{A}) = \sum_{j=0}^{n-1} \sum_{k=0}^{n-1} T_{jk}(F, \bar{F})\alpha^j\bar{\alpha}^k$ $= \sum_{j=0}^{n-1} \sum_{k=0}^{n-1} T_{jk}(F, \bar{F}) = T(F, \bar{F})$. Again, by the reasoning of pp. 33-34, the semi-rational representation $T(F, \bar{F})$ of the full linear group is necessarily of the form $T(F, \bar{F}) = \dfrac{P(F, \bar{F})}{(\det F)^j (\det \bar{F})^k}$; j, k non-negative integers where $P(F, \bar{F})$ is a semi-rational integral representation of the full linear group (i. e. the elements of $P(F, \bar{F})$ are polynomial functions of the real and imaginary parts of the elements of F). In fact if $\phi(F, G)$ denotes the lowest common denominator of the elements of $T(F, G)$ we write $T(F, G) = \dfrac{P(F, G)}{\phi(F, G)}$ where the elements of $P(F, G)$ and $\phi(F, G)$ have no common factor and where $\phi(F, G)$ may be supposed normalised by the condition $\phi(E, E) = 1$. From (7.14) we read off

$$(7.15) \qquad \frac{P(F_1F, G_1G)}{\phi(F_1F, G_1G)} = \frac{P(F_1, G_1) \cdot P(F, G)}{\phi(F_1, G_1) \cdot \phi(F, G)}$$

or, equivalently,

$$\phi(F_1F, G_1G)P(F, G) \div \phi(F, G) = \phi(F_1, G_1)P^{-1}(F_1, G_1)P(F_1F, G_1G).$$

Since the elements of the matrix on the right are polynomials in the elements of F and G (F_1, G_1 being held fixed) the elements of the matrix on the left must be polynomials in the elements of F and G. But the elements of $P(F, G)$ and $\phi(F, G)$ have no factor in common and so $\phi(F, G)$ must divide $\phi(F_1F, G_1G)$. Since these are both polynomials, of the same degree, in the elements of F and G the quotient must be a numerical constant whose value is found to be $\phi(F_1, G_1)$ (on setting $F = G = E_n$). Hence

$$(7.16) \qquad \phi(F_1F, G_1G) = \phi(F_1, G_1)\phi(F, G)$$

implying, from (7.15)

$$(7.17) \qquad P(F_1F, G_1G) = P(F_1, G_1)P(F, G).$$

Now it follows from (7.16) that $\phi(F, E_n)$ is a rational integral one-dimensional representation of the full linear group; for

$$\phi(F_1F, E_n) = \phi(F_1, E_n)\phi(F, E_n) \quad \text{and} \quad \phi(E_n, E_n) = 1.$$

Hence, p. 33, $\phi(F, E_n) = (\det F)^j$, j a non-negative integer. Similarly $\phi(E_n, G) = (\det G)^k$, k a non-negative integer. However it follows from (7.16) that $\phi(F, E_n)\phi(E_n, G) = \phi(F, G)$ so that

$$(7.18) \qquad \phi(F, G) = (\det F)^j (\det G)^k.$$

Hence

$$T(F, G) = \frac{P(F, G)}{(\det F)^j (\det G)^k}$$

where $P(F, \bar{F})$ is, by (7.17), a semi-rational integral representation of the full linear group. When $\det F = 1$, we have $P(F, \bar{F}) = T(F, \bar{F}) = R(F, \bar{F})$. In other words any semi-rational representation of the unimodular group (i.e. any *continuous* representation of the unimodular group) may be imbedded in a semi-rational integral representation of the full linear group. We have in fact proved more: if $R(A, \bar{A})$ is any continuous representation of the unimodular group there exists a $P(F, G)$, defined for all *pairs* of elements F, G of the full linear group, whose elements are polynomials in the elements of F, G, and which satisfies

$$(7.19) \qquad P(F_1, G_1)P(F, G) = P(F_1F, G_1G);$$

furthermore $P(A, \bar{A}) = R(A, \bar{A})$, A any element of the unimodular group. It follows at once from (7.19) that $P(F, E_n)$ is a rational integral representation of the full linear group as also is $P(E_n, G)$. Hence $P(E_n, G)$ is, if reducible, completely reducible

$$P(E_n, G) = \sum_j (E_{c_j} \times M_j(G))$$

where $\{M_j(G)\}$ is an irreducible rational integral representation of the full linear group which is contained in $P(E_n, G)$ c_j times. Since $P(E_n, G)P(F, E_n) = P(F, E_n)P(E_n, G) = P(F, G)$, $P(F, E_n)$, being commutative with every matrix of the representation $P(E_n, G)$ is of the form (p. 104)

$$P(F, E_n) = \sum_j (N_j(F) \times E_{d_j})$$

where d_j is the dimension of the irreducible representation $M_j(G)$ of the full linear group and $N_j(F)$ is of dimension c_j. Since $N_j(F) \times E_{d_j}$

may be transformed by means of a permutation matrix into $E_{d_j} \times N_j(F)$, $N_j(F)$ is a representation of the full linear group which is contained in $P(F, E_n)$ d_j times. For each value of j the Kronecker product $E_{c_j} \times M_j(G)$ is commutative with the Kronecker product $N_j(F) \times E_{d_j}$:

$$(E_{c_j} \times M_j(G))(N_j(F) \times E_{d_j}) \\ = (N_j(F) \times M_j(G)) = (N_j(F) \times E_{d_j})(E_{c_j} \times M_j(G)).$$

If $N_j(F)$ is reducible we write $N_j(F) = \sum_k (E_{c_{j,k}} \times M_k(F))$ where $M_k(F)$ is an irreducible representation of the full linear group and then

$$N_j(F) \times M_j(G) = \sum_k E_{c_{j,k}} \times M_k(F) \times M_j(G).$$

Hence

$$P(F, G) = \sum_j (N_j(F) \times M_j(G)) = \sum_{j,k} E_{c_{j,k}} \times (M_k(F) \times M_j(G))$$

so that the semi-rational representation $P(F, \bar{F})$ of the full linear group appears as the sum of representations $M_k(F) \times M_j(\bar{F})$ where the $M_j(F)$ are irreducible rational integral representations of the full linear group. If $P(F, \bar{F})$ is not analysable it must accordingly be simply a Kronecker product $M_k(F) \times M_j(\bar{F})$ and the irreducibility of $M_k(F)$, $M_j(\bar{F})$ implies that of the Kronecker product $M_k(F) \times M_j(\bar{F})$. In fact if $M_k(F) \times M_j(\bar{F})$ were reducible this would imply, by the argument of p. 191, the reducibility of $M_k(F) \times M_j(G)$, i. e. the vanishing of the set of products $(M_k(F))_s{}^r (M_j(G))_q{}^p$ where (s, q) runs over the first t of the pairs of this type and (r, p) runs over the remaining $d_k d_j - t$ of these pairs. If all the $(M_k(F))_s{}^r$ were zero the representation $\{M_k(F)\}$ of the full linear group would be reducible contrary to hypothesis; since one of the $(M_k(F))_s{}^r \neq 0$ it follows that all the $(M_j(G))_q{}^p = 0$ i. e. that $\{M_j(G)\}$ is reducible contrary to hypothesis. Hence the final principal theorem on continuous representations of the full unimodular group: *every non-analysable continuous representation of the full unimodular group is irreducible and is imbedded in* $M_k(F) \times M_j(\bar{F})$ *where* $M_k(F)$, $M_j(F)$ *are irreducible rational integral representations of the full linear group. Every reducible continuous representation of the unimodular group is analysable into a sum of non-analysable representations* $M_k(A) \times M_j(\bar{A})$.

It follows, by a repetition of the argument on pp. 180-183 that every continuous representation of the extended unimodular group is either irreducible or analysable into a sum of irreducible representations; each irreducible representation belonging to one of two types Γ', Γ'': If C is any element of the extended unimodular group $\Gamma' = \{M_k(C) \times M_j(\bar{C})\}$

whilst $\Gamma'' = \{\det C . M_k(C) \times M_j(\bar{C})\}$. In other words the irreducible rational integral representations of the full linear group are sufficient to construct all continuous representations of (a) the real unimodular group (b) the extended real unimodular group (c) the full unimodular group and (d) the extended full unimodular group; and all reducible continuous representations of these groups are analysable (= completely reducible).

4. The continuous representations of the real linear group and of the full linear group.

If B is any element of the real linear group of dimension n we denote by $r(B)$ the positive n-th root of the absolute value of $\det B$:

$$r(B) = |\det B|^{1/n}$$

and by $R(B)$ the associated scalar matrix

$$R(B) = r(B)E_n.$$

Then $B = R(B)C(B)$ where $\det C(B) = \pm 1$ so that $C(B)$ is an element of the extended, real, unimodular group. If $\Gamma = \{D(B)\}$ is a non-analysable continuous representation of the real linear group the subset of Γ obtained by letting B run over the extended unimodular group (so that $r(B) = 1$, $R(B) = E_n$, $C(B) = B$) constitutes a continuous representation Γ_1 of the extended real unimodular group H'. This representation (obtained from Γ by the principle of selection) of H' is rational and, if reducible, completely reducible. Again when B is a scalar matrix $C(B) = \pm E_n, R(B) = \pm B$; as B runs over the group of positively definite scalar matrices the corresponding elements of Γ constitute a representation Γ_2 of the group of positively definite scalar matrices. Since a scalar matrix commutes with any matrix of the same dimension any element of Γ_2 commutes with any element of Γ_1 and the relation $B = R(B)C(B)$ tells us that any element of Γ is the product of an element of Γ_1 by an element of Γ_2. Let X be a typical element of Γ_1 so that, if Γ_1 is reducible, $X = X_1 \dotplus X_2 \dotplus \cdots \dotplus X_k$. Then any element Y of Γ_2 commuting, as it does, with X will be analysable (p. 181) unless all the $X_1, X_2, \cdots, X_k$ are equivalent; but the analysability of $\Gamma_2 = \{Y\}$ would force that of Γ whose typical matrix is of the type $YX = XY$ and as this is contrary to hypothesis all X_j must be equivalent and we may write

$$X = E_k \times X_1;$$

the commutativity of Y and X (together with the irreducibility of $\{X_1\}$) forcing

$$Y = Y_1 \times E_{d_1}$$

where Y_1 is a $k \times k$ matrix and d_1 is the dimensionality of X_1. Hence the matrices of any non-analysable continuous representation of the real linear group are necessarily of the form

$$XY = (E_k \times X_1)(Y_1 \times E_{d_1}) = Y_1 \times X_1.$$

Since $Y_1 \times X_1$ is a block matrix of the type $(Y_1)_s{}^r X_1$ the Kronecker product $Y_1 \times X_1$ would certainly be analysable if Y_1 were analysable. Dropping the subscript 1 as now useless we may state this preliminary result as follows:

Any non-analysable continuous representation of the real linear group of dimension n is necessarily of the form $\{Y \times X\}$ where $\{X\}$ is an irreducible continuous (hence rational) representation of the extended real unimodular group and $\{Y\}$ is a non-analysable continuous representation of the group of positively definite scalar matrices of dimension n.

Conversely any such Kronecker product $\{Y \times X\}$ constitutes a non-analysable representation of the real linear group. That it constitutes a representation is evident since if $B = B_1 B_2$, $r(B) = r(B_1) r(B_2)$, $R(B) = R(B_1) R(B_2)$ so that $Y(B) = Y(B_1) Y(B_2)$; $C(B) = R^{-1}(B) B = C(B_1) C(B_2)$ so that $X(B) = X(B_1) X(B_2)$. Hence $(Y(B_1) \times X(B_1)) \cdot (Y(B_2) \times X(B_2)) = (Y(B_1) Y(B_2) \times X(B_1) X(B_2)) = Y(B) \times X(B)$. What we have to show is that the representation $\{Y \times X\}$ is non-analysable when $\{X\}$ is irreducible and $\{Y\}$ non-analysable. To do this let rE_n, $r > 0$ be a typical element of the group of positively definite scalar matrices of dimension n and let $Y(r)$ be the matrix of the non-analysable representation Γ_2 which corresponds to the matrix rE_n. Then $Y(r) Y(s) = Y(rs)$ and on setting $r = e^\rho$, $s = e^\sigma$, $Y(r) = Z(\rho)$ we find

$$Z(\rho)\, Z(\sigma) = Z(\rho + \sigma)$$

where the elements of $Z(\rho)$ are continuous functions of ρ (since the elements of $Y(r) = Z(\rho)$ are continuous functions of $r = e^\rho$). The non-analysability and continuity of $Z(\rho)$ tell us that $Z(\rho)$ is presentable in a properly chosen basis in the form (p. 185)

$$Z(\rho) = [\tilde{A}(\rho)]_{(m)} e^{\alpha\rho}; \qquad m = 0, 1, 2, \cdots$$

where Γ_2 is of dimension $d_2 = m + 1$, α is an arbitrary constant, and $\tilde{A}(\rho) = \begin{pmatrix} 1 & 0 \\ \rho & 1 \end{pmatrix}$. Now $Y \times X$ appears, when written in block form as $y_s{}^r X$ where $y_s{}^r = 0$, $r < s$, $y_s{}^s = r^\alpha$ every s (3.4). It is sufficient to illustrate the rest of the discussion by the case where Y is of dimension three so that

$$Y \times X = \begin{pmatrix} y_1{}^1X & 0 & 0 \\ y_1{}^2X & y_2{}^2X & 0 \\ y_1{}^3X & y_2{}^3X & y_3{}^3X \end{pmatrix}$$

Let $P = \begin{pmatrix} P_1{}^1 & P_2{}^1 & P_3{}^1 \\ P_1{}^2 & P_2{}^2 & P_3{}^2 \\ P_1{}^3 & P_2{}^3 & P_3{}^3 \end{pmatrix}$ where each $P_s{}^r$ is a square matrix of the same dimension as X and let us express the fact that P commutes with $Y \times X$. We obtain a set of equations of which one is $y_1{}^1XP_3{}^1 = y_3{}^3P_3{}^1X$; since $y_3{}^3 = y_1{}^1$ this yields $XP_3{}^1 = P_3{}^1X$ and the irreducibility of X tells us that $P_3{}^1$ is a scalar matrix: $P_3{}^1 = p_3{}^1E_{d_1}$. On equating the elements in the second (block) row and third (block) column of $P \cdot (Y \times X)$ and of $(Y \times X) \cdot P$ we find that $P_3{}^2X - XP_3{}^2$ is a scalar multiple of X, say αX, where $\alpha = \dfrac{y_1{}^2}{y_1{}^1}p_3{}^1 = \rho p_3{}^1$. Since $P_3{}^2X - XP_3{}^2$ is independent of ρ we must have $p_3{}^1 = 0$, $P_3{}^2 = p_3{}^2E_{d_1}$. Similarly, on equating the elements in the third row and column (block) we find $p_3{}^2 = 0$, $P_3{}^3 = p_3{}^3E_{d_1}$. Proceeding then to the elements in the second column we find first $P_2{}^1 = p_2{}^1E_{d_1}$; then $p_2{}^1 = 0$, $P_2{}^2 = p_2{}^2E_{d_1}$; then $p_2{}^2 = p_3{}^3$, $P_2{}^3 = p_2{}^3E_{d_1}$. Proceeding in this way we find that P, in order to commute with all the matrices $Y \times X$ must be of the form

$$P = Q \times E_{d_1}$$

where Q is a triangular matrix which commutes with all the matrices Y; in other words Q has all its characteristic numbers equal. Since $Q \times E_{d_1}$ is transformable, by means of a permutation matrix, into $E_{d_1} \times Q$, this means that P has all its characteristic numbers equal. Hence $\{Y \times X\}$ is non-analysable. On setting $\rho = \log r$ we have

$$Y(r) = [\tilde{A}\ (\log r)]_{(m)}r^{a}.$$

Since $\begin{pmatrix} \alpha^{-1} & 0 \\ 0 & \alpha \end{pmatrix}\begin{pmatrix} 1 & 0 \\ s & 1 \end{pmatrix}\begin{pmatrix} \alpha & 0 \\ 0 & \alpha^{-1} \end{pmatrix} = \begin{pmatrix} 1 & 0 \\ \alpha^2 s & 1 \end{pmatrix}$, $\tilde{A}(s)$ is presentable in the form $\tilde{A}(\alpha^2 s)$ by a mere change of basis. Hence $Y(r)$ may be presented in the form $[\tilde{A}\ (n \log r)]_{(m)}r^{a}$

$$= [\tilde{A}\ (\log |\det B|)]_{(m)}\, |\det B|^{a/n}.$$

Since α is an arbitrary constant there is no point in writing α/n and we may state the result just obtained as follows:

Each non-analysable continuous representation of the real linear group is of the form

$$\{|\det B|^{a}\left[\begin{pmatrix} 1 & 0 \\ \log|\det B| & 1 \end{pmatrix}\right]_{(m)} \times X\}$$

where $\{X\}$ *is an irreducible continuous representation of the extended real unimodular group.* The representation $\{X\}$ of the extended real unimodular group may be imbedded in an irreducible rational integral representation of the full linear group; denoting the matrices of this representation by $P(F)$, where F is any element of the full linear group, we have $X = P(A)$ where A is any element of the extended real unimodular group. If B is any element of the real linear group $A = |\det B|^{-1/n} B$ is an element of the extended real unimodular group so that

$$X = P(|\det B|^{-1/n}B) = |\det B|^{-q/n}P(B)$$

where q is the degree of the, necessarily homogeneous, irreducible rational integral representation $\{P(F)\}$ of the full linear group. On absorbing $-q/n$ in the arbitrary constant α we have our main result:

Each non-analysable continuous representation of the real linear group is of the form

$$(7.20) \quad D(B) = |\det B|^{\alpha} \left[\begin{pmatrix} 1 & 0 \\ \log|\det B| & 1 \end{pmatrix}\right]_{(m)} \times P(B)$$

where $\{P(F)\}$ *is an irreducible rational integral representation of the full linear group; and, conversely, each such Kronecker product furnishes a non-analysable continuous representation of the real linear group.* If the representation is not only non-analysable but irreducible we must have $m = 0$; thus, for example, if $m = 1$

$$D(B) = |\det B|^{\alpha} \begin{pmatrix} 1 & 0 \\ \log \det B & 1 \end{pmatrix} \times P(B)$$
$$= |\det B|^{\alpha} \begin{pmatrix} P(B) & 0 \\ \log|\det B|\,P(B) & P(B) \end{pmatrix}$$

which is reducible (and reduced). Hence *not* every non-analysable continuous representation of the real linear group is irreducible. We have proved that

Each irreducible continuous representation of the real linear group is of the form

$$D(B) = |\det B|^{\alpha}\, P(B)$$

where $\{P(F)\}$ *is an irreducible rational integral representation of degree* q *of the full linear group.* Hence $D(B)$ is a positively homogeneous function of B of degree $q + \alpha$.

In order that two irreducible continuous representations Γ, $\tilde{\Gamma}$ of the real linear group be equivalent it is, then, necessary that $\{\tilde{P}(F)\}$ be equivalent to $\{P(F)\}$ so that $\tilde{q} = q$.

The corresponding theorems for continuous representations of the full linear group follow at once. Let F be any element of the full linear group and set $\det F = |\det F|\, e^{i\theta}$; then the matrix A defined by the equation

$$F = |\det F|^{1/n} e^{i\theta/n} A$$

is unimodular and any matrix $D(F)$ of a representation of the full linear group is the product of a matrix Y of a representation (determined by the selection principle), of the group of all positively definite scalar matrices, by a matrix Z of a representation of the group of all scalar matrices of the type $e^{i\theta/n} E_n$, by a matrix X of a representation of the unimodular group. The matrices Y are of the same form as before:

$$Y(r) = \left[\begin{pmatrix} 1 & 0 \\ \log r & 1 \end{pmatrix}\right]_{(m)} r^{\alpha}; \quad r = |\det F|^{1/n}$$

whilst the matrices Z satisfy the equation

$$Z(\theta)Z(\phi) = Z(\theta + \phi).$$

Since they must be periodic (with period 2π) the m for them must be zero (since for any other m some of the elements of $\left[\begin{pmatrix} 1 & 0 \\ \theta & 1 \end{pmatrix}\right]_{(m)}$ are non-periodic, being non-constant polynomials). Hence $Z(\theta) = e^{i\beta\theta}$, β integral. Since any irreducible continuous representation $\{X\}$ of the unimodular group may be imbedded in a semi-rational representation $P_j(F) \times P_k(\bar{F})$ of the full linear group we have the principal theorem:

Each non-analysable continuous representation of the full linear group of dimension n is of the form

$$D(F) = |\det F|^{\alpha} e^{i\beta\theta/n} \left[\begin{pmatrix} 1 & 0 \\ \log|\det F| & 1 \end{pmatrix}\right]_{(m)} \times P_j(F) \times P_k(\bar{F})$$

where $\theta = \arg\det F$, $0 \leq \theta < 2\pi$; α is any complex constant; $\pm\beta$, $m = 0, 1, 2, \cdots$; and $P_j(F)$, $P_k(F)$ are irreducible (hence homogeneous) rational integral representations of the full linear group. The converse is true save that an additional condition is imposed on β; we must have $e^{i\beta(\theta_1+\theta_2)/n} = e^{i\beta\theta/n}$ where $\theta = \arg\det(F_1F_2)$. If $\theta_1 = \theta_2 = \pi$, i. e. if $\det F_1 = \det F_2 = -1$ it follows that $\theta = 0$ since $\det F = 1$; hence $e^{2\pi i\beta/n} = 1$ so that β must be a multiple of n. Hence

Each non-analysable continuous representation of the full linear group is of the form

$$D(F) = |\det F|^{\alpha} e^{i\nu\theta} \left[\begin{pmatrix} 1 & 0 \\ \log|\det F| & 1 \end{pmatrix}\right]_{(m)} \times P_j(F) \times P_k(\bar{F})$$

where $\theta = \arg\det F$, $0 \leq \theta < 2\pi$; α *is any complex constant*; $\pm\nu$, $m = 0, 1, 2, \cdots$; *and* $P_j(F)$, $P_k(F)$ *are irreducible (hence homogeneous) rational integral representations of the full linear group. And, conversely, each such representation of the full linear group is non-analysable.*

In order that a non-analysable continuous representation of the full linear group be irreducible we must have $m = 0$; so that *not* every non-analysable continuous representation of the full linear group is irreducible:

Each irreducible continuous representation of the full linear group is of the form

$$D(F) = |\det F|^{\alpha} e^{\pm i\nu\theta} P_j(F) \times P_k(\bar{F})$$

where $\theta = \arg \det F$, $0 \leq \theta < 2\pi$; α *is any complex constant*, $\nu = 0, 1, 2, \cdots$, *and* $P_j(F)$, $P_k(F)$ *are irreducible (hence homogeneous) rational integral representations of the full linear group and, conversely, each such representation is irreducible.* Two such irreducible representations Γ, $\tilde{\Gamma}$ are equivalent only when $\{\tilde{P}_j(F) \times \tilde{P}_k(\bar{F})\}$ is equivalent to $\{P_j(F) \times P_k(\bar{F})\}$; since this implies, by the argument of p. 191 the equivalence of $\{\tilde{P}_j(F) \times \tilde{P}_k(G)\}$ and $\{P_j(F) \times P_k(G)\}$ it implies (on setting $G = E_n$) the equivalence of $\tilde{P}_j(F)$ and $P_j(F)$ and, similarly, the equivalence of $\tilde{P}_k(F)$ and $P_k(F)$. In particular the degrees of homogeneity of $\{\tilde{P}_j(F)\}$ and $\{P_j(F)\}$ and of $\{\tilde{P}_k(F)\}$ and $\{P_k(F)\}$ must be the same.

CHAPTER EIGHT

GROUP INTEGRATION

In this chapter we shall introduce, by first considering the n-dimensional real linear group, the concept of group-integration and shall obtain expressions for the volume element of the full linear group and of its more important subgroups (with the exception of the orthogonal group which is treated in the following chapter).

1. The volume element of the real linear group.

Each element $X, Y, Z, \cdots$ of the n-dimensional real linear group G is an $n \times n$ non-singular matrix. The n^2 elements of these matrices run, independently of each other, over the set of real numbers (the only condition being that the determinant of each matrix shall not vanish). We express this fact by the statement that G is an n^2-parameter continuous group. We regard the n^2 parameters (i. e. the n^2 elements of any matrix of G) as the components of a vector in an n^2-dimensional "parameter space" and to indicate this we denote by x^{pq} the element $x_q{}^p$ in the p-th row and q-th column of X; in other words we regard the n^2 quantities $x_q{}^p$ as the elements of an $n^2 \times 1$ matrix rather than the elements of an $n \times n$ matrix. Let A be a fixed matrix of G and consider the left translation of G which is induced by A:

$$(8.1) \qquad X \rightarrow Y = AX.$$

This equation is equivalent to the n^2 equations $y_k{}^j = a_a{}^j x_k{}^a$ or, equivalently,

$$(8.2) \qquad y^{jk} = a_a{}^j x^{ak} = a_a{}^j \delta_\beta{}^k x^{a\beta}$$

so that the left-translation (8.1) of G induces in the n^2-dimensional parameter space a linear transformation whose matrix is

$$(8.3) \qquad F(A) = A \times E_n.$$

These linear transformations of the parameter space furnish a representation of G:

$$F(B)F(A) = (B \times E_n)(A \times E_n) = BA \times E_n = F(BA)$$
$$F(E_n) = E_n \times E_n = E_{n^2}; \quad F(A^{-1})F(A) = F(E_n) = E_{n^2}.$$

Let us now consider an arbitrary non-singular $n^2 \times n^2$ matrix. Its columns may be regarded as n^2 linearly independent vectors in the parametric space and on multiplying the matrix by $F(X^{-1}) = F^{-1}(X)$ we obtain, for each element X of G, a new non-singular matrix, i. e. a new set of n^2 linearly independent vectors of the parametric space. Denoting this non-singular $n^2 \times n^2$ matrix, which is thus associated with the element X of G, by $V(X)$, so that the original, arbitrarily chosen, matrix is $V(E_n)$ we have

$$(8.4) \qquad V(X) = F^{-1}(X)V(E_n).$$

Under the left translation (8.1) of G, $V(X) \to V(Y)$ where

$$\begin{aligned} V(Y) &= F^{-1}(Y)V(E_n) = F^{-1}(Y)F(X)V(X) \\ &= F^{-1}(YX^{-1})V(X) = F^{-1}(A)V(X). \end{aligned}$$

It is clear, moreover, from (8.2) that the Jacobian determinant of the transformation from the n^2 variables $(x) = (x^{11}, \cdots, x^{nn})$ to the n^2 variables $(y) = (y^{11}, \cdots, y^{nn})$ is $\det \dfrac{\partial(y)}{\partial(x)} = \det F(A)$ so that

$$(8.5) \qquad d(y) = \det F(A)d(x).$$

Hence

$$\det V(Y) \cdot d(y) = \det F^{-1}(A) \det V(X) \det F(A)d(x) = \det V(X)d(x).$$

In other words the product $\det V(X)d(x)$ is invariant under all left translations of the group G. If, then, we consider any bounded n^2-dimensional region R of the n^2-dimensional parametric space and if this is sent by the non-singular linear transformation $F(A)$ of this space into the n^2-dimensional region R_A of the parametric space; and if $\phi(X)$ is any continuous function defined over G then the integral

$$I_R(\phi) = \int_R \phi(X) \det V(X)d(x)$$

has the same value as the integral $I_{R_A}(\phi_{A^{-1}})$ of the function $\phi_{A^{-1}}(X) = \phi(A^{-1}X)$ over the region R_A. (We assume the region R to be connected, i. e. that any two points of it may be joined by a continuous curve; then the continuous function $\det V(x)d(x)$ preserves its sign over R since it cannot vanish). In fact

$$\begin{aligned} I_{R_A}(\phi_{A^{-1}}) &= \int_{R_A} \phi_{A^{-1}}(Y) \det V(Y)d(y) = \int_R \phi_{A^{-1}}(AX) \det V(X)d(x) \\ &= \int_R \phi(A^{-1} \cdot AX) \det V(X)d(x) = \int_R \phi(X) \det V(X)d(x). \end{aligned}$$

It is convenient to normalise matters by choosing $V(E_n) = E_{n^2}$ so that, from (8.4), $V(X) = F^{-1}(X)$ and the invariant product $d\tau \equiv \det V(x) d(x)$ is

(8.6) $$d\tau = \det F^{-1}(X) d(x).$$

We refer to $d\tau$ as the element of volume of G.

Since $F(X) = X \times E_n$ it may be transformed, by means of a permutation matrix into $E_n \times X$ so that $\det F(X) = (\det X)^n$. Hence the element of volume of the n-dimensional real linear group is

(8.7) $$d\tau = \frac{d(x)}{(\det X)^n}.$$

It is evident that a similar argument may be carried through for the right-translations of G:

(8.8) $$X \rightarrow Y = XA.$$

From this equation we read $y_k{}^j = x_a{}^j a_k{}^a$, i. e.

$$y^{jk} = x^{ja} a_k{}^a = x^{\beta a} \delta_\beta{}^j a_k{}^a$$

so that the linear transformation of the n^2-dimensional parametric space which is induced by the right translation (8.8) of G has for its matrix

(8.9) $$K(A) = E_n \times A'; \ A' \text{ the transposed of } A.$$

On setting $W(X) = K^{-1}(X) = E_n \times \tilde{A}$; $\tilde{A} = (A^{-1})'$ we have $\det W(X) = \det K^{-1}(X) = \{\det K(X)\}^{-1}$ whilst $d(y) = \det K(A) \cdot d(x)$ so that $\det W(Y) \cdot d(y) = \{\det K(Y)\}^{-1} \det K(A) d(x)$. Now it follows from (8.9) that

$$\begin{aligned} K(BA) &= E_n \times A'B' = (E_n \times A')(E_n \times B') = K(A)K(B) \\ K(E_n) &= E_{n^2} \end{aligned}$$

so that, in particular, $K(A^{-1}) = K^{-1}(A)$. Hence $\{\det K(Y)\}^{-1} = \det K(Y^{-1})$ so that

$$\begin{aligned} \det W(Y) d(y) &= \det K(Y^{-1}) \det K(A) d(x) = \det K(Y^{-1}) K(A) d(x) \\ &= \det K(AY^{-1}) d(x) = \det K(X^{-1}) d(x) \\ &= \det K^{-1}(X) d(x) = \det W(X) d(x). \end{aligned}$$

If, then, R is an n^2-dimensional region of our parametric space which is sent by the non-singular linear transformation $K(A)$ (induced by the right translation (8.8) of G) into the n^2-dimensional region R'_A we have by the same reasoning as before

$$I_{R'_A}(\phi'_{A^{-1}}) = I_R(\phi).$$

In this formula ϕ is any continuous function of X defined over G and $\phi'_{A^{-1}}$ is the continuous function of X defined by

$$\phi'_{A^{-1}}(X) = \phi(XA^{-1}).$$

We have, then, apparently two elements of volume of G one of which, namely $\det F^{-1}(X)d(x)$, is suitable for left translations of G whilst the other, namely $\det K^{-1}(X)d(x)$ is suitable for right translations of G. But they are not distinct, simply because $\det X' = \det X$. In fact $\det K(X) = \det(E_n \times X') = (\det X')^n = (\det X)^n = \det F(X)$. Hence the group element of volume $d\tau = \dfrac{d(x)}{(\det X)^n}$ has the properties

$$(8.10) \quad \int_{R_A} \phi(A^{-1}X)\,d\tau = \int_R \phi(X)\,d\tau = \int_{R'_A} \phi(XA^{-1})\,d\tau, \text{ every } A,$$

where R_A, R'_A denote, respectively, the regions of the n^2-dimensional parametric space into which R is sent by the left translation (8.1) and the right translation (8.8) of G. When $\phi(X) = 1$ we may express the result of (8.10) by saying that the volume of R_A equals that of R which also equals that of R'_A; in other words *the volume element of the parametric space has been so defined that the right and left translations of G induce volume preserving transformations of the parametric space.*

On observing that $\det F(A)$ is the Jacobian determinant $\det \dfrac{\partial(y)}{\partial(x)}$ where $Y = AX$ whilst $\det K(A)$ is the Jacobian determinant $\det \dfrac{\partial(y)}{\partial(x)}$ where $Y = XA$ we obtain, on differentiating with respect to (x) the identity $E_n = XX^{-1}$

$$0 = K(X^{-1}) + F(X)\frac{\partial(x^{-1})}{\partial(x)}$$

or, equivalently,

$$(8.11) \qquad \frac{\partial(x^{-1})}{\partial(x)} = -F^{-1}(X)K^{-1}(X)$$

where (x^{-1}) denotes the point of the parametric space which corresponds to X^{-1}. From this matrix equation we obtain

$$\det K^{-1}(X)d(x) = (-1)^n \det F^{-1}(X^{-1})d(x^{-1})$$

so that if R is sent by the inversion $X \to X^{-1}$ into R^{-1} and if we denote by $\phi_{-1}(X)$ the function $\phi(X^{-1})$ then

$$\int_{R^{-1}} \phi_{-1}(X)\,d\tau = (-1)^n \int_R \phi(X)\,d\tau.$$

In fact $\int_{R^{-1}} \phi_{-1}(X)\,d\tau = \int_{R^{-1}} \phi_{-1}(X) \det F^{-1}(X)\,d(x)$

$$= \int_R \phi_{-1}(X^{-1}) \det F^{-1}(X^{-1})\,d(x^{-1})$$

$$= (-1)^{n^2} \int_R \phi(X) \det K^{-1}(X)\,d(x)$$

$$= (-1)^n \int_R \phi(X)\,d\tau.$$

Hence, in particular, not only are volumes preserved under right and left translations of G *but they are also preserved (save possibly in sign) under inversions of* G.

It is important to observe that the element of volume $d\tau = \dfrac{d(x)}{(\det X)^n}$ of the real n-dimensional linear group G is a class function. In fact if X, Y belong to the same class of G we have $Y = A^{-1}XA$ so that $\det Y = \det X$. The transformation of G defined by

$$X \to Y = AXA^{-1};\ A \text{ fixed}$$

is a one to one correspondence of the elements of G with the elements of G with the properties $E_n \to E_n$; $X_1 \to Y_1$, $X_2 \to Y_2$ imply $X_1X_2 \to Y_1Y_2$. It is termed an *automorphism* of G. This automorphism of G, induced by A, may be regarded as the result of *first* performing the left translation $X \to Z = AX$ and *then* performing the right translation $Z \to Y = ZA^{-1}$. Hence the automorphism of G induces a linear transformation in the parametric space whose matrix is

$$H(A) = (E_n \times \tilde{A})(A \times E_n) = (A \times \tilde{A});\ \tilde{A} = (A^{-1})'.$$

The matrices $H(A)$ furnish an n^2-dimensional representation of G and their determinants furnish the identity representation of G. In fact

$$\det H(A) = \det(E_n \times \tilde{A}) \cdot \det(A \times E_n) = \{\det(E_n \times A')\}^{-1} \det F(A)$$
$$= \{\det K(A)\}^{-1} \det F(A) = 1.$$

The representation of G which is furnished by the matrices

(8.12) $$H(A) = (E_n \times \tilde{A})(A \times E_n) = K^{-1}(A)F(A) = (A \times \tilde{A});\ \tilde{A} = (A^{-1})'$$

is known as the *adjoint representation* of G; its characters are given by

(8.13) $$\chi(A) = Tr(A)\,Tr(A^{-1}).$$

The fact that the element of volume is a class function makes it easier to perform the integration over R in terms of other coordinates than the elements $(x_s{}^r)$ of X. If X is any $n \times n$ matrix its characteristic vectors v are defined by the equation

$$Xv = \lambda v. \tag{8.14}$$

If X is such that its characteristic vectors v span the n-dimensional carrier space of X the n characteristic vectors $v_1, \cdots, v_n$ may be regarded as the columns of a non-singular matrix V and then (8.14) may be presented in the form

$$XV = V\Lambda; \quad V^{-1}XV = \Lambda$$

where Λ is the $n \times n$ diagonal matrix whose diagonal elements are the characteristic numbers $(\lambda_1, \cdots, \lambda_n)$ of X. We may suppose these characteristic vectors normalised by the condition that they are all of unit magnitude; or, if none of the diagonal elements of V is zero, we may make the normalization (which is more convenient for us) that these diagonal elements are all unity. If two or more of the diagonal elements of Λ, i. e. of the characteristic numbers of X, are equal V is not determinate so we shall define our new coordinates only for a "generic" element X of G, i. e. for an element X whose characteristic numbers are all distinct (it being certain then that the characteristic vectors of X span the entire carrier space of X; for an assumed relation $c^a v_a = 0$ would yield by repeated operation on it with X the equations $c^a \lambda_a{}^k v_a = 0$, $k = 0, 1, \cdots, n-1$. Taking the j-th components of each of these vector equations we would have a system of n homogeneous equations whose determinant, being the Vandermonde determinant with value $\Delta(\lambda) = \prod_{p<q} (\lambda_p - \lambda_q), \neq 0$. Hence $c^k v_k{}^j = 0$ every k, j; but, for a given k, not all $v_k{}^j = 0$ so that $c^k = 0$). With every generic element X of G, then, there is associated a diagonal matrix Λ, uniquely defined save for transformations by an arbitrary permutation matrix, and a matrix V (uniquely defined when Λ is chosen) whose diagonal elements we shall suppose to be unity. Then we adopt as our n^2 coordinates of the point x of R the n diagonal elements of Λ and the $n^2 - n$ non-diagonal elements of V:

$$\xi^{pp} = \lambda_p; \quad \xi^{pq} = v_q{}^p, \quad p \neq q.$$

The characteristic numbers λ, and the associated characteristic vectors v, will not, in general, be real. If a characteristic number λ is real the associated characteristic vector, defined by $Xv = \lambda v$, may be taken to be real. On the other hand if a characteristic vector $\lambda_1 = \mu + i\nu$ is not real the associated characteristic vector $v_1 = u + iw$ cannot be real since X is real. Then X will have the pair of conjugate complex characteristic numbers $\lambda_1 = \mu + i\nu$ and $\lambda_2 = \mu - i\nu$ and the associated pair of characteristic vectors $v_1 = u + iw$ and $v_2 = u - iw$. We take, then, as our real coordinates for the point x of R the numbers (μ, ν) etc., and the vectors (u, w) etc. and the volume element as calculated for the coordinates $\xi = (\lambda, v)$ will be multiplied by a mere constant when the coordinates are (μ, ν, u, w). In fact

$$\frac{\partial(\lambda_1, \lambda_2)}{\partial(\mu, \nu)} = -2i \quad \text{whilst} \quad \frac{\partial(v_1{}^2, v_2{}^2, v_1{}^3, v_2{}^3, \cdots)}{\partial(u^2, w^2, u^3, w^3, \cdots)} = (-2i)^{n-1}$$

so that the volume element as calculated below for the complex coordinates ξ must be multiplied by $(-2i)^{kn}$, where k is the number of pairs of conjugate complex characteristic numbers λ, to yield the volume element for the real coordinates (μ, ν, u, w). It may be observed that whilst u_j has been normalised so that its $(2j-1)$th component is unity w_j has been normalised so that its $(2j-1)$th component is zero.

The Jacobian $\dfrac{\partial(x)}{\partial(\xi)}$ of the transformation from the parameters x to the coordinates ξ is readily calculated. From the relation $X = V\Lambda V^{-1}$ we read $\dfrac{\partial(x)}{\partial(\lambda)} = H(V) = V \times \tilde{V}$ so that the elements of $\dfrac{\partial(x)}{\partial(\xi)}$ which correspond to the (p, p) column are the elements in the (p, p) column of $V \times \tilde{V}$. On differentiating the equation $X = V\Lambda V^{-1}$ with respect to $v_q{}^p = \xi^{pq}$, holding Λ fixed, we find

$$\begin{aligned}\frac{\partial(x)}{\partial(v)} &= K(\Lambda V^{-1}) + F(V\Lambda)\frac{\partial(v^{-1})}{\partial(v)} \\ &= K(\Lambda V^{-1}) - F(V\Lambda)F(V^{-1})K(V^{-1}), \text{ by (8.11)}, \\ &= (E_n \times \tilde{V}\Lambda) - \{(V\Lambda V^{-1}) \times \tilde{V}\} \\ &= (V \times \tilde{V})[(V^{-1} \times \Lambda) - (\Lambda V^{-1} \times E_n)].\end{aligned}$$

We need only the determinant of $\dfrac{\partial(x)}{\partial(\xi)}$ and this is the same as the determinant of $\dfrac{\partial(z)}{\partial(\xi)}$ where $Z = V_0{}^{-1}XV_0$ the *constant* matrix V_0 coinciding with V at the point where $\dfrac{\partial(x)}{\partial(v)}$ is being evaluated. Since $\dfrac{\partial(z)}{\partial(x)} = V_0{}^{-1} \times V'_0$ (by 8.12) it follows that

$$\frac{\partial z^{rs}}{\partial \xi^{pp}} = \text{the } rs, pp \text{ element of } E_{n^2};$$

$$\frac{\partial z^{rs}}{\partial \xi^{pq}} = \text{the } rs, pq \text{ element of } (V^{-1} \times \Lambda) - (\Lambda V^{-1} \times E_n).$$

Denoting, for a moment, by U the matrix V^{-1} the rs, pq element of

$(V^{-1} \times \Lambda) - (\Lambda V^{-1} \times E_n)$ is $u_p{}^r(\lambda_q - \lambda_r)\delta_q{}^s$ so that the matrix $\dfrac{\partial(z)}{\partial(\xi)}$ is the direct sum of n $n \times n$ matrices of which the q-th has for its (r, p) element:

$$a_p{}^r = u_p{}^r(\lambda_q - \lambda_r); \quad p \neq q; \quad a_q{}^r = \delta_q{}^r.$$

The determinant of this matrix $= \prod_{r \neq q} (\lambda_q - \lambda_r) U_q{}^q$ where $U_q{}^q$ is the cofactor of $u_q{}^q$ in the expansion of det U. Since U is the reciprocal of V $U_q{}^q = \det U v_q{}^q = \det U = (\det V)^{-1}$ (since we have supposed V normalised by the condition that its diagonal elements should be unity). Hence the Jacobian determinant $\dfrac{\partial(z)}{\partial(\xi)}$, or equivalently the Jacobian determinant $\dfrac{\partial(x)}{\partial(\xi)}$, has the value

$$(-)^{n(n-1)/2} \{\Delta(\lambda)\}^2 \div (\det V)^n; \quad \Delta(\lambda) = \prod_{p<q} (\lambda_p - \lambda_q).$$

Since $\det X = \det \Lambda = \lambda_1 \lambda_2 \cdots \lambda_n$ it follows from (8.7) that the element of volume of the group, when expressed in terms of the parameters ξ is

$$(8.15) \quad d\tau = (-)^{n(n-1)/2} [\{\Delta(\lambda)\}^2 \div (\lambda_1 \lambda_2 \cdots \lambda_n)^n (\det V)^n] d(\xi).$$

2. The volume element of subgroups of the real linear group.

The matrices X of a subgroup H of the real linear group of dimension n will generally depend on $r < n^2$ parameters. Thus the group of all real orthogonal matrices consists of the matrices O which satisfy the equation

$$OO' = E_n.$$

The n^2 elements of O satisfy, accordingly, the $n(n+1)/2$ equations

$$\sum_a O_a{}^r O_a{}^s = \delta_s{}^r; \quad r \leq s$$

and the matrices O depend on $n^2 - \dfrac{n(n+1)}{2} = \dfrac{n(n-1)}{2}$ parameters.

(That there are not more than $\dfrac{n(n-1)}{2}$ parameters will appear later when we examine the orthogonal group in detail). The arguments given in the preceding section for the real linear group (for which the number of parameters $= n^2$) are fortunately available with but minor modifications. We shall denote by $(\xi^1, \cdots, \xi^r)$ the parameters on which the matrices X of our subgroup depend; then the left translation

$$(8.17) \quad X \rightarrow Y = AX$$

of our subgroup H (A any fixed element of H) induces a transformation (no longer, in general, linear) of our r-dimensional parametric space; it being tacitly supposed, when we refer to H as an r-parameter group, that as X runs over H, (ξ) runs over an r-dimensional region. We suppose that X is a differentiable function of each of the variables ξ and we obtain from (8.17)

(8.18) $$Y_{,a}\frac{\partial\eta^a}{\partial\xi^q} = AX_{,q}$$

where $X_{,q} = \dfrac{\partial X}{\partial\xi^q}$, $Y_{,j} = \dfrac{\partial Y}{\partial\eta^j}$, the parameters of Y being denoted by η. We denote the $r\times r$ matrix $\dfrac{\partial(\eta)}{\partial(\xi)}$ by $F(\eta,\xi)$ and it follows, on considering the result of performing the two left translations $X\to Y = AX$; $Y\to Z = BY$, which result is itself the left translation $X\to Z = BA\cdot X$ that

(8.19) $$F(\zeta,\xi) = F(\zeta,\eta)F(\eta,\xi)$$

where ξ, η, ζ are the points of the parametric space which correspond to X, Y, Z, respectively. In fact this is merely a transcription of the formula of composite differentiation (for r functions of r variables):

$$\frac{\partial(\zeta)}{\partial(\xi)} = \frac{\partial(\zeta)}{\partial(\eta)}\frac{\partial(\eta)}{\partial(\xi)}.$$

The three points ξ, η, ζ are arbitrary since X, Y, Z may be arbitrarily chosen (A being then $= YX^{-1}$ and B being $= ZY^{-1}$). Furthermore $Y = X$ implies $\eta = \xi$ so that $\dfrac{\partial(\eta)}{\partial(\xi)} = E_r$. Hence, on choosing $\zeta = \xi$ in (8.19) we obtain

(8.20) $$F(\xi,\eta)F(\eta,\xi) = E_r.$$

If ϵ is the point of our parametric space which corresponds to E_n we obtain, on setting $\eta = \epsilon$ in (8.19),

$$F(\zeta,\xi) = F(\zeta,\epsilon)F(\epsilon,\xi)$$

and, on denoting $F(\xi,\epsilon)$ simply by $F(\xi)$, so that $F(\epsilon) = E_r$, $F(\epsilon,\xi) = F^{-1}(\xi)$ this appears as

(8.21) $$F(\zeta,\xi) = F(\zeta)F^{-1}(\xi).$$

Denoting by $V(\xi)$ the non-singular $r\times r$ matrix $F^{-1}(\xi)$ which is attached, in this manner, to each point ξ of our r-dimensional parametric space ($V(\epsilon)$ being the unit matrix E_r) the left translation $X\to Y = AX$ of our group H induces $V(\xi)\to V(\eta) = F^{-1}(\eta)$.

From the equation of definition $\frac{\partial(\eta)}{\partial(\xi)} = F(\eta, \xi) = F(\eta)F^{-1}(\xi)$ follows $\det F^{-1}(\eta) d(\eta) = \det F^{-1}(\xi) d(\xi)$. In other words the product $\det F^{-1}(\xi) d(\xi)$ is invariant under all left translations of our subgroup H. If, then, we consider any bounded r-dimensional region R of our parametric space and if this is sent by the left translation $X \to Y = AX$ of H into the region R_A the integral

$$I_R(\phi) = \int_R \phi(\xi) \det F^{-1}(\xi) d(\xi)$$

of any continuous function defined over the entire parametric space is the same as the integral $I_{R_A}(\phi_{A^{-1}})$ of the function $\phi_{A^{-1}}(\xi)$ over the region R_A, where $\phi_A(\xi)$ is defined, for every A, by the formula $\phi_A(\xi) = \phi(\eta)$; the region R being supposed connected so that the non-vanishing continuous *volume element* $d\tau = \det F^{-1}(\xi) d(\xi)$ preserves its sign through R. In fact

$$I_{R_A}(\phi_{A^{-1}}) = \int_{R_A} \phi_{A^{-1}}(\eta) \det F^{-1}(\eta) d(\eta)$$
$$= \int_R \phi(\xi) \det F^{-1}(\xi) d(\xi) = I_R(\phi).$$

It is evident that a similar argument may be carried through for the right translation of H:

$$X \to Y = XA.$$

On denoting the Jacobian matrix $\frac{\partial(\eta)}{\partial(\xi)}$ of the induced transformation $\xi \to \eta$ of the parametric space by $K(\eta, \xi)$ we find, as before, $K(\zeta, \xi) = K(\zeta, \eta)K(\eta, \xi)$; $K(\xi, \xi) = E_r$; $K(\zeta, \xi) = K(\zeta, \epsilon)K(\epsilon, \xi)$ and on denoting $K(\xi, \epsilon)$ simply by $K(\xi)$

$$K(\eta, \xi) = K(\eta)K^{-1}(\xi).$$

On attaching to each point ξ of our parametric space the non-singular matrix $K^{-1}(\xi)$ we find

$$\det K^{-1}(\xi) d(\xi) = \det K^{-1}(\eta) d(\eta)$$

and show, exactly as before, that if R is any region of our parametric space which is sent into R'_A by the right translation $X \to Y = XA$ of H then

$$I_{R'_A}(\phi'_{A^{-1}}) = I_R(\phi)$$

where ϕ is any continuous function defined over R and $\phi'_{A^{-1}}$ is defined by $\phi'_{A^{-1}}(\eta) = \phi(\xi)$. As before we have, then, apparently two volume elements of our group H of which the first, namely, $\det F^{-1}(\xi)d(\xi)$ is appropriate for left translations of the group whilst the second, namely, $\det K^{-1}(\xi)d(\xi)$ is appropriate for right translations of the group. Both volume elements of the group are, however, readily seen to be the same (save, possibly, for a difference in sign) by the following reasoning. Let us consider the *automorphism* of H which is induced by the element A of H:

$$X \to Z = AXA^{-1}$$

and regard this automorphism as the result of first performing the left translation $X \to Y = AX$ of H and then performing the right translation $Y \to Z = YA^{-1}$ of H. The corresponding transformations $\xi \to \eta$, $\eta \to \zeta$ of the parametric space are such that $\dfrac{\partial(\eta)}{\partial(\xi)} = F(\eta, \xi) = F(\eta)F^{-1}(\xi)$; $\dfrac{\partial(\zeta)}{\partial(\eta)} = K(\zeta, \eta) = K(\zeta)K^{-1}(\eta)$ and so $\dfrac{\partial(\zeta)}{\partial(\xi)} = K(\zeta)K^{-1}(\eta)F(\eta)F^{-1}(\xi)$. When $X = E_n$, $Z = E_n$ so that when $\xi = \epsilon$, $\zeta = \epsilon$ and at this point the matrix $\dfrac{\partial(\zeta)}{\partial(\xi)}$ becomes $K^{-1}(\alpha)F(\alpha)$ where α is the point of the parametric space which corresponds to the element A of H (for $X = E_n$ forces $Y = A$, $\eta = \alpha$). On denoting by $H(\alpha)$ the matrix

$$H(\alpha) = K^{-1}(\alpha)F(\alpha) \tag{8.22}$$

we may say that the automorphism $X \to Z = AXA^{-1}$ of H induces a linear transformation, whose matrix is $H(\alpha)$, on the differentials of the parameters at the point ϵ (which is invariant under the automorphism). Since the collection of automorphisms $X \to Z = AXA^{-1}$ of H, obtained as A runs over H, constitute a group the linear transformations whose matrices are $H(\alpha)$ must furnish an r-dimensional representation of H. This fact, which is essential in the theory, is readily verified as follows. Let A, B be any two elements of H and consider the transformation

$$X \to Z = AXB$$

of H into itself. This may be regarded in two ways

1) as the result of first performing the *left* translation $X \to Y = AX$ and following this with the *right* translation $Y \to Z = YB$. On calculating

$\dfrac{\partial(\zeta)}{\partial(\xi)} = \dfrac{\partial(\zeta)}{\partial(\eta)}\dfrac{\partial(\eta)}{\partial(\xi)}$ we find

$$\frac{\partial(\zeta)}{\partial(\xi)} = K(\zeta, \eta)F(\eta, \xi) = K(\zeta, \alpha\xi)F(\alpha\xi, \xi)$$

where $\alpha\xi$ denotes the point of the parametric space which corresponds to $Y = AX$.

2) as the result of first performing the *right* translation $X \to Y = XB$ and following this with the *left* translation $Y \to Z = AY$. On calculating $\frac{\partial(\zeta)}{\partial(\xi)} = \frac{\partial(\zeta)}{\partial(\eta)} \frac{\partial(\eta)}{\partial(\xi)}$ we find

$$\frac{\partial(\zeta)}{\partial(\xi)} = F(\zeta, \eta) K(\eta, \xi) = F(\zeta, \xi\beta) K(\xi\beta, \xi)$$

where $\xi\beta$ denotes the point of the parametric space which corresponds to $Y = XB$. On equating the results obtained we find

$$F(\zeta, \xi\beta) K(\xi\beta, \xi) = K(\zeta, \alpha\xi) F(\alpha\xi, \xi)$$

which is an identity in α, β, ξ the point ζ being $= \alpha\xi\beta$. On setting $\xi = \epsilon$ we obtain

$$F(\alpha\beta, \beta) K(\beta) = K(\alpha\beta, \alpha) F(\alpha)$$

which is an identity in α, β. On setting $F(\alpha\beta, \beta) = F(\alpha\beta) F^{-1}(\beta)$, $K(\alpha\beta, \alpha) = K(\alpha\beta) K^{-1}(\alpha)$ we obtain

$$K^{-1}(\alpha\beta) F(\alpha\beta) = K^{-1}(\alpha) F(\alpha) K^{-1}(\beta) F(\beta)$$

or, equivalently,

(8.23) $$H(\alpha\beta) = H(\alpha) H(\beta).$$

Since $H(\epsilon) = E_r$ it follows that the matrices $H(\alpha)$ constitute an r-dimensional representation of H. This representation is known as the *adjoint* representation of H. The determinants of the matrices $H(\alpha)$ furnish, accordingly, a continuous one-dimensional representation of H. On the assumption that this one-dimensional representation is bounded (which will certainly be the case if the region R of the parametric space which corresponds to H is bounded and closed, since a continuous function defined over a bounded closed region is itself bounded) it must be unitary and so its 1×1 matrices $= \pm 1$. Hence $\det H(\xi) = \pm 1$, or equivalently, $\det K(\xi) = \pm \det F(\xi)$ so that the two elements of volume of our group, namely, $\det F^{-1}(\xi) d(\xi)$ and $\det K^{-1}(\xi) d(\xi)$ are equal or differ only in sign. The region R, which corresponds to the entire group H, is sent into itself by any right or left translation; denoting simply by $I(\phi)$ the integral of any continuous function ϕ defined over R we have the basic relations

(8.24) $$I(\phi_A) = I(\phi) = I(\phi'_A); \text{ every } A$$

where

$$\phi_A(\xi) = \phi(\alpha\xi); \quad \phi'_A(\xi) = \phi(\xi\alpha); \quad I(\phi) = \int_R \phi(\xi) \det F^{-1}(\xi) d(\xi).$$

It follows also, by the same argument as before, that $I(\phi)$ is invariant, not only with respect to all left and right translations of the integrand ϕ, but with respect to inversions of ϕ. By this we mean that if $\phi^{-1}(\xi) = \phi(\xi^{-1})$ where ξ^{-1} is the point of the parametric space which corresponds to the element X^{-1} of H,

$$I(\phi^{-1}) = I(\phi). \tag{8.25}$$

In fact on differentiating the identity $\epsilon = \xi\xi^{-1}$ with respect to ξ (i. e. on taking the Jacobian matrix of the r constants ϵ with respect to the r independent variables ξ) we find $0 = K(\epsilon, \xi) + F(\epsilon, \xi^{-1}) \dfrac{\partial(\xi^{-1})}{\partial(\xi)}$ so that

$$\det K^{-1}(\xi)\, d(\xi) = -\det F^{-1}(\xi^{-1})\, d(\xi^{-1}) = \pm \det K^{-1}(\xi^{-1})\, d(\xi^{-1}).$$

Hence the element of volume is unaltered, save possibly for sign, under the inversion $\xi \to \xi^{-1}$. As always we assume R connected so that if the element of volume is changed in sign at one point ξ it is changed in sign at all points.

We illustrate the theory of integration over a subgroup of the n-dimensional real linear group by considering the group H of all proper real orthogonal 2×2 matrices. If $A = \begin{pmatrix} a & c \\ b & d \end{pmatrix}$ is an element of H the conditions on the four numbers a, b, c, d, are the following: $a^2 + c^2 = 1$, $ab + cd = 0$, $b^2 + d^2 = 1$, $ad - bc = 1$. Hence we may write $a = \cos\alpha$, $b = \sin\alpha$, $c = -\sin\alpha$, $d = \cos\alpha$. In other words H is a one-parameter continuous group whose typical element is $X = \begin{pmatrix} \cos\xi & -\sin\xi \\ \sin\xi & \cos\xi \end{pmatrix}$ the region R of the parametric space which corresponds to H being the open interval $0 \leq \xi < 2\pi$. We make this interval *closed* by *identifying* its end points 0 and 2π; by this we mean that when we speak, for instance, of a continuous function $\phi(\xi)$ defined over R we imply not only continuity but *periodicity*: $\phi(2\pi) = \phi(0)$. An equivalent way of describing this "closing" of the interval $0 \leq \xi < 2\pi$ is to say that we picture the interval, not as a segment of a line, but as the circumference of the unit circle. The left translation $X \to Y = AX$ of H induces, as is at once seen on performing the matrix multiplication, the *linear* transformation $\xi \to \eta = \alpha + \xi$ of our parametric space R and so the matrix F is the one-dimensional unit matrix. Hence the "element of volume" of H is simply $d\xi$. This example, whilst important, is trivial in the sense that the transformation $\xi \to \eta = \alpha\xi$ of the parametric space which is induced by the left translation $X \to Y = AX$ of H is easily determined. In general the explicit determination of the transformation $\xi \to \eta$ of the parametric space presents considerable difficulties.

3. The orthogonality relations.

Once we are in possession of an invariant element of volume $d\tau$ for a continuous group H whose parametric region R is bounded and closed we may parallel the discussion already given on pp. 80-82 for finite groups, the average of any continuous function ϕ over the group being $\frac{1}{V}\int_R \phi d\tau$ where $V = \int_R d\tau$ is the "volume" of the group. Since R is closed and bounded any continuous representation Γ of H may be presented as a unitary representation (since the matrices $D(s)$ of Γ are bounded, s variable over H) and hence every continuous representation of H is either irreducible or analysable (= completely reducible). Confining our attention therefore to irreducible representations let $\Gamma = \{D(s)\}$ be an irreducible, continuous representation, of dimension d, of H and consider the matrix function

$$\phi(\sigma) = D(s)AD^*(s)$$

defined over R, A being a fixed, but arbitrary, $d \times d$ matrix and σ the point of R which corresponds to the element s of H. The matrix $P = \int_R \phi(\sigma)\,d\tau$ possesses the property

$$D(t)PD^*(t) = P, \text{ every } t. \tag{8.26}$$

In fact $D(t)PD^*(t) = \int_R D(t)D(s)AD^*(s)D^*(t)\,d\tau$

$$= \int_R D(ts)AD^*(ts)\,d\tau = \int_R D(u)AD^*(u)\,d\tau = P,$$

the element of volume $d\tau$ being invariant under the left translation $s \to u = ts$ of H. We may write (8.26) in the form

$$D(t)P = P\{D^*(t)\}^{-1} = P\tilde{D}(t)$$

where $\tilde{\Gamma} = \{\tilde{D}(t)\}$ is the representation of H furnished by the matrices $\tilde{D}(t) = \{D^*(t)\}^{-1}$. Since $\Gamma = \{D(t)\}$ is bounded we may (and shall) suppose it presented in a basis in which its matrices $D(t)$ are unitary implying $\tilde{D}(t) = D(t)$. Γ being irreducible it follows by Schur's lemma that P is a scalar matrix

$$\int_R D(s)AD^*(s)\,d\tau = cE_d.$$

On taking A to be the matrix whose j, k element is unity, all others being zero we find

$$\int_R \{D(s)\}_j{}^r\{D^*(s)\}_t{}^k d\tau = c_j{}^k\delta_t{}^r.$$

On setting $t = r$ and summing with respect to r we obtain

$$\int_R \{D^*(s)D(s)\}_j{}^k d\tau = dc_j{}^k,$$

and since $D(s)$ is unitary this yields $dc_j{}^k = V\delta_j{}^k$ where $V = \int_R d\tau$ is the volume of the group. Hence the first set of orthogonality relations is

$$(8.27)\qquad \int_R \{D(s)\}_j{}^r\{D^*(s)\}_t{}^k d\tau = \frac{V}{d}\,\delta_j{}^k\delta_t{}^r;\ D(s)\text{ unitary.}$$

Similarly if Γ_1 and Γ_2 are any two non-equivalent irreducible continuous representations of H we find, again by an application of Schur's lemma, that P is the zero matrix implying

$$(8.28)\qquad \int \{D_1(s)\}_j{}^r\{D^*{}_2(s)\}_t{}^k d\tau = 0,$$

it being here unnecessary that either $D_1(s)$ or $D_2(s)$ be unitary. If $D_2(s)$ is presented in a basis in which the matrices $D_2(s)$ are unitary we may replace $D^*{}_2(s)$ by $D_2(s^{-1})$ and then both sets of orthogonality relations appears as:

$$(8.29)\qquad \begin{aligned} &\int_R \{D(s)\}_j{}^r\{D(s^{-1})\}_t{}^k d\tau = \frac{V}{d}\,\delta_j{}^k\delta_t{}^r,\\ &\int_R \{D_1(s)\}_j{}^r\{D_2(s^{-1})\}_t{}^k d\tau = 0. \end{aligned}$$

From these follow, on setting $r = j$, $k = t$ and summing with respect to j and t, the orthogonality relations amongst the characters:

$$(8.30)\qquad \int_R \chi(s)\chi(s^{-1})\,d\tau = V;\quad \int_R \chi_1(s)\chi_2(s^{-1})\,d\tau = 0$$

where $\chi(s^{-1})$, $\chi_2(s^{-1})$ may be replaced, if desired, by $\bar{\chi}(s)$, $\bar{\chi}_2(s)$, respectively, since the representations considered are unitary. If Γ is any continuous representation of H it follows from (8. 30) that its analysis into irreducible parts is unique; for $\Gamma = c^1\Gamma_1 + \cdots + c^q\Gamma_q$ implies $\chi(s) = c^1\chi_1(s) + \cdots + c^q\chi_q(s)$ whence $c^j = \frac{1}{V}\int_R \chi(s)\bar{\chi}_j(s)\,d\tau$ showing that c^j is uniquely determined by Γ. Furthermore if two irreducible continuous representations of H have the same characters they must be equivalent; for their non-equivalence would imply $\int_R \chi(s)\bar{\chi}(s)\,ds = 0$ and hence the identical vanishing of the *continuous* function $\chi(s)$ and this cannot be since $\chi(e) = d \neq 0$. Hence any two continuous representations, whatever, reducible or irreducible of H are equivalent if and only if they have the same characters. Furthermore the relation $\chi(s) = c^a \chi_a(s)$ yields $\int_R \chi(s)\bar{\chi}(s)\,d\tau = V \sum_a (c^a)^2$ so that a criterion for irreducibility of Γ is $\frac{1}{V}\int_R \chi(s)\bar{\chi}(s)\,d\tau = 1$.

As an example let us consider the irreducible continuous representations of the Abelian group of proper real orthogonal 2×2 matrices. Since the group is Abelian each irreducible representation is one-dimensional and since the representation is unitary we must have $D(X) = e^{i\theta(\xi)}$ where $\theta(\xi)$ is a real function of ξ which satisfies the equation $\theta(\alpha) + \theta(\xi) = \theta(\alpha + \xi)$. Hence $\theta(\xi) = c\xi$, c a real constant. Since $e^{i\theta(\xi+2\pi)} = e^{i\theta(\xi)}$ we must have $c = m$ where m is an integer. Hence the irreducible continuous (and periodic) representations of the group H of proper real orthogonal 2×2 matrices are exhausted by $D(X) = e^{im\xi}$, $m = 0, \pm 1, \pm 2, \cdots$. The orthogonality relations merely express the familiar facts:

$$\int_0^{2\pi} e^{im\xi} \cdot e^{-in\xi} d\xi = 0; \quad m \neq n.$$
$$= 2\pi; \quad m = n.$$

4. The element of volume of the full linear group and of its subgroups.

A typical element X of the full linear group G of dimension n is a non-singular $n \times n$ matrix with *complex* elements $x_s{}^r = \xi_{1s}{}^r + i\xi_{2s}{}^r$ so that G is a $2n^2$ parameter group; one set of parameters, for instance, being the $2n^2$ real numbers $\xi_{1s}{}^r, \xi_{2s}{}^r$. It is not always most convenient to use real parameters and we suppose, then, that the parameters ξ are subjected to a linear transformation (not necessarily real) $\xi \to \zeta = T\xi$. If $\xi \to \eta$ is, as before, the transformation of the parametric space which is induced by the left translation $X \to Y = AX$ of G, the element of volume, when the parameters ξ are used, is $\{\det \frac{\partial(\eta)}{\partial(\xi)} d(\xi)\}_{\eta=\epsilon}$. If $\omega = T\eta$ are the new, possibly complex, parameters for Y it is clear that $\det \frac{\partial(\omega)}{\partial(\zeta)} = \det \frac{\partial(\eta)}{\partial(\xi)}$ since $\omega = T\eta, \xi = T^{-1}\zeta$ implies $\frac{\partial(\omega)}{\partial(\zeta)} = T \frac{\partial(\eta)}{\partial(\xi)} T^{-1}$.

Hence the element of volume when the new, possibly complex, parameters are used is

$$d\tau = \det\left\{\frac{\partial(\eta)}{\partial(\xi)}\,d(\xi)\right\}_{\eta=\epsilon} = \det\left\{\frac{\partial(\omega)}{\partial(\zeta)}\,d(\xi)\right\}_{\omega=\epsilon'}$$

where $\epsilon' = T\epsilon$ denotes the new parameters of E_n. For example let $x_s{}^r, \bar{x}_s{}^r$ be used as complex parameters for the element X of the full linear group. Then the left translation $X \to Y = AX$ induces the linear transformation whose matrix is $A \times E_n$ on the set $x_s{}^r$ of the $2n^2$ parameters and the linear transformation whose matrix is $\bar{A} \times E_n$ on the remaining set $\bar{x}_s{}^r$ of the $2n^2$ parameters. Hence the transformation of the $2n^2$ parameter space which is induced by the left translation $X \to Y = AX$ is linear and has for its matrix the direct sum of $A \times E_n$ and $\bar{A} \times E_n$. Its determinant is accordingly $(\det A\bar{A})^n$. In order to obtain the element of volume of the full linear group we must evaluate this at $Y = E_n$, i. e. $A = X^{-1}$, and so the element of volume is

$$d\tau = \frac{1}{(\det X\bar{X})^n}\,d(\xi)$$

where the ξ are any real parameters which are connected with $x_s{}^r, \bar{x}_s{}^r$ by a non-singular linear transformation. In particular if $\xi = (\xi_1, \xi_2)$ the element of volume appears as

$$(8.31) \qquad \frac{1}{(\det X\bar{X})^n}\,d(\xi_1, \xi_2).$$

The element of volume when the coordinates in R which are introduced to facilitate the integration are not (ξ_1, ξ_2) but the elements of Λ, V and their conjugates where $X = V\Lambda V^{-1}$ is calculated by the method given on pp. 207-209. We must merely multiply the Jacobian determinant there calculated by its conjugate (since now the change of parameters is not merely from x to (λ, v) but from $(x, \bar{x})$ to $(\lambda, \bar{\lambda}, v, \bar{v})$); we find

$$(8.32)\; d\tau = \frac{\{\Delta(\lambda)\Delta(\bar{\lambda})\}^2}{(\lambda_1 \cdots \lambda_n)^n(\bar{\lambda}_1 \cdots \bar{\lambda}_n)^n}\,\frac{1}{(\det V)^n(\det \bar{V})^n}\,d(\xi).$$

No change is necessary as far as the discussion of the element of volume of a subgroup of the full linear group is concerned. In fact the determination of the element of volume of a subgroup rests on the transformation $\xi \to \eta$ of the parametric space and is unaffected by the nature of the elements X.

5. The characteristic matrices of a subgroup of the full linear group. The left translation $X \to Y = AX$ of any r parameter subgroup H of the full linear group G induces the transformation $\xi \to \eta$ of the parametric region R of H where, (8.18),

$$\frac{\partial Y}{\partial \eta^a} \frac{\partial \eta^a}{\partial \xi^q} = A \frac{\partial X}{\partial \xi^q}.$$

On evaluating this identity in (ξ, η) at $\eta = \epsilon$ so that $Y = E_n$, $A = X^{-1}$, we obtain the following identity in ξ

$$(8.33) \qquad M_a \left(\frac{\partial \eta^a}{\partial \xi^q} \right)_{\eta = \epsilon} = X^{-1} \frac{\partial X}{\partial \xi^q}$$

where the constant matrices M_j are defined by

$$(8.34) \qquad M_j = \left(\frac{\partial Y}{\partial \eta^j} \right)_{\eta = \epsilon} = \left(\frac{\partial X}{\partial \xi^j} \right)_{\xi = \epsilon}; \qquad j = 1, \cdots, r.$$

The matrices M_j are known as the characteristic matrices of the group H (relative to the parameter specification ξ). If they are linearly independent *in the field of real numbers,* i. e. if an hypothecated relation $c^a M_a = 0$, where the c^j are real numbers, implies $c^j = 0$, $j = 1, \cdots, r$, the equation (8.33) furnishes a method for determining the element of volume of H. We have merely to calculate $X^{-1} \dfrac{\partial X}{\partial \xi^q}$ and express it as a linear combination of the characteristic matrices M_j; the coefficient $c_q{}^j$ in this linear combination is, by (8.33) and the hypothecated linear independence in the field of real numbers of the characteristic matrices M_j, $\left(\dfrac{\partial \eta^j}{\partial \xi^q} \right)_{\eta = \epsilon}$. Hence the matrix $(c_q{}^j) = C$ is $F(\epsilon, \xi) = F^{-1}(\xi)$ so that the element of volume of H is

$$d\tau \equiv \det F^{-1}(\xi) d(\xi) = \det C d(\xi).$$

The matrices M_j may well be linearly dependent *in the field of complex numbers*; in other words there may well exist a relation $c^a M_a = 0$ where the complex numbers c^j do not all vanish. It is usually more convenient to calculate all the matrices $X^{-1} \dfrac{\partial X}{\partial \xi^q}$, $q = 1, \cdots, r$, at once by calculating $X^{-1} dX$ where $dX = \dfrac{\partial X}{\partial \xi^a} d\xi^a$; then the result is

$$(8.35) \qquad X^{-1} dX = M_a (d\eta^a)_{\eta = \epsilon}$$

and the element of volume is found by taking the determinant of the coefficients of the r linear forms $(d\eta^j)_{\eta=\epsilon}$, $j=1,\cdots,r$, in the differentials $d\xi^k$ and multiplying it by $d(\xi)$. The matrix $X^{-1}dX$ is known as the general infinitesimal matrix associated with H and the collection of matrices

(8.36) $$\delta X \equiv X^{-1}dX;\ X \text{ variable over } H$$

is said to constitute the infinitesimal group of H.

In order to illustrate the theory, let us consider the group H of unitary unimodular 2×2 matrices. The typical element of H is

$$X=\begin{pmatrix} x_4-ix_3 & -x_1-ix_2 \\ x_1-ix_2 & x_4+ix_3 \end{pmatrix}$$

where $x_1^2+x_2^2+x_3^2+x_4^2=\det X=1$. Hence H is a three parameter group and we take (x_1,x_2,x_3) as the three parameters ξ. Since E_2 is furnished by $\xi=0$, $x_4=1$, and since $x_1dx_1+x_2dx_2+x_3dx_3+x_4dx_4=0$ we have $(dx_4)_{\xi=\epsilon}=0$ so that the three characteristic matrices are

$$M_1=\begin{pmatrix} 0 & -1 \\ 1 & 0 \end{pmatrix};\quad M_2=\begin{pmatrix} 0 & -i \\ -i & 0 \end{pmatrix};\quad M_3=\begin{pmatrix} -i & 0 \\ 0 & +i \end{pmatrix}.$$

On calculating $\delta X=X^{-1}dX$ and writing it in the form c^aM_a we find

$$\begin{aligned} c^1 &= x_4dx_1-x_3dx_2+x_2dx_3-x_1dx_4 \\ c^2 &= x_3dx_1+x_4dx_2-x_1dx_3-x_2dx_4 \\ c^3 &= -x_2dx_1+x_1dx_2+x_4dx_3-x_3dx_4. \end{aligned}$$

On eliminating dx_4 by means of the relation $x_1dx_1+x_2dx_2+x_3dx_3+x_4dx_4=0$ and multiplying each row of the resulting determinant by x_4 we see that we have to evaluate the determinant

$$\begin{vmatrix} x_4^2+x_1^2 & -x_4x_3+x_1x_2 & x_4x_2+x_1x_3 \\ x_4x_3+x_1x_2 & x_4^2+x_2^2 & -x_4x_1+x_2x_3 \\ -x_4x_2+x_1x_3 & x_4x_1+x_2x_3 & x_4^2+x_3^2 \end{vmatrix}.$$

This turns out to be x_4^2 and so the element of volume is $\dfrac{1}{x_4}d(x_1,x_2,x_3)$ (since the determinant must be divided by x_4^3 to neutralise the previous multiplication of each of its three rows by x_4). On writing $x_4=\cos\theta$ so that $x_1^2+x_2^2+x_3^2=\sin^2\theta$ it becomes convenient to introduce new parameters $(\zeta_1,\zeta_2,\zeta_3)$ defined by $\xi=\dfrac{\sin\theta}{\theta}\zeta$, i.e. $\xi_1=x_1=\dfrac{\sin\theta}{\theta}\zeta_1$, $\xi_2=x_2=\dfrac{\sin\theta}{\theta}\zeta_2$; $\xi_3=x_3=\dfrac{\sin\theta}{\theta}\zeta_3$; the new parametric space becoming the interior of the sphere $0\leq\theta<2\pi$ (since $\zeta_1^2+\zeta_2^2+\zeta_3^2=\theta^2$). An easy calculation yields $\frac{\partial(\xi)}{\partial(\zeta)}=\frac{\sin^2\theta}{\theta^2}\cos\theta$ so that $\left(\frac{\partial(\zeta)}{\partial(\xi)}\right)_{\zeta=\epsilon'}=1$. Hence the volume element when the parameters ζ are used is $\frac{1}{\cos\theta}\,\frac{\sin^2\theta\cos\theta}{\theta^2}\,d(\zeta)$ $=\frac{\sin^2\theta}{\theta^2}\,d(\zeta)$. In fact if ω corresponds to η, as ζ does to ξ, $\left\{\frac{\partial(\omega)}{\partial(\zeta)}\right\}_{\omega=\epsilon'}$ $=\left\{\frac{\partial(\omega)}{\partial(\eta)}\right\}_{\omega=\epsilon'}\left\{\frac{\partial(\eta)}{\partial(\xi)}\right\}_{\eta=\epsilon}\frac{\partial(\xi)}{\partial(\zeta)}$. On introducing polar coordinates θ, λ, μ the integration may be performed by means of the formula $\int_R \phi d\tau=\int_R \phi\sin^2\theta\,d\theta\sin\lambda d\lambda d\mu$. Since the characteristic numbers of X are $e^{\pm i\theta}$ any *class function* ϕ is a function $\phi(\theta)$ of θ alone and our integral simplifies to

$$\int_R \phi d\tau = 4\pi\int_0^{2\pi}\phi(\theta)\sin^2\theta d\theta. \tag{8.37}$$

Note that the polar coordinates θ, λ, μ are merely convenient tools for performing the integration (after the element of volume has been already calculated) and cannot serve as parameters for H; for the origin $\theta=0$ of the parametric space, which corresponds to the unit point of the group, is a singular point of the polar coordinates. It is important to observe that a typical element X of the group H is of the form

$$X=\cos\theta E_2+\sin\theta I \tag{8.38}$$

where $I=\frac{-i}{\theta}\begin{pmatrix}\zeta_3 & \zeta_2+i\zeta_1\\ \zeta_2-i\zeta_1 & -\zeta_3\end{pmatrix}$ so that $I^2=-E_2$. In other words $X=e^{\theta I}$ where I is the product by i of a 2×2 Hermitian matrix whose trace is zero. On writing

$$I_1=\begin{pmatrix}0 & +1\\ -1 & 0\end{pmatrix},\quad I_2=\begin{pmatrix}0 & -i\\ -i & 0\end{pmatrix},\quad I_3=\begin{pmatrix}-i & 0\\ 0 & +i\end{pmatrix}$$

we may write $X=\cos\theta E_2+\frac{\sin\theta}{\theta}(\zeta_1 I_1+\zeta_2 I_2+\zeta_3 I_3)$ where the matrices E_2, I_1, I_2, I_3 obey the rules of quaternion multiplication:

$$I_1^2=I_2^2=I_3^2=-E_2;\ I_2I_3=I_1=-I_3I_2 \text{ etc.}$$

Hence the group H is a representation of the group of all real unit quaternions (under quaternion multiplication as the law of combination) the representation being *faithful* (i. e. to each element X of H there corresponds one and only one unit quaternion). The subgroup of H which is composed of its *real* elements is the proper real orthogonal group of dimension 2; any element O of this group is of the form

(8.39) $$O = \cos\theta E_2 + \sin\theta I$$

where $I = \begin{pmatrix} 0 & 1 \\ -1 & 0 \end{pmatrix}$ is a skew symmetric matrix whose square is $-E_2$. Since E_2, I obey the rules of multiplication of ordinary complex numbers $I^2 = -E_2$ the group of proper real orthogonal 2×2 matrices is a faithful representation of the group of all unit complex numbers (i. e. complex numbers of unit modulus).

We have seen, p. 213, that the automorphism of H

$$X \to Z = AXA^{-1}$$

which is induced by the element A of H gives rise to an r-dimensional representation $\Gamma = \{H(\alpha)\}$, known as the adjoint representation, of H. The matrices $H(\alpha)$ are the Jacobian matrices $\dfrac{\partial(\zeta)}{\partial(\xi)}$ evaluated at $\xi = \epsilon$ or, what is the same thing, $\zeta = \epsilon$. On differentiating the equation $Z = AXA^{-1}$ with respect to ξ^q and evaluating at $\xi = \epsilon$ we obtain

$$M_a \left(\frac{\partial \zeta^a}{\partial \xi^q}\right)_{\xi=\epsilon} = AM_qA^{-1}.$$

On regarding the set of matrices $M_j, j = 1, \cdots, r$, as a $1 \times r$ vector M we may say that the automorphism $X \to Z = AXA^{-1}$ of H induces the linear transformation

$$M \to N = MH(\alpha)$$

of the r-dimensional real vector space which is spanned by the characteristic vector-matrices M. Since the determinant of $H(\alpha)$ is unity (on the supposition that any point of the parametric region R may be connected by a continuous curve with the unit point ϵ; for $\det H(\epsilon) = 1$ and the continuous function $\det H(\alpha)$ can take only the values ± 1) it is clear that if C is any $r \times r$ matrix and if we write the vector-matrix MC (whose j-th component is the matrix $M_a c_j{}^a$) in the form ND then $\det D = \det C$. In fact $C = H(\alpha)D$ so that $\det C = \det H(\alpha) \det D = \det D$. The useful implication of this result for our immediate purpose is the following. We know that in order to calculate the element of volume of H we must express $\delta X = X^{-1}dX$ as a linear combination $c^a M_a = (c_\beta{}^a d\xi^\beta) M_a$ of the characteristic matrices M_j and must then take the determinant of the matrix $C = (c_j{}^k)$. We now see that, if it proves more convenient, we may express δX just as well as a linear combination of the matrices $N_j = AM_jA^{-1}$ where A is any element of H; or, equivalently, we may express $A^{-1}\delta XA$, instead of δX, as a linear combination of the characteristic matrices M_j; the only thing remaining to do being then to take the determinant of the linear forms in the $d\xi$ which appear as the coefficients in this linear combination.

We illustrate these remarks by considering the element of volume of the n-dimensional unitary group H. Since the Schur canonical form of any element X of H is diagonal (X being normal) and unitary the diagonal representative Λ of the class to which X belongs is

$$\Lambda = \begin{pmatrix} e^{i\theta_1} & & & \\ & \cdot & & \\ & & \cdot & \\ & & & e^{i\theta_n} \end{pmatrix} = e^{i\Theta}$$

where Θ is the real diagonal (hence Hermitian) matrix

$$\Theta = \begin{pmatrix} \theta_1 & & & & \\ & \theta_2 & & & \\ & & \cdot & & \\ & & & \cdot & \\ & & & & \theta_n \end{pmatrix}.$$

Hence $X = V\Lambda V^{-1} = Ve^{i\Theta}V^{-1} = e^{Vi\Theta V^{-1}} = e^{iH}$ where $H = V\Theta V^{-1} = V\Theta V^*$ is Hermitian. Conversely every matrix $X = e^{iH}$, H an arbitrary Hermitian matrix, is unitary since $X^* = e^{-iH} = X^{-1}$. Since an arbitrary Hermitian matrix depends on $n + \frac{1}{2}(n^2 - n)2 = n^2$ real parameters the unitary n-dimensional group is an n^2 parameter group; we take as our parameters for X the n-diagonal elements $h_p{}^p$ and the $n^2 - n$ real and imaginary parts of the non-diagonal elements $h_p{}^q$, $q < p$, of H. Since $X = e^{iH} = E_n + iH - \dfrac{H^2}{2!} - \dfrac{iH^3}{3!} + \cdots$ and since $H = 0$ yields the unit element of our group the characteristic matrices M_q are simply $i\dfrac{\partial H}{\partial \xi^q}$, $q = 1, \cdots, n^2$. In fact $dH^2 = HdH + dH \cdot H = 0$, when $H = 0$; $d \cdot H^3 = dH \cdot H^2 + H \cdot dH^2 = 0$ when $H = 0$ and so on. The first n characteristic matrices $M_1, \cdots, M_n$ are, accordingly, diagonal:

$$M_1 = \begin{pmatrix} i & & & \\ & 0 & & \\ & & \cdot & \\ & & & \cdot \\ & & & & 0 \end{pmatrix} \cdots M_n = \begin{pmatrix} 0 & & & \\ & 0 & & \\ & & \cdot & \\ & & & i \end{pmatrix}$$

whilst the remainder are of the type $M_2^1 = \begin{pmatrix} 0 & i & & & \\ +i & 0 & & & \\ & & 0 & & \\ & & & \cdot & \\ & & & & 0 \end{pmatrix}$

$\tilde{M}_2^1 = \begin{pmatrix} 0 & 1 & & \\ -1 & 0 & & \\ & & 0 & \\ & & & 0 \end{pmatrix}$. The element V of our group which transforms X into Λ is undetermined to the extent of a right-factor diagonal unitary matrix D (it being understood that we are confining our attention to the "generic" unitary matrix X, no two of whose characteristic numbers $e^{i\theta_1}, \cdots, e^{i\theta_n}$ are equal). We use this diagonal unitary matrix D which is at our disposal to arrange that the diagonal elements of V are real and positive so that V depends on $n^2 - n$, instead of n^2 parameters.

We are now ready to proceed with the calculation of $\delta X = X^{-1}dX$. Since $X = V\Lambda V^{-1}$, $XV = V\Lambda$ so that $dX \cdot V + X \cdot dV = dV \cdot \Lambda + Vd\Lambda$ or, equivalently, $dX = (dV \cdot \Lambda + V \cdot d\Lambda - X \cdot dV)V^{-1}$. Hence

$$\delta X = X^{-1}dX = V(\Lambda^{-1}V^{-1}dV\Lambda + \Lambda^{-1}d\Lambda - V^{-1}dV)V^{-1}$$

or, equivalently,

$$V^{-1}\delta XV = \Lambda^{-1}\delta V\Lambda + \delta\Lambda - \delta V.$$

We have now merely to express this as a linear combination of the characteristic matrices M_j, $M_p{}^q$, $\tilde{M}_p{}^q$. Since the diagonal elements of $\Lambda^{-1}\delta V\Lambda$ and δV are the same the coefficient c^j of M_j is $d\theta_j$. The j, k element of the matrix $V^{-1}\delta XV$ $(j \neq k)$ is $(e^{i(\theta_k - \theta_j)} - 1)\delta v_k{}^j$ and if $\delta V = c_\beta{}^\alpha M_\alpha{}^\beta + \tilde{c}_\beta{}^\alpha \tilde{M}_\alpha{}^\beta$, $(\delta v)_k{}^j = (ic_j{}^k + \tilde{c}_j{}^k)$, $k > j$ so that the coefficient of $M_k{}^j$ in $V^{-1}\delta XV$ is the imaginary part of $(\tilde{c}_j{}^k + ic_j{}^k)(e^{i(\theta_k - \theta_j)} - 1)$ whilst the coefficient of $\tilde{M}_j{}^k$ is the real part of this expression. Since a determinant is multiplied by $-2i$ when the first of two of its columns is replaced by the first $+i$ times the second whilst the second is replaced by the first $-i$ times the second the determinant of the $n(n-1)$ linear forms which constitute the coefficients of the $M_p{}^q$, $\tilde{M}_p{}^q$ in $V^{-1}\delta XV$ is $\dfrac{1}{(2i)^{n(n-1)}}$ times the determinant of the $n(n-1)$ linear forms

$$(c_j{}^k + ic_j{}^k)\{e^{i(\theta_k - \theta_j)} - 1\}, \quad (\tilde{c}_j{}^k - ic_j{}^k)\{e^{-i(\theta_k - \theta_j)} - 1\}.$$

In order to facilitate the integration we shall introduce as new coordinates (not as *parameters* for the group) the n numbers $(\theta_1, \cdots, \theta_n)$ and $n^2 - n$ numbers which specify the elements of V; then the numbers

$\bar{c}_j^k$, c_j^k are independent of θ and the volume element is factorable into a product one factor of which depends only on the coordinates θ and the other on the $n^2 - n$ parameters for V. In integrating any *class* function over R we need only pay attention to the integration with respect to the cooordinates θ, the part which comes from the integration with respect to the remaining $n^2 - n$ cooordinates dividing out in the averaging process over the group. We shall call the part which depends only on θ, for the sake of brevity, the element of volume $d\tau$ of the group and shall absorb all awkward constants in the other factor which cancels out. For the unitary group $d\tau$ is, accordingly $\prod_{k>j}(e^{i\theta_k} - e^{i\theta_j})(e^{-i\theta_k} - e^{-i\theta_j})d(\theta)$ or, equivalently, since numerical factors are without significance,

$$d\tau = \prod_{k>j} \sin^2 \frac{(\theta_k - \theta_j)}{2} d(\theta_1, \cdots, \theta_n). \tag{8.40}$$

For the unimodular unitary group only a slight change has to be made. Since $X = V\Lambda V^{-1}$, $\det X = 1$ forces $\det \Lambda = 1$, or, equivalently $\theta_1 + \cdots + \theta_n = 0$. The group is an $n^2 - 1$ parameter group and if we use as coordinates $\theta_1, \cdots, \theta_{n-1}$ together with the $n^2 - n$ coordinates which specify V the element of volume is

$$d\tau = \prod_{k>j} \sin^2 \frac{\theta_k - \theta_j}{2} d(\theta_1, \cdots, \theta_{n-1});\quad \theta_n = -(\theta_1 + \cdots + \theta_{n-1}). \tag{8.41}$$

Thus for the unimodular two-dimensional unitary group

$$d\tau = \sin^2 \theta d\theta$$

as given in (8.37) (only in that simple case the complete expression for $d\tau$ involving the factor depending on the other coordinates was given).

CHAPTER NINE

THE ORTHOGONAL GROUP

In this chapter we shall discuss the irreducible representations of the n-dimensional real orthogonal group and shall derive from these the irreducible representations of the n-dimensional rotation group (= group of $n \times n$ real orthogonal matrices of determinant unity).

1. The canonical representative of a class of the real orthogonal group.

The typical element X of the group R' of all real orthogonal matrices of dimension n is defined by

$$XX' = X'X = E_n.$$

Since $X' = X^*$, X being real, R' is a subgroup of the unitary group so that the characteristic numbers of X are all of unit modulus. If a characteristic number is real it must be ± 1 and we shall suppose, for the moment, that X has at least one characteristic number 1. This characteristic number 1 has at least one characteristic vector v_1 associated with it and since v_1 satisfies the equation $Xv_1 = v_1$ it may be taken to be real and of unit magnitude; in fact the ratios of the n coordinates of v_1 are real and v_1 is undetermined to the extent of a scalar factor. We know, from the orthogonalisation process of Schmidt, that v_1 may be taken as the first column of a real $n \times n$ orthogonal matrix A; the discussion of this process given on p. 24 dealt with vectors *in the complex field* (i. e. vectors whose coordinates are complex numbers) but it may be repeated for vectors *in the real* field (i. e. vectors whose coordinates are real numbers) and then the adjective *unitary* may be replaced by *real orthogonal*. Since, then, $Ae_1 = v_1$ the equation $Xv_1 = v_1$ may be replaced by $A^{-1}XAe_1 = e_1$ so that the real orthogonal matrix $A^{-1}XA$ is of the form $\begin{pmatrix} 1 & u' \\ 0 & Y \end{pmatrix}$ where u' is a $1 \times n-1$ and Y an $n-1 \times n-1$ matrix. The fact that $\begin{pmatrix} 1 & u' \\ 0 & Y \end{pmatrix}$ is orthogonal finds its expression in the equation

$$\begin{pmatrix} 1 & u' \\ 0 & Y \end{pmatrix}\begin{pmatrix} 1 & 0 \\ u & Y' \end{pmatrix} = E_n,$$

and this implies first $u'u = 0$, so that $u = 0$, and next $YY' = E_{n-1}$

so that Y is a real orthogonal matrix. The same reduction is feasible if X has a characteristic number $= -1$. If Y has a real characteristic number we can find, by the same argument, a real orthogonal $n-1 \times n-1$ matrix B such that

$$B^{-1}YB = \begin{pmatrix} \pm 1 & 0 \\ 0 & Z \end{pmatrix}; \; Z \text{ a real orthogonal } n-2 \times n-2 \text{ matrix.}$$

Then the $n \times n$ real orthogonal matrix $A_1 = \begin{pmatrix} 1 & 0 \\ 0 & B \end{pmatrix}$ is such that

$$A_1^{-1}A^{-1}XAA_1 = \begin{pmatrix} F_2 & 0 \\ 0 & Z \end{pmatrix}$$

where F_2 is a two-rowed diagonal real orthogonal matrix (hence with diagonal elements ± 1) and Z is an $n-2 \times n-2$ real orthogonal matrix. Continuing this argument we see that if X possesses j real characteristic numbers ± 1 (each counted according to its multiplicity) we can find a real n-dimensional orthogonal matrix A such that

$$A^{-1}XA = \begin{pmatrix} F_j & 0 \\ 0 & Y \end{pmatrix}$$

where F_j is a real diagonal orthogonal matrix (hence with diagonal elements ± 1) and Y is an $n-j$ dimensional real orthogonal matrix none of whose characteristic numbers are real. Since the complex characteristic numbers occur in conjugate pairs $n-j$ must be even, $= 2m$, say. If B is a $2m$-dimensional real orthogonal matrix and $B^{-1}YB = Z$ then $A_2 = \begin{pmatrix} E_j & 0 \\ 0 & B \end{pmatrix}$ is a real n-dimensional orthogonal matrix such that $A_2^{-1}A^{-1}XAA_2 = \begin{pmatrix} F_j & 0 \\ 0 & Z \end{pmatrix}$. In order to find, therefore, a canonical representative for the class of R' to which X belongs we have merely to find a canonical form under transformations by real orthogonal matrices for a $2m$-dimensional real orthogonal matrix Y which has no real characteristic number. If $e^{i\theta}$ is a characteristic number of Y no characteristic vector v associated with $e^{i\theta}$ can be real since $Yv = e^{i\theta}v$: $v = v_1 + iv_2$; $v_2 \neq 0$; v_1, v_2 real. In addition $v_1 \neq 0$ for if $v_1 = 0$, $v/i = v_2$ would be a real characteristic vector; also v_1 and v_2 are linearly independent since otherwise v_1 would be a multiple of v and hence a characteristic vector associated with $e^{i\theta}$ which is impossible since v_1 is real. Let, then, u_1, u_2 be two mutually perpendicular real unit vectors in the plane determined by v_1, v_2 and (again by the orthogonalisation process of Schmidt) let B be a real $2m$-dimensional orthogonal matrix of which u_1, u_2 are the first two columns. Since $Yv = e^{i\theta}v$ we have

$$Yv_1 = \cos\theta v_1 - \sin\theta v_2; \quad Yv_2 = \sin\theta v_1 + \cos\theta v_2.$$

On writing u_1, u_2 as linear combinations (with real coefficients) of v_1, v_2, and vice versâ, we obtain Yu_1, Yu_2 as linear combinations (with real coefficients) of u_1 and u_2, i. e. $B^{-1}YBe_1$, $B^{-1}YBe_2$ as linear combinations of e_1, e_2:

$$B^{-1}YB = \begin{pmatrix} C & L' \\ 0 & M \end{pmatrix}$$

where C is a real 2×2 matrix, L' is a real $2 \times 2m - 2$ matrix and M a real $2m - 2 \times 2m - 2$ matrix. Expressing that $B^{-1}YB$ is orthogonal:

$$\begin{pmatrix} C' & 0 \\ L & M' \end{pmatrix}\begin{pmatrix} C & L' \\ 0 & M \end{pmatrix} = E_{2m}$$

we find first $C'C = E_2$ so that C is a real orthogonal 2×2 matrix; next $LC = 0$ so that $L = 0$ (on multiplying on the right by C') and finally that $M'M = E_{2m-2}$ so that M is a real orthogonal $2m - 2 \times 2m - 2$ matrix. Continuing this process we see that we can find a real orthogonal matrix V so that

$$V^{-1}XV = \begin{pmatrix} F_j & & & & & \\ & C_1 & & & & \\ & & C_2 & & & \\ & & & \cdot & & \\ & & & & \cdot & \\ & & & & & C_m \end{pmatrix}$$

where F_j is a real diagonal orthogonal matrix and each C_j, $j = 1, \cdots, m$, is a real 2×2 orthogonal matrix. Furthermore each C_j is a proper 2×2 orthogonal matrix since every improper real 2×2 orthogonal matrix, being of the type $\begin{pmatrix} \cos\theta & \sin\theta \\ \sin\theta & -\cos\theta \end{pmatrix}$ has the *real* characteristic numbers ± 1. Hence each C_j is of the type

$$C_j = \begin{pmatrix} \cos\theta_j & \sin\theta_j \\ -\sin\theta_j & \cos\theta_j \end{pmatrix}.$$

Since E_2, $-E_2$ are of the type C_j with $\theta_j = 0, \pi$, respectively, an *even* number of $+1$'s and of (-1)'s may be absorbed from F_j and so a canonical representative of the class of R' to which X belongs is of the following type:

1. n even.

$$\Lambda = \begin{pmatrix} C_1 & & & \\ & \cdot & & \\ & & \cdot & \\ & & & C_{n/2} \end{pmatrix} \text{ if } X \text{ is proper; } \begin{pmatrix} C_1 & & & \\ & \cdot & & \\ & & \cdot & \\ & & & C_{(n/2)-1} & \\ & & & & F \end{pmatrix}$$

if X is improper, where $F = \begin{pmatrix} 1 & 0 \\ 0 & -1 \end{pmatrix}$.

2. n odd $= 2k + 1$.

$$\begin{pmatrix} C_1 & & & & \\ & C_2 & & & \\ & & \cdot & & \\ & & & C_k & \\ & & & & 1 \end{pmatrix} \text{ if } X \text{ is proper; } \begin{pmatrix} C_1 & & & & \\ & \cdot & & & \\ & & \cdot & & \\ & & & C_k & \\ & & & & -1 \end{pmatrix}$$

if X is improper. If we consider the classes of the rotation subgroup R of R' it is clear that a distinction must be made between the cases n even and n odd. If n is odd R does not effect any refinement of the classes of R'. For if V transforms X into any element Y of R so also does $V(-E_n) = -V$ and of the two matrices, V and $-V$, one is proper. If n is even there is a refinement of the classes of R' by R. In fact $C(\theta) = \begin{pmatrix} \cos\theta & \sin\theta \\ -\sin\theta & \cos\theta \end{pmatrix}$ and $C(-\theta) = \begin{pmatrix} \cos\theta & -\sin\theta \\ \sin\theta & \cos\theta \end{pmatrix}$ are transformable into one another by the improper 2×2 real orthogonal matrix $F = \begin{pmatrix} 1 & 0 \\ 0 & -1 \end{pmatrix}$ but are not transformable into one another by any element of the 2-dimensional rotation group (since this group is Abelian). On writing $n = 2k$ and denoting by $\Lambda(\theta_1, \cdots, \theta_k)$ the canonical representative of the class of R' to which X belongs:

$$\Lambda(\theta_1, \cdots, \theta_k) = \begin{pmatrix} C_1 & & & & \\ & C_2 & & & \\ & & \cdot & & \\ & & & \cdot & \\ & & & & C_k \end{pmatrix}$$

we see that $\Lambda(\pm\theta_1, \cdots, \pm\theta_k)$ all belong to the same class of R' whilst they belong to two distinct classes of R. Those for which an *even* number of the $(\theta_1, \cdots, \theta_k)$ carry a negative sign belong to the class containing $\Lambda(\theta_1, \cdots, \theta_k)$ whilst those for which an *odd* number of the $(\theta_1, \cdots, \theta_k)$ carry a negative sign belong to the class containing

$\Lambda(-\theta_1, \theta_2, \cdots, \theta_k)$. Since the matrix inverse to $\Lambda(\theta_1, \cdots, \theta_k)$ is $\Lambda(-\theta_1, \cdots, -\theta_k)$ each class of R' contains the inverse of each of its members. Hence the characters of any continuous representation of R' are *real*; for the representation, being bounded, is necessarily equivalent to a unitary representation so that the character of any element is the conjugate complex of the character of the reciprocal of that element.

In closing this section we remark that the argument we have given shows that any *real* $n \times n$ matrix may be transformed by means of a real orthogonal $n \times n$ matrix into a canonical form analogous to the canonical form due to Schur (in the complex field). If n is even $(= 2m)$ the canonical form is an $m \times m$ matrix (whose elements are 2×2 matrices) the elements below the main diagonal being zero. In other words the canonical form is precisely the triangular canonical form of Schur but the elements of the $n/2 \times n/2$ "block" matrix, which furnishes the canonical form, are 2×2 real matrices (instead of 1×1 complex matrices). When n is odd $(= 2m + 1)$ the canonical form is obtained from the canonical form just given for $n = 2m$ by adding a last column of real elements and a last row all of whose elements are zero save the last (i. e. diagonal) element.

2. The element of volume of the *n*-dimensional rotation group.

Since $C_j = \begin{pmatrix} \cos\theta_j & \sin\theta_j \\ -\sin\theta_j & \cos\theta_j \end{pmatrix} = e^{S_j}$ where S_j is the skew-symmetric matrix: $S_j = \begin{pmatrix} 0 & \theta_j \\ -\theta_j & 0 \end{pmatrix}$ any *proper* real n-dimensional orthogonal matrix may be written in the form $X = e^S$ where S is a real n-dimensional skew-symmetric matrix. In fact the canonical representative of the class of R' to which X belongs is of the form e^{Σ} where Σ is the skew-symmetric real matrix, of dimension n,

$$\Sigma = \begin{bmatrix} S_1 & & & \\ & \cdot & & \\ & & \cdot & \\ & & & \cdot \\ & & & & S_k \end{bmatrix}; \text{ if } n \text{ is even } (= 2k)$$

$$\Sigma = \begin{bmatrix} S_1 & & & & \\ & \cdot & & & \\ & & \cdot & & \\ & & & \cdot & \\ & & & & S_k & \\ & & & & & 0 \end{bmatrix}; \text{ if } n \text{ is odd } (= 2k + 1).$$

Hence $X = Ve^{\Sigma}V^{-1} = e^{V\Sigma V^{-1}} = e^S$ where S is a real skew-symmetric matrix of dimension n. In fact $S = V\Sigma V^{-1}$ so that $S' = (V^{-1})'\Sigma' V' = -V\Sigma V^{-1} = -S$. Since a skew-symmetric real matrix involves $\frac{1}{2}(n^2 - n) = \frac{1}{2}n(n-1)$ parameters the n-dimensional rotation group is an $\frac{1}{2}n(n-1)$ parameter group. We shall adopt as parameters the elements $\xi_p{}^q$, $p > q$, of S which lie above the main diagonal of S ($\xi_p{}^q$ being the element in the q-th row and p-th column of S). Since the set of matrices $X(t) = e^{tS}$ furnishes, as t varies continuously from 0 to 1, a set of elements of R varying continuously from E_n to X the rotation group R is connected. We proceed to determine its element of volume $d\tau$. Since $S = 0$ furnishes the unit element E_n of R and since $X = e^S = E_n + S + \frac{S^2}{2!} + \cdots$ the characteristic matrices

$$M_p{}^q = \left(\frac{\partial X}{\partial \xi_p{}^q}\right)_{\xi=0} = \frac{\partial S}{\partial \xi_p{}^q};\ p > q.$$

On denoting by $e_j{}^k$ the n-dimensional matrix all of whose elements are zero save the one in the j-th row and k-th column, which one is unity, we have

$$(9.1) \qquad M_p{}^q = e_q{}^p - e_p{}^q.$$

As always our problem in calculating the element of volume of our group is to express $\delta X = X^{-1}dX$ as a linear combination

$$\delta X = c_\beta{}^\alpha M_\alpha{}^\beta$$

of the characteristic matrices $M_q{}^p$ and then to calculate the determinant of the $\frac{1}{2}n(n-1)$ linear forms $c_p{}^q$ in the differentials $d\xi$. We have already seen (p. 223) that if it proves more convenient we may just as well express $V^{-1}\delta XV$, where V is any element of our group, as a linear combination of the characteristic matrices $M_q{}^p$. In finding this linear combination we may adopt any convenient basis whatever in which to express the elements of our group. Thus if A is any fixed non-singular matrix whatever (not necessarily a member of our group) we may express $A^{-1}V^{-1}\delta XVA$ as a linear combination of the matrices $A^{-1}M_q{}^pA$. If we denote the presentations of $V, X, \Lambda, M_q{}^p$ in the new basis by $W, Y, \Theta, N_q{}^p$, respectively:

$$W = A^{-1}VA;\quad Y = A^{-1}XA,\quad \Theta = A^{-1}\Lambda A,\quad N_q{}^p = A^{-1}M_q{}^pA,$$

the equation $XV = V\Lambda$ appears in the form $YW = W\Theta$, and the equation

$$V^{-1}\delta XV = \Lambda^{-1}\delta V\Lambda + \delta\Lambda - \delta V$$

appears in the form

$$W^{-1}\delta YW = \Theta^{-1}\delta W\Theta + \delta\Theta - \delta W.$$

Since $W^{-1}\delta Y W = A^{-1}V^{-1}\delta X V A$ (δY being $A^{-1}\delta X A$) we have merely to express $\Theta^{-1}\delta W\Theta + \delta\Theta - \delta W$ as a linear combination of the matrices $N_q{}^p$ and then to take the determinant of the $\frac{1}{2}n(n-1)$ linear forms in the differentials $d\xi$ which appear as the coefficients of the matrices $N_q{}^p$. We shall take our transforming matrix A unitary so that whilst Θ, Y, W are no longer members of our real orthogonal group they will be members of the containing n-dimensional unitary group. Hence δW will be a linear combination (with specialized coefficients, to be sure), of the characteristic matrices M_j, $M_p{}^q$, $\tilde{M}_p{}^q$ $(p > q)$ of the unitary group (pp. 223-4). Denoting by J the 2×2 unitary matrix

$$J = \frac{1}{\sqrt{2}}\begin{pmatrix} 1 & 1 \\ +i & -i \end{pmatrix}$$

we shall choose for A, according as n is even or odd, the following:

1) n even, $= 2k$, $A = E_k \times J$; 2) n odd, $= 2k+1$, $A = E_k \times J \dotplus E_1$.

It is at once clear that

$$J^{-1}C_j J = \begin{pmatrix} e^{i\theta_j} & 0 \\ 0 & e^{-i\theta_j} \end{pmatrix}; \quad C_j = \begin{pmatrix} \cos\theta_j & \sin\theta_j \\ -\sin\theta_j & \cos\theta_j \end{pmatrix}$$

and so Θ has the following forms, according as n is even or odd:

1) n even $= 2k$;

$$(9.2) \qquad \Theta_{2k} = \begin{pmatrix} e^{i\theta_1} & & & & & \\ & e^{-i\theta_1} & & & & \\ & & \cdot & & & \\ & & & \cdot & & \\ & & & & e^{i\theta_k} & \\ & & & & & e^{-i\theta_k} \end{pmatrix}$$

2) n odd, $= 2k+1$;

$$(9.3) \qquad \Theta_{2k+1} = \Theta_{2k} \dotplus E_1.$$

On denoting, as before, by $e_p{}^q$ the $n \times n$ matrix all of whose elements are zero save the one in the p-th row and q-th column, which one is unity, an easy calculation yields the following results (it being understood that when n is even we write $n = 2k$ and when n is odd we write $n = 2k+1$):

$$(9.4) \qquad \left.\begin{aligned} A^{-1}e_{2p-1}^{2q-1}A &= \tfrac{1}{2}(e_{2p-1}^{2q-1} + e_{2p-1}^{2q} + e_{2p}^{2q-1} + e_{2p}^{2q}) \\ A^{-1}e_{2p-1}^{2q}A &= \frac{i}{2}(e_{2p-1}^{2q-1} - e_{2p-1}^{2q} + e_{2p}^{2q-1} - e_{2p}^{2q}) \\ A^{-1}e_{2p}^{2q-1}A &= -\frac{i}{2}(e_{2p-1}^{2q-1} + e_{2p-1}^{2q} - e_{2p}^{2q-1} - e_{2p}^{2q}) \\ A^{-1}e_{2p}^{2q}A &= \tfrac{1}{2}(e_{2p-1}^{2q-1} - e_{2p-1}^{2q} - e_{2p}^{2q-1} + e_{2p}^{2q}) \end{aligned}\right\} ; \quad p, q = 1, \cdots, k.$$

$$(9.5)\qquad \begin{aligned} A^{-1}e^{2p-1}_{2k+1}\,A &= \frac{1}{\sqrt{2}}\,(e^{2p-1}_{2k+1}+e^{2p}_{2k+1})\\ A^{-1}e^{2p}_{2k+1}\,A &= \frac{i}{\sqrt{2}}\,(e^{2p-1}_{2k+1}-e^{2p}_{2k+1})\\ A^{-1}e^{2k+1}_{2p-1}\,A &= \frac{1}{\sqrt{2}}\,(e^{2k+1}_{2p-1}+e^{2k+1}_{2p})\\ A^{-1}e^{2k+1}_{2p}\,A &= \frac{-i}{\sqrt{2}}\,(e^{2k+1}_{2p-1}-e^{2k+1}_{2p}) \end{aligned}\;;\qquad p=1,\cdots,k$$

(the second set being necessary only when n is odd). From these formulae it is easy to evaluate the presentations $N_p{}^q$ of the characteristic matrices of our group in the adopted basis; in fact $N_p{}^q = A^{-1}M_p{}^qA = A^{-1}(e_q{}^p - e_p{}^q)A$. On adopting the following notations

$$(9.6)\qquad \begin{aligned} &e^{2p}_{2q} - e^{2q-1}_{2p-1} = K^{2q-1}_{2p-1};\; e^{2p}_{2q-1} - e^{2q}_{2p-1} = K^{2q}_{2p-1}\\ &e^{2p-1}_{2q} - e^{2q-1}_{2p} = K^{2q-1}_{2p};\; e^{2p-1}_{2q-1} - e^{2q}_{2p} = K^{2q}_{2p}\\ &e^{2k+1}_{2p} - e^{2p-1}_{2k+1} = K^{2p-1}_{2k+1};\; e^{2k+1}_{2p-1} - e^{2p}_{2k+1} = K^{2p}_{2k+1} \end{aligned}$$

we find

$$(9.7)\qquad \begin{aligned} N^{2q-1}_{2p-1} &= \tfrac{1}{2}(K^{2q-1}_{2p-1}+K^{2q}_{2p-1}+K^{2q-1}_{2p}+K^{2q}_{2p})\\ N^{2q}_{2p-1} &= \frac{i}{2}\,(K^{2q-1}_{2p-1}-K^{2q}_{2p-1}+K^{2q-1}_{2p}-K^{2q}_{2p})\\ N^{2q-1}_{2p} &= -\frac{i}{2}\,(K^{2q-1}_{2p-1}+K^{2q}_{2p-1}-K^{2q-1}_{2p}-K^{2q}_{2p})\\ N^{2q}_{2p} &= \tfrac{1}{2}(K^{2q-1}_{2p-1}-K^{2q}_{2p-1}-K^{2q-1}_{2p}+K^{2q}_{2p}) \end{aligned}\;;\quad \begin{aligned}&p>q;\\ &p,q=1,\cdots,k.\end{aligned}$$

When n is even $(=2k)$ these equations express all the $N_p{}^q$, $p>q$, save those for which p is even and $q=p-1$, in terms of the matrices $K_p{}^q$, $p>q$ (the matrices $K_p{}^q$ for which p is even and $q=p-1$ not appearing in these expressions). The exceptional matrices N^{2j-1}_{2j} are furnished by the formulae

$$(9.8)\qquad N^{2j-1}_{2j} = i(e^{2j-1}_{2j-1}-e^{2j}_{2j});\qquad j=1,2,\cdots,k.$$

There are $\frac{1}{2}\,\frac{n}{2}(\frac{n}{2}-1)$ sets of matrices $(N^{2q-1}_{2p-1}, N^{2q}_{2p-1}, N^{2q-1}_{2p}, N^{2q}_{2p})$ and as each set contains four matrices there are $\frac{1}{2}n(n-2)$ matrices of this type; adding to these the $\frac{1}{2}n$ matrices of the special diagonal type N^{2j-1}_{2j} we have the entire set of $\frac{1}{2}n(n-1)$ matrices $N_p{}^q$, $p>q$. We see, then, that when n is even, the expression $\Theta^{-1}\delta W\Theta + \delta\Theta - \delta W$ which we know to be a linear combination of the matrices $N_p{}^q$, $p>q$, may equally well be expressed as a linear combination of the $\frac{1}{2}n(n-2)$ matrices $(K^{2q-1}_{2p-1}, K^{2q}_{2p-1}, K^{2q-1}_{2p}, K^{2q}_{2p})$, $p>q$, together with the $n/2$ diagonal matrices N^{2j-1}_{2j},

$j = 1, \cdots, k$. Furthermore the determinant of the four equations connecting each set $(K^{2q-1}_{2p-1}, K^{2q}_{2p-1}, K^{2q-1}_{2p}, K^{2q}_{2p})$ with the corresponding set $(N^{2q-1}_{2p-1}, N^{2q}_{2p-1}, N^{2q-1}_{2q}, N^{2q}_{2p})$ is unity so that the determinant of the $\frac{1}{2}n(n-1) \times \frac{1}{2}n(n-1)$ matrix which connects the set (K, N^{2j-1}_{2j}) with the set $N_p{}^q$ is unity. This assures us that in order to find the element of volume of the rotation group, for n even $(= 2k)$, we may, if it proves more convenient, express $\Theta^{-1}\delta W\Theta + \delta\Theta - \delta W$ as a linear combination of the matrices (K, N^{2j-1}_{2j}) (instead of the matrices $N_p{}^q$, $p > q$) and then take the determinant of the linear forms in the differentials $d\xi$ which appear as the coefficients of the matrices (K, N^{2j-1}_{2j}).

The following relations follow at once from the definition of $\Theta = \Theta_{2k}$:

$$(9.9) \qquad \begin{aligned} \Theta^{-1}e^{2q-1}_{2p-1}\Theta &= e^{-i(\theta_p-\theta_q)}e^{2q-1}_{2p-1}; \quad \Theta^{-1}e^{2q}_{2p-1}\Theta = e^{-i(\theta_p-\theta_q)}e^{2q}_{2p-1} \\ \Theta^{-1}e^{2q-1}_{2p}\Theta &= e^{+i(\theta_p+\theta_q)}e^{2q-1}_{2p}; \quad \Theta^{-1}e^{2q}_{2p}\Theta = e^{i(\theta_p-\theta_q)}e^{2q}_{2p} \end{aligned}$$

and these furnish

$$(9.10) \qquad \begin{aligned} \Theta^{-1}K^{2q-1}_{2p-1}\Theta &= e^{-i(\theta_p-\theta_q)}K^{2q-1}_{2p-1}; \quad \Theta^{-1}K^{2q}_{2p-1}\Theta = e^{-i(\theta_p+\theta_q)}K^{2q}_{2p-1} \\ \Theta^{-1}K^{2q-1}_{2p}\Theta &= e^{i(\theta_p+\theta_q)}K^{2q-1}_{2p}; \quad \Theta^{-1}K^{2q}_{2p}\Theta = e^{i(\theta_p-\theta_q)}K^{2q}_{2p}; \\ \Theta^{-1}N^{2j-1}_{2j}\Theta &= N^{2j-1}_{2j}. \end{aligned}$$

Hence if $\delta W = \sum_j c^j N^{2j-1}_{2j} + \sum_{p>q} c_q{}^p K^{2q-1}_{2p-1} + \sum_{p>q} (c_q{}^p)' K^{2q}_{2p-1} + \sum_{p>q} (c_q{}^p)'' K^{2q-1}_{2p} + \sum_{p>q} (c_q{}^p)''' K^{2q}_{2p}$ the coefficients of the various matrices N^{2j-1}_{2j}, K^{2q-1}_{2p}, K^{2q}_{2p-1}, K^{2q-1}_{2p}, K^{2q}_{2p} in the expression $\Theta^{-1}\delta W\Theta + \delta\Theta - \delta W$ are, respectively $d\theta_j$,

$$c_q{}^p\{e^{-i(\theta_p-\theta_q)} - 1\}, (c_q{}^p)'\{e^{-i(\theta_p+\theta_q)} - \}, (c_q{}^p)''\{e^{i(\theta_p+\theta_q)} - 1\}, (c_q{}^p)'''\{e^{i(\theta_p-\theta_q)} - 1\}.$$

Adopting as coordinates in terms of which it is convenient to carry out the integration the k numbers $(\theta_1, \cdots, \theta_k)$ and $\frac{1}{2}n(n-2)$ parameters ϕ specifying W the coefficients $c_q{}^p$, $(c_q{}^p)'$, $(c_q{}^p)''$, $(c_q{}^p)'''$ depend only on the parameters ϕ. Now any class function i. e. any function depending only on the canonical representative Λ of the class of R to which X belongs is a function of the numbers $\theta_1, \cdots, \theta_k$ alone; in fact a function of particular type since it must be a symmetric function which is, moreover, unaffected by a change of sign of an *even* number of the θ's. For such functions we need only calculate the part of the multiple integral (with respect to the θ's and ϕ's) which depends on the θ's alone (the other part cancelling out in the process of *averaging* over the group). Hence the element of volume (for class functions) of the rotation group of even dimension $2k$ is

$$d\tau = (e^{-i(\theta_p-\theta_q)} - 1)(e^{-i(\theta_p+\theta_q)} - 1)(e^{i(\theta_p+\theta_q)} - 1)(e^{i(\theta_p-\theta_q)} - 1)\,d(\theta_1, \cdots, \theta_k)$$
$$= \prod_{p>q} 4\{1 - \cos(\theta_p - \theta_q)\}\{1 - \cos(\theta_p + \theta_q)\}\,d(\theta_1, \cdots, \theta_k)$$
$$= \prod_{p>q} \left\{ 16 \sin^2 \frac{\theta_p - \theta_q}{2} \sin^2 \frac{\theta_p + \theta_q}{2} \right\} d(\theta_1, \cdots, \theta_k).$$

The numerical factor 16 may be removed from each parenthesis as unimportant and so we write

$$(9.11) \qquad d\tau = \prod_{p>q} \left\{ \sin^2 \frac{\theta_p - \theta_q}{2} \sin^2 \frac{\theta_p + \theta_q}{2} \right\} d(\theta_1, \cdots, \theta_k).$$

Here (p, q) run over the $\dfrac{k(k-1)}{2}$ pairs which may be selected from $k = \dfrac{n}{2}$ numbers. For the trivial case $n = 2$ there are no such pairs and $d\tau$ is simply $d\theta$ (there being no matrices K in this case but simply the one matrix $N_2{}^1$). For $n = 4$ we have

$$d\tau = \sin^2 \frac{(\theta_2 - \theta_1)}{2} \sin^2 \frac{(\theta_2 + \theta_1)}{2}\, d(\theta_1, \theta_2).$$

When n is odd, $= 2k + 1$, we have, in addition to the $\dfrac{2k(2k-1)}{2}$ matrices $(K^{2q-1}_{2p-1}, K^{2q}_{2p-1}, K^{2q-1}_{2p}, K^{2q}_{2p})$, $p > q$, the $2k$ matrices

$$(9.12) \qquad K^{2p-1}_{2k+1} = e^{2k+1}_{2p} - e^{2p-1}_{2k+1}; \quad K^{2p}_{2k+1} = e^{2k+1}_{2p-1} - e^{2p}_{2k+1}; \quad p = 1, \cdots, k.$$

Using the equations (9.5) we derive

$$(9.13) \qquad \begin{aligned} N^{2p-1}_{2k+1} &= A^{-1} M^{2p-1}_{2k+1} A = A^{-1}(e^{2k+1}_{2p-1} - e^{2p-1}_{2k+1}) A = \frac{1}{\sqrt{2}} (K^{2p-1}_{2k+1} + K^{2p}_{2k+1}) \\ N^{2p}_{2k+1} &= A^{-1} M^{2p}_{2k+1} A = A^{-1}(e^{2k+1}_{2p} - e^{2p}_{2k+1}) A = \frac{i}{\sqrt{2}} (K^{2p-1}_{2k+1} - K^{2p}_{2k+1}) \end{aligned}$$

so that our $\dfrac{n(n-1)}{2}$ matrices $N_p{}^q$ are replaceable by the k diagonal matrices N^{2j-1}_{2j}, the $\frac{1}{2}k(k-1)$ sets of four matrices $(K^{2q-1}_{2p-1}, K^{2q}_{2p-1}, K^{2q-1}_{2p}, K^{2q}_{2p})$ and the k sets of two matrices $(K^{2p-1}_{2k+1}, K^{2p}_{2k+1})$. Furthermore, the determinant of the linear transformation from these new matrices (N^{2j-1}_{2j}, K) to the old matrices $(N_p{}^q)$ is $(-i)^k$. The relations (9.9) are unaffected by the change in definition of Θ, namely, $\Theta = \Theta_{2k} \dotplus E_1$ (instead of $\Theta = \Theta_{2k}$) but we must add now the additional relations

$$(9.14) \qquad \begin{aligned} &\Theta^{-1} e^{2k+1}_{2p-1} \Theta = e^{-i\theta_p} e^{2k+1}_{2p-1}; \quad \Theta^{-1} e^{2k+1}_{2p} \Theta = e^{i\theta_p} e^{2k+1}_{2p}; \\ &\Theta^{-1} e^{2p-1}_{2k+1} \Theta = e^{i\theta_p} e^{2p-1}_{2k+1}; \quad \Theta^{-1} e^{2p}_{2k+1} \Theta = e^{-i\theta_p} e^{2p}_{2k+1}. \end{aligned}$$

From these and (9.12) we obtain

$$(9.15) \qquad \Theta^{-1} K^{2p-1}_{2k+1} \Theta = e^{i\theta_p} K^{2p-1}_{2k+1}; \quad \Theta^{-1} K^{2p}_{2k+1} \Theta = e^{-i\theta_p} K^{2p}_{2k+1}$$

so that the element of volume, as calculated for the $2k$ dimensional rotation group, must be multiplied by $\prod_{p=1}^{k}(e^{i\theta_p}-1)(e^{-i\theta_p}-1)$. Removing as before unimportant numerical factors we obtain as the element of volume of the $(2k+1)$ dimensional rotation group (appropriate for the integration of *class* functions over the group)

$$(9.16) \quad d\tau = \prod_{p=1}^{k} \sin^2\frac{\theta_p}{2} \prod_{p>q} \left\{ \sin^2\frac{\theta_p-\theta_q}{2} \sin^2\frac{\theta_p+\theta_q}{2} \right\} d(\theta_1,\cdots,\theta_k).$$

For the three dimensional rotation group there are no pairs (p,q) and the element of volume is simply $\sin^2\frac{\theta}{2}\,d\theta$.

In order to determine the region of the $(\theta_1,\cdots,\theta_k)$ space over which the integration is to be effected we remark that the relation $X=e^S$ implies that any characteristic vector of S is a characteristic vector of X; for $Sv=i\theta v$ forces $Xv=e^{i\theta}v$. Hence if $X=e^{S_1}=e^{S_2}$ the two real n-dimensional skew-symmetric matrices S_1, S_2 have the same (non-singular) matrix of characteristic vectors and when these characteristic vectors are adopted as the vectors of a basis both S_1 and S_2 appear simultaneously in diagonal form. Hence S_2 permutes with S_1 and so $e^{S_1}=e^{S_2}$ implies $e^{S_1-S_2}=E$. If the normal forms of S_1 and S_2 are

$$\begin{pmatrix} i\theta_1 & & & & \\ & -i\theta_1 & & & \\ & & \cdot & & \\ & & & \cdot & \\ & & & & \cdot \end{pmatrix} \quad\text{and}\quad \begin{pmatrix} i\theta'_1 & & & & \\ & -i\theta'_1 & & & \\ & & \cdot & & \\ & & & \cdot & \\ & & & & \cdot \end{pmatrix}$$

respectively, it follows that $\theta'_j=\theta_j+2m_j\pi$ where m_j is an integer. Conversely when the characteristic vectors of S are prescribed it is sufficient to let each θ_j vary in the range $0\leq\theta_j<2\pi$ to obtain the entire set of matrices X of our rotation group; and any two points θ of this region furnish distinct matrices X. If n is odd a change of sign of any θ_j does not affect the class so that in integrating a class function we may restrict each θ to the range $0\leq\theta_j\leq\pi$. When n is even, on the other hand, we may restrict all of the θ's but one, θ_1 say, to this range whilst θ_1 itself varies over the entire range $0\leq\theta_1<2\pi$. When $n=3$, for example, the parametric region (three dimensional) is the interior of a sphere of radius π together with *half* of its surface (diametrically opposite points $\theta=\pm\pi$ having to be identified since they yield the same X). In this (physically important) case it is easy to write down in finite terms the dependence of X on S. In fact S satisfies the equation $S^3+\theta^2S=0$ so that $X=e^S$ is expressible as a quadratic polynomial in S.

$$X=\alpha E_3+\beta S+\gamma S^2.$$

The coefficients are at once determined by writing S in its normal form $\begin{pmatrix} i\theta & & \\ & -i\theta & \\ & & 0\end{pmatrix}$ and noting that X then appears in its normal form $\begin{pmatrix} e^{i\theta} & & \\ & e^{-i\theta} & \\ & & 1\end{pmatrix}$. We find $\alpha=1$, $e^{\pm i\theta}=(1-\theta^2)\pm i\beta\theta$ so that $\beta=\dfrac{\sin\theta}{\theta}$, $\gamma=\dfrac{1-\cos\theta}{\theta^2}$; hence

$$X=E_3+\frac{\sin\theta}{\theta}S+\frac{1-\cos\theta}{\theta^2}S^2.$$

S is of the form

$$S=\begin{pmatrix} 0 & -n & m\\ n & 0 & -l\\ -m & l & 0\end{pmatrix} \text{ with } l^2+m^2+n^2=\theta^2.$$

The two remaining parameters (which specify the different members of a given class) may be taken to be the angles (λ,ϕ) of a system of polar coordinates in which θ is the radius so that

$$\frac{S}{\theta}=\begin{pmatrix} 0 & -\cos\lambda & \sin\lambda\sin\phi\\ +\cos\lambda & 0 & -\sin\lambda\cos\phi\\ -\sin\lambda\sin\phi & \sin\lambda\cos\phi & 0\end{pmatrix};\ 0\leq\lambda\leq\pi;\ 0\leq\phi<2\pi$$

and it is then clear that a change of sign of θ is equivalent to keeping θ fixed and replacing λ by $\pi-\lambda$ and ϕ by $\pi+\phi$ (i. e. to a passage to the diametrically opposite point of the sphere of radius θ).

3. Integration over the *n*-dimensional real orthogonal group.

If X is any element of R and A is any fixed element of R' which is not in R the matrices X and $Y=AX$ exhaust R' as X runs over R. Denoting the element of volume of R by $d\tau$ we define the integral over R' of a function ϕ defined over R' as follows. Writing $\phi(AX)=\psi(X)$ we construct the two integrals $\int\phi d\tau$ and $\int\psi d\tau$ over R and we term their sum the integral of ϕ over R'

$$(9.17)\qquad I_{R'}(\phi)\equiv\int_{R'}\phi d\tau=\int_R\phi d\tau+\int_R\psi d\tau.$$

It is clear that $I_{R'}(\phi)$ is unaffected by any left translation of its integrand by an element of R (simply because each of its component parts $I_R(\phi)$, $I_R(\psi)$ is invariant under such a left translation; a left translation $\phi(X) \to \phi_B(X) = \phi(BX)$ of ϕ inducing the left translation $\psi(X) = \phi(AX) \to \phi(BAX) = \phi(A \cdot A^{-1}BAX) = \psi(A^{-1}BAX)$ of ψ). But it is also invariant under a left translation by any "improper" element of R'. In fact any such improper element of R' is of the form AB where B is an element of R and

$$\begin{aligned} I_{R'}(\phi_{AB}) &= \int_R \phi(ABX)d\tau + \int_R \phi(ABAX)d\tau \\ &= \int_R \psi(BX)d\tau + \int_R \phi(CX)d\tau \\ &= \int_R \psi(X)d\tau + \int_R \phi(X)d\tau = I_{R'}(\phi) \end{aligned}$$

where C is the element ABA. This invariance under left translations enables us to derive the orthogonality relations connecting irreducible continuous representations of R'. In fact we first derive, as on p. 216, the relation

$$\int_{R'} \{D(s)\}_j{}^r\{D^*(s)\}_t{}^k d\tau = c_j{}^k\delta_t{}^r$$

it being understood that the irreducible continuous representation $\Gamma = \{D(s)\}$ of R' is presented in a basis in which its matrices $D(s)$ are unitary. On setting $t = r$ and summing with respect to r we obtain

$$\int_{R'} \{D^*(s)D(s)\}_j{}^k d\tau = dc_j{}^k; \ d \text{ the dimension of } \{D(s)\}.$$

Since $D(s)$ is unitary we have $D^*(s)D(s) = E_d$ so that

$$\delta_j{}^k V' = dc_j{}^k$$

where $V' = \int_{R'} d\tau$ is the volume of R'. Since the volume of R' is obtained by integrating over R' the unit function $\phi(X) = 1 = \phi(AX)$, $V' = \int_R d\tau + \int_R d\tau = 2V$ where V is the volume of the rotation group R. Hence

$$(9.18) \qquad \int_{R'} \{D^*(s)\}_j{}^r\{D(s)\}_t{}^k d\tau = \frac{2V}{d}\,\delta_j{}^k\delta_t{}^r,$$

it being understood that the irreducible representation $\Gamma = \{D(s)\}$ of R' is presented in a basis in which its matrices $D(s)$ are unitary (which understanding involves no lack of generality since the continuous representation Γ of R' is bounded, its matrices being of the types $D(X)$, $D(A)D(X)$, X an arbitrary element of R). On setting $j=r$, $t=k$ in (9.18) and summing with respect to r and k we obtain

$$\frac{1}{2V}\int_{R'}\bar{\chi}(s)\chi(s)\,d\tau=1.$$

By continuing with the argument of pp. 216-7 we see that this relation is a criterion for irreducibility of the representation Γ whose characters are $\chi(s)$; in other words it is not only necessary but sufficient to guarantee the irreducibility of Γ. Further the argument there given shows that the analysis of any reducible representation Γ of R':

$$\Gamma=c^a\Gamma_a$$

into its irreducible components is unique; the coefficients c^j being determined by the characters of Γ:

$$c^j=\frac{1}{2V}\int_{R'}\chi(s)\chi_j(s)\,d\tau$$

(it being unnecessary to write $\bar{\chi}_j(s)$ since the characters of any continuous representation of R' are real (p. 230)). It follows that any two continuous representations of R' which possess the same characters are equivalent.

In order to effectively carry out the integration which is defined by (9.17) we must be able to perform the integration $\int_R \psi(X)\,d\tau = \int_R \phi(Y)\,d\tau$ where $Y=AX$. This involves the expression of $d\tau$ in terms of the elements of Y (of which the integrand $\phi(Y)$ is a function) or in terms of some variables which are convenient for the description of $\phi(Y)$. When n is odd there is no difficulty since A may then be chosen as $-E_n$ so that $Y=-X$ and the coordinates in terms of which it is convenient to specify $\phi(Y)$ are simply the coordinates in terms of which it is convenient to specify X. We have, then, when n is odd:

$$I_{R'}(\phi)=\int_R\{\phi(X)+\phi(-X)\}\,d\tau$$

where, when $\phi(X)$ is a class-function, $d\tau$ is given by (9.11). When n is even $(=2k)$ matters are not so simple and it is necessary to evaluate $d\tau$ (associated with the element X of R) in terms of the element $Y=AX$ of R'. We shall choose for A the matrix

$$A=\begin{pmatrix}E_{n-1} & 0\\ 0 & -1\end{pmatrix};\ \text{so that } A^2=E_n.$$

The canonical form of $Y = AX$ under *proper* orthogonal transformations is

$$\Lambda(\theta_1, \cdots, \theta_k) = C_1 \dotplus \cdots \dotplus C_{k-1} \dotplus \begin{pmatrix} \cos\theta_k & \sin\theta_k \\ \sin\theta_k & -\cos\theta_k \end{pmatrix}$$

where $C_j = \begin{pmatrix} \cos\theta_j & \sin\theta_j \\ -\sin\theta_j & \cos\theta_j \end{pmatrix}$; $j = 1, \cdots, k-1$. Thus $V^{-1}YV = \Lambda$ and from this follows, by the calculation on p. 224,

$$V^{-1}\delta YV = \Lambda^{-1}\delta V\Lambda + \delta\Lambda - \delta V.$$

Now $Y = AX$ so that

$$\delta Y = Y^{-1}dY = X^{-1}A^{-1}d(AX) = X^{-1}A^{-1}(AdX) = X^{-1}dX = \delta X$$

so that

$$V^{-1}\delta XV = \Lambda^{-1}\delta V\Lambda + \delta\Lambda - \delta V.$$

In proceeding, therefore, with the calculation of the element of volume $d\tau$ of R which is attached to the element X of R we have merely to repeat the argument of pp. 231-5 the only difference being that $\Lambda(\theta_1, \cdots, \theta_k)$ now has the form $C_k \dotplus \cdots \dotplus C_{k-1} \dotplus FC_k$ instead of, as before, the form $C_1 \dotplus \cdots \dotplus C_{k-1} \dotplus C_k$. On transforming all of our matrices by the matrix $E_k \times J \left(J = \frac{1}{\sqrt{2}} \begin{pmatrix} 1 & 1 \\ i & -i \end{pmatrix} \right)$ Λ takes the form

$$\Theta = \begin{pmatrix} e^{i\theta_1} & & & & & & & \cdot \\ & e^{-i\theta_1} & & & & & & \\ & & \cdot & & & & & \\ & & & \cdot & & & & \\ & & & & \cdot & & & \\ & & & & & e^{i\theta_{k-1}} & & \\ & & & & & & e^{-i\theta_{k-1}} & \\ & & & & & & 0 & e^{-i\theta_k} \\ \cdot & & \cdot & \cdot & \cdot & & e^{i\theta_k} & 0 \end{pmatrix}$$

instead of the form (9. 2) as before. We define the matrices $K_p{}^q$, $p > q$, as in (9. 6) and the presentations $N_p{}^q$, $p > q$, of our characteristic matrices $M_p{}^q$ in our new basis, are furnished by (9. 7) and (9. 8). The relations (9. 9) are still valid *so long as neither p nor $q = k$* whilst when either p or q (or both) takes the value k we must replace (9. 9) by

$$\begin{aligned}
&\Theta^{-1}e_{2p-1}^{2k-1}\Theta = e^{-i(\theta_p+\theta_k)}e_{2p-1}^{2k}; &&\Theta^{-1}e_{2k-1}^{2p-1}\Theta = e^{i(\theta_p+\theta_k)}e_{2k}^{2p-1};\\
&\Theta^{-1}e_{2p-1}^{2k}\Theta = e^{-i(\theta_p-\theta_k)}e_{2p-1}^{2k-1}; &&\Theta^{-1}e_{2k}^{2p-1}\Theta = e^{i(\theta_p-\theta_k)}e_{2k-1}^{2p-1};\\
&\Theta^{-1}e_{2p}^{2k-1}\Theta = e^{i(\theta_p-\theta_k)}e_{2p}^{2k}; &&\Theta^{-1}e_{2k-1}^{2p}\Theta = e^{-i(\theta_p-\theta_k)}e_{2k}^{2p};\\
&\Theta^{-1}e_{2p}^{2k}\Theta = e^{i(\theta_p+\theta_k)}e_{2p}^{2k-1}; &&\Theta^{-1}e_{2k}^{2p}\Theta = e^{-i(\theta_p+\theta_k)}e_{2k-1}^{2p};\\
&\Theta^{-1}e_{2k-1}^{2k}\Theta = e_{2k}^{2k-1}; &&\Theta^{-1}e_{2k}^{2k-1}\Theta = e_{2k-1}^{2k}.
\end{aligned}$$

The relations (9.10) must accordingly, when either p or $j = k$, be replaced by the following

$$\Theta^{-1}K^{2q-1}_{2k-1}\Theta = e^{i(\theta_q+\theta_k)}K^{2q-1}_{2k}; \quad \Theta^{-1}K^{2q}_{2k-1}\Theta = e^{-i(\theta_q-\theta_k)}K^{2q}_{2k}$$
$$\Theta^{-1}K^{2q-1}_{2k}\Theta = e^{i(\theta_q-\theta_k)}K^{2q-1}_{2k-1}; \quad \Theta^{-1}K^{2q}_{2k}\Theta = e^{-i(\theta_q+\theta_k)}K^{2q}_{2k-1}$$

$(q = 1, \cdots, k-1)$; $\Theta^{-1}N^{2k-1}_{2k}\Theta = -N^{2k-1}_{2k}$. If, then,

$$\delta W = \sum_j c^j N^{2j-1}_{2j} + \sum_{p>q} c_q{}^p K^{2q-1}_{2p-1} + \sum_{p>q} (c_q{}^p)' K^{2q}_{2p-1} + \sum_{p>q} (c_q{}^p)'' K^{2q-1}_{2p} + \sum_{p>q} (c_q{}^p)''' K^{2q}_{2p}$$

the coefficients of the various matrices N^{2j-1}_{2j}, K^{2q-1}_{2p-1}, K^{2q}_{2p-1}, K^{2q-1}_{2p}, K^{2q}_{2p} in the expression $\Theta^{-1}\delta W\Theta + \delta\Theta - \delta W$ are the same as those given on p. 234 *when neither p nor $j = k$*. When $j = k$ there is a trivial change: $d\theta_k$ must be replaced by $d\theta_k - 2c^k$, but when $p = k$ the change is more serious. The coefficients of K^{2q-1}_{2k-1}, K^{2q}_{2k-1}, K^{2q-1}_{2k}, K^{2q}_{2k}, $q = 1, \cdots k-1$, are, respectively,

$$(c_q{}^k)'' e^{i(\theta_q-\theta_k)} - c_q{}^k; \quad (c_q{}^k)''' e^{-i(\theta_q+\theta_k)} - (c_q{}^k)';$$
$$(c_q{}^k) e^{i(\theta_q+\theta_k)} - (c_q{}^k)''; \quad e^{-i(\theta_q-\theta_k)}(c_q{}^k)' - (c_q{}^k)'''.$$

In evaluating the determinant of the linear forms in the differentials $d\xi$ which constitute the coefficients of the matrices $K_p{}^q$, N^{2j-1}_{2j} we may combine $(c_q{}^k)'' e^{i(\theta_q-\theta_k)} - c_q{}^k$ with $(c_q{}^k) e^{i(\theta_q+\theta_k)} - (c_q{}^k)''$, the latter being multiplied by $e^{i(\theta_q-\theta_k)}$, when we obtain $(c_q{}^k)(e^{2i\theta_q} - 1)$. On factoring out $(e^{2i\theta_q} - 1)$ the remaining linear form $(c_q{}^k) e^{i(\theta_q+\theta_k)} - (c_q{}^k)''$ may be replaced by $-(c_q{}^k)''$ in evaluating the determinant. Dealing similarly with the two linear forms $(c_q{}^k)''' e^{-i(\theta_q+\theta_k)} - (c_q{}^k)'$ and $e^{-i(\theta_q-\theta_k)}(c_q{}^k)' - (c_q{}^k)'''$ we see that the four linear forms which constituted the coefficients of K^{2q-1}_{2k-1}, K^{2q}_{2k-1}, K^{2q-1}_{2k}, K^{2q}_{2k} may be replaced by $c_q{}^k$, $(c_q{}^k)'$, $(c_q{}^k)''$, $(c_q{}^k)'''$ provided the determinant is multiplied by $(e^{2i\theta_q} - 1)(e^{-2i\theta_q} - 1) = 4\sin^2\theta_q$. We shall be interested only in the case where the function being integrated is a class function (the classes being classes of R' and not of R); since the canonical form of Y, under transformations by elements of R', is $C_1 \dot{+} \cdots \dot{+} C_{k-1} \dot{+} F$ where $F = \begin{pmatrix} 1 & 0 \\ 0 & -1 \end{pmatrix}$ such a class function is a function of the variables $\theta_1, \theta_2, \cdots, \theta_{k-1}$ alone. The factor of $\int_R \phi(Y)d\tau$ which comes from the integration with respect to θ_k and the variables ϕ which specify W will cancel out in forming the quotient $\frac{1}{2V}\int_R \phi(Y)\,d\tau$ and so we take for $d\tau$ the factor of $d\tau$ which involves only the variables $\theta_1, \cdots, \theta_{k-1}$:

$$(9.19)\quad d\tau = \prod_{q=1}^{k-1} \sin^2\theta_q \prod_{\substack{p>q\\1}}^{k-1} \left\{ \sin^2\frac{(\theta_p-\theta_q)}{2} \sin^2\frac{(\theta_p+\theta_q)}{2} \right\} d(\theta_1, \cdots, \theta_{k-1}).$$

4. The irreducible continuous representations of the real orthogonal group R'.

The symmetrized Kronecker m-th power $[X]_{(m)}$, $[Y]_{(m)}$ of the matrices of R' furnishes a rational integral representation Γ_m of dimension $\binom{n+m-1}{m}$ of R' whose characters are the functions $q_m(\mathbf{s})$ where $s_1 = TrX$ (or TrY), $s_2 = TrX^2$ (or TrY^2) etc. This representation may be regarded as operating in a carrier space in which the power products $(x^1)^{j_1}(x^2)^{j_2}\cdots(x^n)^{j_n}$, $j_1 + j_2 + \cdots + j_n = m$, constitute a basis, $x = (x^1, \cdots, x^n)$ being an arbitrary vector in the carrier space of the matrices X, $Y = AX$ of R'. Since $(x^1)^2 + \cdots + (x^n)^2$ is left invariant by all the matrices X, Y of R' the subspace of the carrier space of Γ_m which is spanned by the vectors $\{(x^1)^2 + \cdots + (x^n)^2\} \times (x^1)^{k_1}\cdots(x^n)^{k_n}$ where $k_1 + k_2 + \cdots + k_n = m - 2$ is invariant under all the matrices of Γ_m and the representation of R' which is induced by Γ_m in this invariant space is the symmetrized Kronecker $(m-2)$-nd power whose characters are $q_{m-2}(\mathbf{s})$. Γ_m induces, therefore, in a space complementary to this invariant space of its carrier space a rational integral representation of R' whose characters are $q_m(\mathbf{s}) - q_{m-2}(\mathbf{s}) = q'_m(\mathbf{s})$. Since $q_m(\mathbf{s}) = p_m(\mathbf{z})$, where the $(\mathbf{z}) = (z_1, \cdots, z_n)$ are the characteristic numbers of X, or Y as the case may be, and since $\frac{1}{(1-z_1t)\cdots(1-z_nt)} = \sum_{k=0}^{\infty} p_k(\mathbf{z})t^k$ it follows that

$$(9.20)\quad \frac{1-t^2}{(1-z_1t)\cdots(1-z_nt)} = \sum_{0}^{\infty} p'_k(\mathbf{z})t^k;\ p'_k(\mathbf{z}) = p_k(\mathbf{z}) - p_{k-2}(\mathbf{z})$$

(the usual conventions $p_0(\mathbf{z}) = 1$, $p_{-1}(\mathbf{z}) = p_{-2}(\mathbf{z}) = \cdots = 0$ being followed).

Since $q'_m(\mathbf{s})$ furnishes the characters of a representation of R' any product such as $q'_{m_1}(\mathbf{s})\cdots q'_{m_j}(\mathbf{s})$ furnishes the characters of a representation of R'; in fact of the representation which is the Kronecker product of the representations whose characters are furnished by

$q'_{m_1}(s), \cdots, q'_{m_j}(s)$ respectively. If $(\lambda) = (\lambda_1, \lambda_2, \cdots, \lambda_k)$, $\lambda_1 \geq \lambda_2 \geq \cdots \geq \lambda_k \geq 0$ are any k numbers the determinantal function

$$\{\lambda\}'(s) = \begin{vmatrix} q'_{\lambda_1}, & q'_{\lambda_1+1} + q'_{\lambda_1-1}, & \cdots & \\ q'_{\lambda_2-1}, & \cdot & & \cdot \\ & \cdot & & \cdot \\ q'_{\lambda_k-(k-1)}, & \cdots & & , q'_{\lambda_k} + q'_{\lambda_k-2(k-1)} \end{vmatrix}$$

(where the various elements are obtained by methodically increasing and decreasing by unity the label attached to the symbol q' as we move from each column to its neighbor on the right and then writing in each column after the first the sum of the two q' thus obtained, each q' carrying a negative label being zero) is accordingly a linear combination with integral coefficients (some of which might, so far as we yet know, be negative) of the simple characters of R'. We propose to show that $\{\lambda\}'(s)$ furnishes, for each choice of (λ), a *simple* character of R' and that no two of the simple characters obtained in this way are the same. In order to do this it is necessary to make a preliminary evaluation of some integrals over R.

The denominator of the fraction on the left of (9. 20) is $\prod_{j=1}^{k}(1-2\cos\theta_j t + t^2)$ if $n(=2k)$ is even and is the product of this by $(1-t)$ if $n\ (=2k+1)$ is odd. We shall assign to the indeterminate t the k distinct values $(t_1, \cdots, t_k)$ and shall denote by g_p the expression

$$g_p = \prod_{j=1}^{k}(1-2\cos\theta_j t_p + t_p^2); \qquad p = 1, \cdots, k.$$

The corresponding denominator of the fraction in (9. 20) will be denoted by f_p so that $f_p = g_p$ if $n = 2k$ is even; $f_p = (1-t_p)g_p$ if $n = 2k+1$ is odd. The first integral we propose to evaluate is that of the reciprocal of the product $g_1 \cdots g_k$ over R: $\int_R \frac{d\tau}{g_1 \cdots g_k}$. To do this it is convenient to introduct the notations

$$T_p = 1 + t_p^2; \quad u_p = \frac{2t_p}{1+t_p^2}; \qquad p = 1, \cdots, k,$$

for then a factor such as $(1-2\cos\theta_j t_p + t_p^2)$ of g_p appears as $T_p(1-\cos\theta_j u_p)$ so that

$$(g_1 \cdots g_k)^{-1} = (T_1 T_2 \cdots T_k)^{-k} \{\prod_{1}^{p,j}(1-\cos\theta_j u_p)\}^{-1}.$$

But we know, from Cauchy's determinantal relation (p. 115), that

$\{\prod_{p,j\ 1}^{k}(1 - \cos\theta_j u_p)\}^{-1}$ is the quotient of the k-th order determinant, of which the element in the p-th row and j-th column is $\dfrac{1}{1 - \cos\theta_j u_p}$, by $\Delta(\boldsymbol{u})\Delta(\cos\theta)$, the Δ symbol denoting, as usual the difference product. Thus

$$\Delta(\boldsymbol{u}) = \prod_{p<q\ 1}^{k}(u_p - u_q) = \{2^{k(k-1)/2}\Delta(\boldsymbol{t})\prod_{p<q\ 1}^{k}(1 - t_p t_q)\} \div (T_1 \cdots T_k)^{k-1}.$$

Since $\cos\theta_p - \cos\theta_q = -2\sin\dfrac{\theta_p - \theta_q}{2}\sin\dfrac{\theta_p + \theta_q}{2}$ the element of volume $d\tau$, given when $n = 2k$ is even by (9.11), may be written as

$$d\tau = \{\Delta(\cos\theta)\}^2 d(\theta_1, \cdots, \theta_k)$$

the numerical factor -2 being without significance as the constant multiplier it gives rise to cancels out in the process of averaging over R. Hence the integral we wish to evaluate appears as:

$$\int_R \frac{d\tau}{g_1 \cdots g_k} = \int_R \det\left(\frac{1}{1 - \cos\theta_j u_p}\right)\Delta(\cos\theta)\, d(\theta)$$
$$\div\, 2^{k(k-1)/2}\Delta(\boldsymbol{t})\{\prod_{p<q\ 1}^{k}(1 - t_p t_q)\}T_1 \cdots T_k.$$

Since $1 - \cos\theta_j u_p = (1 - 2\cos\theta_j t_p + t_p^2) \div T_p$ the factor $T_1 \cdots T_k$ may be absorbed in the determinant and we may write

$$2^{k(k-1)/2}\Delta(\boldsymbol{t})\prod_{p<q\ 1}^{k}(1 - t_p t_q)\int_R \frac{d\tau}{g_1 \cdots g_k}$$
$$= \int_R \det\left(\frac{1}{1 - 2\cos\theta_j t_p + t_p^2}\right)\Delta(\cos\theta)\, d(\theta).$$

Now a typical term in the expansion of the determinant is

$$\pm \{(1 - 2\cos\theta_{j_1} t_1 + t_1^2) \cdots (1 - 2\cos\theta_{j_k} t_k + t_k^2)\}^{-1}$$

where $(j_1, \cdots, j_k)$ is a permutation of the numbers $1, \cdots, k$ and the plus (minus) sign is used according as this permutation is even (odd). But an interchange of two of the variables $(\theta_1, \cdots, \theta_k)$ of integration cannot affect the value of the integral; such an interchange changes the nature of the permutation $(j_1, \cdots, j_k)$ (from even to odd or vice versâ) and changes the sign of $\Delta(\cos\theta)$. Hence every one of the $k!$ terms in the expansion of $\det\left(\dfrac{1}{1 - 2\cos\theta_j t_p + t_p^2}\right)$ yields, on integration, the same result so that we need only take the leading term and multiply the result by $k!$ Hence

$$2^{k(k-1)/2}\Delta(t)\{\prod_{\substack{p<q\\1}}^{k}(1-t_pt_q)\}\int_R \frac{d\tau}{g_1\cdots g_k}$$
$$= k!\int_R\{\prod_{j=1}^{k}(1-2\cos\theta_jt_j+t_j^2)\}^{-1}\Delta(\cos\theta)\,d(\theta).$$

On writing $\Delta(\cos\theta)$ as a Vandermonde determinant, of order k, of which the element in the p-th row and j-th column is $(\cos\theta_j)^{k-p}$ we have merely to integrate a determinant of which the element in the p-th row and j-th column is $(\cos\theta_j)^{k-p}\div(1-2\cos\theta_jt_j+t_j^2)$. Since the variables are now separated (each of the k columns being a function of only one of the k variables $\theta_1,\cdots,\theta_k$) the integral of each term in the expansion of the determinant is found by integrating each of its factors with respect to the single variable contained in it. Hence we have merely to evaluate a determinant of order k of which the element in the p-th row and j-th column is

$$\int_0^{2\pi}\frac{(\cos\theta)^{k-p}d\theta}{(1-2\cos\theta t_j+t_j^2)}.$$

On writing

$$(1-2\cos\theta t_j+t_j^2)^{-1}=(1-t_je^{i\theta})^{-1}(1-t_je^{-i\theta})^{-1}$$

we find

$$(1-2\cos\theta t_j+t_j^2)^{-1}=1+2\sum_1^{\infty}c'_qt_j^q$$

where

$$c'_q=\cos q\theta+\cos(q-2)\theta+\cdots;\ q=1,2,\cdots$$

(the summation ending in $\frac{1}{2}$ if q is even). Hence

$$(1-t_j^2)\{(1-2\cos\theta t_j+t_j^2)\}^{-1}=1+2\sum_1^{\infty}\cos q\theta t_j^q.$$

Furthermore

$$(\cos\theta)^{k-p}=\left\{\frac{e^{i\theta}+e^{-i\theta}}{2}\right\}^{k-p}$$
$$=\{\cos(k-p)\theta+(k-p)\cos(k-p-2)\theta+\cdots\}$$
$$\div 2^{k-p-1};\ k-p=1,2,\cdots$$

From the orthogonality relations

$$\int_0^{2\pi}\cos p\theta\cos q\theta d\theta=0;\ p\neq q;\ \int_0^{2\pi}\cos^2 p\theta d\theta=\pi$$

it follows that $(1-t_j^2)\int_0^{2\pi}\frac{\cos^{k-p}\theta d\theta}{1-2\cos\theta t_j+t_j^2}$ is a polynomial in t_j of degree $k-p$ the coefficient of the highest power t_j^{k-p} being $2\pi \div 2^{k-p-1}$, $p=1, 2, \cdots, k-1$. For $p=k$, on the other hand the value of the integral is 2π. On removing the factor $\frac{2\pi}{2^{k-p-1}}$ from the p-th row of our determinant, $p=1, \cdots, k-1$, and the factor 2π from the k-th row we obtain a determinant of which the element in the p-th row and j-th column is a polynomial of degree $k-p$ in t_j the coefficient of the highest power t_j^{k-p} of t_j being unity. Since the polynomials in a given row are the same, only the argument t_j varying from column to column, we may simplify our determinant by subtracting from each row an appropriate linear combination of the rows beneath it; it then appears as the Vandermonde determinant of which the element in the p-th row and j-th column is t_j^{k-p} so that its value is $\Delta(\boldsymbol{t})$. On dividing out by the factors $(1-t_j^2)$, $j=1, \cdots, k$, which were introduced for convenience, we obtain

$$2^{(k-1)^2}\{\prod_{\substack{p<q\\1}}^{k}(1-t_pt_q)\}\{\prod_{p=1}^{k}(1-t_p^2)\}\int_R\frac{d\tau}{g_1\cdots g_k}=(2\pi)^k k!$$

On setting $t_1=t_2=\cdots=t_k=0$ each of the quantities $g_1, \cdots, g_k$ assumes the value unity and we find

$$V=(2\pi)^k\cdot k!\div 2^{(k-1)^2}. \tag{9.21}$$

Hence

$$\frac{1}{V}\int_R\frac{d\tau}{g_1, \cdots, g_k}=\{\prod_{\substack{p\leq q\\1}}^{k}(1-t_pt_q)\}^{-1}$$

(the factors $(1-t_j^2)$ being absorbed amongst the factors $1-t_pt_q$ by permitting $p=q$). Since $n=2k$ is even we may identify each g_p with f_p so that

$$\frac{1}{V}\int_R\frac{d\tau}{f_1\cdots f_k}=\{\prod_{\substack{p\leq q\\1}}^{k}(1-t_pt_q)\}^{-1};\quad n \text{ even }=2k. \tag{9.22}$$

We may observe that the element of volume (9.11) may be normalised, by use of (9.21), so that the volume V of the $n=2k$ dimensional group becomes unity. We have merely to write

$$d\tau=\frac{2^{(k-1)^2}}{(2\pi)^k k!}\prod_{\substack{p<q\\1}}^{k}(\cos\theta_p-\cos\theta_q)^2 d(\theta_1, \cdots, \theta_k);\quad n=2k. \tag{9.23}$$

When $n = 2k + 1$ is odd we have to use the element of volume (9.16) or, equivalently, the element of volume

$$d\tau = \{\prod_{p=1}^{k} (1 - \cos\theta_p)\}\{\prod_{\substack{p<q \\ 1}}^{k} (\cos\theta_p - \cos\theta_q)^2\}\, d(\theta_1 \cdot\cdot\cdot, \theta_k).$$

The argument proceeds as before the only difference in the end result being that we must evaluate a k-th order determinant of which the element in the p-th row and j-th column is

$$\int_0^{2\pi} \frac{(\cos\theta)^{k-p}(1 - \cos\theta)}{1 - 2\cos\theta t_j + t_j^2}\, d\theta$$

instead of

$$\int_0^{2\pi} \frac{(\cos\theta)^{k-p} d\theta}{1 - 2\cos\theta t_j + t_j^2}$$

as before. We have seen

(by expanding $(\cos\theta)^{k-p} = \left(\dfrac{e^{i\theta} + e^{-i\theta}}{2}\right)^{k-p} = \dfrac{1}{2^{k-p-1}}[\cos(k-p)\theta + \binom{k-p}{1}\cos(k-p-2)\theta + \cdot\cdot\cdot]$)

that

$$(1 - t^2)\int_0^{2\pi} \frac{(\cos\theta)^{k-p} d\theta}{1 - 2\cos\theta t + t^2}$$

is the polynomial

$$\frac{2\pi}{2^{k-p-1}}[t^{k-p} + \binom{k-p}{1} t^{k-p-2} + \cdot\cdot\cdot].$$

The polynomial $P_{k-p}(t) = t^{k-p} + \binom{k-p}{1} t^{k-p-2} + \cdot\cdot\cdot$ has, when $t = 1$, one half the value of $(t + \frac{1}{t})^{k-p}$ when $t = 1$ and so when $t = 1$ the expression

$$(1 - t^2)\int_0^{2\pi} \frac{(\cos\theta)^{k-p} d\theta}{1 - 2\cos\theta t + t^2}$$

has the value 2π. Since this value is independent of p the difference

$$(1 - t^2)\int_0^{2\pi} \frac{(\cos\theta)^{k-p} - (\cos\theta)^{k-p-1}}{1 - 2\cos\theta t + t^2}\, d\theta$$

is divisible by $1 - t$ and

$$(1 + t)\int_0^{2\pi} \frac{(\cos\theta)^{k-p}(1 - \cos\theta)}{1 - 2\cos\theta t + t^2}\, d\theta$$

is a polynomial of degree $k - p$ in t the coefficient of the highest power of t being $\frac{2\pi}{2^{k-p}}$. Hence the value of the determinant (which becomes the simple Vandermonde determinant $\Delta(t)$ on removing the common factors $\frac{2\pi}{2^{k-p}}$ from each row and the factors $1 + t_j$ from each column followed by subtraction from each row of an appropriate linear combination of the rows below it) is $\frac{(2\pi)^k}{2^{k(k-1)/2}}\Delta(t)$. On dividing out by the factors $1 + t_p$ we obtain

$$2^{k(k-1)}\{\prod_{\substack{p<q\\1}}^{k}(1 - t_p t_q)\}\{\prod_{j=1}^{k}(1 + t_j)\}\int_R \frac{d\tau}{g_1 \cdots g_k} = (2\pi)^k k!$$

On replacing g_p by $f_p \div (1 - t_p)$ we obtain

$$\int_R \frac{d\tau}{f_1 \cdots f_k} = \frac{(2\pi)^k k!}{2^{k(k-1)}}\{\prod_{\substack{p\leq q\\1}}^{k}(1 - t_p t_q)\}^{-1}.$$

On setting $t_1 = \cdots = t_k = 0$ each $f_p = 1$ and we find

(9.24) $$V = \frac{(2\pi)^k}{2^{k(k-1)}}k!$$

so that

(9.25) $$\frac{1}{V}\int_R \frac{d\tau}{f_1 \cdots f_k} = \{\prod_{\substack{p\leq q\\1}}^{k}(1 - t_p t_q\}^{-1};\ n \text{ odd} = 2k + 1.$$

We observe that the volume element (9.16) may be normalised, by use of (9.24) so that the volume V of the $n = 2k + 1$ dimensional rotation group becomes unity. We have merely to write

(9.26) $$d\tau = \frac{2^{k(k-1)}}{(2\pi)^k k!}\{\prod_{j=1}^{k}(1 - \cos\theta_j)\}\{\prod_{\substack{p<q\\1}}^{k}(\cos\theta_p - \cos\theta_q)^2\}\,d(\theta_1, \cdots, \theta_k).$$

In order to evaluate the integral of $(f_1 \cdots f_k)^{-1}$ over R' we have to consider separately the trivial case when $n = 2k + 1$ is odd and the case when $n = 2k$ is even. When n is odd $Y = -X$ and f_p evaluated for $Y = f(-t_p)$. Since the right hand side of (9.25) is unaffected when the sign of each and every t_p is changed it follows that the two integrals whose sum gives the integral over R' are equal. Hence

(9.27) $$\frac{1}{2V}\int_{R'} \frac{d\tau}{f_1 \cdots f_k} = \{\prod_{\substack{p\leq q\\1}}^{k}(1 - t_p t_q)\}^{-1};\quad n = 2k + 1.$$

The same result holds when $n = 2k$ is even but to prove this some further calculations are necessary. We have seen that, whether n is odd or even, the integral of $(f_1 \cdots f_k)^{-1}$ over R, divided by the volume V of R, $= \{\prod_{\substack{p \leq q \\ 1}}^{k} (1 - t_p t_q)\}^{-1} = \{\prod_{p=1}^{k} (1 - t_p^2) L_k(\boldsymbol{t})\}^{-1}$ where $L_k(\boldsymbol{t}) = \prod_{\substack{p<q \\ 1}}^{k} (1 - t_p t_q)$. If j is one of the numbers $1, 2, \cdots, k-1$ we may set $t_{j+1} = t_{j+2} = \cdots = t_k = 0$ forcing $f_{j+1} = f_{j+2} = \cdots = f_k = 1$ and we see that the result

$$\frac{1}{V}\int_R \frac{d\tau}{f_1 \cdots f_j} = \{\prod_{p=1}^{j} (1 - t_p^2) L_j(\boldsymbol{t})\}^{-1}; \quad L_j(\boldsymbol{t}) = \prod_{\substack{p<q \\ 1}}^{j} (1 - t_p t_q)$$

is valid not only when $j = k$ but also when $j = 1, 2, \cdots, k-1$. To see that happens when $j > k$ let us consider the function

$$g_p = \prod_{q=1}^{k} (1 - 2 \cos \theta_q t_p + t_p^2)$$

which $= f_p$ when $n = 2k$ is even and $= f_p \div (1 - t_p)$ when $n = 2k + 1$ is odd. g_p is a polynomial in t_p and $T_p = 1 + t_p^2$:

$$g_p = c_k t_p^k + c_{k-1} t_p^{k-1} T_p + \cdots + c_1 t_p T_p^{k-1} + T_p^k$$

so that the determinant of order $k+1$ of which the elements in the p-th row are $(t_p^k, t_p^{k-1}T_p, \cdots, t_p T_p^{k-1}, g_p)$ has the same value as the determinant of order $k+1$ of which the elements in the p-th row are $(t_p^k, t_p^{k-1}T_p, \cdots, t_p T_p^{k-1}, T_p^k)$. This determinant may be readily evaluated; in the first place $\Delta_{k+1}(\boldsymbol{t}) = \prod_{\substack{p<q \\ 1}}^{k+1} (t_p - t_q)$ is a factor of it. Secondly the elements of the p-th row become, on division by t_p^{2k}, the same functions of $\frac{1}{t_p}$ that they were originally of t_p. Hence not only is $t_p - t_q$ a factor of the determinant but $1 - t_p t_q$ is also. Hence $\Delta_{k+1}(\boldsymbol{t}) L_{k+1}(\boldsymbol{t})$ is a factor of the determinant; the remaining factor is seen to be unity on comparing the coefficients of the leading term $t_1^k t_2^{k+1} \cdots t_{k+1}^{2k}$ which is unity in both expressions. The cofactors of the last column of the determinant of order $k+1$, of which the elements in the p-th row are $(t_p^k, \cdots, t_p T_p^{k-1}, g_p)$, are readily evaluated; for example the cofactor of g_1, when multiplied by $(-1)^k$, is the product by $t_2 \cdots t_{k+1}$ of the determinant of order k of which the q-th row is $(t_{q+1}^{k-1}, t_{q+1}^{k-2} T_{q+1}, \cdots, t_{q+1} T_{q+1}^{k-2}, T_{q+1}^{k-1})$ and the value of this determinant is, as we have just

seen, $\Delta_k^1(\boldsymbol{t})L_k^1(\boldsymbol{t})$ (the superscripts 1 indicating that $\Delta_k^1(\boldsymbol{t})$ and $L_k^1(\boldsymbol{t})$ are obtained from $\Delta_{k+1}(\boldsymbol{t})$ and $L_{k+1}(\boldsymbol{t})$, respectively, by omitting the factors which involve t_1). We have, accordingly, proved the relation

$$(9.28)\quad \Delta_{k+1}(\boldsymbol{t})L_{k+1}(\boldsymbol{t}) = (-1)^k t_2\cdots t_{k+1}\Delta_k^1(\boldsymbol{t})L_k^1(\boldsymbol{t})g_1 + (-1)^{k-1}t_1t_3\cdots t_{k+1}\Delta_k^2(\boldsymbol{t})L_k^2(\boldsymbol{t})g_2 + \cdots$$

and we divide this relation by $V(f_1\cdots f_{k+1})$ and then integrate the resulting equation over R. The first term on the right becomes

$$(-1)^k t_2\cdots t_{k+1}\Delta_k^1(\boldsymbol{t})L_k^1(\boldsymbol{t})\int_R \frac{d\tau}{f_2\cdots f_{k-1}} \div V$$

if n is even and the quotient of this by $(1-t_1)$ if n is odd. But the quantity $\frac{1}{V}\int_R \frac{d\tau}{f_2\cdots f_{k+1}}$ has the value $\{\prod_2^{k+1}(1-t_p^2)L_k^1(\boldsymbol{t})\}^{-1}$ and so the first term yields $[(-1)^k t_2\cdots t_{k+1}\Delta_k^1(\boldsymbol{t})/\prod_{p=1}^{k+1}(1-t_p^2)]$ times $(1-t_1^2)$, if n is even, and times $1+t_1$ if n is odd. The product $t_2\cdots t_{k+1}\Delta_k^1(\boldsymbol{t})$ may be written as a determinant of order k of which the elements in the q-th row are $(t_{q+1}^k, t_{q+1}^{k-1},\cdots, t_{q+1})$ and so we obtain, on multiplying both sides of our equation by $\prod_{p=1}^{k+1}(1-t_p^2)$,

$$\Delta_{k+1}(\boldsymbol{t})\{\prod_{\substack{p\leq q\\1}}^{k+1}(1-t_pt_q)\}\frac{1}{V}\int_R \frac{d\tau}{f_1\cdots f_{k+1}} = \begin{vmatrix} t_1^k & t_1^{k-1}\cdots t_1 & s_1 \\ \cdot & \cdot & \cdot \\ \cdot & \cdot & \cdot \\ t_{k+1}^k & t_{k+1}^{k-1}\cdots t_{k+1} & s_{k+1}\end{vmatrix}$$

where $s_j = 1-t_j^2$ if n is even and $=1+t_j$ if n is odd. In either event the determinant on the right is equivalent to the Vandermonde determinant whose value is $\Delta_{k+1}(\boldsymbol{t})$ as may be seen by adding the $(k-1)$-st column to the last if n is even and by subtracting the k-th column from the last if n is odd. Hence the basic relation

$$(9.29)\qquad \frac{1}{V}\int_R \frac{d\tau}{f_1\cdots f_j} = \{\prod_{\substack{p\leq q\\1}}^{j}(1-t_pt_q)\}^{-1}$$

holds, not only when $j=1,2,\cdots,k$, but when $j=k+1$ as well. Exactly the same argument goes through for higher values of j; thus if $j=k+2$, we divide the basic equation (9.28) by $V(f_1\cdots f_{k+2})$ and integrate the result over R. The first term yields

$$(-1)^k t_2\cdots t_{k+1}\Delta_k^1(\boldsymbol{t})L_k^1(\boldsymbol{t})/\prod_{p=2}^{k+2}(1-t_p^2)\prod_{\substack{p<q\\2}}^{k+2}(1-t_pt_q)$$

if n is even and the quotient of this by $1-t_1$ if n is odd; this may be written as

$$(-1)^k t_2 \cdots t_{k+1}\Delta_k^1(\boldsymbol{t})L_{k+1}(\boldsymbol{t})/\{\prod_{\substack{p\leq q\\1}}^{k+2}(1-t_pt_q)\}$$

$$\text{times } (1-t_1^2)(1-t_1t_{k-2})$$

if n is even and the quotient of this by $1-t_1$ if n is odd. On dividing through by $L_{k+1}(\boldsymbol{t})$ we obtain

$$\Delta_{k+1}(\boldsymbol{t})\frac{1}{V}\int_R\frac{d\tau}{f_1\cdots f_{k+2}}=\{\prod_{\substack{p\leq q\\1}}^{k+2}(1-t_pt_q)\}^{-1}\begin{vmatrix} t_1^k & \cdots & t_1 & s'_1\\ \cdot & & \cdot & \cdot\\ \cdot & & \cdot & \cdot\\ t_{k+1}^k & \cdots & t_{k+1} & s'_{k+1}\end{vmatrix}$$

where $s'_p=s_p(1-t_pt_{k+2})$. As before the determinant on the right is the Vandermonde determinant of order $k+1$ whose value is $\Delta_{k+1}(\boldsymbol{t})$ and we see that (9.29) is valid when $j=k+2$. Proceeding in this way from each value of j to the next higher we see that the basic relation (9.29) is valid for each value of j from 1 to $n-1$ inclusive; in passing from $j=n-1$ to $j=n$ the quantities s_p which occur in the last column of the determinant on the right in the final step of the argument are $(1-t_p^2)(1-t_pt_{k+2})(1-t_pt_{k+3})\cdots(1-t_pt_n)$, if n is even, and the quotient of this by $1-t_p$ if n is odd. In either event s_p is a polynomial of degree $k+1$ with lowest term 1 and highest term $(-1)^k t_p^{k+2}t_{k+2}\cdots t_n$; the determinant on the right splits up into the sum of two determinants of which the first is the Vandermonde determinant of order $k+1$ whose value is $\Delta_{k+1}(\boldsymbol{t})$ the second being the product of this by $t_1t_2\cdots t_n$. Hence when $j=n$ the relation (9.29) must be replaced by

$$(9.30)\qquad \frac{1}{V}\int_R\frac{d\tau}{f_1\cdots f_n}=\{\prod_{\substack{p\leq q\\1}}^{n}(1-t_pt_q)\}^{-1}(1+t_1t_2\cdots t_n).$$

We are now ready to proceed with the final step of our preliminary calculations, namely, the evaluation of $\dfrac{1}{2V}\displaystyle\int_{R'}\frac{d\tau}{f_1\cdots f_j}$, $j=1,2,\cdots,n$. When n is odd there is no difficulty since then we may set $Y=-X$ and f_p for Y is obtained from the f_p for X by changing the sign of t_p as already pointed out in the derivation of (9.27). This change of sign of each t_p does not affect $\prod_{\substack{p\leq q\\1}}^{j}(1-t_pt_q)$ and each of the two integrals, which occur, by definition, in $\dfrac{1}{2V}\displaystyle\int_{R'}\frac{d\tau}{f_1\cdots f_j}$ has, for

$j = 1, \cdots, n-1$, the same value, namely one-half of $\frac{1}{V}\int_R \frac{d\tau}{f_1 \cdots f_j}$.
On the other hand when $j = n$ the second of the two integrals has the value

$$\tfrac{1}{2}\{\prod_{p \leq q}^{n} (1 - t_p t_q)\}^{-1}\{1 + (-t_1)(-t_2)\cdots(-t_n)\}$$

$$= \tfrac{1}{2}\{\prod_{p \leq q}^{n} (1 - t_p t_q)\}^{-1}(1 - t_1 t_2 \cdots t_n)$$

since n is odd. Hence the integral over $R' = \{\prod_{p \leq q}^{n} (1 - t_p t_q)\}^{-1}$. In other words for all values of j from 1 up to n, inclusive, (not merely up to $n-1$ inclusive as is the case for the rotation group)

$$(9.31) \qquad \frac{1}{2V}\int_{R'} \frac{d\tau}{f_1 \cdots f_j} = \{\prod_{p \leq q}^{j} (1 - t_p t_q)\}^{-1}; \quad n = 2k+1 \text{ odd.}$$

This relation holds also when $n = 2k$ is even but to prove it we have to turn to the form (9.19) for $d\tau$; apart from numerical factors which have no essential significance this may be written as

$$d\tau = \prod_{q=1}^{k-1} (1 - \cos^2 \theta_q) \prod_{p<q}^{k-1} (\cos\theta_p - \cos\theta_q)^2\, d(\theta_1, \cdots, \theta_{k-1}).$$

We shall first treat the case $j = k-1$. Writing $f_p(Y) = (1 - t_p{}^2)h_p$ so that $h_p = \prod_{j=1}^{k-1} (1 - 2\cos\theta_j t_p + t_p{}^2)$ the integral $\int_R (f_1 \cdots f_{k-1})^{-1} d\tau$ takes the form $\prod_{p=1}^{k-1} (1 - t_p{}^2)^{-1} \int_R \frac{d\tau}{h_1 \cdots h_{k-1}}$. The calculations proceed exactly as before save that k must be replaced by $k-1$ and allowance made for the difference in form of $d\tau$. We find, as on p. 245, that $2^{(k-1)(k-2)/2}\Delta_{k-1}(\boldsymbol{t})\{\prod_{p<q}^{k-1} (1 - t_p t_q)\} \int_R \frac{d\tau}{h_1 \cdots h_{k-1}}$ is the product of $(k-1)!$ by a determinant of order $k-1$ of which the element in the p-th row and j-th column is $\int_0^{2\pi} \frac{(\cos\theta)^{k-1-p} - (\cos\theta)^{k+1-p}}{1 - 2\cos\theta \cdot t_j + t_j{}^2} d\theta$. We have seen that $\int_0^{2\pi} \frac{(\cos\theta)^{k-p} d\theta}{1 - 2\cos\theta \cdot t + t^2}$ multiplied by $(1 - t^2)$ is a polynomial $P_{k-p}(t)$ of degree $k-p$ in t:

$$2^{k-p-1} P_{k-p}(t) = 2\pi\{t^{k-p} + \binom{k-p}{1} t^{k-p-2} + \cdots\}.$$

When $t=1$, $P_{k-p}(t)$ has the value 2π so that $P_{k-p}(t)-P_{k-p+2}(t)$ is divisible by $1-t$ (since it vanishes when $t=1$). When $t=-1$, $P_{k-p}(t)$ has the value $2\pi(-1)^{k-p}$ so that $P_{k-p}(t)-P_{k-p+2}(t)$ is also divisible by $1+t$; hence $P_{k-p}(t)-P_{k-p+2}(t)$ is divisible by $1-t^2$ the quotient being a polynomial of degree $k-p$ in t whose highest degree term is $\frac{2\pi}{2^{k-p+1}}$. In other words the element in the p-th row and j-th column of the determinant of order $k-1$ which we have to evaluate is a polynomial of degree $k-1-p$ in t_j the coefficient of the highest power being $\frac{2\pi}{2^{k-p}}$. On removing the common factor $\frac{2\pi}{2^{k-p}}$ from the p-th row, $p=1,2,\cdots,k-1$, the determinant becomes the Vandermonde determinant of order $k-1$ whose value is $\Delta_{k-1}(\boldsymbol{t})$. We obtain, then, the result

$$(9.32)\qquad \int_R \frac{d\tau}{f_1\cdots f_{k-1}}=\frac{(2\pi)^{k-1}(k-1)!}{2^{(k-1)^2}}\{\prod_{\substack{p\leq q\\1}}^{k-1}(1-t_pt_q)\}^{-1}.$$

On setting $t_1=\cdots=t_{k-1}=0$ we see that our choice of $d\tau$ yields $V=\dfrac{(2\pi)^{k-1}(k-1)!}{2^{(k-1)^2}}$ and so

$$(9.33)\qquad \frac{1}{V}\int_R \frac{d\tau}{f_1\cdots f_{k-1}}=\{\prod_{\substack{p\leq q\\1}}^{k-1}(1-t_pt_q)\}^{-1}.$$

It follows that $d\tau$ may be normalised so that V is unity:

$$(9.34)\ d\tau=\frac{2^{(k-1)^2}}{(2\pi)^{k-1}(k-1)!}\{\prod_{p=1}^{k-1}(1-\cos^2\theta_p)\}\{\prod_{\substack{p<q\\1}}^{k-1}(\cos\theta_p-\cos\theta_q)\}^2 d(\theta_1,\cdots,\theta_{k-1}).$$

It follows at once from (9.33), on setting $t_{j+1}=t_{j+2}=\cdots=t_{k-1}=0$ that

$$(9.35)\qquad \frac{1}{V}\int_R \frac{d\tau}{f_1\cdots f_j}=\{\prod_{\substack{p\leq q\\1}}^{j}(1-t_pt_q)\}^{-1};\quad j=1,2,\cdots,k-1;$$

and this, in combination with (9.29), yields

$$(9.36)\qquad \frac{1}{2V}\int_{R'} \frac{d\tau}{f_1\cdots f_j}=\{\prod_{\substack{p\leq q\\1}}^{j}(1-t_pt_q)\}^{-1};\quad j=1,2,\cdots,k-1.$$

To evaluate the integral for higher values of j we write down (9.28) with k replaced by $k-1$ and g_p by h_p and integrate over R the equation obtained by dividing each side of our equation by $V(f_1 \cdots f_k)$. The first term on the right becomes

$$(-1)^{k-1} t_2 \cdots t_k \Delta^1_{k-1}(\boldsymbol{t}) L^1_{k-1}(\boldsymbol{t}) \int_R \frac{d\tau}{f_2 \cdots f_k} \div V(1 - t_1^2)$$

and so the right hand side of our equation yields on performing the indicated integrations by means of (9.33), the quotient of the Vandermonde determinant of order k whose p-th row is $(t_p^{k-1}, t_p^{k-2}, \cdots, t_p, 1)$ by $\{\prod_1^k (1 - t_p^2)\}$. On dividing out by the common factor $\Delta_k(\boldsymbol{t})$, which equals the Vandermonde determinant, we find

$$\frac{1}{V} \int_R \frac{d\tau}{f_1 \cdots f_k} = \{\prod_{\substack{p \leq q \\ 1}}^{k} (1 - t_p t_q)\}^{-1}$$

which, together with (9.22), yields

$$\frac{1}{2V} \int_{R'} \frac{d\tau}{f_1 \cdots f_k} = \{\prod_{\substack{p \leq q \\ 1}}^{k} (1 - t_p t_q)\}^{-1}. \tag{9.37}$$

From (9.37) we pass to $\frac{1}{2V} \int_{R'} \frac{d\tau}{f_1 \cdots f_{k+1}}$ in exactly the same way that we have passed from (9.33) to (9.37). In this way we obtain the general formula

$$\frac{1}{2V} \int_{R'} \frac{d\tau}{f_1 \cdots f_j} = \{\prod_{\substack{p \leq q \\ 1}}^{j} (1 - t_p t_q)\}^{-1}; \quad j = 1, 2, \cdots, n-1. \tag{9.38}$$

In passing from $j = n - 1$ to $j = n$ we obtain on the right a determinant of order k of which the elements in the p-th row are $(t_p^{k-1}, t_p^{k-2}, \cdots, t_p, s_p)$ where $s_p = (1 - t_p t_{k+1}) \cdots (1 - t_p t_{2k})$. The value of this determinant $= \Delta_k(\boldsymbol{t})(1 - t_1 \cdots t_{2k})$ so that the second of our integrals in the calculation of $\frac{1}{2V} \int_{R'} \frac{d\tau}{f_1 \cdots f_n}$ has the value

$$\tfrac{1}{2}\{\prod_{\substack{p \leq q \\ 1}}^{n} (1 - t_p t_q)\}^{-1}(1 - t_1 \cdots t_{2k}).$$

Since the first of the two integrals

$$= \tfrac{1}{2}\{\prod_{\substack{p \leq q \\ 1}}^{n} (1 - t_p t_q)\}^{-1}(1 + t_1 \cdots t_{2k})$$

(by (9.30)) we have

$$\frac{1}{2V} \int_{R'} \frac{d\tau}{f_1 \cdots f_n} = \{\prod_{\substack{p \leq q \\ 1}}^{n} (1 - t_p t_q)\}^{-1}; \quad n = 2k. \tag{9.39}$$

After these somewhat lengthy calculations we return to a consideration of the representation of R whose characters are the functions $\{\lambda\}'(s)$ defined on p. 243. The relation (9.20) may be written $(1-t^2)\{f(t)\}^{-1} = \sum_0^\infty p'_k t^k$ and on setting, in turn, $t = t_1, t_2, \cdots, t_k$ we obtain the k relations

$$\frac{1-t_p{}^2}{f_p} = \sum_0^\infty p'_{j_p} t_p{}^{j_p}.$$

On multiplying these relations together we obtain

$$\frac{\prod_1^k (1-t_p{}^2)}{f_1\cdots f_k} = \sum_{(j)=0}^\infty p'_{j_1} p'_{j_2} \cdots p'_{j_k} t_1{}^{j_1}\cdots t_k{}^{j_k}.$$

We now multiply both sides of this equation by $\Delta_k(\boldsymbol{t})L_k(\boldsymbol{t})$; this expression is equivalent to the determinant of order k of which the elements in the p-th row are $(t_p{}^{k-1}, t_p{}^{k-2}T_p, \cdots, t_pT_p{}^{k-2}, \cdots, T_p{}^{k-1})$ and this is equivalent to the determinant of order k of which the elements in the p-th row are $(t_p{}^{k-1}, t_p{}^{k-2}+t_p{}^k, t_p{}^{k-3}+t_p{}^{k+1}, \cdots, 1+t_p{}^{2k-2})$ (since this determinant is obtainable from the previous one by subtracting from each column an appropriate linear combination of the columns which precede it). On multiplying the elements of this p-th row by $\sum_0^\infty p'_{j_p}t_p{}^{j_p}$ we obtain a determinant of which the elements in the p-th row are

$$\Big(\sum_0^\infty p'_{j_p-(k-1)}t_p{}^{j_p}, \sum_0^\infty \{p'_{j_p-(k-2)}+p'_{j_p-k}\}t_p{}^{j_p}, \cdots, \sum_0^\infty \{p'_{j_p}+p'_{j_p-2k+2}\}t_p{}^{j_p}\Big).$$

On setting $l_1 = \lambda_1 + (k-1)$, $l_2 = \lambda_2 + (k-2), \cdots, l_k = \lambda_k$, this determinant is the sum over all sets of numbers $\lambda_1 \geqq \lambda_2 \geqq \cdots \geqq \lambda_k \geqq 0$ of $\{\lambda\}' A(l_1, \cdots, l_k)$ where $A(l_1, \cdots, l_k)$ is the determinant of order k of which the elements in the p-th row are $(t_p{}^{l_1}, \cdots, t_p{}^{l_k})$. On dividing through by $\Delta_k(\boldsymbol{t})$, $A(l_1, \cdots, l_k) \div \Delta_k(\boldsymbol{t})$ becomes the simple characteristic $\{\lambda\}(\boldsymbol{t})$ of the symmetric group on $\lambda_1+\lambda_2+\cdots+\lambda_k$ letters. Hence

$$\frac{\prod_{\substack{p\leqq q\\1}}^k (1-t_pt_q)}{f_1\cdots f_k} = \sum_{(\lambda)} \{\lambda\}'\{\lambda\}(\boldsymbol{t}). \tag{9.40}$$

On denoting by $(u_1, \cdots, u_k)$ a second set of k indeterminates and setting $f(u_1)=f_{k+1},\cdots,f(u_k)=f_{2k}$ we find on multiplying (9.40) by the result of substituting $\boldsymbol{u}$ for $\boldsymbol{t}$ in it

$$(9.41)\qquad \frac{\prod_{\substack{p\leq q\\1}}^{k}(1-t_pt_q)\prod_{\substack{p\leq q\\1}}^{k}(1-u_pu_q)}{f_1f_2\cdots f_{2k}}=\sum_{(\lambda)(\mu)}\{\lambda\}'\{\mu\}'\{\lambda\}(\boldsymbol{t})\{\mu\}(\boldsymbol{u}).$$

On integrating this equation divided by $2V$ over R' we obtain

$$\{\prod_{\substack{p,q\\1}}^{k}(1-t_pu_q)\}^{-1}=\sum_{(\lambda)(\mu)}\{\lambda\}(\boldsymbol{t})\{\mu\}(\boldsymbol{u})\frac{1}{2V}\int_{R'}\{\lambda\}'\{\mu\}'d\tau.$$

The expression on the left $=\sum_{(\lambda)}\{\lambda\}(\boldsymbol{t})\{\lambda\}(\boldsymbol{u})$; in fact

$$\{\prod_{\substack{p,q\\1}}^{k}(1-t_pu_qx)\}^{-1}=\sum_{0}^{\infty}p_m(\boldsymbol{tu})x^m=\sum_{0}^{\infty}\{\Sigma\{\lambda\}(\boldsymbol{t})\{\lambda\}(\boldsymbol{u})\}x^m$$

where the summation in the coefficient of x^m is over all partitions of m (see p. 116). On setting $x=1$ we obtain the result stated. Hence we have the relation

$$\sum_{(\lambda)}\{\lambda\}(\boldsymbol{t})\{\lambda\}(\boldsymbol{u})=\sum_{(\lambda)(\mu)}\{\lambda\}(\boldsymbol{t})\{\mu\}(\boldsymbol{u})\frac{1}{2V}\int_{R'}\{\lambda\}'\{\mu\}'d\tau.$$

On regarding $\boldsymbol{u}$ as fixed and $\boldsymbol{t}$ variable we have on each side of the equation a combination of homogeneous polynomials $\{\lambda\}(\boldsymbol{t})$ of the variable $\boldsymbol{t}=(t_1,\cdots,t_k)$. The parts of each side which are homogeneous of a given degree m must equal each other and so

$$\sum_{(\lambda)}\{\lambda\}(\boldsymbol{t})\{\lambda\}(\boldsymbol{u})=\sum_{(\lambda)(\mu)}\{\lambda\}(\boldsymbol{t})\{\mu\}(\boldsymbol{u})\frac{1}{2V}\int_{R'}\{\lambda\}'\{\mu\}'d\tau$$

where the summation is now over all partitions (λ) of m. Since the simple characteristics of the symmetric group on m letters are linearly independent it follows that

$$\{\lambda\}(\boldsymbol{u})=\sum_{(\mu)}\{\mu\}(\boldsymbol{u})\frac{1}{2V}\int_{R'}\{\lambda\}'\{\mu\}'d\tau$$

where (λ) is a given partition of m. Regarding now $\boldsymbol{u}$ as variable we have first

$$\frac{1}{2V}\int_{R'}\{\lambda\}'\{\mu\}'d\tau=0$$

unless (μ) is a partition of m and then

$$(9.42) \qquad \frac{1}{2V}\int_{R'} \{\lambda\}'\{\mu\}' d\tau = 0$$

unless $(\mu) = (\lambda)$ in which case

$$(9.43) \qquad \frac{1}{2V}\int_{R'} \{\lambda\}'\{\lambda\}' d\tau = 1.$$

We know that $\{\lambda\}'$ is a combination with integral coefficients, positive or negative, of simple characters (i. e. characters of irreducible representations) of R'. We now learn from (9.43) that $\{\lambda\}'$ is either a simple character of R' or the product of a simple character by -1; and from (9.42) that no two of the simple characters $\{\lambda\}'$, $\{\mu\}'$ of R' obtained in this way are the same.

In order to show that $\{\lambda\}'$ is actually a simple character of R' (and not the negative of a simple character) we calculate its value for E_n, the unit element of R'; this calculation will at the same time furnish the dimension of the irreducible representation of R' whose characters are furnished by $\{\lambda\}'$. It is convenient to modify the form of $\{\lambda\}'$ and this modification will be clearly understood if we illustrate it by considering the case $k = 4$ (i. e. $n = 8$ or 9). $\{\lambda\}'$ is, in this case, a determinant of order 4 of which the elements in the p-th row are

$$(p'_{l_p-3},\ p'_{l_p-2} + p'_{l_p-4},\ p'_{l_p-1} + p'_{l_p-5},\ p'_{l_p} + p'_{l_p-6})$$

where $l_1 = \lambda_1 + 3$, $l_2 = \lambda_2 + 2$, $l_3 = \lambda_3 + 1$, $l_4 = \lambda_4$ (in general, $l_1 = \lambda_1 + (k-1)$, $l_2 = \lambda_2 + (k-2), \cdots, l_k = \lambda_k$). On denoting by ξ_p an operator which reduces by unity any label in the p-th row we may write $\{\lambda'\}$ as a determinant of order 4 ($= k$) of which the elements in the p-th row are

$$(\xi_p{}^3 p'_{l_p},\ \xi_p{}^2(1+\xi_p{}^2)p'_{l_p},\ \xi_p(1+\xi_p{}^4)p'_{l_p},\ (1+\xi_p{}^6)p'_{l_p}).$$

Denoting, for a moment, the various columns of this determinant by C_1, C_2, C_3, C_4 we subtract $6C_3 - 15C_2 + 20C_1$ from C_4 and the element in the p-th row of the 4-th column becomes $(1-\xi_p)^6 p'_{l_p}$; we next subtract $4C_2 - 6C_1$ from C_3 when the element in the p-th row of the third column becomes $\xi_p(1-\xi_p)^4 p'_{l_p}$; finally we subtract $2C_1$ from C_2 when the element in the p-th row of the second column becomes $\xi_p{}^2(1-\xi_p)^2 p'_{l_p}$. Carrying through this argument for any value of k we see that $\{\lambda\}'$ may be written as a determinant of order k of which the elements in the p-th row are

$$(\xi_p{}^{k-1} p'_{l_p},\ \xi_p{}^{k-2}(1-\xi_p)^2 p'_{l_p}, \cdots, \xi_p(1-\xi_p)^{2k-4} p'_{l_p},\ (1-\xi_p)^{2k-2} p'_{l_p}).$$

Since $p'_{l_p} = (1 - \xi_p^2) p_{l_p}$ we see that $\{\lambda\}'$ may also be written as a determinant of order k of which the elements in the p-th row are

$$(9.44) \quad (\xi_p^{k-1}(1-\xi_p^2)p_{l_p}, \cdots, \\ \xi_p(1-\xi_p)^{2k-4}(1-\xi_p^2)p_{l_p}, (1-\xi_p)^{2k-2}(1-\xi_p^2)p_{l_p})$$

or, equivalently,

$$(9.45) \quad \{\lambda\}' = \{\prod_{p=1}^{k}(1-\xi_p^2)\} \begin{vmatrix} \xi_1^{k-1}, \xi_1^{k-2}(1-\xi_1)^2, \cdots, (1-\xi_1)^{2k-2} \\ \cdot \quad \cdot \quad \cdots \quad \cdot \\ \xi_k^{k-1}, \xi_k^{k-2}(1-\xi_k)^2, \cdots, (1-\xi_k)^{2k-2} \end{vmatrix} p_{l_1} \cdots p_{l_k}.$$

The expression which operates on the product $p_{l_1} p_{l_2} \cdots p_{l_k}$ in (9.45) may be written as

$$\prod_{p=1}^{k}(1-\xi_p^2) \cdot \begin{vmatrix} \xi_1^{k-1}, \xi_1^{k-2}(1+\xi_1^2), \xi_1^{k-3}(1+\xi_1^2)^2, \cdots, (1+\xi_1^2)^{k-1} \\ \cdot \quad \cdot \quad \cdot \quad \cdots \\ \xi_k^{k-1}, \quad \cdot \quad \cdot \quad , \cdots, (1+\xi_k^2)^{k-1} \end{vmatrix}$$

and, by the argument of p. 249, this $= \prod_{\substack{p \leq q \\ 1}}^{k} (1-\xi_p\xi_q)\Delta_k(\xi)$. Since

$$\{\lambda\} = \begin{vmatrix} \xi_1^{k-1}, \xi_1^{k-2}, \cdots, 1 \\ \cdot \quad \cdot \quad \cdots \quad \cdot \\ \xi_k^{k-1}, \quad \cdots, 1 \end{vmatrix} p_{l_1} \cdots p_{l_k} = \Delta_k(\xi) p_{l_1} \cdots p_{l_k}$$

we have

$$(9.45^{\text{bis}}) \qquad \{\lambda\}' = \prod_{\substack{p \leq q \\ 1}}^{k} (1-\xi_p\xi_q)\{\lambda\}.$$

The evaluation of $\{\lambda\}'$ for the unit element E_n of R' is easily performed when $\{\lambda\}'$ is written in the form (9.44). In fact, since p_j is the coefficient of t^j in the development of $\{(1-z_1t)\cdots(1-z_nt)\}^{-1}$ and since $z_1 = z_2 = \cdots = z_n = 1$ for the element E_n of R', $\phi(\xi)p_j$ is the coefficient of t^j in $\dfrac{\phi(t)}{(1-t)^n}$, ϕ being any polynomial function. Hence in order to evaluate $\{\lambda\}'$ at E_n we have to evaluate a determinant of order k of which the elements in the p-th row are the coefficients of t^{l_p} in the developments of the functions

$$(t^{k-1}(1+t)(1-t)^{-(n-1)}, t^{k-2}(1+t)(1-t)^{-(n-3)}, \cdots, \\ t(1+t)(1-t)^{-(n-2k+3)}, (1+t)(1-t)^{-(n-2k+1)})$$

as power series in t. The element in the p-th row and j-th column of our determinant, being the coefficient of t^{l_p+j-k} in the development of

$(1+t)(1-t)^{-(n-2j+1)}$ is, accordingly, zero if $l_p+j-k<0$, unity if $l_p+j-k=0$ and

$$\binom{n-2j+l_p+j-k}{n-2j}+\binom{n-2j+l_p+j-k-1}{n-2j}$$
$$=\frac{(n-2j+l_p+j-k-1)\cdots(l_p+j-k+1)}{(n-2j)\,!}(n+2l_p-2k)$$

if $l_p+j-k\geqq 1$. This last expression can be used if $l_p+j-k<0$ since it gives the correct value zero; in fact $l_p=\lambda_p+k-p\geqq k-p$ so that $l_p+j-k\geqq j-p$ so that $n-2j+l_p+j-k-1\geqq n-j-p-1\geqq 0$ unless $j=k=p$; $n=2k$. But this case cannot arise with $l_p+j-k<0$ since $l_p\geqq 0$. The general formula valid when $l_p+j-k>0$ and $l_p+j-k<0$ may also be used when $l_p+j-k=0$ since it furnishes the proper value unity. When n is even $(=2k)$ the last column is exceptional; in it we have to develop $(1+t)(1-t)^{-1}=1+2t+2t^2+\cdots$ so that the elements in the last column, being the coefficients of t^{l_p} are the same, namely 2, for all l_p save $l_p=0$. $l_p=0$ forces $p=k$ and the elements in the last row are all zero save the last which is unity. If, then, $n=2k$ and $l_k=0$ we shall double the last row in order to have a determinant in which *all* elements of the last column are 2 (instead of all but one) and we shall divide our result by 2 at the end. Since the element in the p-th row and j-th column of our determinant is

$$\frac{(n-2j+l_p+j-k-1)\cdots(l_p+j-k+1)}{(n-2j)\,!}(n+2l_p-2k)$$

(i. e. a polynomial of degree $(n-2j)$ in l_p, the polynomial being the same for every row—here the doubling of the last row in the case $n=2k$, $l_p=0$ is essential) our determinant contains $\Delta(\boldsymbol{l})=\prod_{p<q}^{k}{}_{1}(l_p-l_q)$ as a factor. Furthermore it is evident that if l_p is replaced by $2k-n-l_p$ the expression given above for the element in the p-th row and j-th column of our determinant is multiplied by $(-1)^{n-2j}$ so that not only is l_p-l_q a factor of our determinant but so also is (l_p+l_q+n-2k). When $n=2k$ is even, therefore, our determinant has the factor $\prod_{p<q}^{k}{}_{1}(l_p-l_q)(l_p+l_q)$ and the remaining factor is numerical since the product $\prod_{p<q}^{k}{}_{1}(l_p^2-l_q^2)$ is of degree $2k-2=n-2$ in l_1 as is also the determinant being evaluated. Since the coefficient of $l_1^{n-2}l_2^{n-4}\cdots l_{k-1}^2$

in the expansion of the determinant is $2^k \div (n-2)!\cdots 2!$ we see that when n is even ($=2k$) the desired value of our determinant, which furnishes $\{\lambda\}'$ for the element E_n of R' is

$$\text{(9.46)}\quad \left.\begin{array}{l} \dfrac{2^k}{(2k-2)!\cdots 4!2!}\prod_{\substack{p<q\\1}}^{k}(l_p^2-l_q^2);\quad l_k\neq 0 \\ \dfrac{2^{k-1}}{(2k-2)!\cdots 4!2!}\prod_{\substack{p<q\\1}}^{k}(l_p^2-l_q^2);\quad l_k=0 \end{array}\right\};\quad n=2k.$$

Since this value is positive we see that, when $n=2k$ is even, $\{\lambda\}'$ furnishes the characters of an irreducible representation of R' whose dimension is given by (9.46). When $n=2k+1$ is odd the p-th row of our determinant has the factor $n+2l_p-2k$ (this does not happen when $n=2k$ is even for then the last column consists solely of 2's). Since the determinant is of degree $n-2=2k-1$ in l_1 the remaining factor, other than

$$\{\prod_{p=1}^{k}(n+2l_p-2k)\}\{\prod_{\substack{p<q\\1}}^{k}(l_p+l_q+n-2k)(l_p-l_q)\}$$

is numerical and its value is found as before. On writing $l'_p=l_p+\frac{1}{2}$ the value of the determinant is

$$\text{(9.47)}\quad \frac{2^k}{(2k-1)!\cdots 3!1!}l'_1\cdots l'_k\{\prod_{\substack{p<q\\1}}^{k}(l'_p-l'_q)(l'_p+l'_q)\}.$$

Hence, again, when $n=2k+1$ is odd $\{\lambda\}'$ furnishes the characters of an irreducible representation of R' whose dimension is given by (9.47). We shall see in the next section, after we have discussed the irreducible representations of the n-dimensional rotation group R, that there are no other continuous representations of R' than those described above.

5. The irreducible representations of the *n*-dimensional rotation group.

If Γ is an irreducible representation of the n-dimensional full orthogonal (real) group R' we obtain from it, by the principle of selection, a representation, which may or may not be irreducible, of the subgroup R of R'. Denoting the characters of Γ by $\{\chi(X),\chi(AX)\}$ the hypothecated irreducibility of Γ furnishes the equation:

$$\text{(9.48)}\quad \frac{1}{2V}\int_R\{\chi(X)\}^2d\tau+\frac{1}{2V}\int_R\{\chi(AX)\}^2d\tau=1.$$

Now R' has two basic representations of dimension 1 (hence irreducible) namely

(a) the identity representation Γ^{+}_{0}

and (b) the alternating representation Γ^{-}_{0} for which $\chi(X) = 1$, $\chi(AX) = -1$. The Kronecker product $\Gamma \times \Gamma^{-}_{0}$ of any given irreducible representation Γ of R' by Γ^{-}_{0} is also irreducible (since it has the same squared characters as Γ) and it is equivalent to Γ when and only when the characters $\chi(AX)$ of Γ are zero, every X. When this is not the case the two non-equivalent representations Γ and $\Gamma \times \Gamma^{-}_{0}$ of R' are termed *associated*; a representation Γ of R' whose characters $\chi(AX)$ are zero, every X, being termed *self-associated*. For a self-associated representation Γ of R' we have, from (9.48) $\frac{1}{2V}\int_R \{\chi(X)\}^2 d\tau = 1$ or, equivalently, $\frac{1}{V}\int_R \{\chi(X)\}^2 d\tau = 2$. Hence the representation of R which is obtained from Γ by the principle of selection is not irreducible, being the sum of precisely two (since $\sum_j (c^j)^2 = 2$) irreducible representations of R. On the other hand if Γ is an irreducible representation of R' which is not self-associated the representation of R which is obtained from Γ by the principle of selection is irreducible. In fact the non-equivalence of Γ and $\Gamma \times \Gamma^{-}_{0}$ yields (by (8.30))

$$\frac{1}{2V}\int_R \{\chi(X)\}^2 d\tau - \frac{1}{2V}\int_R \{\chi(AX)\}^2 d\tau = 0$$

and this, together with (9.48), forces $\frac{1}{V}\int_R \{\chi(X)\}^2 d\tau = 1$ so that the representation of R whose characters are $\chi(X)$ is irreducible (p. 239). When $n = 2k + 1$ we may set $A = -E_n$ and it is clear that no representation of R' is self-associated since this would force $\chi(-E_n)$, which $= -\chi(E_n)$, to be zero. Hence when $n = 2k + 1$ is odd all representations of R which are obtained by the principle of selection from irreducible representations of R' are themselves irreducible.

Denote now by Γ any representation, irreducible or not, of R: $\Gamma = \{D(X)\}$. Then the collection of matrices $\{\tilde{D}(X)\}$ where

$$\tilde{D}(X) = D(A^{-1}XA) = D(AXA) \quad (\text{since } A^{-1} = A)$$

furnishes a representation $\tilde{\Gamma}$ of R. When n is odd, so that $A = -E_n$ we have $A^{-1}XA = X$ so that $\tilde{\Gamma}$ coincides with Γ. When n is even $\tilde{\Gamma}$ may or may not coincide with Γ; it will coincide with Γ if Γ is derivable from a representation of R' by the principle of selection for then $\tilde{D}(X) = D^{-1}(A)D(X)D(A)$ and $\tilde{\chi}(X) = \chi(X)$. If $\tilde{\Gamma}$ is different from Γ it will be irreducible when Γ is irreducible and vice versâ. In fact the volume element $d\tau$ of R is invariant under the *outer automorphism* of R: $X \to Y = AXA$; for $d\tau$ is an even function of the angles $(\theta_1, \cdots, \theta_k)$ and the angles for $Y = AXA$ are $(\theta_1, \cdots, -\theta_k)$. Hence

$$\frac{1}{V}\int_R \{\tilde{\chi}(X)\}^2 d\tau = \frac{1}{V}\int_R \{\chi(AXA)\}^2 d\tau = \frac{1}{V}\int_R \{\chi(X)\}^2 d\tau.$$

We term $\tilde{\Gamma}$ the adjoint representation of R to Γ it being clear that the relationship of adjointness is reflexive: Γ is the adjoint representation of R to $\tilde{\Gamma}$; also Γ and $\tilde{\Gamma}$ have the same dimension since $\tilde{D}(E) = D(AEA) = D(E)$. When Γ and $\tilde{\Gamma}$ coincide we term Γ a self-adjoint representation of R; so that, in particular, all representations of R are self-adjoint when n is odd. If $\Gamma = \{D(X)\}$ is obtained from a self-associated irreducible representation $\{D(X), D(AX)\}$ of R' by the principle of selection Γ is reducible: $\Gamma = \Gamma_1 + \Gamma_2$; $D(X) = D_1(X) + D_2(X)$. We write $D(A)$ in block form suggested by the analysis of Γ:

$$D(A) = \begin{pmatrix} L & M \\ N & P \end{pmatrix}$$

and observe that this implies $D(AX) = D(A)D(X) = \begin{pmatrix} LD_1(X) & MD_2(X) \\ ND_1(X) & PD_2(X) \end{pmatrix}$

Since $\{D(X), D(AX)\}$ is irreducible it follows that N is not the zero matrix. Now $\tilde{D}(X) = D(AXA) = D_1(AXA) + D_2(AXA) = \tilde{D}_1(X) + \tilde{D}_2(X)$; and $\tilde{D}(X)D(A) = D(AXA)D(A) = D(AX) = D(A)D(X)$ so that

$$\begin{pmatrix} \tilde{D}_1(X)L & \tilde{D}_1(X)M \\ \tilde{D}_2(X)N & \tilde{D}_2(X)P \end{pmatrix} = \begin{pmatrix} LD_1(X) & MD_2(X) \\ ND_1(X) & PD_2(X) \end{pmatrix}.$$

From the relation $\tilde{D}_2(X)N = ND_1(X)$ and the fact that N is not the zero matrix we deduce, by Schur's lemma, that $\tilde{\Gamma}_2$ coincides with Γ_1; and that N is a scalar square matrix; in other words the two representations Γ_1, Γ_2 of R are adjoint (and hence of the same dimension). Since Γ_2 and Γ_1 are non-equivalent Γ_2 and $\tilde{\Gamma}_2$ are non-equivalent and so the relation $\tilde{D}_2(X)P = PD_2(X)$ tells us, again by an application of Schur's lemma, that P is the zero matrix; similarly L is the zero matrix. Hence $D(A)$ is of the form $\begin{pmatrix} 0 & cE_d \\ c'E_d & 0 \end{pmatrix}$ where d is the common dimension of Γ_1 and Γ_2. The fact that $\{D(A)\}^2 = D(A^2) = D(E_n) = E_{2d}$ tells us that $cc' = 1$; and on transforming all the matrices $D(X)$,

$D(AX)$) by the matrix $\begin{pmatrix} c^{\frac{1}{2}}E_d & 0 \\ 0 & c^{-\frac{1}{2}}E_d \end{pmatrix}$ we see that the representation Γ may be presented in a basis in which

$$D(A) = \begin{pmatrix} 0 & E_d \\ E_d & 0 \end{pmatrix}.$$

We have seen in the preceding section that associated with each set of k numbers $\lambda_1 \geqq \lambda_2 \geqq \cdots \geqq \lambda_k \geqq 0$ there is an irreducible representation $\Gamma_{(\lambda)}$ of R' ($n = 2k$ or $2k+1$). When n is odd each of these furnishes, by the principle of selection, an irreducible representation of R. To see whether or not any two of the representations $\Gamma_{(\lambda)}$ constitute a pair of associated representations of R' or whether, when n is even, any one of the representations $\Gamma_{(\lambda)}$ is self-associated we integrate the basic equation (9.41), divided by V, over R (instead of, as before, integrating this equation, divided by $2V$, over R'). When $n = 2k+1$ is odd we find

$$\{\prod_{p,q}^{k}{}_{1} (1 - t_p u_q)\}^{-1} = \sum_{(\lambda)(\mu)} \{\lambda\}(\boldsymbol{t})\{\mu\}(\boldsymbol{u}) \frac{1}{V}\int_R \{\lambda\}'\{\mu\}' d\tau$$

or, equivalently

$$\sum_{(\lambda)} \{\lambda\}(\boldsymbol{t})\{\lambda\}(\boldsymbol{u}) = \sum_{(\lambda)(\mu)} \{\lambda\}(\boldsymbol{t})\{\mu\}(\boldsymbol{u}) \frac{1}{V}\int_R \{\lambda\}'\{\mu\}' d\tau.$$

This implies, by the reasoning of p. 256,

(9.49) $\frac{1}{V}\int_R \{\lambda\}'\{\mu\}' d\tau = 0$ unless $(\lambda) = (\mu)$ and $\frac{1}{V}\int_R [\{\lambda\}']^2 d\tau = 1.$

It follows from (9.49) that no two of the representations $\Gamma_{(\lambda)}$ of R' form a pair of associated representations of R'. We obtain, then, further irreducible representations of R' by adding to the set $\Gamma_{(\lambda)}$ the set $\Gamma_{(\lambda)} \times \Gamma^{-}_{0}$ no two of the latter set being equivalent (if they were the pair $\Gamma_{(\lambda)}, \Gamma_{(\mu)}$, having the same characters, would be equivalent) nor any one of the set $\Gamma_{(\lambda)} \times \Gamma^{-}_{0}$ being equivalent to any one, $\Gamma_{(\mu)}$ of the set $\Gamma_{(\lambda)}$ (if it was $\Gamma_{(\lambda)}$ and $\Gamma_{(\mu)}$ would form an associated pair). When, on the other hand, $n = 2k$ is even we find

(9.50) $$[\sum_{(\lambda)} \{\lambda\}(\boldsymbol{t})\{\lambda\}(\boldsymbol{u})(1 + t_1 \cdots t_k u_1 \cdots u_k)]$$
$$= \sum_{(\lambda)(\mu)} \{\lambda\}(\boldsymbol{t})\{\mu\}(\boldsymbol{u}) \frac{1}{V}\int_R \{\lambda\}'\{\mu\}' d\tau.$$

Since $\{\lambda\}(\boldsymbol{t}) = A(l_1, \cdots, l_k) \div \Delta(\boldsymbol{t})$, where $A(l_1, \cdots, l_k)$ is the k-th order determinant of which the elements in the p-th row are $(t_1^{l_p}, \cdots, t_k^{l_p})$, we have

$$\{\lambda\}(\boldsymbol{t}) \cdot t_1 \cdots t_k = A(l_1+1, \cdots, l_k+1) \div \Delta(\boldsymbol{t})$$
$$= (\lambda_1+1, \lambda_2+1, \cdots, \lambda_k+1).$$

Hence we may write (9. 50) in the form

$$\sum_{(\lambda)} [\{\lambda\}(\boldsymbol{t})\{\lambda\}(\boldsymbol{u}) + \{\lambda_1+1, \cdots, \lambda_k+1\}(\boldsymbol{t})\{\lambda_1+1, \cdots, \lambda_k+1\}(\boldsymbol{u})]$$
$$= \sum_{(\lambda)(\mu)} \{\lambda\}(\boldsymbol{t})\{\mu\}(\boldsymbol{u}) \frac{1}{V}\int_R \{\lambda\}'\{\mu\}' d\tau.$$

Hence, again by the reasoning of p. 256, $\frac{1}{V}\int_R \{\lambda\}'\{\mu\}' d\tau = 0$ unless $(\lambda) = (\mu)$; so that, again, no two of the representations $\Gamma_{(\lambda)}, \Gamma_{(\mu)}$ of R' form an associated pair. If $\lambda_k = 0$ we never find a member $\{\lambda\}(\boldsymbol{t})$ in the set $\{\lambda_1+1, \cdots, \lambda_k+1\}(\boldsymbol{t})$ so that when $n = 2k$ is even and $\lambda_k = l_k = 0$ we again have $\frac{1}{V}\int_R [\{\lambda\}']^2 d\tau = 1$ so that the representation of R which is obtained by the principle of selection from $\Gamma_{(\lambda)}$ is irreducible; in other words $\Gamma_{(\lambda)}$ is not self-associated when $n = 2k$ and $\lambda_k = 0$. On the other hand, when $\lambda_k > 0$ we find each $\{\lambda\}(\boldsymbol{t})$ once (and only once) in the set $\{\lambda_1+1, \cdots, \lambda_k+1\}(\boldsymbol{t})$ so that $\frac{1}{V}\int_R [\{\lambda\}']^2 d\tau = 2$ showing that the representation of R which is obtained from $\Gamma_{(\lambda)}$ by the principle of selection is reducible, being the sum of two adjoint representations of R; or, equivalently, that $\Gamma_{(\lambda)}$ is a self-associated representation of R' when $n = 2k$ is even and $\lambda_k = l_k > 0$. It is clear that neither member of the adjoint pair of representations of R obtained from the self-associated representation $\Gamma_{(\lambda)}$ of R' is equivalent to the representation of R obtained from the non-self associated representation $\Gamma_{(\mu)}$ of R'. In fact

$$\frac{1}{V}\int_R \{\lambda\}'\{\mu\}' d\tau = 0 \text{ so that } \frac{1}{V}\int_R [\{\lambda_1\}' + \{\lambda_2\}']\{\mu\}' d\tau = 0$$

(the suffixes 1, 2 referring to the two members of the adjoint pair). But $d\tau$ is an even function of $(\theta_1, \cdots, \theta_k)$ and $\{\mu\}'$ is also (since it is a class function over R') so that

$$\int_R \{\lambda_1\}'\{\mu\}' d\tau = \int_R \{\lambda_2\}'\{\mu\}' d\tau$$

forcing

$$\frac{1}{V}\int_R \{\lambda_1\}'\{\mu\}' d\tau = \frac{1}{V}\int_R \{\lambda_2\}'\{\mu\}' d\tau = 0,$$

which proves the statement made. Similarly we show that neither member of the adjoint pair of representations of R obtained from the self-associated representation $\Gamma_{(\lambda)}$ of R' is equivalent to either member of the adjoint-pair of representations of R obtained from the self-associated representations $\Gamma_{(\mu)}$ of R' $((\lambda) \neq (\mu))$. In fact $\{\lambda_1\}'(X) = \{\mu_1\}'(X)$ forces $\{\lambda_2\}'(X) = \{\mu_2\}'(X)$ and this forces

$$\{\lambda\}'(X) \equiv \{\lambda_1\}'(X) + \{\lambda_2\}'(X) = \{\mu_1\}'(X) + \{\mu_2\}'(X) \equiv \{\mu\}'(X)$$

which is impossible since the self-associated representations $\Gamma_{(\lambda)}$, $\Gamma_{(\mu)}$ of R' (for which $\{\lambda\}'(AX) = 0 = \{\mu\}'(AX)$) are non-equivalent.

We now proceed to show that there are no other continuous irreducible representations of R than those obtained in this way: i. e. by the principle of selection from the representations $\Gamma_{(\lambda)}$ of R' when n is odd $(= 2k + 1)$, or when n is even and $\lambda_k = 0$, combined with the pairs of adjoint representations of R obtained from the analysis of the representations of R which follow, again by the principle of selection, from the representations of R' where $n = 2k$ is even and $\lambda_k > 0$. To do this let us first consider an arbitrary continuous *self-adjoint* representation $\Gamma = \{D(X)\}$ of R. On denoting, as before, by C_j the 2×2 proper real orthogonal matrix $\begin{pmatrix} \cos\theta_j & \sin\theta_j \\ -\sin\theta_j & \cos\theta_j \end{pmatrix}$ the canonical representative of the class of R to which an arbitrary element X of R belongs is (p. 229)

$$\Lambda = \Lambda(\theta_1, \cdots, \theta_k) = C_1 \dotplus \cdots \dotplus C_k \dotplus E_1; \quad n = 2k + 1$$
$$\Lambda = \Lambda(\theta_1, \cdots, \theta_k) = C_1 \dotplus \cdots \dotplus C_k \qquad n = 2k.$$

On denoting $\Lambda(\theta_1, 0, \cdots, 0)$ by Λ_1 and so on we have

$$\Lambda = \Lambda_1 \Lambda_2 \cdots \Lambda_k$$

so that

$$D(\Lambda) = D(\Lambda_1) \cdots D(\Lambda_k). \tag{9.51}$$

Now the matrices $D(\Lambda_j)$ constitute a continuous, periodic representation Γ_j of the Abelian group whose elements are $\begin{pmatrix} \cos\theta_j & \sin\theta_j \\ -\sin\theta_j & \cos\theta_j \end{pmatrix}$ and so a basis exists in which $\{D(\Lambda_j)\}$ is in diagonal form; the diagonal elements being of the type $e^{im\theta_j}$, m an integer, positive, negative or zero. Hence, in any basis whatever, the elements of $D(\Lambda_j)$ are polynomials in $e^{i\theta_j}$, $e^{-i\theta_j}$ and so, by (9.51), each element of $D(\Lambda)$ is a linear combination of expressions of the type $e^{i(m_1\theta_1 + m_2\theta_2 + \cdots + m_k\theta_k)}$ where the coefficients $m_1, \cdots, m_k$ are integers, positive, negative or zero. In particular the trace of $D(\Lambda)$ is such a linear combination. But $\chi(\Lambda)$ is unaffected by any permutation of $(\theta_1, \cdots, \theta_k)$ (since any permutation of these angles may be effected by transforming Λ by an appropriate permutation matrix—i. e. by an element of R') or by a change of sign of any of the θ's (since any such change of sign may, again, be effected by transforming Λ by an appropriate element of R'). On applying these operations to $\chi(\Lambda)$ and averaging we see that $\chi(\Lambda) = \chi(X)$ is a linear combination of expressions $\sigma_{(m)}$ where $\sigma_{(m)} = \Sigma e^{i(m_1\theta_1 + \cdots + m_k\theta_k)}$ the summation being over all those permutations and changes of sign of $(\theta_1, \cdots, \theta_k)$ which actually change the term $e^{i(m_1\theta_1 + \cdots + m_k\theta_k)}$. We arrange the notation so that $m_1 \geq m_2 \geq \cdots \geq m_k \geq 0$ and establish a dictionary order of the sets (m) according to which (m) precedes (m') if $\Sigma m > \Sigma m'$ or if, these sums being equal, the *first* non-vanishing member of the set $(m_1 - m'_1, \cdots, m_k - m'_k)$ is positive. Terming the first member of the linear combination of the $\sigma_{(m)}$ which furnishes $\chi(X)$ when the $\sigma_{(m)}$ are arranged in the order described, the *leader* of $\chi(X)$ we now prove the basic result: *the leader of* $\{\lambda\}'$ *is* $\sigma_{(\lambda)}$; $\{\lambda\}'$ furnishing the characters of the representation of R which is obtained, by the principle of selection, from the representation $\Gamma_{(\lambda)}$ of R'. To do this we start with the relation

$$f_p^{-1} \equiv \{(1 - z_1 t_p) \cdots (1 - z_n t_p)\}^{-1} = \sum_{k=0}^{\infty} p_k t_p^k$$

and, by the method by which (9.40) was derived, obtain

$$(f_1 \cdots f_k)^{-1} = \sum_{(\lambda)} \{\lambda\}(z)\{\lambda\}(t).$$

On multiplying this relation by $\{\prod_{p \leq q \atop 1}^{k} (1 - t_p t_q)\}$ the left-hand side becomes $\sum_{(\lambda)} \{\lambda\}'(z)\{\lambda\}(t)$, by (9.40), whilst on the right the product $\{\lambda\}(t)$ by $\{\prod_{p \leq q \atop 1}^{k} (1 - t_p t_q)\}$ becomes $\{\lambda\}(t) + \sum_{(\mu)} c^{(\mu)}\{\mu\}(t)$ where each $\{\mu\}$ precedes $\{\lambda\}$. In fact $\{\lambda\}(t) = A(l_1, \cdots, l_k) \div \Delta(t)$ so that

$$\begin{aligned}\{\lambda\}(t) \times t_1^{j_1} \cdots t_k^{j_k} &= A(l_1 + j_1, \cdots, l_k + j_k) \\ &\div \Delta(t) = \{\lambda_j + j_1, \cdots, \lambda_k + j_k\}\end{aligned}$$

and this precedes $\{\lambda\}$ since $\Sigma(\lambda + j) > \Sigma\lambda$. On comparing, then, the coefficients of $\{\lambda\}(t)$ we find

$$\{\lambda\}'(z) = \{\lambda\}(z) + \sum_{(\nu)} d^{(\nu)}\{\nu\}(z) \tag{9.52}$$

where each $\{\nu\}$ is preceded by $\{\lambda\}$. But $\{\lambda\}(z)$ is a symmetric function of $(z_1, \cdots, z_n)$ whose leading term is $T_{(\lambda)}(z) = \Sigma z_1^{\lambda_1} \cdots z_k^{\lambda_k}$ (p. 164) and since $(z_1, \cdots, z_n) = (e^{i\theta_1}, \cdots, e^{-i\theta_k})$, $T_{(\lambda)}(z) = \sigma_{(\lambda)}$. Hence the leading term of $\{\lambda\}(z)$ and, equivalently by (9.52), of $\{\lambda\}'(z)$ is $\sigma_{(\lambda)}$. It follows that we may, by a recurrence method, express each of the $\sigma_{(\lambda)}$ as a linear combination, with integral coefficients, of the $\{\lambda\}'$ the first term in this linear combination being $\{\lambda\}'$ with the numerical coefficient unity. Hence $\chi(X)$ is a linear combination

$$\chi(X) = \Sigma c^{(\lambda)}\{\lambda\}'.$$

Not all the coefficients $c^{(\lambda)}$ can be zero since $\chi(E) \neq 0$; let $c^{(\mu)} \neq 0$ and calculate $\frac{1}{V}\int_R \chi(X)\{\mu\}'d\tau$. Since $\frac{1}{V}\int_R \{\lambda\}'\{\mu\}'d\tau = 0$ when $(\lambda) \neq (\mu)$ ((9.49)) we have $\frac{1}{V}\int_R \chi(X)\{\mu\}'d\tau = c^\mu$ (or $2c^\mu$ if $n = 2k$, $\lambda_k > 0$). Hence there does not exist any continuous self-adjoint representation of R whose characters are orthogonal to all the $\{\lambda\}'$; *in other words not all the numbers* $\frac{1}{V}\int_R \chi(X)\{\lambda\}'d\tau = 0$. But this means that every irreducible continuous representation of R is equivalent to one of the irreducible representations of R already obtained: *the set of continuous representations of R already obtained is complete.* In fact this is evident if the proposed new irreducible representation of R is self-adjoint for if it were distinct from the representations of R already furnished we would have $\frac{1}{V}\int_R \chi(X)\{\lambda\}'d\tau = 0$ for every (λ) (each $\{\lambda\}'$ furnishing either the characters of one of our irreducible representations or the sum of the characters of an adjoint pair of our irreducible representations). If the proposed new irreducible representation is not self-adjoint we consider the representation obtained by adding it to its adjoint; the characters of this (reducible) representation of R are $\chi(X) + \tilde{\chi}(X)$ so that we know that not all the integrals

$$\frac{1}{V}\int_R [\chi(X) + \chi(X)]\{\lambda\}'d\tau$$

vanish. But $d\tau$, being an even function of $(\theta_1, \cdots, \theta_k)$ and $\{\lambda\}'$ being a class function over R' (not merely a class function over R) the integral

$$\frac{1}{V}\int_R \tilde{\chi}(X)\{\lambda\}'d\tau = \frac{1}{V}\int_R \chi(X)\{\lambda\}'d\tau$$

so that not all the integrals

$$\frac{1}{V}\int_R \chi(X)\{\lambda\}'d\tau$$

vanish. As before this shows that the proposed irreducible continuous representation of R is equivalent to one of those already in our possession.

We are now able to show that there are no other continuous irreducible representations of R' than the representations $\Gamma_{(\lambda)}$, $\Gamma_{(\lambda)} \times \Gamma^{-}_{0}$ already obtained. In fact let Γ be a proposed *new* irreducible continuous representation of R' with characters $\{\chi(X), \chi(AX)\}$. If Γ is not self-associated the numbers $\{\chi(X)\}$ are the characters of an irreducible self-adjoint representation of R (p. 261) so that $\chi(X) = \{\lambda\}'(X)$; if Γ is self-associated the numbers $\{\chi(X)\}$ are the sums of the characters of a pair of adjoint irreducible representations of R so that again $\chi(X) = \{\lambda\}'(X)$ (where now $n = 2k$ is even and $\lambda_k > 0$). On combining the orthogonality relations between the characters of Γ and $\Gamma_{(\lambda)}$ and of Γ and $\Gamma_{(\lambda)} \times \Gamma^{-}_{0}$ we obtain

$$\frac{1}{V}\int_R \chi(X)\{\lambda\}'(X)\,d\tau = 0, \text{ i. e. } \frac{1}{V}\int_R [\{\lambda\}']^2 d\tau = 0$$

which is absurd since the continuous function $\{\lambda\}'$ does not vanish at $X = E_n$ (its value there being the dimension of Γ).

We call explicit attention to an important corollary of the results obtained in the present section. We have seen that the characters $\{\lambda\}'$ of any irreducible continuous representation $\Gamma_{(\lambda)}$ of R' are expressible as determinants of order k whose individual elements are linear combinations, with integral coefficients of the quantities $p'_j(z)$. On expanding this determinant we secure a series of products $p'_{j_1}(z) \cdots p'_{j_k}(z)$ some with positive and some with integral coefficients. Each product $p'_{j_1}(z) \cdots p'_{j_k}(z)$ furnishes the characters of a rational integral representation of R'; for each factor $p'_{j_v}(z)$ furnishes the characters of a rational integral representation of R' (p. 242) and the Kronecker product of these various rational integral representations of R' is itself a rational integral representation of R' whose characters are $p'_{j_1}(z) \cdots p'_{j_k}(z)$. On putting on one side the products $p'_{j_1} \cdots p'_{j_k}$ carrying positive integral coefficients (the other products being transferred to the side containing $\{\lambda\}'$) we see that $\Gamma_{(\lambda)}$ is part of the analysis of a rational integral representation of R'; hence $\Gamma_{(\lambda)}$ *is itself a rational integral representation of* R'. Hence any continuous representation of R' is a rational integral representation since it is a linear combination of certain of the representations $\Gamma_{(\lambda)}$. Furthermore any self-adjoint irreducible representation of R, being obtainable from one of the $\Gamma_{(\lambda)}$ by the principle of selection, is a rational integral representation of R; and each member of a pair of adjoint representations of R which are obtained, when $n = 2k$ is even, by analysing the representation of R which is derived from $\Gamma_{(\lambda)}$ by the principle of selection ($\lambda_k > 0$) is also a rational integral representation since it is part of the analysis of a rational integral representation of R. *Hence every continuous representation of R' and of R is rational integral.*

In concluding this section we point out that the results are particularly simple in the physically important case $n = 3$. Here $k = 1$; $\{\lambda\}' = p'_\lambda = p_\lambda - p_{\lambda-2}$ is the coefficient of t^λ in the expansion of

$$\frac{1-t^2}{(1-t)(1-2\cos\theta\cdot t+t^2)} = \frac{1+t}{1-2\cos\theta\cdot t+t^2}.$$

We have seen (p. 245) that

$$\frac{1}{1-2\cos\theta t+t^2} = 1 + 2\sum_1^\infty c'_q t_j{}^q$$

where

$$c'_q = \cos q\theta + \cos(q-2)\theta + \cdots$$

(the summation ending in $\frac{1}{2}$ if q is even). Hence

$$(9.53) \qquad \{\lambda\}' = 2(c'_\lambda + c'_{\lambda-1}) = 2\cos\lambda\theta + 2\cos(\lambda-1)\theta + \cdots + 2\cos\theta + 1 = \frac{\sin(\lambda+\frac{1}{2})\theta}{\sin\frac{1}{2}\theta}.$$

Since $n = 3$ is odd the complete set of irreducible continuous representations of R is furnished by the principle of selection from $\Gamma_0, \Gamma_1, \Gamma_2, \cdots$, the representations of R obtained in this way being of dimensions $1, 3, 5, \cdots, (2j+1), \cdots$ respectively. We obtain the complete set of representations of R' by adding to $\Gamma_0, \Gamma_1, \Gamma_2, \cdots$ their associates.

6. The analysis of the Kronecker product of irreducible representations of the real orthogonal group.

The characteristic numbers of any element X of the n dimensional rotation group R are $(e^{\pm i\theta_1}, \cdots, e^{\pm i\theta_k})$, if $n = 2k$ is even, and $(e^{\pm i\theta_1}, \cdots, e^{\pm i\theta_k}, 1)$ if $n = 2k+1$ is odd; and the characteristic numbers of any element AX of R' which is not in R are $(e^{\pm i\theta_1}, \cdots, e^{\pm i\theta_{k-1}}, \pm 1)$, if $n = 2k$ is even, and $(e^{\pm i\theta_1}, \cdots, e^{\pm i\theta_k}, -1)$ if $n = 2k+1$ is odd. Denoting by $(\boldsymbol{z}) = (z_1, \cdots, z_n)$ the set of n characteristic numbers (in any one of the four cases) the set $(1/\boldsymbol{z})$ is the same as the set $\boldsymbol{z}$; and the product $\sigma_n = z_1 \cdots z_n$ is $+1$ if evaluated for an element X of R and -1 if evaluated for an element AX of R' which is not in R. We shall denote this product by ϵ so that $\epsilon(X) = 1$; $\epsilon(AX) = -1$. On indicating the elementary symmetric functions of the characteristic numbers $(\boldsymbol{z})$ by $(\sigma_0, \sigma_1, \cdots, \sigma_n)$ we have

$$(9.54) \qquad \sigma_{n-j} = \epsilon\sigma_j; \qquad j = 0, 1, 2, \cdots, n.$$

In fact $\Sigma(1/z)\,(=\sigma_{n-1}/\sigma_n)=\Sigma z\,(=\sigma_1)$ so that $\sigma_{n-1}=\sigma_n\sigma_1$ and so for the other values of j. We have seen (p. 112) that the functions $p_k(z)$ are connected with the $\sigma(z)$ by the relations

$$p_0\sigma_0=1;\ p_1\sigma_0-p_0\sigma_1=0;\ p_2\sigma_0-p_1\sigma_1+p_0\sigma_2=0;\ \cdots.$$

These relations may be treated as special cases of the basic relation

$$(9.55)\qquad p_j\sigma_0-p_{j-1}\sigma_1+\cdots+(-1)^n p_{j-n}\sigma_n=0$$

provided the p_{-j}, $j=1,2,\cdots$ are properly defined. It is clear that if we set $p_{-1}=p_{-2}=\cdots=p_{-(n-1)}=0$ we obtain all the relations first written save the single one $p_0\sigma_0=1$. To obtain this as the special instance $j=0$ of (9.55) we have to set $(-1)^n p_{-n}\epsilon=-1$ i.e. $p_{-n}=(-1)^{n+1}\epsilon$. By use of (9.54), (9.55) may be written in the form

$$p_{j-n}\sigma_0-p_{j-n+1}\sigma_1+\cdots+(-1)^n p_j\sigma_n=0;$$

if, then, we set $j=-k$ and $p_{-(n+k)}=(-1)^{n+1}\epsilon p_k$, $k=0,1,2,\cdots$ the relation (9.55) is universally valid i.e. valid when j is any integer positive, negative or zero. On replacing j by $j-2$ in (9.55) and subtracting the resulting equation from (9.55) we obtain

$$(9.56)\quad p'_j\sigma_0-p'_{j-1}\sigma_1+\cdots+(-1)^n p'_{j-n}\sigma_n=0;\ j=0,\pm1,\pm2,\cdots.$$

At this stage it is convenient to discuss separately the cases n even and n odd and $\epsilon=\pm1$.

1. $n=2k$; $\epsilon=1$.

On using (9.54) and setting $j=\lambda+k$ in (9.56) we find

$$p'_\lambda\sigma_k-(p'_{\lambda+1}+p'_{\lambda-1})\sigma_{k-1}+\cdots+(-1)^k(p'_{\lambda+k}+p'_{\lambda-k})\sigma_0=0.$$

Hence if $\lambda_1\geqq\lambda_2\geqq\cdots\geqq\lambda_{k+1}$ are any $k+1$ integers the determinant

$$(9.57)\quad D(\lambda_1,\cdots,\lambda_{k+1})\equiv\begin{vmatrix} p'_{\lambda_1}, & p'_{\lambda_1+1}+p'_{\lambda_1-1}, & \cdots & p'_{\lambda_1+k}+p'_{\lambda_1-k}\\ \cdot & & & \cdot\\ \cdot & & & \cdot\\ p'_{\lambda_{k+1}-k}, & & \cdots & p'_{\lambda_{k+1}}+p'_{\lambda_{k+1}-2k}\end{vmatrix}$$

vanishes. In general we shall denote by $D(\lambda_1,\cdots,\lambda_j)$ the determinant of order j of which the elements in the p-th row are

$$(p'_{\lambda_p-(p-1)},\ p'_{\lambda_p-p+2}+p'_{\lambda_p-p},\ \cdots,\ p'_{\lambda_p-p+j}+p'_{\lambda_p-p-j+2})$$

and it is then clear that $D(\lambda_1,\cdots,\lambda_k)$ has the same *formal* definition as the function $\{\lambda\}'$ which furnishes the characters of the irreducible representation $\Gamma_{(\lambda)}$ of R'. But there is one essential difference: in $\{\lambda\}'$

all the p's which carry negative subscripts are assigned the value zero whilst in $D(\lambda_1, \cdots, \lambda_k)$ those p's which carry a negative subscript whose *numerical* value $\geq n$ are differently defined. We shall denote by $\Delta(\lambda_1, \cdots, \lambda_j)$ the determinant of order j whose formal definition is the same as that of $D(\lambda_1, \cdots, \lambda_j)$ but where *all* p's carrying negative subscripts are assigned the value zero (so that, in particular, $\Delta(\lambda_1, \cdots, \lambda_k) = \{\lambda\}'$). The least subscript attached to a p' in $D(\lambda_1, \cdots, \lambda_k)$ is found as the subscript of the second member of the element in the k-th row and k-th column and is $\lambda_k - 2k + 2$; on replacing each p'_j by $p_j - p_{j-2}$ the least subscript attached to a p is $\lambda_k - 2k$. Hence if $\lambda_k > 0$ no p with a label $< -(n-1)$ enters $D(\lambda_1, \cdots, \lambda_k)$ and we have

$$D(\lambda_1, \cdots, \lambda_k) = \Delta(\lambda_1, \cdots, \lambda_k) = \{\lambda\}'; \ \lambda_k > 0.$$

On the other hand if $\lambda_k = 0$ all the elements of the last row of $D(\lambda_1, \cdots, \lambda_{k-1}, 0)$ are zero save the last which $= 2p_0$ whilst all the elements of the last row of $\Delta(\lambda, \cdots, \lambda_{k-1}, 0)$ are zero save the last which $= p_0$. Hence

$$D(\lambda_1, \cdots, \lambda_{k-1}, 0) = 2\Delta(\lambda_1, \cdots, \lambda_{k-1}, 0) = 2\{\lambda\}'.$$

Similar connections may be established between $D(\lambda_1, \cdots, \lambda_{k+1})$, whose value we know to be zero, and $\Delta(\lambda_1, \cdots, \lambda_{k+1})$. The least label attached to a p in $D(\lambda_1, \cdots, \lambda_{k+1})$ is $\lambda_{k+1} - 2k - 2$ and so

$$(9.58) \quad \Delta(\lambda_1, \cdots, \lambda_{k+1}) = D(\lambda_1, \cdots, \lambda_{k+1}) = 0; \quad \lambda_{k+1} \geq 3.$$

If $\lambda_{k+1} = 2$ we find, in the same way,

$$(9.59) \qquad \Delta(\lambda_1, \cdots, \lambda_k, 2) = -\Delta(\lambda_1, \cdots, \lambda_k) = -\{\lambda\}'.$$

Similarly

$$\Delta(\lambda_1, \cdots, \lambda_k, 1) = \tfrac{1}{2}D(\lambda_1, \cdots, \lambda_k, 1) = 0 \text{ if } \lambda_k > 1$$

whilst

$$\Delta(\lambda_1, \cdots, \lambda_{k-1}, 1, 1) = \Delta(\lambda_1, \cdots, \lambda_{k-1}, 0) = \{\lambda_1, \cdots, \lambda_{k-1}, 0\}'$$

(the element in the k-th row and $(k+1)$-st column of $D(\lambda_1, \cdots, \lambda_{k-1}, 1, 1)$ being $p_2 + p_0$ whilst the element in the k-th row and $(k+1)$-st column of $\Delta(\lambda_1, \cdots, \lambda_{k-1}, 1, 1)$ is simply p_2).

2. $n = 2k + 1$; $\epsilon = 1$.

Here $(\sigma_0, \sigma_1, \cdots, \sigma_n)$ are the elementary symmetric functions of the $n = 2k + 1$ quantities $(e^{\pm i\theta_1}, \cdots, e^{\pm i\theta_k}, 1)$; if, then, we denote by $(\sigma'_0, \cdots, \sigma'_{2k})$ the elementary symmetric functions of the $2k$ quantities $(e^{\pm i\theta_1}, \cdots, e^{\pm i\theta_k})$ we have

$$\sigma_0 = \sigma'_0 + 1;\ \sigma_1 = \sigma'_1 + \sigma'_0;\ \cdots\ \sigma_n = \sigma'_{2k}$$

so that the basic relation (9.55) may be written in the form

$$p_j\sigma'_0 - p_{j-1}(\sigma'_1 + \sigma'_0) + \cdots - p_{j-n}\sigma'_{2k} = 0.$$

On using the relations $\sigma'_{2k-j} = \sigma'_j$, $j = 0, 1, 2, \cdots, 2k$, we obtain, by varying j, a system of homogeneous linear equations in the $k+1$ quantities $(\sigma'_k, \cdots, \sigma'_0)$ and these force us to the conclusion that $D(\lambda_1, \cdots, \lambda_{k+1})$ again vanishes. The reasoning will be entirely clear if we write the argument for the case $k = 2$ $(n = 5)$. Our set of equations is

$$(p_{j-2} - p_{j-3})\sigma'_2 - (p_{j-1} - p_{j-2} + p_{j-3} - p_{j-4})\sigma'_1 \\ + (p_j - p_{j-1} + p_{j-4} - p_{j-5})\sigma'_0 = 0$$

and on adding to this equation the one obtained from it by replacing j by $j-1$ we find

$$p'_{j-2}\sigma'_2 - (p'_{j-1} + p'_{j-3})\sigma'_1 + (p'_j + p'_{j-4})\sigma'_0 = 0.$$

On setting, in turn, $j = \lambda_1 + 2, \lambda_2 + 1, \lambda_3$ we obtain three homogeneous equations whose determinant is $D(\lambda_1, \lambda_2, \lambda_3)$. In this way we obtain the general result, valid whether n is even or odd,

(9.60) $$D(\lambda_1, \cdots, \lambda_{k+1}) = 0.$$

Since the least label attached to a p in $D(\lambda_1, \cdots, \lambda_k)$ is $\lambda_k - 2k$ it follows that

$$D(\lambda_1, \cdots, \lambda_k) = \Delta(\lambda_1, \cdots, \lambda_k) = \{\lambda\}';\ n = 2k+1,\ \lambda_k \geq 0.$$

The least label attached to a p in $D(\lambda_1, \cdots, \lambda_{k+1})$ is $\lambda_{k+1} - 2k - 2$ so that

(9.61) $$\Delta(\lambda_1, \cdots, \lambda_{k+1}) = D(\lambda_1, \cdots, \lambda_{k+1}) = 0;\ \lambda_{k+1} \geq 2.$$

Similarly

$$\Delta(\lambda_1, \cdots, \lambda_k, 1) = \Delta(\lambda_1, \cdots, \lambda_k) = \{\lambda\}'.$$

3. $n = 2k$; $\epsilon = -1$.

Here $(\sigma_0, \sigma_1, \cdots, \sigma_{2k})$ are the elementary symmetric functions of the quantities $(e^{\pm i\theta_1}, \cdots, e^{\pm i\theta_{k-1}}, \pm 1)$; if, then, we denote by $(\sigma'_0, \cdots, \sigma'_{2k-2})$ the elementary symmetric functions of the $2k-2$ quantities $(e^{\pm i\theta_1}, \cdots, e^{\pm i\theta_{k-1}})$ we have

$$\sigma_0 = \sigma'_0;\ \sigma_1 = \sigma'_1;\ \sigma_2 = \sigma'_2 - \sigma'_0;\ \cdots.$$

On substituting these expressions in (9.55) and using the relations

$\sigma'_{2k-2-j} = \sigma'_j$ we obtain a set of homogeneous equations in the k quantities $\sigma'_{k-1}, \cdots, \sigma'_0)$ and these lead to the conclusion

$$D(\lambda_1, \cdots, \lambda_k) = 0. \tag{9.62}$$

The argument will be quite clear on writing it out for the case $k = 3$ $(n = 6)$. Our equations are

$$p'_{j-2}\, \sigma'_2 - (p'_{j-1} + p'_{j-3})\sigma'_1 + (p'_j + p'_{j-4})\sigma'_0 = 0$$

and on setting j, in turn, equal to $\lambda_1 + 2$, $\lambda_2 + 1$, λ_3 we obtain $D(\lambda_1, \lambda_2, \lambda_3) = 0$. As before we have

$$\{\lambda\}' = \Delta(\lambda_1, \cdots, \lambda_k) = D(\lambda_1, \cdots, \lambda_k) = 0;\ \lambda_k > 0. \tag{9.63}$$

It follows, à fortiori (by expanding in terms of the last column) from (9.62) that

$$D(\lambda_1, \cdots, \lambda_{k+1}) = 0;\ \Delta(\lambda_1, \cdots, \lambda_{k+1}) = 0 \text{ unless } \lambda_{k+1} = 1.$$

To evaluate $\Delta(\lambda_1, \cdots, \lambda_k, 1)$ we expand it in terms of the last row obtaining, since $\Delta(\lambda_1, \cdots, \lambda_k) = 0$, $\lambda_k > 0$,

$$\Delta(\lambda_1, \cdots, \lambda_k, 1) = -\xi_1^k \cdots \xi_k^k \begin{vmatrix} 1 & \eta_1 & \cdots & \eta_1^{k-2} & \eta_1^k \\ \cdot & \cdot & \cdots & \cdot & \cdot \\ \cdot & \cdot & \cdots & \cdot & \cdot \\ 1 & \eta_k & \cdots & \eta_k^{k-2} & \eta_k^k \end{vmatrix} \prod_1^k (1 - \xi_p^2)\, p_{\lambda_1+k} \cdots p_{\lambda_k+1}$$

where $\eta_p = \xi_p + 1/\xi_p$. The determinant $= \prod_{\substack{p>q \\ 1}}^{k} (\eta_p - \eta_q)(\eta_1 + \cdots + \eta_k)$ and so

$$\begin{aligned} \Delta(\lambda_1, \cdots, \lambda_k, 1) &= \prod_{\substack{p \leq q \\ 1}}^{k} (1 - \xi_p \xi_q) \Delta_k(\xi)(\eta_1 + \cdots \eta_k)\, p_{\lambda_1+k-1} \cdots p_{\lambda_k} \\ &= (\eta_1 + \cdots + \eta_k)\{\lambda_1, \cdots, \lambda_k\}'. \end{aligned}$$

Since $\{\lambda_1, \cdots, \lambda_k\}' = 0$ if $\lambda_k > 0$ we have

$$\begin{aligned} &\Delta(\lambda_1, \cdots, \lambda_k, 1) = 0 \text{ if } \lambda_k > 1; \\ &\Delta(\lambda_1, \cdots, \lambda_{k-1}, 1, 1) = -\{\lambda_1, \cdots, \lambda_{k-1}\}'. \end{aligned} \tag{9.64}$$

4. $n = 2k + 1;\ \epsilon = -1$.

Here $(\sigma_0, \cdots, \sigma_{2k+1})$ are the elementary symmetric functions of the quantities $(e^{\pm i\theta_1}, \cdots, e^{\pm i\theta_k}, -1)$; if, then, we denote by $(\sigma'_0, \cdots, \sigma'_{2k})$ the elementary symmetric functions of the $2k$ quantities $(e^{\pm i\theta_1}, \cdots, e^{\pm i\theta_k})$ we have

$$\sigma_0 = \sigma'_0;\quad \sigma_1 = \sigma'_1 - \sigma'_0;\quad \sigma_2 = \sigma'_2 - \sigma'_1;\ \cdots.$$

On substituting these values in (9.55) and using the relations σ'_{2k-j}

$= \sigma'_j$, $j = 0, 1, \cdots, 2k$ we obtain a system of homogeneous equations in the $k+1$ quantities $(\sigma'_k, \sigma'_{k-1}, \cdots, \sigma'_0)$ which lead to the conclusion

$$D(\lambda_1, \cdots, \lambda_{k+1}) = 0. \tag{9.65}$$

The argument will be clear if we write it out for the case $k = 2$ $(n = 5)$. Our equations then are

$$(p_{j-2} + p_{j-3})\sigma'_2 - (p_{j-1} + p_{j-2} + p_{j-3} + p_{j-4})\sigma'_1 \\ + (p_j + p_{j-1} + p_{j-4} + p_{j-5})\sigma'_0 = 0,$$

and on replacing j by $j - 1$ and subtracting, these yield

$$p'_{j-2}\sigma'_2 - (p'_{j-1} + p'_{j-3})\sigma'_1 + (p'_j + p'_{j-4})\sigma'_0 = 0.$$

On setting, in turn, $j = \lambda_1 + 2, \lambda_2 + 1, \lambda_3$ we obtain three homogeneous equations in $(\sigma'_2, -\sigma'_1, \sigma'_0)$ whose determinant $D(\lambda_1, \lambda_2, \lambda_3)$ must vanish. In this way the validity of (9.65) is proved. Exactly as in the case $n = 2k + 1$, $\epsilon = 1$ we find

$$\Delta(\lambda_1, \cdots, \lambda_{k+1}) = D(\lambda_1, \cdots, \lambda_{k+1}) = 0 \text{ if } \lambda_{k+1} > 1,$$

whilst

$$\Delta(\lambda_1, \cdots, \lambda_k, 1) = -\{\lambda\}' \text{ (instead of } +\{\lambda\}' \text{ as before).}$$

We are now able to deal with the problem of analysing the Kronecker product of two irreducible representations $\Gamma_{(\lambda)}$ and $\Gamma_{(\mu)}$ of R'. We shall first dispose of the trivial case $n = 2$. Here $k = 1$ and the two irreducible representations of R' have characters $\{\lambda_1\}' = p'_{\lambda_1} = (1 - \xi_1^2)p_{\lambda_1}$, $\{\lambda_2\}' = p'_{\lambda_2} = (1 - \xi_2^2)p_{\lambda_2}$, $\lambda_1 \geq \lambda_2 > 0$, respectively. (There is no point in including the trivial case $\lambda_2 = 0$ since Γ_0 is the identity representation of R'). Our task is to write

$$\{\lambda_1\}'\{\lambda_2\}' = (1 - \xi_1^2)(1 - \xi_2^2)p_{\lambda_1}p_{\lambda_2}$$

as a linear combination of the $\{\lambda\}'$. To do this we use the result

$$\begin{aligned}\{\lambda_1, \lambda_2\} &= (\xi_1 - \xi_2)p_{l_1}p_{l_2} \ (l_1 = \lambda_1 + 1, l_2 = \lambda_2) \\ &= (1 - \xi_2/\xi_1)p_{\lambda_1}p_{\lambda_2}\end{aligned}$$

or, equivalently,

$$p_{\lambda_1}p_{\lambda_2} = (1 - \xi_2/\xi_1)^{-1}\{\lambda_1, \lambda_2\} = \{\lambda_1, \lambda_2\} \\ + \{\lambda_1 + 1, \lambda_2 - 1\} + \cdots + \{\lambda_1 + \lambda_2\}.$$

We have, accordingly, merely to evaluate expressions of the type $(1 - \xi_1^2)(1 - \xi_2^2)\{\mu_1, \mu_2\}$ and we shall do this first for elements of R, i.e. for $\epsilon = 1$. Now

$$\Delta(\mu_1, \mu_2) = (1-\xi_1^2)(1-\xi_2^2)\begin{vmatrix} \xi_1 & 1+\xi_1^2 \\ \xi_2 & 1+\xi_2^2 \end{vmatrix} p_{m_1}p_{m_2}$$
$$= (1-\xi_1^2)(1-\xi_2^2)(1-\xi_1\xi_2)(\xi_1-\xi_2)p_{m_1}p_{m_2}$$
$$= (1-\xi_1^2)(1-\xi_2^2)(1-\xi_1\xi_2)\{\mu_1, \mu_2\}$$

and

$$\Delta(\mu_1, \mu_2) = 0 \text{ if } \mu_2 > 2 \text{ or if } \mu_2 = 1, \mu_1 > 1$$

whilst

$$\Delta(\mu_1, 2) = -\{\mu_1\}' \quad \text{and} \quad \Delta(1, 1) = \{0\}'.$$

Hence if $\mu_2 > 2$ we have

$$(1-\xi_1^2)(1-\xi_2^2)\{\mu_1, \mu_2\} = (1-\xi_1^2)(1-\xi_2^2)\{\mu_1-1, \mu_2-1\}$$

and continuing this on we obtain

$$(1-\xi_1^2)(1-\xi_2^2)\{\mu_1, \mu_2\} = (1-\xi_1^2)(1-\xi_2^2)\{\mu_1-\mu_2+2, 2\}$$

and this

$$= (1-\xi_1^2)(1-\xi_2^2)\{\mu_1-\mu_2+1, 1\} - \{\mu_1-\mu_2+2\}'.$$

If $\mu_1 \neq \mu_2$ the first term of this

$$= (1-\xi_1^2)(1-\xi_2^2)\{\mu_1-\mu_2\} = (1-\xi_1^2)\{\mu_1-\mu_2\} = \{\mu_1-\mu_2\}'$$

so that

$$(1-\xi_1^2)(1-\xi_2^2)\{\mu_1, \mu_2\} = \{\mu_1-\mu_2\}' - \{\mu_1-\mu_2+2\}'.$$

If, on the other hand, $\mu_1 = \mu_2$ the term

$$(1-\xi_1^2)(1-\xi_2^2)\{1, 1\} = 2\{0\}'$$

and so

$$(1-\xi_1^2)(1-\xi_2^2)\{\mu_1, \mu_1\} = 2\{0\}' - \{2\}'.$$

On applying these results to the expressions given above for $p_{\lambda_1}p_{\lambda_2}$ we obtain

$$\{\lambda_1\}'\{\lambda_2\}' = \{\lambda_1-\lambda_2\}' + \{\lambda_1+\lambda_2\}'; \quad \lambda_1 \neq \lambda_2 \neq 0$$
$$\{\lambda_1\}'\{\lambda_1\}' = 2\{0\}' + \{2\lambda_1\}'.$$

These relations will be true also for the elements of R' which are not in R (for which $\epsilon = -1$) provided we replace $2\{0\}'$ by $\Gamma^+_0 + \Gamma^-_0$ for $\{\lambda\}'$ is zero when $\epsilon = -1$ (save when $\lambda = 0$). Hence the general result

$$(9.66) \qquad \begin{aligned} \Gamma_{\lambda_1} \times \Gamma_{\lambda_2} &= \Gamma_{\lambda_1-\lambda_2} + \Gamma_{\lambda_1+\lambda_2}; \quad \lambda_1 \neq \lambda_2 \\ \Gamma_{\lambda_1} \times \Gamma_{\lambda_1} &= \Gamma^+_0 + \Gamma^-_0 + \Gamma_{2\lambda_1}. \end{aligned}$$

We now turn to the equally trivial (but physically important) case

$n=3$. Since $k=1$ the argument is practically the same. But now $\Delta(\mu_1, \mu_2)=0$ if $\mu_2>1$ so that

$$(1-\xi_1^2)(1-\xi_2^2)\{\mu_1, \mu_2\} = (1-\xi_1^2)(1-\xi_2^2)\{\mu_1-\mu_2+1, 1\}$$

and this $=\{\mu_1-\mu_2\}'+\{\mu_1-\mu_2+1\}'$. On applying these results (valid for $\epsilon=1$) to the expression given above for $p_{\lambda_1}p_{\lambda_2}$ we obtain

$$\{\lambda_1\}'\{\lambda_2\}' = \{\lambda_1-\lambda_2\}'+\{\lambda_1-\lambda_2+1\}'+\cdots+\{\lambda_1+\lambda_2\}'.$$

Since each $\{\lambda\}'$ is the character of an irreducible representation of the three-dimensional rotation group we have, for this group, the formula

$$(9.67)\qquad \Gamma_{\lambda_1}\times\Gamma_{\lambda_2} = \Gamma_{\lambda_1-\lambda_2}+\Gamma_{\lambda_1-\lambda_2+1}+\cdots+\Gamma_{\lambda_1+\lambda_2}.$$

This important result is known as the Clebsch-Gordan formula.

When we are evaluating $\{\lambda_1\}'\{\lambda_2\}'$ for an element of R' which is not in R (i.e. for $\epsilon=-1$) we obtain $\{\mu_1-\mu_2\}'-\{\mu_1-\mu_2+1\}'$ (instead of $\{\mu_1-\mu_2\}'+\{\mu_1-\mu_2+1\}'$ as before). On denoting by Γ^*_λ the associated representation $\Gamma_\lambda\times\Gamma^-_0$ of R' to Γ_λ we have

$$(9.68)\qquad \Gamma_{\lambda_1}\times\Gamma_{\lambda_2} = \Gamma_{\lambda_1-\lambda_2}+\Gamma^*_{\lambda_1-\lambda_2+1}+\Gamma_{\lambda_1-\lambda_2+2}+\cdots+\Gamma_{\lambda_1+\lambda_2}.$$

This form of the Clebsch-Gordan formula is available for both R and R' since Γ and Γ^* coincide over R.

When $k\geq 2$ $(n\geq 4)$ the evaluation of the Kronecker product may be carried out as follows. From the relation

$$\{\mu_1, \mu_2\}' = (1-\xi_1^2)(1-\xi_2^2)(1-\xi_1\xi_2)\{\mu_1, \mu_2\}$$

we read off

$$\begin{aligned}(1-\xi_1^2)(1-\xi_2^2)\{\mu_1, \mu_2\} &= (1-\xi_1\xi_2)^{-1}\{\mu_1, \mu_2\}' \\ &= (1+\xi_1\xi_2+\xi_1^2\xi_2^2+\cdots)\{\mu_1, \mu_2\}' \\ &= \{\mu_1, \mu_2\}'+\{\mu_1-1, \mu_2-1\}'+\cdots+\{\mu_1-\mu_2\}'.\end{aligned}$$

Since the characters of $\Gamma_{\lambda_1}\times\Gamma_{\lambda_2}$ are furnished by the expression

$$\begin{aligned}\{\lambda_1\}'\{\lambda_2\}' &= (1-\xi_1^2)(1-\xi_2^2)p_{\lambda_1}p_{\lambda_2} \\ &= (1-\xi_1^2)(1-\xi_2^2)[\{\lambda_1, \lambda_2\} \\ &\qquad +\{\lambda_1+1, \lambda_2-1\}+\cdots+\{\lambda_1+\lambda_2\}]\end{aligned}$$

we obtain

$$(9.69)\qquad \Gamma_{\lambda_1}\times\Gamma_{\lambda_2} = \begin{cases}\Gamma_{\lambda_1+\lambda_2}+\Gamma_{\lambda_1+\lambda_2-2}+\cdots+\Gamma_{\lambda_1-\lambda_2} \\ +\Gamma_{\lambda_1+\lambda_2-1,1}+\Gamma_{\lambda_1+\lambda_2-3,1}+\cdots+\Gamma_{\lambda_1-\lambda_2+1,1} \\ +\Gamma_{\lambda_1+\lambda_2-2,2}+\cdots+\Gamma_{\lambda_1-\lambda_2+2,2} \\ +\cdots \\ +\Gamma_{\lambda_1,\lambda_2}\end{cases}$$

E.g., $\quad \Gamma_3\times\Gamma_2 = (\Gamma_5+\Gamma_3+\Gamma_1)+(\Gamma_{(4,1)}+\Gamma_{(2,1)})+\Gamma_{(3,2)}.$

For $n=4$, Γ_3 and Γ_2 are, by (9. 46), of dimensions 16 and 9, respectively, and we have the check by dimensions

$$16 \times 9 = (36+16+4)+(48+16)+24.$$

It is important to notice that (9. 69), which we shall term the *generalized Clebsch-Gordan* formula, is a universal formula being valid even when $k=1$ ($n=2$ or 3). When $n=2$ all $\{\mu_1,\mu_2\}'$ for which $\mu_2>2$ vanish by (9. 58) and p. 273 whilst $\{\mu_1,2\}'=-\{\mu_1\}'$; also all $\{\mu_1,1\}'$ for which $\mu_1>1$ vanish and $\{1,1\}'=\epsilon\{0\}'$. Hence when $n=2$ (9. 69) reduces to

$$\Gamma_{\lambda_1}\times\Gamma_{\lambda_2}=\Gamma_{\lambda_1+\lambda_2}+\Gamma_{\lambda_1+\lambda_2-2}+\cdots+\Gamma_{\lambda_1-\lambda_2}$$
$$-\Gamma_{\lambda_1+\lambda_2-2}-\Gamma_{\lambda_1+\lambda_2-4}-\cdots-\Gamma_{\lambda_1-\lambda_2+2}$$

and to this plus $\epsilon\{0\}'$ if $\lambda_1=\lambda_2$. In other words

$$\Gamma_{\lambda_1}\times\Gamma_{\lambda_2}=\Gamma_{\lambda_1+\lambda_2}+\Gamma_{\lambda_1-\lambda_2};\quad \lambda_1\neq\lambda_2$$
$$\Gamma_{\lambda_1}\times\Gamma_{\lambda_1}=\Gamma_{2\lambda_1}+\Gamma^{+}_{0}+\Gamma^{-}_{0}.$$

Similarly when $n=3$ all $\{\mu_1,\mu_2\}'$ for which $\mu_2>1$ vanish and $\{\mu_1,1\}'=\epsilon\{\mu_1\}'$ (pp. 272 and 274) so that

$$\Gamma_{\lambda_1}\times\Gamma_{\lambda_2}=\Gamma_{\lambda_1+\lambda_2}+\Gamma_{\lambda_1+\lambda_2-2}+\cdots+\Gamma_{\lambda_1-\lambda_2}$$
$$+\Gamma^{*}_{\lambda_1+\lambda_2-1}+\Gamma^{*}_{\lambda_1+\lambda_2-2}+\cdots+\Gamma^{*}_{\lambda_1-\lambda_2+1}.$$

The same method is available for the general Kronecker product $\Gamma_{(\lambda)}\times\Gamma_{(\mu)}$ where $(\lambda)=(\lambda_1,\cdots,\lambda_{j_1})$, $(\mu)=(\mu_1,\cdots,\mu_{j_2})$ provided $\lambda_{j_1}\geqq\mu_1$. We shall first treat $\Gamma_{(\lambda)}\times\Gamma_1$. Since

$$\{\lambda\}'=[\prod_{p=1}^{j_1}(1-\xi_p{}^2)\prod_{\substack{p<q\\1}}^{j_1}(1-\xi_p\xi_q)]\{\lambda\}$$

and $$\{1\}'=(1-\xi^2{}_{j_1+1})\{1\}$$

we have to evaluate the result of operating with $[\prod_{p=1}^{j_1+1}(1-\xi_p{}^2)\prod_{\substack{p<q\\1}}^{j_1}(1-\xi_p\xi_q)]$ upon $\{\lambda\}\{1\}$ this latter product being by (5. 17)

$$\{\lambda_1+1,\cdots,\lambda_{j_1}\}+\cdots+\{\lambda_1,\cdots,\lambda_{j_1}+1\}+\{\lambda_1,\cdots,\lambda_{j_1},1\}.$$

Upon operating on our expression with the product $\prod_{p=1}^{j_1}(1-\xi_p\xi_{j_1+1})$ we obtain $\{\lambda_1+1,\cdots,\lambda_{j_1}\}'+\cdots+\{\lambda_1,\cdots,\lambda_{j_1},1\}'$ so that the result we desire is found by operating with the reciprocal of $\prod_{p=1}^{j_1}(1-\xi_p\xi_{j_1+1})$ i. e. with

$$\prod_{p=1}^{j_1} (1 - \xi_p \xi_{j_1+1})^{-1} = \prod_{p=1}^{j_1} (1 + \xi_p \xi_{j_1+1} + \xi^2{}_p \xi^2{}_{j_1+1} + \cdots)$$

upon the expressions $\{\lambda_1 + 1, \cdots, \lambda_{j_1}\}', \cdots, \{\lambda_1, \cdots, \lambda_{j_1}, 1\}'$ and combining the results. The number in the $(j_1 + 1)$-st place of the parentheses $\{\lambda_1 + 1, \cdots, \lambda_{j_1}\}', \cdots, \{\lambda_1, \cdots, \lambda_{j_1} + 1\}$ being, in each instance, zero, we obtain from these parentheses merely the result of operating by unity whilst from the last parentheses $\{\lambda_1, \cdots, \lambda_{j_1}, 1\}'$ we obtain

$$\{\lambda_1, \cdots, \lambda_{j_1}, 1\} + \{\lambda_1 - 1, \cdots, \lambda_{j_1}\}' + \cdots \{\lambda_1, \cdots, \lambda_{j_1} - 1\}.$$

Hence the final result

$$\begin{aligned} \{\lambda\}'\{1\}' = {} & \{\lambda_1 + 1, \cdots, \lambda_{j_1}\}' + \cdots \\ & + \{\lambda_1, \cdots, \lambda_{j_1} + 1\}' + \{\lambda_1, \cdots, \lambda_{j_1}, 1\}' \\ & + \{\lambda_1 - 1, \cdots, \lambda_{j_1}\}' + \cdots + \{\lambda_1, \cdots, \lambda_{j_1} - 1\}'. \end{aligned} \tag{9.70}$$

E. g.

$$\{2, 1\}'\{1\}' = \{3, 1\}' + \{2^2\}' + \{1^2\}' + \{2\}' + \{2, 1^2\}'.$$

When $k = 2$, i. e. $n = 4$ or 5, the last term must be modified since it contains more than k elements. When $n = 4$ it must be replaced by $\epsilon\{2\}'$ so that, when $n = 4$,

$$\Gamma_{(2,1)} \times \Gamma_1 = \Gamma_{(3,1)} + \Gamma_{(2^2)} + \Gamma_{(1^2)} + \Gamma_2 + \Gamma^*{}_2$$

the check by dimensions being

$$16 \times 4 = 30 + 10 + 6 + 9 + 9.$$

On the other hand when $n = 5$ the term $\{2, 1^2\}'$ must be replaced by $\epsilon\{2, 1\}'$ so that, when $n = 5$

$$\Gamma_{(2,1)} \times \Gamma_1 = \Gamma_{(3,1)} + \Gamma_{(2^2)} + \Gamma_{(1^2)} + \Gamma_2 + \Gamma^*{}_{(2,1)}$$

the check by dimensions being (by (9. 47))

$$35 \times 5 = 81 + 35 + 10 + 14 + 35.$$

As a second example we calculate $\Gamma_{(3,2)} \times \Gamma_2$. The product

$$\{3, 2\}\{2\} = \{5, 2\} + \{4, 3\} + \{4, 2, 1\} + \{3^2, 1\} + \{3, 2^2\}.$$

(Table 6, *American Journal of Mathematics*, Vol. LIX, p. 484, (1937)) and we have merely to accent the expressions on the right and to apply to each of them the operator

$$\begin{aligned} (1 - \xi_1\xi_3)^{-1}(1 - \xi_2\xi_3)^{-1} &= (1 + \xi_1\xi_3 + \xi_1{}^2\xi_3{}^2 + \cdots)(1 + \xi_2\xi_3 + \xi_2{}^2\xi_3{}^2 + \cdots) \\ &= 1 + (\xi_1 + \xi_2)\xi_3 + (\xi_1{}^2 + \xi_1\xi_2 + \xi_2{}^2)\xi_3{}^2 + \cdots. \end{aligned}$$

The two element parentheses are unaffected; $\{4,2,1\}'$ yields $\{4,2,1\}' + \{4,1\}' + \{3,2\}'$; $\{3^2,1\}'$ yields $\{3^2,1\}' + \{3,2\}'$ whilst $\{3,2^2\}'$ yields $\{3,2^2\}' + \{3,1^2\}' + \{3\}' + \{2^2,1\}' + \{2,1\}'$ so that

$$\{3,2\}'\{2\}' = \{5,2\}' + \{4,3\}' + \{4,2,1\}' + \{4,1\}' + \{3^2,1\}' + \{3,2^2\}' + 2\{3,2\}' + \{3,1^2\}' + \{3\}' + \{2^2,1\}' + \{2,1\}'.$$

For $n=4$, $k=2$ the parentheses containing three elements must be modified; each $\{\lambda_1,\lambda_2,\lambda_3\}'$ for which $\lambda_3 = 1$, $\lambda_2 > 1$ vanishes; each $\{\lambda_1,1,1\}'$ is replaced by $\epsilon\{\lambda_1,0\}'$ and each $\{\lambda_1,\lambda_2,2\}'$ is replaced by $-\{\lambda_1,\lambda_2\}'$ (cf. pp. 271 and 273). We obtain, then, when $n=4$

$$\Gamma_{(3,2)} \times \Gamma_2 = \Gamma_{(5,2)} + \Gamma_{(4,3)} + \Gamma_{(4,1)} + \Gamma_{(3,2)} + \Gamma_3 + \Gamma^*_3 + \Gamma_{(2,1)}$$

the check by dimensions being

$$24 \times 9 = 64 + 32 + 48 + 24 + 16 + 16 + 16.$$

On multiplying this again by Γ_1 we readily find $(n=4)$

$$\Gamma_{(3,2)} \times \Gamma_2 \times \Gamma_1 = \Gamma_{(6,2)} + 2\Gamma_{(5,3)} + 2\Gamma_{(5,1)} + \Gamma_{(4^2)} + 4\Gamma_{(4,2)} + 2\Gamma_{(3^2)} + 2\Gamma_4 + 2\Gamma^*_4 + 5\Gamma_{(3,1)} + 2\Gamma_{(2^2)} + 2\Gamma_2 + 2\Gamma^*_2 + \Gamma_{(1^2)}.$$

In order that the method may be entirely clear we shall carry through the analysis of $\Gamma_{(3,2)} \times \Gamma_{(2,1)}$. Here we have

$$\{3,2\}' = (1-\xi_1^2)(1-\xi_2^2)(1-\xi_1\xi_2)\{3,2\};$$
$$\{2,1\}' = (1-\xi_3^2)(1-\xi_4^2)(1-\xi_3\xi_4)\{2,1\}$$

so that

$$\{3,2\}'\{2,1\}' = (1-\xi_1^2)(1-\xi_2^2)(1-\xi_3^2)(1-\xi_4^2) \times (1-\xi_1\xi_2)(1-\xi_3\xi_4)\cdot\{3,2\}\{2,1\}.$$

The product

$$\{3,2\}\{2,1\} = \{5,3\} + \{5,2,1\} + \{4^2\} + 2\{4,3,1\} + \{4,2^2\} + \{4,2,1^2\} + \{3^2,2\} + \{3^2,1^2\} + \{3,2^2,1\}$$

(see the table *American Journal of Mathematics*, Vol. LIX, p. 485, (1937)) so that we have merely to evaluate expressions of the type

$$\prod_{p=1}^{4}(1-\xi_p^2)\cdot(1-\xi_1\xi_2)(1-\xi_3\xi_4)\{\lambda_1,\lambda_2,\lambda_3,\lambda_4\}.$$

Since

$$\{\lambda_1,\lambda_2,\lambda_3,\lambda_4\}' = \Big[\prod_{p=1}^{4}(1-\xi_p^2)\prod_{\substack{p<q\\1}}^{4}(1-\xi_p\xi_q)\Big]\{\lambda_1,\lambda_2,\lambda_3,\lambda_4\} \quad (9.45^{\text{bis}})$$

we have

$$[\prod_{p=1}^{4}(1-\xi_p^2)](1-\xi_1\xi_2)(1-\xi_3\xi_4)\{\lambda_1,\lambda_2,\lambda_3,\lambda_4\}$$
$$=(1-\xi_1\xi_3)^{-1}(1-\xi_1\xi_4)^{-1}(1-\xi_2\xi_3)^{-1}(1-\xi_2\xi_4)^{-1}\{\lambda_1,\lambda_2,\lambda_3,\lambda_4\}'.$$

In evaluating the expression on the right-hand side it is convenient to work first with $(1-\xi_2\xi_4)^{-1}=1+\xi_2\xi_4+\xi_2^2\xi_4^2+\cdots$. If $\lambda_4=0$ the terms $\xi_2\xi_4, \xi_2^2\xi_4^2,\cdots$ contribute nothing since they all yield $\{\lambda\}'$'s ending in a negative number. We list the results of applying the operator $[(1-\xi_1\xi_3)(1-\xi_1\xi_4)(1-\xi_2\xi_3)(1-\xi_2\xi_4)]^{-1}$ to the various expressions $\{5,3\}', \{5,2,1\}',\cdots$ which are obtained by accenting the terms in the analysis of the product $\{3,2\}\{2,1\}$:

$$\{5,3\}'\to\{5,3\}';\ \{5,2,1\}'\to\{5,2,1\}'+\{5,1\}'+\{4,2\}';$$
$$\{4^2\}'\to\{4^2\}';\ 2\{4,3,1\}'\to2\{4,3,1\}'+2\{4,2\}'+2\{3^2\}';$$
$$\{4,2^2\}'\to\{4,2^2\}'+\{4,1^2\}'+\{3,2,1\}'+\{4\}'+\{3,1\}'+\{2^2\}';$$
$$\{4,2,1^2\}'\to\{4,2,1^2\}'+\{4,1^2\}'+\{3,2,1\}'+\{3,1\}';$$
$$\{3^2,2\}'\to\{3^2,2\}'+\{3,2,1\}'+\{3,1\}';$$
$$\{3^2,1^2\}'\to\{3^2,1^2\}'+\{3,2,1\}'+\{2^2\}';$$
$$\{3,2^2,1\}'\to\{3,2^2,1\}'+\{3,1^3\}'+\{2^3\}'+\{2^2,1^2\}'+2\{2,1^2\}'+\{2\}'+\{1^2\}'.$$

Hence the net result of the analysis is

$$\begin{aligned}\{3,2\}'\{2,1\}'=&\{5,3\}'+\{5,2,1\}'+\{4^2\}'+2\{4,3,1\}'+\{4,2^2\}'\\&+\{4,2,1^2\}'+\{3^2,2\}'+\{3^2,1^2\}'+\{3,2^2,1\}'\\&+\{5,1\}'+3\{4,2\}'+2\{4,1^2\}'+2\{3^2\}'\\&+4\{3,2,1\}'+\{3,1^3\}'+\{2^3\}'+\{2^2,1^2\}'+\{4\}'\\&+3\{3,1\}'+2\{2^2\}'+2\{2,1^2\}'+\{2\}'+\{1^2\}'.\end{aligned}$$

Some idea of the complexity of the problem being treated may be grasped by computing (by means of (9.46) or (9.47)) the dimensions of the representations involved. Thus for $k=4$, $n=8$, $\Gamma_{(3,2)}$ is of dimension $\frac{2^3}{6!\,4!\,2!}20.\,35.\,36.\,15.\,16=1400$ (since $l_1=6$, $l_2=4$, $l_3=1$, $l_4=0$) whilst $\Gamma_{(2,1)}$ is of dimension 160; the Kronecker product is accordingly of dimension $1400\times160=224{,}000$. On calculating the dimensions of the various representations on the right of the expression given for $\{3,2\}'\{2,1\}'$ we obtain the check

$$\begin{aligned}224{,}000=&21{,}840+32{,}768+8{,}918+2(25{,}725)+15{,}092+17{,}820\\&+8{,}910+8{,}624+7{,}350+3{,}696+3(4{,}312)+2(3{,}675)\\&+2(1{,}925)+4(4{,}096)+1{,}680+840+1{,}134+294\\&+3(567)+2(300)+2(350)+35+28.\end{aligned}$$

From the analysis of $\Gamma_{(3,2)} \times \Gamma_{(2,1)}$ which we have just furnished for $k \geq 4$ we can read off the analysis of this same product when $k = 2$ or 3. Thus when $n = 4$, $k = 2$ we have to discard all $\{\lambda_1, \lambda_2, \lambda_3\}'$ for which $\lambda_3 \geq 3$ (pp. 271 and 273) whilst all $\{\lambda_1, \lambda_2, 2\}'$ must be replaced by $-\{\lambda_1, \lambda_2\}$ (p. 271); also all $\{\lambda_1, \lambda_2, 1\}'$ are to be discarded save those for which $\lambda_2 = 1$, $\{\lambda_1, 1, 1\}'$ being replaced by $\epsilon\{\lambda_1\}'$. The $\{\lambda_1, \lambda_2, \lambda_3, \lambda_4\}$ for which $\lambda_4 \neq 0$ cause more difficulty. Thus, in dealing with $\{4, 2, 1^2\}'$ we expand it in terms of the last row. In this expansion we are confronted with the evaluation of

$$-(1-\xi_1^2)(1-\xi_2^2)(1-\xi_3^2)\begin{vmatrix} \xi_1^3 & \xi_1^2(1+\xi_1^2) & 1+\xi_1^6 \\ \xi_2^3 & \xi_2^2(1+\xi_2^2) & 1+\xi_2^6 \\ \xi_3^3 & \xi_3^2(1+\xi_3^2) & 1+\xi_3^6 \end{vmatrix} p_7p_4p_2$$

(this being the cofactor of the element in the fourth row and third column). On setting $\xi + 1/\xi = \eta$ the third order determinant appearing here takes the form

$$\xi_1^3\xi_2^3\xi_3^3\begin{vmatrix} 1 & \eta_1 & \eta_1^3 \\ 1 & \eta_2 & \eta_2^3 \\ 1 & \eta_3 & \eta_3^3 \end{vmatrix} = -\xi_1^3\xi_2^3\xi_3^3\Delta(\boldsymbol{\eta})(\eta_1+\eta_2+\eta_3)$$
$$= (1-\xi_1\xi_2)(1-\xi_1\xi_3)(1-\xi_2\xi_3)\Delta(\boldsymbol{\xi})\{\xi_1\xi_2\xi_3(\xi_1+\xi_2+\xi_3) + \xi_2\xi_3+\xi_3\xi_1+\xi_1\xi_2\}.$$

Hence the expression we have to evaluate is

$$-[\xi_1\xi_2\xi_3(\xi_1+\xi_2+\xi_3)+\xi_2\xi_3+\xi_3\xi_1+\xi_1\xi_2]\{5,3,2\}'$$
$$= -[\{3,2,1\}'+\{4,1^2\}'+\{4,2\}'+\{4,2^2\}'+\{4,3,1\}'+\{5,2,1\}'].$$

The cofactor $\{4, 2, 1\}'$ of the element in the fourth row and fourth column of $\{4, 2, 1^2\}'$ vanishes and so, on discarding the terms which vanish and modifying the remainder as described above, we find $\{4, 2, 1^2\}' \to -\epsilon\{4\}'$. Similarly $\{3^2, 1^2\}' \to 0$;

$$\{3,1^3\}' = \{3,1^2\}'\{1\}' - [\{2,1^2\}'+\{3,1\}'+\{4,1^2\}'+\{3,2,1\}'] \to 0;$$

$\{2^2, 1^2\}' \to -\epsilon\{2\}'$. In the evaluation of $\{3, 2^2, 1\}'$ we have to make use of the analysis of $\{3, 2\}'\{1\}'$:

$$\{3,2\}'\{1\}' = \{4,2\}'+\{3^2\}'+\{3,1\}'+\{2^2\}'+\{3,2,1\}'$$
$$\to \{4,2\}'+\{3^2\}'+\{3,1\}'+\{2^2\}'$$

and we find $\{3, 2^2, 1\}' \to -\{3, 1\}'$. On combining these results we find, for $n = 4$,

$$\Gamma_{(3,2)} \times \Gamma_{(2,1)} = \Gamma_{(5,3)} + \Gamma_{(5,1)} + \Gamma_{(4^2)} + 2\Gamma_{(4,2)} + \Gamma_4 + \Gamma^*_4 + \Gamma_{(3^2)}$$
$$+ 2\Gamma_{(3,1)} + \Gamma_{(2^2)} + \Gamma_2 + \Gamma^*_2 + \Gamma_{(1^2)}$$

the check by dimensions being

$$24 \times 16 = 54 + 70 + 18 + 84 + 25 + 25 + 14 + 60 + 10 + 9 + 9 + 6.$$

In order to evaluate a product such as $\Gamma_{(3,2)} \times \Gamma_{(3)}$ it is simplest to use the relation

$$\{2,1\}' = \begin{vmatrix} p'_2 & p'_3 + p'_1 \\ p'_0 & p'_1 \end{vmatrix} \quad \text{i. e. } \{3\}' = \{2\}'\{1\}' - \{2,1\}' - \{1\}'.$$

From the analyses already given of $\Gamma_{(3,2)} \times \Gamma_2 \times \Gamma_1$, $\Gamma_{(3,2)} \times \Gamma_{(2,1)}$, $\Gamma_{(3,2)} \times \Gamma_{(1)}$ we read off $(n = 4)$

$$\Gamma_{(3,2)} \times \Gamma_{(3)} = \Gamma_{(6,2)} + \Gamma_{(5,3)} + \Gamma_{(5,1)} + \Gamma_{(4,2)} + \Gamma_4 + \Gamma^*_4 + 2\Gamma_{(3,1)} + \Gamma_2 + \Gamma^*_2$$

the check by dimensions being

$$24 \times 16 = 90 + 54 + 70 + 42 + 25 + 25 + 60 + 9 + 9.$$

7. The modification rules for the n-dimensional orthogonal group.

In the analysis of the Kronecker product of two irreducible representatives of the n-dimensional orthogonal group we are confronted with the quantities $\Delta(\lambda_1, \cdots, \lambda_j) = \{\lambda_1, \cdots, \lambda_j\}'$, $j > k$, and it is necessary to express these in terms of the simple characters $\Delta(\lambda_1, \cdots, \lambda_j) = \{\lambda_1, \cdots, \lambda_j\}'$ $j \leq k$, of the n-dimensional orthogonal group ($n = 2k+1$ if n is odd; $n = 2k$ if n is even). We have already given the necessary modification rules in the particular case $j = k+1$; they are as follows: n, odd, $(= 2k+1)$; $\{\lambda_1, \cdots, \lambda_{k+1}\}' = 0$ if $\lambda_{k+1} > 1$; $\{\lambda_1, \cdots, \lambda_k, 1\}' = \epsilon\{\lambda_1, \cdots, \lambda_k\}'$ where $\epsilon = \pm 1$ according as the element of R' is proper / improper.

n, even, $= 2k$; $\{\lambda_1, \cdots, \lambda_{k+1}\}' = 0$ if $\lambda_{k+1} > 2$; $\{\lambda_1, \cdots, \lambda_k, 2\}' = -\epsilon\{\lambda_1, \cdots, \lambda_k\}'$; $\{\lambda_1, \cdots, \lambda_k, 1\}' = 0$ if $\lambda_k > 1$; $\{\lambda_1, \cdots, \lambda_{k-1}, 1^2\}' = \epsilon\{\lambda_1, \cdots, \lambda_{k-1}\}'$.

To derive the necessary modification rules when $j = k+2$ we proceed as follows. Considering first the case n odd, $(= 2k+1)$ we have

$$g_p = f_p \div (1 - \epsilon t_p) = c_k t_p{}^k + c_{k-1} t_p{}^{k-1} T_p + \cdots + T_p{}^k$$

so that

$$T_p g_p = c_k t_p{}^k T_p + \cdots + T_p{}^{k+1}.$$

Hence the determinant of order $k+2$:

$$| t_p{}^{k+1}, t_p{}^k T_p, \cdots, t_p T_p{}^k, T_p g_p |$$

has the same value as the determinant of order $k+2$:

$$| t_p^{k+1}, t_p^k T_p, \cdots, t_p T_p^k, T_p^{k+1} |$$

whose value is $\Delta_{k+2}(t) L_{k+2}(t)$. On multiplying through by $\prod_1^{k+1} (1 - t_p^2) \div f_p$ and denoting, for the moment, by $M_j(t)$ the product

$$\{\prod_1^j (1 - t_p^2)\} \cdot L_j(t) = \prod_{\substack{p \leq q \\ 1}}^{j} (1 - t_p t_q),$$

we obtain

$$\frac{\Delta_{k+2}(t) M_{k+2}(t)}{f_1 \cdots f_{k+2}} = | t_p^{k+1}, \cdots, t_p T_p^k, (1 + \epsilon t_p) T_p \Pi'_p (1 - t_q^2) \div f_q |$$

where Π'_p denotes the product of the $k+1$ terms obtained by assigning to q, in turn, the values $1, 2, \cdots, k+2$, *with the exception of* p. We now expand the determinant on the right in terms of the last column and observe that the cofactor of the element in the p-th row and last column has $L^p_{k+1}(t)$ as a factor. Since

$$\frac{M_j(t)}{f_1 \cdots f_j} = \sum_{(\lambda)} \{\lambda\}' \{\lambda\}(t)$$

(cf. the derivation of (9. 40)) we obtain

$$\frac{\Delta_{k+2}(t) M_{k+2}(t)}{f_1 \cdots f_{k+2}} = \sum_{(\lambda)} \{\lambda\}' \, | t_p^{l_1+1}, \cdots, t_p^{l_{k+1}+1}, (1 + \epsilon t_p) T_p |$$

where $l_1 = \lambda_1 + k, \cdots, l_{k+1} = \lambda_{k+1}$, and the summation on the right is over all parentheses (λ) of not more than $k+1$ elements. If (μ) denotes a typical parenthesis of not more than $k+2$ elements we obtain, accordingly, on division by $\Delta_{k+2}(t)$ and expanding $(1 + \epsilon t_p) T_p$ in the form $1 + \epsilon t_p + t_p^2 + \epsilon t_p^3$

$$\sum_{(\mu)} \{\mu\}' \{\mu\}(t) = \sum_{(\lambda)} \{\lambda\}' [\{\lambda_1, \cdots, \lambda_{k+1}\}(t) + \epsilon \{\lambda_1, \cdots, \lambda_{k+1}, 1\}(t)$$
$$+ \{\lambda_1, \cdots, \lambda_{k+1}, 2\}(t) + \epsilon \{\lambda_1, \cdots, \lambda_{k+1}, 3\}(t)].$$

Owing to the linear independence of the quantities $\{\lambda_1, \cdots, \lambda_{k+2}\}(t)$ it follows that $\{\lambda_1, \cdots, \lambda_{k+2}\}' = 0$ if $\lambda_{k+2} > 3$. Furthermore, since $\{\lambda_1, \cdots, \lambda_{k+1}\}' = 0$ if $\lambda_{k+1} > 1$ only those $\{\lambda_1, \cdots, \lambda_{k+1}, 3\}'$ have a value differing, possibly, from zero which are disordered and end in $(1, 3)$ or $(0, 3)$. On comparing coefficients of $\{\lambda_1, \cdots, \lambda_{k+2}\}(t)$ we obtain the following modification rules for $\{\lambda_1, \cdots, \lambda_{k+2}\}'$ when $n (= 2k+1)$ is odd. *All* $\{\lambda_1, \cdots, \lambda_{k+2}\}'$ *vanish save the following:*

$$\{\lambda_1, \cdots, \lambda_k, 2^2\}' = -\{\lambda_1, \cdots, \lambda_k\}';$$
$$\{\lambda_1, \cdots, \lambda_k, 2, 1\}' = -\epsilon \{\lambda_1, \cdots, \lambda_k\}';$$
$$\{\lambda_1, \cdots, \lambda_{k-1}, 1^3\}' = \epsilon \{\lambda_1, \cdots, \lambda_{k-1}\}'.$$

When $n(=2k)$ is even we proceed in a similar manner but here the two cases $\epsilon = \pm 1$ must be treated separately. Taking first the case $\epsilon = 1$ we have $g_p = f_p$ so that the element in the p-th row and last column of the $(k+2)$ order determinant (which equals $\Delta_{k+2}(\boldsymbol{t}) M_{k+2}(\boldsymbol{t}) \div f_1 \cdots f_{k+2}$) is $(1 - t_p^2) T_p \Pi'_p (1 - t_q^2) \div f_q$ instead of $(1 + \epsilon t_p) \times T_p \Pi'_p (1 - t_q^2) \div f_q$. Hence our basic equation is

$$\sum_{(\mu)} \{\mu\}'\{\mu\}(\boldsymbol{t}) = \sum_{(\lambda)} \{\lambda\}'[\{\lambda_1, \cdots, \lambda_{k+1}\}(\boldsymbol{t}) - \{\lambda_1, \cdots, \lambda_{k+1}, 4\}(\boldsymbol{t})].$$

We read from this equation the fact that all $\{\lambda_1, \cdots, \lambda_{k+2}\}'$ vanish save those for which $\lambda_{k+2} = 4$ and $\{\lambda_1, \cdots, \lambda_{k+1}, 4\}' = -\{\lambda_1, \cdots, \lambda_{k+1}\}'$. On setting $\lambda_{k+1} = 2$ we find $\{\lambda_1, \cdots, \lambda_k, 3^2\}' = -\{\lambda_1, \cdots, \lambda_k\}'$; on setting $\lambda_{k+1} = 1$ we find $\{\lambda_1, \cdots, \lambda_{k-1}, 2^3\} = -\{\lambda_1, \cdots, \lambda_{k-1}\}'$; and on setting $\lambda_{k+1} = 0$ we find $\{\lambda_1, \cdots, \lambda_k, 3, 1\}' = \{\lambda_1, \cdots, \lambda_k\}'$. This last yields (when $\lambda_k < 3$) the results $\{\lambda_1, \cdots, \lambda_{k-1}, 2^2, 1\}' = -\{\lambda_1, \cdots, \lambda_{k-1}, 1\}'$; $\{\lambda_1, \cdots, \lambda_{k-1}, 2, 1^2\}' = -\{\lambda_1, \cdots, \lambda_{k-1}\}'$ and this last yields, when $\lambda_{k-1} < 2$ $\{\lambda_1, \cdots, \lambda_{k-2}, 1^4\}' = \{\lambda_1, \cdots, \lambda_{k-2}\}'$. All the other $\{\lambda_1, \cdots, \lambda_{k+2}\}'$ vanish. E.g., $n = 4$, $\epsilon = 1$, $\{4, 2, 1^2\}' = -\{4\}'$; $\{2^2, 1^2\}' = -\{2\}'$; $\{3, 2^2, 1\}' = -\{3, 1\}'$ (see the somewhat tedious derivation of these results on p. 281).

When $\epsilon = -1$, $n = 2k$, we have to start with $h_p = f_p \div (1 - t_p^2)$ rather than f_p. Since $h_p = c_{k-1} t_p^{k-1} + \cdots + T_p^{k-1}$ we write $h_p T_p^2 = c_{k-1} t_p^{k-1} T_p^2 + \cdots + T_p^{k+1}$ and the element in the p-th row and last column of the $(k+2)$ order determinant (which equals $\Delta_{k+2}(\boldsymbol{t}) M_{k+2}(\boldsymbol{t}) \div f_1 \cdots f_{k+2}$) is $T_p^2 \Pi'_p (1 - t_q^2) \div f_q$. Since $T_p^2 = 1 + 2t_p^2 + t_p^4$ our basic equation is

$$\sum_{(\mu)} \{\mu\}'\{\mu\}(\boldsymbol{t}) = \sum_{(\lambda)} \{\lambda\}'[\{\lambda_1, \cdots, \lambda_{k+1}\}(\boldsymbol{t}) + 2\{\lambda_1, \cdots, \lambda_{k+1}, 2\}(\boldsymbol{t}) + \{\lambda_1, \cdots, \lambda_{k+1}, 4\}(\boldsymbol{t})].$$

Since, when $\epsilon = -1$, all $\{\lambda_1, \cdots, \lambda_{k+1}\}'$, $\lambda_{k+1} > 0$, vanish save $\{\lambda_1, \cdots, \lambda_{k-1}, 1^2\}'$ which $= -\{\lambda_1, \cdots, \lambda_{k-1}\}'$ we see that all $\{\lambda_1, \cdots, \lambda_{k+2}\}'$ vanish save $\{\lambda_1, \cdots, \lambda_{k-1}, 2^3\}' = -\{\lambda_1, \cdots, \lambda_{k-1}\}'$; $\{\lambda_1, \cdots, \lambda_{k-1}, 2, 1^2\}' = \{\lambda_1, \cdots, \lambda_{k-1}\}'$; $\{\lambda_1, \cdots, \lambda_{k-2}, 1^4\}' = -\{\lambda_1, \cdots, \lambda_{k-2}\}'$ On combining the results for $\epsilon = \pm 1$ we obtain the modification rules for $n = 2k$, $j = k + 2$:

$$\{\lambda_1, \cdots, \lambda_k, 3^2\}' = -\{\lambda_1, \cdots, \lambda_k\}';$$
$$\{\lambda_1, \cdots, \lambda_{k-1}, 2^3\}' = -\{\lambda_1, \cdots, \lambda_{k-1}\}';$$
$$\{\lambda_1, \cdots, \lambda_k, 3, 1\}' = \{\lambda_1, \cdots, \lambda_k\}';$$
$$\{\lambda_1, \cdots, \lambda_{k-1}, 2^2, 1\}' = -\{\lambda_1, \cdots, \lambda_{k-1}, 1\}';$$
$$\{\lambda_1, \cdots, \lambda_{k-1}, 2, 1^2\} = -\epsilon\{\lambda_1, \cdots, \lambda_{k-1}\}';$$
$$\{\lambda_1, \cdots, \lambda_{k-2}, 1^4\}' = \epsilon\{\lambda_1, \cdots, \lambda_{k-2}\}'.$$

These modification rules furnish complete information when $k=2$, i. e, $n=5$ or 4. When $n=7$ or 6 we have to derive similarly the modification rules for $j=k+3$. We now have to deal with a determinant of order $k+3$ whose last column carries an additional factor $T_p=1+t_p^2$ in the p-th row; and so on.

8. The analysis of the representations of R' which are furnished, by the principle of selection, by the irreducible representations of the full linear group.

This analysis follows at once from the relation

$$\{\lambda_1,\cdots,\lambda_j\}'=\{\prod_{p=1}^{j}(1-\xi_p^2)\prod_{\substack{p<q\\1}}^{j}(1-\xi_p\xi_q)\}\{\lambda_1,\cdots,\lambda_j\}$$

which implies

$$(9.71)\quad \{\lambda_1,\cdots,\lambda_j\}=\{\prod_{p=1}^{j}(1-\xi_p^2)^{-1}\prod_{\substack{p<q\\1}}^{j}(1-\xi_p\xi_q)^{-1}\}\{\lambda_1,\cdots,\lambda_j\}'.$$

If $j=1$ the result is trivially simple:

$$\{\lambda_1\}=(1-\xi_1^2)^{-1}\{\lambda_1\}'=\{\lambda_1\}'+\{\lambda_1-2\}'+\cdots.$$

E. g., $\{3\}=\{3\}'+\{1\}'$; $\{4\}=\{4\}'+\{2\}'+\{0\}'$.

When $j=2$ we first operate with $(1-\xi_2^2)^{-1}$, then with $(1-\xi_1\xi_2)^{-1}$ and finally with $(1-\xi_1^2)^{-1}$. Thus

$$\begin{aligned}\{4,2\}&=(1-\xi_1^2)^{-1}(1-\xi_1\xi_2)^{-1}(1-\xi_2^2)^{-1}\{4,2\}'\\&=(1-\xi_1^2)^{-1}(1-\xi_1\xi_2)^{-1}[\{4,2\}'+\{4\}']\\&=(1-\xi_1^2)^{-1}[\{4,2\}'+\{4\}'+\{3,1\}'+\{2\}']\\&=\{4,2\}'+\{4\}'+\{3,1\}'+\{2^2\}'+2\{2\}'+\{0\}'.\end{aligned}$$

Here in operating with $(1-\xi_1^2)^{-1}$ upon $\{4,2\}'$, for instance, we obtain

$$\{4,2\}'+\{2^2\}'+\{0,2\}'=\{4,2\}'+\{2^2\}'-\{1^2\}'$$

and in operating on $\{3,1\}'$ with $(1-\xi_1^2)^{-1}$ we obtain

$$\{3,1\}'+\{1^2\}'+\{-1,1\}'=\{3,1\}'+\{1^2\}'-\{0\}'.$$

When $k=1$, $n=2$ or 3, the parentheses containing two elements must be modified as explained in the previous section. Thus when $n=2$, $\{4,2\}'$ must be replaced by $-\{4\}'$ etc. and we find

$$\{4,2\}'=\{2\}'+\{0\}';\quad n=2$$

the check by dimensions being

$$3=2+1\quad (\text{see } (4.41)).$$

If, on the other hand $n = 3$, we find

$$\{4, 2\}' = \{4\}' + \epsilon\{3\}' + 2\{2\}' + \{0\}';$$

the check by dimensions being

$$27 = 9 + 7 + 10 + 1.$$

The simplest irreducible representations of the full linear group to deal with in this way are those for which each $\lambda = 1$: $\{\lambda\} = \{1^j\}$, $j = 1, \cdots, n$. Since $\{1^j\} = \sigma_j$ (4.27) it follows (from (9.54)) that the representation of R' obtained by the principle of selection from $\{1^{n-j}\}$ is the associate of the representation of R' obtained from $\{1^j\}$ so that we may limit ourselves to the cases $j \leq k$. It is at once clear that the representations of R' obtained, by the principle of selection, from $\{1^j\}$, $j = 1, \cdots, k$, are all irreducible. Thus when $j = 2$ the application of $(1 - \xi_2{}^2)^{-1}$ to $\{1^2\}'$ yields $\{1^2\}'$; the sequential application of $(1 - \xi_1\xi_2)^{-1}$ yields $\{1^2\}' + \{0\}'$ and the final application of $(1 - \xi_1{}^2)^{-1}$ yields $\{1^2\}' + \{-1, 1\}' + \{0\}' = \{1^2\}'$. The proof in the general case is immediate: in evaluating the effect of the operators $(1 - \xi_p\xi_q)^{-1}$, $p < q$, upon $\{1^j\}'$ we get simply $\{1^j\}'$ if $q < j$ and from $(1 - \xi_p{}^2)^{-1}$ we again get simply $\{1^j\}'$ if $p < j - 1$. The operators $(1 - \xi_p\xi_j)^{-1}$ also yield simply $\{1^j\}'$ save when $p = j - 1$ and $(1 - \xi_j{}^2)^{-1}$ also yields $\{1^j\}'$. There remain only $(1 - \xi^2{}_{j-1})^{-1}(1 - \xi_{j-1}\xi_j)^{-1}$ and so

$$\begin{aligned}\prod_{\substack{1 \\ p \leq q}}^{j} (1 - \xi_p\xi_q)^{-1}\{1^j\}' &= (1 - \xi^2{}_{j-1})^{-1}(1 - \xi_{j-1}\xi_j)^{-1}\{1^j\}' \\ &= (1 - \xi^2{}_{j-1})^{-1}[\{1^j\}' + \{1^{j-2}\}'] \\ &= \{1^j\}' - \{1^{j-2}\}' + \{1^{j-2}\}' = \{1^j\}'\end{aligned}$$

i. e. $\{1^j\} = \{1^j\}'$ proving the irreducibility of the representation of R' obtained from the irreducible representation $\{1^j\}$ of the full linear group by the principle of selection. When n is odd or when $n = 2k$ is even and $j < k$ the representation of the rotation group R obtained from $\{1^j\}$ by the principle of selection is again irreducible but when $n = 2k$ is even the representation of R obtained from $\{1^k\}$ by the principle of selection is reducible being the sum of two adjoint representations of R.

9. The analysis of the representation of R'_{n-1} which is induced, i. e. furnished, by the principle of selection, by the irreducible representation $\Gamma_{(\lambda)}$ of R'_n.

The elements of R'_{n-1} are in one-to-one correspondence with those elements of R'_n whose last row and column consist entirely of zeros save for their common diagonal element which is unity. On indicating by a superposed bar quantities having reference to R'_{n-1} it follows that

$$f \equiv \prod_{1}^{n}(1 - z_n t) = (1 - t)\bar{f}$$

and, hence, that

$$\bar{p}_j = p_j - p_{j-1} = (1 - \xi_j) p_j; \qquad j = 0, 1, 2, \cdots$$

or, equivalently,

$$p_j = (1 - \xi_j)^{-1}\bar{p}_j = \bar{p}_j + \bar{p}_{j-1} + \cdots.$$

The desired analysis is obtained by combining this relation with

$$\{\lambda\}' = \{\prod_{\substack{p \leq q \\ 1}}^{k} (1 - \xi_p\xi_q)\}\{\lambda\} = \{\prod_{\substack{p \leq q \\ 1}}^{k} (1 - \xi_p\xi_q)\}\Delta_k(\boldsymbol{\xi}) p_{l_1} \cdots p_{l_k}.$$

Let us first consider the case when $n = 2k + 1$ is odd so that the k for $n - 1$ is the same as for n. Then

$$(9.72) \qquad \{\lambda\}' = \{\prod_{p=1}^{k} (1 - \xi_p)^{-1}\}\{\bar{\lambda}\}'$$

furnishes the desired analysis. The one-element representations are trivially simple to analyse:

$$\{\lambda_1\}' = \{\bar{\lambda}_1\}' + \{\overline{\lambda_1 - 1}\}' + \cdots + \{\bar{0}\}'.$$

E. g.,

$\{2\}' = \{\bar{2}\}' + \{\bar{1}\}' + \{\bar{0}\}'$. For $n = 3$ we have the check by dimensions $5 = 2 + 2 + 1$. For two element partitions we have

$$\{\lambda_1, \lambda_2\}' = (1 - \xi_1)^{-1}(1 - \xi_2)^{-1}\{\overline{\lambda_1, \lambda_2}\}'$$
$$= \{1 + p_1(\xi_1, \xi_2) + p_2(\xi_1, \xi_2) + \cdots\}\{\overline{\lambda_1, \lambda_2}\}'.$$

E. g.,

$$\{3, 2\}' = \{\overline{3, 2}\}' + \{\overline{3, 1}\}' + \{\bar{3}\}' + \{\overline{2^2}\}' + \{\overline{2, 1}\}'.$$

For $n = 5$ the check by dimensions is

$$105 = 24 + 30 + 16 + 10 + 16 + 9.$$

The general result is

$$(9.73) \quad \{\lambda_1, \cdots, \lambda_j\}' = \{1 + p_1(\xi_1, \cdots, \xi_j) + p_2(\xi_1, \cdots, \xi_j) + \cdots\}\{\overline{\lambda_1, \cdots, \lambda_j}\}' \quad j = 1, 2, \cdots, k.$$

When n is even the same formula holds, when $j < k$, but when $j = k$ the parentheses on the right containing k elements, must be modified according to the rules already given. All $\{\overline{\lambda_1, \cdots, \lambda_k}\}'$ for which $\lambda_k > 1$ must be dropped whilst all $\{\overline{\lambda_1, \cdots, \lambda_{k-1}, 1}\}'$ must be replaced by $\epsilon\{\overline{\lambda_1, \cdots, \lambda_{k-1}}\}'$. Thus when $n = 4$ we find, from the expression given above for $\{3, 2\}'$, the formula

$$\{3, 2\}' = \epsilon\{\overline{3}\}' + \{\overline{3}\}' + \epsilon\{\overline{2}\}' + \{\overline{2}\}'$$

or, equivalently,

$$\Gamma_{(3,2)} = \bar{\Gamma}_3 + \bar{\Gamma}^*{}_3 + \bar{\Gamma}_2 + \bar{\Gamma}^*{}_2,$$

the check by dimensions being $24 = 7 + 7 + 5 + 5$.

The results of the present paragraph are known as the *branching rules* for the full real n-dimensional orthogonal group R'_n. When $n = 2k + 1$ is odd they furnish the branching rules for R_n, the rotation n-dimensional group, and when n is even they furnish the branching rules for those irreducible representations $\Gamma_{(\lambda)}$ of R_n for which $\lambda_k = 0$; when $\lambda_k > 0$ they furnish the branching rules for the sum of a pair of adjoint representations of R_n.

10. The characters of those irreducible representations of R_{2k} which appear in the analysis of the representation of R_{2k} which is induced by the irreducible representation $\Gamma_{(\lambda)}, \lambda_k > 0$, of R'_{2k}.

We have seen that the irreducible representation $\Gamma_{(\lambda)}$ of R', $n = 2k$, $\lambda_k > 0$, induces a representation of R which is the sum of two adjoint irreducible representations of R. The sum of the characters of this pair of adjoint representations of R is $\{\lambda\}'$ and our present task is the evaluation of the individual characters of each member of the pair of adjoint representations. Preliminary to this we shall find it convenient to transform the expression $\{\lambda\}'$ which furnishes the characters of the irreducible representation $\Gamma_{(\lambda)}$ of R'. We have seen, pp. 243-4, that when $n = 2k$ is even

$$2^{k(k-1)/2}\Delta(t)\Delta(\cos\theta)\prod_{\substack{1\\p<q}}^{k}(1 - t_p t_q) \div f_1 f_2 \cdots f_k$$

is equivalent to the k-th order determinant of which the element in the p-th row and j-th column is $(1 - 2\cos\theta_j t_p + t_p^2)^{-1}$. On multiplying through by $\prod_{p=1}^{k}(1 - t_p^2)$ we see that

$$2^{k(k-1)/2}\Delta(t)\Delta(\cos\theta)\prod_{\substack{1\\p\leq q}}^{k}(1 - t_p t_q) \div f_1 \cdots f_k$$

is equivalent to the k-th order determinant of which the element in the p-th row and j-th column is

$$\frac{1 - t_p^2}{1 - 2\cos\theta_j t_p + t_p^2} = 1 + 2\sum_{q_j=1}^{\infty}\cos q_j\theta_j t_p^{q_j}$$

(p. 245). We denote the coefficients of this infinite series by $c_{q_j}(\theta_j)$ so that $c_0(\theta_j) = 1$, $c_q(\theta_j) = 2\cos q\theta_j$, $q = 1, 2, \cdots$; then our determinant is the sum over all sets of numbers $l_1 > l_2 > \cdots > l_k \geq 0$ of the products

$$c(l)A(l_1, \cdots, l_k)$$

where $c(l)$ is the determinant of order k of which the element in the p-th row and j-th column is $c_{l_j}(\theta_p)$:

$$(9.74) \qquad c(l) = \begin{vmatrix} c_{l_1}(\theta_1) & c_{l_2}(\theta_1) & \cdots & c_{l_k}(\theta_1) \\ \cdot & & \cdots & \cdot \\ \cdot & & \cdots & \cdot \\ c_{l_1}(\theta_k) & \cdot & \cdots & c_{l_k}(\theta_k) \end{vmatrix}.$$

On dividing our equation through by $\Delta(\boldsymbol{t})$ we have

$$2^{k(k-1)/2}\Delta(\cos\theta)\prod_{\substack{p\leq q\\1}}^{k}(1 - t_p t_q) \div f_1 f_2 \cdots f_k = \sum_{(\lambda)} c(l)\{\lambda\}(\boldsymbol{t})$$

and a comparison of this with (9.40) yields, owing to the homogeneous nature of the functions $\{\lambda\}(\boldsymbol{t})$ and the linear independence of the simple characteristics of the symmetric group on m letters,

$$(9.75) \quad \{\lambda\}' = \frac{c(l)}{2^{k(k-1)/2}\Delta(\cos\theta)} = \frac{c(l)}{\Delta(c_1)} = \frac{c(l)}{c(k-1, k-2, \cdots, 1, 0)}$$

(for $c_1(\theta_j) = 2\cos\theta_j = e^{i\theta_j} + e^{-i\theta_j}$ so that the Vandermonde determinant of which the element in the p-th row and j-th column is $c_1{}^p(\theta_j)$, $p = 0, 1, \cdots, k-1$, is the same as the determinant of which the element in the p-th row and j-th column is $c_p(\theta_j) = 2\cos p\theta_j$). Hence $\{\lambda\}'$ is the quotient of a determinant of which the element in the p-th row and j-th column is $c_{l_p}(\theta_j) = 2\cos l_p\theta_j$ by the determinant of which the element in the p-th row and j-th column is $c_p(\theta_j) = 2\cos p\theta_j$ (it being understood that when l_p or p is zero the factor 2 is missing). We now proceed to evaluate the quotient $s(l) \div c(k-1, \cdots, 1, 0)$ where $l_1 > l_2 > \cdots > l_k > 0$, $s_{l_j}(\theta_p) = 2i\sin l_j\theta_p$ and $s(l)$ is the determinant of order k which the element in the p-th row and j-th column is $s_{l_j}(\theta_p)$:

$$(9.76) \qquad s(l) = \begin{vmatrix} s_{l_1}(\theta_1) & \cdots & s_{l_k}(\theta_1) \\ \cdot & & \cdot \\ \cdot & & \cdot \\ s_{l_1}(\theta_k) & \cdots & s_{l_k}(\theta_k) \end{vmatrix}.$$

It is clear that $s(l)$ is divisible by $c(k-1, \cdots, 1, 0)$ the quotient being a symmetric polynomial in the variables $e^{\pm i\theta_j}$; for

$$c(k-1,\cdots,1,0)=\prod_{\substack{p<q\\1}}^{k}(e^{i\theta_p}+e^{-i\theta_p}-e^{-i\theta_q}-e^{-i\theta_q})$$

$$=\prod_{\substack{p<q\\1}}^{k}(e^{i\theta_p}-e^{i\theta_q})(1-e^{-i(\theta_p+\theta_q)})$$

and $s(l)$ is a polynomial in $e^{\pm i\theta_j}$ which vanishes when $\theta_p=\pm\theta_q$. If we denote the quotient $s(l)\div c(k-1,\cdots,1,0)$ by $\{\lambda\}''$, where $\lambda_k=l_k>0$, the combinations $\frac{1}{2}[\{\lambda\}'\pm\{\lambda\}'']$ are linear combinations with integral coefficients of simple characters of R; for they are linear combinations with integral coefficients of expressions $\sigma_{(m)}=\Sigma e^{i(m_1\theta_1+\cdots+m_k\theta_k)}$ the summation being over all those permutations and *even* numbers of changes of sign of $(\theta_1,\cdots,\theta_k)$ which actually change the term $e^{i(m_1\theta_1+\cdots+m_k\theta_k)}$. (Note the difference between the argument here and the corresponding argument on p. 266, there $\chi(X)$ was an even function of the angles $(\theta_1,\cdots,\theta_k)$ whilst here it is affected when an odd number of these angles are changed in sign, $\{\lambda\}''$ being an odd function of $(\theta_1,\cdots,\theta_k)$). In arranging our dictionary order of the sets $(m_1,\cdots,m_k)$ we have to allow for the fact that the last number m_k may be negative but we set $m_1\geq m_2\geq\cdots\geq m_{k-1}\geq|m_k|$. The leading member of $\{\lambda\}'$ is $e^{i(\lambda_1\theta_1+\cdots+\lambda_k\theta_k)}$, by (9.75), and when $\lambda_k>0$, $\{\lambda\}'$ splits into two simple characters; since $\{\lambda\}'$ contains $e^{i(\lambda_1\theta_1+\cdots+\lambda_{k-1}\theta_{k-1}-\lambda_k\theta_k)}$, being an even function of all the θ's, we see that one of the simple characters has $e^{i(\lambda_1\theta_1+\cdots+\lambda_k\theta_k)}$ as its leading term and that the other has $e^{i(\lambda_1\theta_1+\cdots+\lambda_{k-1}\theta_{k-1}-\lambda_k\theta_k)}$ as its leading term. Thus to each set of k numbers $m_1\geq m_2\geq\cdots\geq m_{k-1}\geq|m_k|$ belongs a unique simple character with the leader $\sigma_{(m)}=\Sigma e^{i(m_1\theta_1+\cdots+m_k\theta_k)}$ and this implies, by a recursive method, that each $\sigma_{(m)}$ is a linear combination of simple characteristics.

It is clear that the quantities $\frac{1}{2}[\{\lambda\}'\pm\{\lambda\}'']$ are actually simple characters since they are, respectively, the sums $\Sigma\, e^{i(\lambda_1\theta_1+\cdots+\lambda_k\theta_k)}$ and $\Sigma\, e^{i(\lambda_1\theta_1+\cdots-\lambda_k\theta_k)}$. It is, indeed, easy to verify their simplicity by the methods already given. We have seen, p. 245, that

$$(1-2\cos\theta_j t_p+t_p^2)^{-1}=1+2\sum_{1}^{\infty}(\cos q\theta_j+\cos(q-2)\theta_j+\cdots)t_p^q$$

and the coefficient of t_p^q is readily shown, on multiplying it by $\sin\theta_j$, to be $\sin(q+1)\theta_j\div\sin\theta_j=s_{q+1}(\theta_j)\div s_1(\theta_j)$. In other words the coefficient of t_p^q in the development of

$$\frac{t_p s_1(\theta_j)}{1-2\cos\theta_j t_p+t_p^2}$$

is $s_q(\theta_j)$ and it follows by the argument of pp. 288-9 that

$$2^{k(k-1)/2}\Delta(\boldsymbol{t})\Delta(\cos\theta)s_1(\theta_1)\cdots s_1(\theta_k)t_1\cdots t_k\prod_{\substack{p<q\\1}}^{k}(1-t_pt_q)\div f_1\cdots f_k$$

is the sum over all $l_1 > l_2 > \cdots > l_k$ for which $l_k > 0$ of the products $s(l)A(l_1,\cdots,l_k)$. On dividing out by $\Delta(\boldsymbol{t})$ we obtain

$$(9.77)\qquad 2^{k(k-1)/2}\Delta(\cos\theta)s_1(\theta_1)\cdots s_1(\theta_k)t_1\cdots t_k\prod_{\substack{p<q\\1}}^{k}(1-t_pt_q)$$
$$\div f_1\cdots f_k = \Sigma' s(l)\{\lambda\}(\boldsymbol{t})$$

the prime attached to the sign of summation indicating $\lambda_k > 0$.

But we may proceed as on p. 255. Thus

$$f_p^{-1} = \sum_0^{\infty} p_{j_p}t_p^{j_p};\qquad p = 1,\cdots,k$$

so that

$$(f_1\cdots f_k)^{-1} = \sum_{(j)=0}^{\infty} p_{j_1}\cdots p_{j_k}t_1^{j_1}\cdots t_k^{j_k}.$$

On multiplication by $\Delta_k(\boldsymbol{t})L_k(\boldsymbol{t})t_1\cdots t_k$ we obtain on the right a sum of products of determinants $A(l_1,\cdots,l_k)$, $l_k > 0$, by determinants $\{\lambda\}'''$

$$(9.78)\qquad \{\lambda\}''' = \begin{vmatrix} p_{\lambda_1-1}, p_{\lambda_1}+p_{\lambda_1-2},\cdots, p_{\lambda_1+k-2}+p_{\lambda_1-k} \\ \cdot \qquad\qquad\qquad \cdot \\ \cdot \qquad\qquad\qquad \cdot \\ \cdot \qquad\qquad\qquad \cdot \\ p_{\lambda_k-k}, \qquad\qquad \cdots, p_{\lambda_k-1}+p_{\lambda_k-2k+1} \end{vmatrix}.$$

On division through by $\Delta_k(\boldsymbol{t})$ we find

$$(9.79)\qquad \frac{t_1\cdots t_k\prod_{\substack{p<q\\1}}^{k}(1-t_pt_q)}{f_1\cdots f_k} = \Sigma'\{\lambda\}'''\{\lambda\}(\boldsymbol{t})$$

and comparison of this with (9.77) yields

$$(9.80)\qquad \{\lambda\}'' = \frac{s(l)}{c(k-1,\cdots,1,0)} = s_1(\theta_1)\cdots s_1(\theta_k)\{\lambda\}'''$$
$$= (2i)^k \sin\theta_1\cdots\sin\theta_k\{\lambda\}'''.$$

It is clear from (9.78) that $\{1^k\}''' = 1$, since all the elements below the main diagonal vanish and all the diagonal elements are unity. Hence $\{1^k\}'' = (2i)^k\sin\theta_1\cdots\sin\theta_k$ and we shall denote this quantity by $i^k\delta$

$$(9.81)\qquad \{1^k\}'' = s_1(\theta_1)\cdots s_1(\theta_k) = (2i)^k\sin\theta_1\cdots\sin\theta_k = i^k\delta$$
$$\delta = 2^k\sin\theta_1\cdots\sin\theta_k.$$

On multiplication by δ (9.79) takes the form

$$t_1 \cdots t_k \prod_{\substack{p<q \\ 1}}^{k} (1-t_p t_q) \frac{\delta}{f_1 \cdots f_k} = (-i)^k \Sigma' \{\lambda\}'' \{\lambda\} (\boldsymbol{t});$$

on replacing $(t_1, \cdots, t_k)$ by a second set of variables $(u_1, \cdots, u_k)$, multiplication and integration over R we obtain

$$\begin{aligned}(9.82) \quad & t_1 \cdots t_k u_1 \cdots u_k \prod_{\substack{p<q \\ 1}}^{k} (1-t_p t_q) \prod_{\substack{p<q \\ 1}}^{k} (1-u_p u_q) \\ & \times \frac{1}{V} \int_R \frac{\delta^2 d\tau}{f_1 \cdots f_{2k}} = \Sigma' \{\lambda\} (\boldsymbol{t}) \{\mu\} \{\boldsymbol{u}\} \frac{1}{V} \int_R \{\lambda\}'' \overline{\{\mu\}''} d\tau\end{aligned}$$

where the bar over $\{\mu\}''$ denotes, as always, the conjugate complex. The integral $\frac{1}{V} \int_R \frac{\delta^2 d\tau}{f_1 \cdots f_{2k}}$ has already, to all intents and purposes, been calculated. Thus from (9.32) we obtain, on replacing $k-1$ by k and observing that there $f_p = (1-t_p^2) h_p$

$$\frac{1}{2^{2k}} \int_R \frac{\delta^2 d\tau}{f_1 \cdots f_k} = \frac{(2\pi)^k k!}{2^{k^2}} \{\prod_{\substack{p<q \\ 1}}^{k} (1-t_p t_q)\}^{-1}.$$

On using the expression (9.21) for V we find

$$\frac{1}{V} \int_R \frac{\delta^2 d\tau}{f_1 \cdots f_k} = 2 \{\prod_{\substack{p<q \\ 1}}^{k} (1-t_p t_q)\}^{-1}.$$

From this we proceed as before to $\frac{1}{V} \int_R \frac{\delta^2 d\tau}{f_1 \cdots f_j}$, $j = k+1, k+2, \cdots, 2k$. Thus on multiplying (9.28), with g_p replaced by f_p, by $\delta^2 \div V(f_1 \cdots f_{k+1})$ and integrating the resulting equation over R we get on the right a series of terms of which the first is

$$(-1)^k t_2 \cdots t_{k+1} \Delta_k^1 (\boldsymbol{t}) \times 2(-1)^k$$

and so, as on p. 250, we obtain

$$\frac{1}{V} \int_R \frac{\delta^2 d\tau}{f_1 \cdots f_{k+1}} = 2 \{\prod_{\substack{p<q \\ 1}}^{k+1} (1-t_p t_q)\}^{-1}.$$

Proceeding in this way we obtain finally

$$(9.83) \qquad \frac{1}{V} \int_R \frac{\delta^2 d\tau}{f_1 \cdots f_{2k}} = 2 \{\prod_{\substack{p<q \\ 1}}^{2k} (1-t_p t_q)\}^{-1}.$$

The difference between (9.83) and the corresponding formula (9.30) should be noted; the factor $\prod_{p=1}^{2k}(1-t_p^2)$ is missing from the denominator on the right of (9.83), simply because the f_p of p. 252 $=(1-t_p^2)h_p$. Further the factor $(1+t_1\cdots t_n)$ of (9.30) is missing from (9.83) simply because the factors $(1-t_p^2)$ of p. 251 are here missing.

On substituting (9.83) in (9.82) we obtain

$$2\frac{t_1\cdots t_k u_1\cdots u_k}{\Pi(1-t_pu_q)}=\Sigma'\{\lambda\}(\boldsymbol{t})\mu(\boldsymbol{u})\frac{1}{V}\int_R\{\lambda\}''\overline{\{\mu\}''}d\tau.$$

The left hand side $=2\Sigma'\{\lambda\}(\boldsymbol{t})\{\lambda\}(\boldsymbol{u})$ (p. 264) and so

$$\frac{1}{V}\int_R[|\{\lambda\}''|]^2d\tau=2;\quad \lambda_k>0$$

$$\frac{1}{V}\int_R\{\lambda\}''\overline{\{\mu\}''}d\tau=0;\quad (\lambda)\neq(\mu).$$

Furthermore the integral $\frac{1}{V}\int_R\{\lambda\}'\overline{\{\lambda\}''}d\tau=0$ since $\{\lambda\}''$ is an *odd* periodic function of $(\theta_1,\cdots,\theta_k)$, with period 2π, and $\{\lambda\}'$ is an *even* periodic function of $(\theta_1,\cdots,\theta_k)$, with period 2π (the periodicity allowing us to replace the intervals $(0,2\pi)$ of integration by the intervals $(-\pi,\pi)$). Hence, since $\frac{1}{V}\int_R[\{\lambda\}']^2d\tau=2$

$$\frac{1}{V}\int_R[\tfrac{1}{2}(|\{\lambda\}'\pm\{\lambda\}''|)]^2d\tau=1,$$

showing that $\frac{1}{2}[\{\lambda\}'\pm\{\lambda\}'']$ are *simple* characters (the oddness of $\{\lambda\}''$ showing that they have the value of $\frac{1}{2}\{\lambda\}'$ at the unit element). Their sum is $\{\lambda\}'$ so that they are the characters of the two irreducible representations of R which are contained in the reducible representation of R which is induced by the irreducible representation $\Gamma_{(\lambda)}$ of R', $\lambda_k>0$.

The quantity $\delta=2^k\sin\theta_1\cdots\sin\theta_k$ which appears (9.80) as a factor of $\{\lambda\}''$ may be conveniently expressed as follows. We have

$$f(t)=\prod_{p=1}^{n}(1-z_pt)=\prod_{p=1}^{k}(1-2\cos\theta_pt+t^2)$$

so that

$$f(1)=\prod_{p=1}^{k}2(1-\cos\theta);\quad f(-1)=\prod_{p=1}^{k}2(1+\cos\theta).$$

Hence $f(1)f(-1)=\prod_{p=1}^{k}(2\sin\theta_k)^2=\delta^2$. Since $f(1)=\det(E_n-X)$, $f(-1)=\det(E_n+X)=\det(E_n+X')$

(9.84) $$\delta^2 = \det (E_n - X)(E_n + X') = \det (X' - X), \text{ since } XX' = E_n.$$

The determinant of the skew symmetric matrix $X' - X$, of even degree, is a perfect square of a polynomial in the elements of X (known as a Pfaffian) and δ is this polynomial.

11. Alternative form for the simple characters $\{\lambda\}'$ of the real orthogonal group of odd dimension $n = 2k + 1$.

It is easy to obtain, when n is odd, an expression for $\{\lambda\}'$ analogous to (9.75) (which is valid when $n = 2k$ is even). Exactly as on p. 288 we see that

$$2^{k(k-1)/2}\Delta(t)\Delta(\cos\theta)\prod_{\substack{p\leq q\\1}}^{k}(1 - t_p t_q) \div g_1 \cdots g_k$$

is equivalent to the k-th order determinant of which the element in the p-th row and j-th column is $(1 - t_p^2)/(1 - 2\cos\theta_j t_p + t_p^2)$. Since $g_p = f_p \div (1 - t_p)$ (p. 243) the statement just made is equivalent to the following:

$$2^{k(k-1)/2}\Delta(t)\Delta(\cos\theta)\prod_{\substack{p\leq q\\1}}^{k}(1 - t_p t_q) \div f_1 \cdots f_k$$

is equivalent to the k-th order determinant of which the element in the p-th row and j-th column is $(1 + t_p) \div (1 - 2\cos\theta_j t_p + t_p^2)$. Since (p. 245)

$$(1 - 2\cos\theta t_p + t_p^2)^{-1} = 1 + 2\sum_{1}^{\infty} c'_q t_p^q$$

where $c'_q = \cos q\theta + \cos (q-2)\theta + \cdots$ (the summation ending in $\frac{1}{2}$ if q is even) the element in the p-th row and j-th column of our determinant is a power series in t_p of which the coefficient of t_p^q is

$$2\{c'_q(\theta_j) + c'_{q-1}(\theta_j)\} = 2\{\cos q\theta_j + \cos (q-1)\theta_j + \cdots\} = \sin (q + \tfrac{1}{2})\theta_j \div \sin \tfrac{1}{2}\theta_j.$$

Hence, by the same argument as on pp. 290-1, $\{\lambda\}'$ is obtained from the formula (9.80) for $\{\lambda\}''$ by increasing each of the numbers $(l_1, \cdots, l_k)$ by $\frac{1}{2}$ and dividing by $(2i)^k \sin\theta_1/2 \cdots \sin\theta_k/2$. Since $2\sin\theta/2\cos p\theta = \sin (p + \frac{1}{2})\theta - \sin (p - \frac{1}{2})\theta$ the product

$$2^k \sin\theta_1/2 \cdots \sin\theta_k/2 \begin{vmatrix} \cos(k-1)\theta_1 & \cdots & \cos(k-1)\theta_k \\ \cdot & & \cdot \\ \cdot & & \cdot \\ 1 & \cdots & 1 \end{vmatrix}$$

$$= \begin{vmatrix} \sin(k-\frac{1}{2})\theta_1 & \cdots & \sin(k-\frac{1}{2})\theta_k \\ \cdot & & \cdot \\ \cdot & & \cdot \\ \sin\theta_1/2 & \cdots & \sin\theta_k/2 \end{vmatrix}$$

and so

$$(2i)^k \sin\theta_1/2 \cdots \sin\theta_k/2 \; c(k-1, k-2, \cdots, 1, 0) = s(k-\tfrac{1}{2}, \cdots, \tfrac{3}{2}, \tfrac{1}{2}).$$

Hence

$$(9.85) \qquad \{\lambda\}' = \frac{s(l_1+\frac{1}{2}, \cdots, l_k+\frac{1}{2})}{s(k-\frac{1}{2}, \cdots, \frac{1}{2})}.$$

Since $2^{k(k-1)/2}\Delta(\cos\theta) = c(k-1, \cdots, 1, 0)$ (see (9.75)) the normalised element of volume (9.23) of the $n = 2k$ dimensional rotation group may be written in the form

$$(9.86) \quad d\tau = [\{c(k-1, \cdots, 1, 0)\}^2 \div (2\pi)^k k!\, 2^{k-1}]\, d(\theta_1, \cdots, \theta_k).$$

Similarly the normalised element of volume (9.26) of the $n = 2k+1$ dimensional rotation group may be written in the form

$$(9.87) \quad d\tau = [2^k \sin^2\frac{\theta_1}{2} \cdots \sin^2\frac{\theta_k}{2} \{c(k-1, \cdots, 1, 0)\}^2 \div (2\pi)^k k!]\, d(\theta_1, \cdots, \theta_k)$$
$$= [\,| s(k-\tfrac{1}{2}, \cdots, \tfrac{3}{2}, \tfrac{1}{2})|^2 \div (2\pi)^k k!\, 2^k]\, d(\theta_1, \cdots, \theta_k).$$

CHAPTER TEN

SPIN REPRESENTATIONS OF THE ROTATION GROUP

In this chapter we shall show that there exist two-valued (= spin) representations of the n-dimensional rotation group and shall determine the characters of the irreducible representations of the two-sheeted "covering group" of the rotation group.

1. The two-valued representations of the three-dimensional rotation group.

The general 2×2 Hermitian matrix whose trace is zero is of the form

$$P(x) = \begin{pmatrix} x^3 & x^1 + ix^2 \\ x^1 - ix^2 & -x^3 \end{pmatrix}$$

where (x^1, x^2, x^3) are arbitrary real numbers. On setting

$$(10.1) \qquad P_1 = \begin{pmatrix} 0 & 1 \\ 1 & 0 \end{pmatrix}; \quad P_2 = \begin{pmatrix} 0 & i \\ -i & 0 \end{pmatrix}; \quad P_3 = \begin{pmatrix} 1 & 0 \\ 0 & -1 \end{pmatrix}$$

we have

$$P(x) = x^1 P_1 + x^2 P_2 + x^3 P_3.$$

If $P(x)$ is subjected to an arbitrary unitary transformation $P(x) \to Q = UPU^*$, Q is also Hermitian with trace zero so that

$$Q = P(y) = y^1 P_1 + y^2 P_2 + y^3 P_3.$$

Since $\det Q = \det P(x)$ the real linear transformation $x \to y$ induced by $P(x) \to Q = P(y)$ is such that $(x^1)^2 + (x^2)^2 + (x^3)^2 = (y^1)^2 + (y^2)^2 + (y^3)^2$; in other words $y = Ox$ where O is a real orthogonal 3×3 matrix. If V is any second unitary 2×2 matrix and if $Q \to R = VQV^*$ induces the orthogonal transformation $y \to z = O(V)y = O(V)O(U)x$ we see that $P \to R = VQV^* = (VU)P(VU)^*$ induces the orthogonal transformation $O(V)O(U)$; in other words $O(VU) = O(V)O(U)$. Since $O(E_2) = E_3$ it follows that the collection of 3×3 real orthogonal matrices $O(U)$, obtained by letting U wander over the 2×2 unitary group, constitutes a representation of this group. It is clear that the representation is not faithful: the same orthogonal matrix O will correspond to many elements U of the 2×2 unitary group. In fact if $V = mU$ where m is a complex number (necessarily of unit modulus since $V^*V = E_2$ forces $m\bar{m} = 1$) $VPV^* = UPU^*$ so that $O(V) = O(U)$. We may, accordingly, restrict ourselves to unimodular unitary 2×2 matrices U, i.e. to matrices U for which

$\det U = 1$ but even with this restriction the representation of the 2×2 unimodular unitary group $\{U\}$ furnished by the collection of real 3×3 orthogonal matrices $\{O(U)\}$ is not faithful. In fact the necessary and sufficient condition that $O(U) = O(V)$ is that $VPV^* = UPU^*$, every P, i. e. that $WP = PW$, every P, where $W = U^*V$. On setting $P = P_3$ we see that W must be diagonal; and, on setting $P = P_1$, that it must be scalar. Since W is unimodular it must be $\pm E_2$ so that $V = \pm U$; and this necessary condition is evidently sufficient. Hence $\{O(U)\}$ is a representation of the 2×2 unimodular unitary group having the property that $O(U) = O(V)$ is equivalent to (i. e. implies and is implied by) $V = \pm U$.

It is easy to see that the collection of matrices $\{O(U)\}$ is the entire 3-dimensional rotation group. To prove this let us denote by $R_{p,q}(\theta)$, $p < q$, the "plane rotation" $x \to x'$:

$$\begin{aligned} x'_p &= \cos\theta\, x_p + \sin\theta\, x_q \\ x'_q &= -\sin\theta\, x_p + \cos\theta\, x_q \\ x'_r &= x_r \qquad\qquad\qquad r \neq p;\ r \neq q, \end{aligned}$$

so that $R_{p,q}(-\theta) = \{R_{p,q}(\theta)\}^{-1}$. If $A = (a_p{}^q)$ is any element of the 3-dimensional rotation group we can determine α so that the element $B = AR_{2,3}(\alpha)$ of the 3-dimensional rotation group has $b_3{}^1 = 0$; in fact we have merely to set $a_2{}^1 \sin\alpha + a_3{}^1 \cos\alpha = 0$. Similarly we can determine β so that $C = BT_{1,2}(\beta) = AR_{2,3}(\alpha)T_{1,2}(\beta)$ has $c_2{}^1 = 0$. Since $c_3{}^1 = b_3{}^1 = 0$ it follows, since C is an element of the 3-dimensional rotation group, that $(c_1{}^1)^2 = 1$, i. e. $c_1{}^1 = \pm 1$. If $c_1{}^1 = -1$ we can make it $+1$ by changing β into $\beta + \pi$ and it follows that $C = T_{2,3}(\psi)$ is a plane rotation. Hence $A = T_{2,3}(\psi)T_{1,2}(-\beta)R_{2,3}(-\alpha)$; on writing $\alpha = -\phi$, $\beta = -\theta$ we have

$$A = T_{2,3}(\psi)T_{1,2}(\theta)T_{2,3}(\phi) \tag{10.2}$$

which is the classical factorisation (due to Euler) of any three-dimensional rotation into a product of three-plane rotations. Now when U is diagonal:

$$U = \begin{pmatrix} e^{-i\theta} & 0 \\ 0 & e^{i\theta} \end{pmatrix}$$

an easy calculation yields

$$UP_1U^* = \begin{pmatrix} 0 & e^{-2i\theta} \\ e^{2i\theta} & 0 \end{pmatrix} = \cos 2\theta\, P_1 - \sin 2\theta\, P_2$$

$$UP_2U^* = \begin{pmatrix} 0 & ie^{-2i\theta} \\ -ie^{2i\theta} & 0 \end{pmatrix} = \sin 2\theta\, P_1 + \cos 2\theta\, P_2$$

$$UP_3U^* = \begin{pmatrix} 1 & 0 \\ 0 & -1 \end{pmatrix} = P_3.$$

Hence

$$\begin{aligned} y^1 &= \cos 2\theta\, x^1 + \sin 2\theta\, x^2 \\ y^2 &= -\sin 2\theta\, x^1 + \cos 2\theta\, x^2 \\ y^3 &= \qquad\qquad\qquad\qquad x^3 \end{aligned}$$

so that $O(U) = T_{1,2}(2\theta)$. Similarly if

$$V = \begin{pmatrix} \cos\theta & -i\sin\theta \\ -i\sin\theta & \cos\theta \end{pmatrix}$$

we find $O(V) = T_{2,3}(2\theta)$. Hence the general matrix

$$A = T_{2,3}(\psi)T_{1,2}(\theta)T_{2,3}(\phi)$$

of the 3-dimensional rotation group appears in the collection $O(U)$; in fact $A = O(W)$ where

$$(10.3) \quad W = V\left(\frac{\psi}{2}\right)U\left(\frac{\theta}{2}\right)V\left(\frac{\phi}{2}\right)$$

$$= \begin{pmatrix} \cos\frac{\psi}{2} & -i\sin\frac{\psi}{2} \\ -i\sin\frac{\psi}{2} & \cos\frac{\psi}{2} \end{pmatrix} \begin{pmatrix} e^{-i\theta/2} & 0 \\ 0 & e^{i\theta/2} \end{pmatrix} \begin{pmatrix} \cos\frac{\phi}{2} & -i\sin\frac{\phi}{2} \\ -i\sin\frac{\phi}{2} & \cos\frac{\phi}{2} \end{pmatrix}.$$

The matrix A is, conversely, a *proper* real orthogonal matrix; the easiest way to see this being the following. The 2×2 Hermitian matrix

$$H = P(x) + x^4E_2 = x^1P_1 + x^2P_2 + x^3P_3 + x^4E_2 = \begin{pmatrix} x^4 + x^3 & x^1 + ix^2 \\ x^1 - ix^2 & x^4 - x^3 \end{pmatrix}$$

(x^4 real) induces, when subjected to the transformation

$$H \to K = UHU^*$$

a linear transformation $x \to y$ under which the determinant and trace of H remain unaltered. This transformation is accordingly a real 4-dimensional orthogonal transformation for which $y^4 = x^4$. Its determinant is, therefore, the same as that of $O(U)$. But the determinant of the linear transformation $x \to y$ is the same as that of the similar transformation $h \to k$ where $h^1 = h_1{}^1, h^2 = h_1{}^2, h^3 = h_2{}^1, h^4 = h_2{}^2$ and this linear transformation has $U \times \bar{U}$ as its matrix so that its determinant is 1 (it being evident from the relation $U \times \bar{U} = (U \times E_2)(E_2 \times \bar{U})$ that $\det(U \times \bar{U}) = (\det U \det \bar{U})^2$).

We have, accordingly, proved that the three-dimensional rotation group furnishes a representation $U \to O(U)$ of the 2×2 unimodular unitary group with the property $O(V) = O(U)$ when, and only when $V = \pm U$. Conversely we may regard the 2×2 unimodular unitary group as a representation $O(U) \to \pm U$ of the 3-dimensional rotation group; but then the representation is *two-valued:* to a given element $O(U)$ of the three-dimensional rotation group corresponds *either* U *or* $-U$. If we consider the closed continuum of three dimensional rotations found by holding ϕ, ψ fixed in (10. 2) and allowing θ to vary from 0 to 2π the corresponding continuum of matrices W, given by (10. 3), is not closed since $U(\theta/2)$ begins at E_2 and ends at $-E_2$. In order therefore that we may properly speak of the 2×2 unimodular unitary group as furnishing a representation of the rotation group we must introduce a refinement of definition in accordance with which the element $A = T_{2,3}(\psi)T_{1,2}(\theta)T_{2,3}(\phi)$ is distinguishable from the element obtained from this by holding ϕ and ψ fixed and allowing θ to vary through 2π whilst it is indistinguishable from the element obtained by holding ϕ and ψ fixed and allowing θ to vary through 4π. The elements of the group of which the 2×2 unimodular group is a representation are not, then, merely the matrices of the three-dimensional rotation group but these matrices together with the manner by which they are reached, starting from some convenient element (say the unit element) of the rotation group. We term this new group the "covering group" of the rotation group but we postpone its precise definition till we have considered the two-valued representations of the n-dimensional rotation group (= group of all real orthogonal $n \times n$ matrices of determinant unity). The two-valued representations are known as spin representations; and vectors in the carrier space of a two-valued representation are known as *spinors.* In particular the vectors in the carrier space of the representation furnished by the unimodular two-dimensional unitary group $\{U\}$ are known as *two-component spinors.*

2. Two-valued representations of the *n*-dimensional rotation group.

The two cases n even $(=2k)$ and n odd $(=2k+1)$ must be treated differently.

Case 1. $n = 2k$.

We consider the four 2×2 matrices

$$(10.4)\quad P_1 = \begin{pmatrix} 0 & 1 \\ 1 & 0 \end{pmatrix};\ P_2 = \begin{pmatrix} 0 & i \\ -i & 0 \end{pmatrix};\ P_3 = \begin{pmatrix} 1 & 0 \\ 0 & -1 \end{pmatrix};\ P_4 = E_2$$

of the previous section. It is at once clear that

$$P_1^2 = P_2^2 = P_3^2 = P_4^2 = E_2;$$
$$P_2P_3 = -P_3P_2;\ P_3P_1 = -P_1P_3;\ P_1P_2 = -P_2P_1;\ iP_1P_2P_3 = E_2.$$

Any 2×2 matrix $\begin{pmatrix} a_1^1 & a_2^1 \\ a_1^2 & a_2^2 \end{pmatrix}$ may be written as a linear combination

$c^1P_1 + c^2P_2 + c^3P_3 + c^4P_4$ of the matrices P_1, P_2, P_3, P_4 (it being merely necessary to set $c^1 = \frac{1}{2}(a_1{}^2 + a_2{}^1)$; $c^2 = \frac{i}{2}(a_1{}^2 - a_2{}^1)$; $c^3 = \frac{1}{2}(a_1{}^1 + a_2{}^2)$; $c^4 = \frac{1}{2}(a_1{}^1 - a_2{}^2)$) and we express this fact by the statement that the four matrices (P_1, P_2, P_3, P_4) constitute a basis for the full matrix algebra of dimension 2 and order 4. We now introduce $n = 2k$ matrices of dimension 2^k each of which is the Kronecker product of k 2×2 matrices selected from the set (P_1, P_2, P_3, P_4):

$$
\begin{aligned}
M_1 &= P_1 \times P_4 \times \cdots \times P_4 \times P_4 \times P_4 \\
M_2 &= P_3 \times P_1 \times P_4 \times \cdots \times P_4 \times P_4 \\
M_3 &= P_3 \times P_3 \times P_1 \times P_4 \times \cdots \times P_4 \\
&\cdots\cdots \\
M_k &= P_3 \times P_3 \times \cdots \qquad \times P_3 \times P_1 \\
&\cdots\cdots \\
M_{k+1} &= P_2 \times P_4 \times \cdots \qquad \times P_4 \\
M_{k+2} &= P_3 \times P_2 \times P_4 \times \cdots \times P_4 \\
&\cdots \\
M_{2k} &= P_3 \times P_3 \times \cdots \times P_3 \times P_2.
\end{aligned} \tag{10.5}
$$

Since each $P_j{}^2 = E_2$ and since

$$(A_1 \times A_2 \times \cdots \times A_k)(B_1 \times B_2 \times \cdots \times B_k) = A_1B_1 \times A_2B_2 \times \cdots \times A_kB_k$$

it follows that $M_j{}^2 = E_2 \times \cdots \times E_2 = E_{2^k}$, $j = 1, 2, \cdots, 2k$. Furthermore $M_pM_q = -M_qM_p$; $p < q = 1, 2, \cdots, 2k$. E. g.

$$
\begin{aligned}
M_1M_3 &= P_1P_3 \times P_3 \times P_1 \times P_4 \times \cdots \times P_4 \quad (\text{since } P_4 = E_2) \\
M_3M_1 &= P_3P_1 \times P_3 \times P_1 \times P_4 \times \cdots \times P_4.
\end{aligned}
$$

The collection of matrices $M_1{}^{\alpha_1}M_2{}^{\alpha_2} \cdots M_{2k}^{\alpha_{2k}}$, where each of the exponents $\alpha_1, \alpha_2, \cdots, \alpha_{2k}$ takes one of the two values 0, 1 consists of 2^{2k} matrices and these constitute a basis for the full matrix algebra of dimension 2^k. To prove this we first observe that since $iP_1P_2 = P_3$ the product

$$N_j \equiv iM_jM_{k+j} = E_2 \times E_2 \times \cdots \times P_3 \times E_2 \times \cdots \times E_2, \qquad j = 1, 2, \cdots, k$$

(the factor P_3 occurring in the j-th place). Hence, since

$$
\begin{aligned}
E_{2^k} &= E_2 \times E_2 \times \cdots \times E_2, \\
{}_jR_1{}^1 &\equiv \tfrac{1}{2}(E_{2^k} + N_j) = E_2 \times E_2 \times \cdots \times Q_1{}^1 \times E_2 \times \cdots \times E_2 \\
{}_jR_2{}^2 &\equiv \tfrac{1}{2}(E_{2^k} - N_j) = E_2 \times E_2 \times \cdots \times Q_2{}^2 \times E_2 \times \cdots \times E_2
\end{aligned}
$$

where $Q_p{}^q$ denotes the 2×2 matrix all of whose elements are zero save the element in the p-th row and q-th column which element is unity; nothing more being involved in these statements than the obvious relations

$$A \times (B + C) = (A \times B) + (A \times C);$$
$$(A + B) \times C = (A \times C) + (B \times C)$$

which imply

$$A \times (B + C) \times D = A \times B \times D + A \times C \times D.$$

Again it is clear from the definition of N_j that

$$N_1 N_2 \cdots N_j = P_3 \times P_3 \times \cdots \times P_3 \times E_2 \times \cdots \times E_2,$$

there being j factors P_3 and this implies the two relations

$$L_j \equiv N_1 \cdots N_{j-1} M_j = E_2 \times E_2 \times \cdots \times P_1 \times E_2 \times \cdots \times E_2$$
$$L_{k+j} \equiv N_1 \cdots N_{j-1} M_{k+j} = E_2 \times E_2 \times \cdots \times P_2 \times E_2 \times \cdots \times E_2,$$

the factors P_1, P_2 occurring in the j-th place $(j = 1, 2, \cdots, k)$. Hence, as before

$${}_jR_2{}^1 \equiv \tfrac{1}{2}(L_j + iL_{k+j}) = E_2 \times E_2 \times \cdots \times Q_2{}^1 \times E_2 \times \cdots \times E_2$$
$${}_jR_1{}^2 \equiv \tfrac{1}{2}(L_j - iL_{k+j}) = E_2 \times E_2 \times \cdots \times Q_1{}^2 \times E_2 \times \cdots \times E_2,$$

the factors $Q_2{}^1, Q_1{}^2$ again occurring in the j-th place. It is convenient to use a binary scale notation to indicate the rows and columns of our 2^k dimensional matrices; thus $a^{r_1 \cdots r_k}_{s_1 \cdots s_k}$ denotes the element in the $(r_1, \cdots, r_k)$ row and the $(s_1, \cdots, s_k)$ column where each of the labels r, s takes one or other of the two values 1, 2. The matrix $\prod_j {}_jR_{r_j}{}^{s_j} = Q_{r_1}{}^{s_1} \times Q_{r_2}{}^{s_2} \times \cdots \times Q_{r_k}{}^{s_k}$ and all elements of this are zero save the one in the $(r_1, r_2, \cdots, r_k)$ column and the $(s_1, s_2, \cdots, s_k)$ row which one is unity. Owing to the basic relations $M_j{}^2 = E_{2^k}$; $M_p M_q = -M_q M_p$ each L_j, L_{k+j} and hence each ${}_jR_{r_j}{}^{s_j}$ is a linear combination of the matrices $M_1{}^{a_1} \cdots M_{2k}^{a_{2k}}$ and hence $\prod_j {}_jR_{r_j}{}^{s_j}$ is such a linear combination of matrices of the type $M_1{}^{a_1} \cdots M_{2k}^{a_{2k}}$. The $2k$ matrices $M_1, \cdots, M_{2k}$ generate a group whose typical element is $\pm M_1{}^{a_1} \cdots M_{2k}^{a_{2k}}$ and we may express our result as follows:

The group generated by the matrices $(M_1, \cdots, M_{2k})$ *has the complete* 2^k *dimensional matrix algebra as its enveloping algebra*; the phrase enveloping algebra of a group of matrices meaning simply the collection of matrices obtained by forming all linear combinations of matrices of the group. If we have any representation of a group of matrices the enveloping algebra of the representation is termed a representation of the enveloping algebra of the group; it being understood that if $\Gamma = \{D(A)\}$ is the representation of the given matrix group $\{A\}$ then

$$D(\lambda A) = \lambda D(A);\ \lambda \text{ any complex number};$$
$$D(A + B) = D(A) + D(B).$$

If $\{A\}$ is a given matrix algebra of which M is any given fixed non-singular element the correspondence $A \to D(A) = M^{-1}AM$ defines a particularly simple representation of $\{A\}$ which is known as an inner automorphism (the word inner implying that the transforming matrix M itself belongs to $\{A\}$). There is a basic theorem which is essential for our immediate purpose and which runs as follows:

Every automorphism of the complete matrix algebra of a given dimension is an inner automorphism.

Thus if we can construct a second set of matrices $\tilde{M}_1, \cdots, \tilde{M}_{2k}$ of dimension 2^k satisfying the basic relations

$$\tilde{M}_j^2 = E_{2^k};\quad \tilde{M}_p\tilde{M}_q = -\tilde{M}_q\tilde{M}_p$$

the correspondence $M_j \to \tilde{M}_j$ furnishes an automorphism of the complete matrix 2^k-dimensional algebra. Hence this automorphism must be an *inner* automorphism; in other words there must exist a non-singular 2^k-dimensional matrix T which transforms M_j into $\tilde{M}_j$, every j:

$$\tilde{M}_j = T^{-1}M_jT; \qquad j = 1, 2, \cdots, 2k.$$

To prove that every automorphism of the complete matrix algebra of a given dimension, m say, is an inner automorphism we proceed as follows. Let A be any $m \times m$ matrix; then the columns of any $m \times m$ matrix X which satisfies $AX = \lambda X$ must be characteristic vectors of A associated with the characteristic number λ. If the given automorphism of our complete m-dimensional matrix algebra is indicated by $A \to \tilde{A}$ we have $\tilde{A}\tilde{X} = \lambda X$ so that λ is a characteristic constant of $\tilde{A}$. If, then, D is a diagonal $m \times m$ matrix with m distinct characteristic constants $(\lambda_1, \cdots, \lambda_m)$, D has $(\lambda_1, \cdots, \lambda_m)$ as characteristic constants and so $\tilde{D}$ is similar to D: $\tilde{D} = T^{-1}DT$. Hence the given automorphism $A \to \tilde{A}$ followed by the inner automorphism $\tilde{A} \to T\tilde{A}T^{-1}$ is an automorphism of the complete m-dimensional matrix algebra which leaves D invariant. We shall denote this automorphism by $A \to A^{\#}$. Denoting by $E_i{}^j$ the $m \times m$ matrix all of whose elements are zero save the element in the i-th row and j-th column, which is unity, we have

$$DE_i{}^j = \lambda_i E_i{}^j;\quad E_i{}^jD = \lambda_j E_i{}^j$$

and these imply, since $D^\# = D$,

$$D(E_i{}^j)^\# = \lambda_i(E_i{}^j)^\#; \quad (E_i{}^j)^\# D = \lambda_j(E_i{}^j)^\#.$$

The first of these two equations says that all elements of $(E_i{}^j)^\#$ save those in the i-th row, vanish whilst the second of the two equations says that all elements of $(E_i{}^j)^\#$, save those in the j-th column, vanish. Hence $(E_i{}^j)^\# = c_j{}^i E_i{}^j$. Since $(E_i{}^i)^2 = E_i{}^i$ we have $(E_i{}^{i\#})^2 = E_i{}^{i\#}$ so that $(c_i{}^i)^2 = c_i{}^i$. $c_i{}^i$ cannot be zero since $E_i{}^i$, and hence $(E_i{}^i)^\#$, has one characteristic number unity; hence $(E_i{}^i)^\#$ is not the zero matrix so that $c_i{}^i \neq 0$. This forces $c_i{}^i = 1$, $i = 1, 2, \cdots, m$ and then the obvious relation $E_j{}^i = E_j{}^1 E_1{}^i$ forces $c_i{}^j = c_1{}^j c_i{}^1$. This being valid when $j = i$ we have $c_1{}^i c_i{}^1 = 1$ so that $c_i{}^j = c_1{}^j \div c_1{}^i$. If then C is the diagonal matrix whose i-th diagonal element is $c_1{}^i$ $(E_i{}^j)^\# = C^{-1} E_i{}^j C$, every i, j. Since any matrix of the complete m-dimensional matrix algebra is a linear combination of the $E_i{}^j$ it follows that the automorphism $A \rightarrow A^\#$ is an inner automorphism and this implies that the original automorphism $A \rightarrow \tilde{A}$ is also an inner automorphism (since the product, or sequential performance, of two inner automorphisms is an inner automorphism).

Having proved our main theorem we have merely to observe that if O is any $2k \times 2k$ orthogonal matrix, proper or not, the matrices

$$\tilde{M}_j = M_a O_j{}^a$$

satisfy the basic relations $(\tilde{M}_j)^2 = E_{2^k}$; $\tilde{M}_q \tilde{M}_p = -\tilde{M}_p \tilde{M}_q$. Hence, corresponding to each orthogonal matrix O of dimension $2k$, is a non-singular matrix $T(O)$ of dimension 2^k such that $\tilde{M}_j = T^{-1}(O) M_j T(O)$. Regarding the $2k$ matrices $(M_1, \cdots, M_{2k})$ as a one row, $2k$ column matrix (whose elements are $2^k \times 2^k$ matrices) $\boldsymbol{M}$ we see that $\boldsymbol{M} \rightarrow \tilde{\boldsymbol{M}} = \boldsymbol{M} O_1$ implies $\tilde{M}_j = T^{-1}(O_1) M_j T(O_1)$, $j = 1, \cdots, 2k$. If O_1 is followed by a second orthogonal matrix O_2: $\tilde{\boldsymbol{M}} \rightarrow \boldsymbol{M}^\# = \tilde{\boldsymbol{M}} O_2 = \boldsymbol{M} O_1 O_2$ we have

$$M^\#_j = T^{-1}(O_2) \tilde{M}_j T(O_2) = T^{-1}(O_2) T^{-1}(O_1) M_j T(O_1) T(O_2)$$
$$\text{so that } T(O_1 O_2) = T(O_1) T(O_2).$$

In other words the matrices $T(O)$, of dimension 2^k, constitute a representation of the $2k$ dimensional orthogonal group. The same inner automorphism of the 2^k dimensional complete matrix group that is furnished by $T(O)$ is furnished by $\lambda T(O)$ where λ is any complex number $(\neq 0)$. It is clear that this is the only ambiguity; for if two matrices $T(O)$, $T^\#(O)$ exist such

$$\tilde{M}_j = T^{-1}(O) M_j T(O) = \{T^\#(O)\}^{-1} M_j T^\#(O)$$

the matrix $T^{\#}(O)T^{-1}(O)$ is commutative with all M_j and hence with the complete matrix algebra of dimension 2^k; hence, by Schur's lemma $\{T^{\#}(O)\}T^{-1}(O)$ is a scalar matrix: $T^{\#}(O) = \lambda T(O)$.

The indeterminate multiplier λ can be normalised by the following considerations. Since P_1 and P_3 are symmetric the k matrices $M_1, \cdots, M_k$ are symmetric:

$$M'_j = M_j; \qquad j = 1, \cdots, k$$

(this being an immediate consequence of the evident relation

$$(A \times B \times C \times \cdots)' = (A' \times B' \times C' \times \cdots).$$

Since P_2 is skew symmetric so also are the M_{k+j}:

$$M'_{k+j} = -M_{k+j}; \qquad j = 1, \cdots, k.$$

Hence the $2k$ matrices M'_j, $j = 1, \cdots, 2k$, satisfy the basic relations

$$(M'_j)^2 = E_{2^k}; \quad M'_p M'_q = -M'_q M'_p$$

and so there exists a non-singular matrix C such that

$$M'_j = C^{-1} M_j C, \qquad j = 1, \cdots, 2k.$$

It is easy to see that we may take $C = M_1 \cdots M_k$ if k is odd and $C = M_{k+1} \cdots M_{2k}$ if k is even for M_j commutes (and M_{k+j} anticommutes) with $M_1 \cdots M_k$ if k is odd whilst M_j commutes (and M_{k+j} anticommutes) with $M_{k+1} \cdots M_{2k}$ is k is even. From $M_j \to \tilde{M}_j = T^{-1}(O)M_jT(O)$ we read $\tilde{M}'_j = T'(O)M'_j(T^{-1}(O))'$. However $\tilde{M}_j = M_a O_j{}^a$ so that

$$\begin{aligned} \tilde{M}'_j = M'_a O_j{}^a = C^{-1} M_a C O_j{}^a = C^{-1}\tilde{M}_j C \\ = C^{-1}T^{-1}(O)M_jT(O)C = C^{-1}T^{-1}(O)CM'_jC^{-1}T(O)C \end{aligned}$$

so that $\{T^{-1}(O)\}' = \rho C^{-1}T(O)C$ where ρ is any complex number. When $T(O)$ is replaced by $\lambda T(O)$, $\{T^{-1}(O)\}'$ is replaced by $(1/\lambda)\{T^{-1}(O)\}'$ and we normalise λ by choosing it so that $\rho = 1$; in other words $T(O)$ is transformed into $\{T^{-1}(O)\}'$ by $C = M_1 \cdots M_k$ (if k is odd) or $C = M_{k+1} \cdots M_{2k}$ (if k is even). $T(O)$ is now uniquely determined save for sign (λ being determined by the equation $\rho\lambda^2 = 1$): the representation is two valued:

$$O \to \pm T(O).$$

The simplest case is that for which $n = 2$, $k = 1$. Here $M_1 = P_1$, $M_2 = P_2$; if O is proper it is of the form $O = \begin{pmatrix} \cos\theta & \sin\theta \\ -\sin\theta & \cos\theta \end{pmatrix}$ and so

$$\tilde{M}_1 = P_1 \cos\theta - P_2 \sin\theta = \begin{pmatrix} 0 & e^{-i\theta} \\ e^{i\theta} & 0 \end{pmatrix}$$

$$\tilde{M}_2 = P_1 \sin\theta + P_2 \cos\theta = \begin{pmatrix} 0 & ie^{-i\theta} \\ -ie^{i\theta} & 0 \end{pmatrix}.$$

On setting $T(O) = \begin{pmatrix} a & b \\ c & d \end{pmatrix}$ and equating $M_1T(O)$ to $T(O)\tilde{M}_1$ and $M_2T(O)$ to $T(O)\tilde{M}_2$ we find that $T(O)$ is a scalar multiple of $\Delta(\theta) = \begin{pmatrix} e^{i\theta/2} & 0 \\ 0 & e^{-i\theta/2} \end{pmatrix}$:

$$T(O) = \lambda\Delta(\theta) = \begin{pmatrix} \lambda e^{i\theta/2} & 0 \\ 0 & \lambda e^{-i\theta/2} \end{pmatrix}.$$

Since $k = 1$ is odd $C = M_1 = \begin{pmatrix} 0 & 1 \\ 1 & 0 \end{pmatrix}$ and on equating $T(O)$ to $C\{T^{-1}(O)\}'$ we find $\lambda = \pm 1$. Hence

$$(10.6) \qquad T(O) = \Delta(\theta) = \begin{pmatrix} e^{i\theta/2} & 0 \\ 0 & e^{-i\theta/2} \end{pmatrix}.$$

When O is improper it is in the same class as $F = \begin{pmatrix} 1 & 0 \\ 0 & -1 \end{pmatrix}$. Then $\tilde{M}_1 = M_1$; $\tilde{M}_2 = -M_2$ and we find as above that $T(O)C$ is a scalar multiple of $\begin{pmatrix} 0 & 1 \\ 1 & 0 \end{pmatrix}$ the scalar multiple being again ± 1. Hence

$$(10.7) \qquad \Delta(F) = \begin{pmatrix} 0 & 1 \\ 1 & 0 \end{pmatrix}.$$

Case 2. n odd $= 2k + 1$.

We have merely to add to the $2k$ matrices $M_1, \cdots, M_{2k}$, the matrix

$$(10.8) \qquad M_{2k+1} = P_3 \times P_3 \times \cdots \times P_3 \quad (k \text{ factors}).$$

It is immediately evident that $(M_{2k+1})^2 = E_{2^k}$, $M_jM_{2k+1} = -M_{2k+1}M_j$, $j = 1, \cdots, 2k$. Instead of considering the 2^{2k+1} matrices $M_1^{\alpha_1} \cdots M_{2k}^{\alpha_{2k}} M_{2k+1}^{\alpha_{2k+1}}$ where $\alpha_j = 0$ or 1, $j = 1, \cdots, 2k+1$ we confine our attention to the 2^{2k} matrices obtained by choosing $\alpha_1 + \alpha_2 + \cdots + \alpha_{2k+1}$ even. Since

$$N_j = iM_jM_{k+j} = E_2 \times E_2 \times \cdots \times P_3 \times E_2 \times \cdots \times E_2$$

we have $N_1N_2 \cdots N_kM_{2k+1} = E_{2^k}$ or, equivalently,

$$i^k(-1)^{k(k-1)/2} M_1M_2 \cdots M_{2k}M_{2k+1} = E_{2^k}.$$

Hence the collection of matrices $M_1^{\alpha_1} \cdots M_{2k+1}^{\alpha_{2k+1}}$ for which $\alpha_1 + \cdots + \alpha_{2k+1}$ is even is enveloped by the same algebra as the collection $M_1^{\alpha_1} \cdots M_{2k}^{\alpha_{2k}}$, $\alpha_1 + \cdots + \alpha_{2k}$ even or odd, i.e. by the complete matrix algebra of dimension 2^k. E. g., when $n=3$, $M_1=P_1$, $M_2=P_2$, $M_3=P_3$; $M_1M_3=iP_2$, $M_2M_3=-iP_1$ so that the complete matrix algebra of dimension 2 is spanned indifferently by (E_2, P_1, P_2, P_1P_2) or $(E_2, M_1M_2, M_1M_3, M_2M_3)$. The relation which connects the $(2k+1)$ matrices $M_1, \cdots, M_{2k+1}$ may be written in the form $(-1)^{k^2/2} M_1, \cdots, M_{2k+1}=E_{2^k}$; it follows that each matrix of the complete matrix algebra of dimension 2^k appears twice in the enveloping algebra of the set $M_1{}^{a_1}\cdots M_{2k+1}^{a_{2k+1}}$, once as an element of the even sub-algebra and once as an element of the complementary set (namely the product of the element of the even sub-algebra by the odd element $(-1)^{k^2/2} M_1\cdots M_{2k+1}$). The correspondence $M_j \rightarrow \tilde{M}_j = -M_j$, $j=1,2,\cdots,2k+1$, sets up a two-valued representation of the complete 2^k-dimensional matrix algebra, the unit matrix being represented by $\pm E_{2^k}$. In order to have a one-valued representation of the complete matrix algebra we must be sure that $(-1)^{k^2/2} \times M_1\cdots M_{2k+1}$ is represented by the unit matrix. On setting

$$\tilde{M}_j = M_a O_j{}^a, \qquad j=1,2,\cdots,2k+1$$

we obtain $\tilde{M}_1\cdots\tilde{M}_{2j+1}=\{\det O\}(M_1\cdots M_{2j+1})$ (owing to the relations $M_pM_q=-M_qM_p$). Hence in order to obtain a spin representation

$$\tilde{M}_j = T^{-1}(O)M_jT(O)$$

we must confine our attention to the proper orthogonal matrices (for which $\det O=1$). From this two-valued representation of the rotation group we may obtain a two-valued representation of the full real orthogonal n-dimensional group by assigning to $-E_{2k+1}$ the matrix $\pm E_{2^k}$.

3. The character of the spin representation of the *n*-dimensional real orthogonal group.

We first treat the somewhat trivial but physically important case $n=3$. Since every element of the three-dimensional rotation group is transformable, by an element of this group, into a plane rotation $T_{1,2}(\theta)$ we have merely to calculate the trace of $\Delta(\theta)=\begin{pmatrix} e^{+i\theta/2} & 0 \\ 0 & e^{-i\theta/2}\end{pmatrix}$ (cf. (10.6)). Denoting the spin representation by Δ we have the result

$$\chi(\Delta)=2\cos\theta/2=e^{i\theta/2}+e^{-i\theta/2}. \tag{10.9}$$

It follows at once that Δ is irreducible; in fact the element of volume of the 3-dimensional rotation group is (9.16) $d\tau=\sin^2\theta/2\,d\theta$ and the range of integration is from 0 to 4π (since we are dealing with a two-valued representation so that the rotation group is *doubly covered*). Hence

$$\frac{1}{V}\int \{\chi(\Delta)\}^2 d\tau = \int_0^{4\pi} 4\sin^2\theta/2\cos^2\theta/2\,d\theta \div \int_0^{4\pi}\sin^2\theta/2\,d\theta$$
$$= \int_0^{4\pi}\sin^2\theta\,d\theta \div 2\int_0^{2\pi}\sin^2\phi\,d\phi = 1.$$

The irreducible one-valued representations of the 3-dimensional rotation group are all of the type Γ_λ, $\lambda = 0, 1, 2, \cdots$ where

$$\chi(\Gamma_\lambda) = \sin(\lambda + \tfrac{1}{2})\theta \div \sin\tfrac{1}{2}\theta$$

(see (9.53) or (9.85)). It follows that the Kronecker product $\Delta \times \Gamma_\lambda$ is reducible, being the sum of two irreducible representations of the doubly covered rotation group. In fact

$$\chi(\Delta \times \Gamma_\lambda) = 2\cos\theta/2\sin(\lambda + \tfrac{1}{2})\theta \div \sin\theta/2$$

so that

$$\frac{1}{V}\int \chi^2 d\tau = \frac{1}{2\pi}\int_0^{4\pi}\{2\cos\theta/2\sin(\lambda+\tfrac{1}{2})\theta\}^2 d\theta$$
$$= \frac{1}{4\pi}\int_0^{4\pi}\{\sin(\lambda+1)\theta + \sin\lambda\theta\}^2 d\theta$$
$$= 2; \quad (\lambda \neq 0).$$

The character of $\Delta \times \Gamma_\lambda$ is the quotient by $2i\sin\theta/2$ of

$$(e^{i\theta/2} + e^{-i\theta/2})(e^{i(\lambda+\frac{1}{2})\theta} - e^{-i(\lambda+\frac{1}{2})\theta});$$

but we know (p. 265) that the characters of any representation are linear combination of expressions $\sigma_m = 2\cos m\theta$ and so the product of any character by $2i\sin\theta/2$ is a linear combination of expressions $\sin(m + \tfrac{1}{2})\theta$. Hence the characters of the two irreducible representations contained in $\Delta \times \Gamma_\lambda$ are $\dfrac{\sin(\lambda+1)\theta}{\sin\theta/2}$ and $\dfrac{\sin\lambda\theta}{\sin\theta/2}$. Thus the characters of the irreducible two-valued representations of the 3-dimensional rotation group are given by

$$\text{(10.10)} \qquad \{\lambda\}' = \frac{\sin\lambda\theta}{\sin\theta/2}; \qquad \lambda = 1, 2, 3, \cdots,$$

the characters of the irreducible one-valued representations being given by

$$\{\lambda\}' = \frac{\sin(\lambda+\tfrac{1}{2})\theta}{\sin\theta/2}; \qquad \lambda = 0, 1, 2, \cdots.$$

It will appear later that there are no other continuous irreducible representations of the 3-dimensional rotation group.

The Kronecker square $\Delta \times \Delta$ is one-valued and readily analysable; for

$$\chi(\Delta \times \Delta) = 4\cos^2 \theta/2 = 2(1 + \cos\theta)$$
$$= 1 + 2(\cos\theta + \tfrac{1}{2}) = 1 + \frac{\sin 3\theta/2}{\sin\theta/2}$$

so that

(10. 11) $$\Delta \times \Delta = \Gamma_0 + \Gamma_1.$$

Passing now to the case where n is general ($= 2k$ or $2k+1$) we observe that any proper real n-dimensional orthogonal matrix may be transformed, by means of a proper real n-dimensional orthogonal matrix, into the product

$$T_{1,k+1}(\theta_1)T_{2,k+2}(\theta_2)\cdots T_{k,2k}(\theta_k)$$

of plane rotations (cf. p. 229). From the equations of definition (10. 5) we see that

$$\tilde{M}_1 = \cos\theta\, M_1 - \sin\theta\, M_{k+1} = \begin{pmatrix} 0 & e^{-i\theta} \\ e^{+i\theta} & 0 \end{pmatrix} \times E_2 \times \cdots \times E_2$$

$$\tilde{M}_{k+1} = \sin\theta\, M_1 + \cos\theta\, M_{k+1} = \begin{pmatrix} 0 & ie^{-i\theta} \\ -ie^{+i\theta} & 0 \end{pmatrix} \times E_2 \times \cdots \times E_2.$$

Hence

$$\Delta(T_{1,k+1}(\theta_1)) = \begin{pmatrix} e^{+i\theta_1/2} & 0 \\ 0 & e^{-i\theta_1/2} \end{pmatrix} \times E_2 \times \cdots \times E_2$$

the argument being precisely the same as in the case $n = 2$. Similarly

$$\Delta(T_{j,k+j}(\theta_j)) = E_2 \times \cdots \times \begin{pmatrix} e^{+i\theta_j/2} & 0 \\ 0 & e^{-i\theta_j/2} \end{pmatrix} \times E_2 \times \cdots \times E_2$$

(the factor $\begin{pmatrix} e^{+i\theta_j/2} & 0 \\ 0 & e^{-i\theta_j/2} \end{pmatrix}$ being in the j-th place). Hence for any rotation with angles $(\theta_1, \cdots, \theta_k)$

(10. 12) $$\Delta = \begin{pmatrix} e^{+i\theta_1/2} & 0 \\ 0 & e^{-i\theta_1/2} \end{pmatrix} \times \begin{pmatrix} e^{+i\theta_2/2} & 0 \\ 0 & e^{-i\theta_2/2} \end{pmatrix} \times \cdots \times \begin{pmatrix} e^{+i\theta_k/2} & 0 \\ 0 & e^{-i\theta_k/2} \end{pmatrix}$$

it being clear from this explicit formula that Δ is actually a two-valued representation. Its character is given by:

(10. 13) $$\chi(\Delta) = 2^k \cos\theta_1/2 \cdots \cos\theta_k/2.$$

The Kronecker square $\Delta \times \Delta$ is a one-valued representation whose analysis can be written down at once. In fact

$$\chi(\Delta \times \Delta) = 2^k(1 + \cos\theta_1)\cdots(1 + \cos\theta_k)$$
$$= (1 + e^{i\theta_1})(1 + e^{-i\theta_1}) \cdots (1 + e^{i\theta_k})(1 + e^{-i\theta_k})$$
$$= \sigma_0 + \sigma_1 + \cdots + \sigma_n$$

where σ_j denotes the j-th elementary symmetric function of the $2k$ characteristic numbers $e^{\pm i\theta_1}, \cdots, e^{\pm i\theta_k}$. Hence (see (9.54) and p. 286)

$$(10.14)\quad \begin{aligned} \Delta \times \Delta &= \left\{ \begin{matrix} \Gamma_0 + \cdots + \Gamma_k \\ + \Gamma^*_0 + \cdots + \Gamma^*_k \end{matrix} \right\}; \quad n = 2k+1 \\ \Delta \times \Delta &= \left\{ \begin{matrix} \Gamma_0 + \cdots + \Gamma_{k-1} \\ + \Gamma^*_0 + \cdots + \Gamma^*_{k-1} \end{matrix} \right\} + \Gamma_k (= \Gamma'_k + \Gamma''_k); \quad n = 2k. \end{aligned}$$

The two valued representation Δ of the n-dimensional rotation group is irreducible when $n = 2k+1$ is odd and is the sum of two irreducible representations Δ' and Δ'', each of dimension 2^{k-1}, when $n = 2k$ is even. To prove this we show that the integral $\frac{1}{V}\int \{\chi(\Delta)\}^2 d\tau$, taken over the doubly covered rotation group, is unity when n is odd and two when n is even.

Case 1. $n = 2k+1$.

Since the range of integration for each of the angles $\theta_1, \cdots, \theta_k$ is 0 to 4π (and not 0 to 2π as for the simply covered group) the normalised element of volume (9.87) must be divided by 2^k in order that the total volume of the doubly covered group may be unity:

$$(10.15)\quad d\tau = \{|s(k-\tfrac{1}{2}, \cdots, \tfrac{1}{2})|^2 \div (2\pi)^k k!\, 2^{2k}\} d(\theta_1, \cdots, \theta_k).$$

On multiplying this by $\{\chi(\Delta)\}^2$, as given in (10.11), and integrating we find, since $2\cos\theta/2 \sin(p+\tfrac{1}{2})\theta = \sin(p+1)\theta + \sin p\theta$,

$$\frac{1}{V}\int \{\chi(\Delta)\}^2 d\tau = \int [|s(k, \cdots, 2, 1)|^2 \div (2\pi)^k k!\, 2^{2k}] d(\theta_1, \cdots, \theta_k).$$

The determinant $s(k, \cdots, 1)$ contains when expanded $k!$ terms and its squared modulus contains, accordingly, $k!$ square terms and a number of product terms. The product terms integrate to zero and each of the square terms integrates to $2^{2k}(2\pi)^k$ (the range of integration for each angle being from 0 to 4π). Hence $\frac{1}{V}\int \{\chi(\Delta)\}^2 d\tau = 1$ so that the representation Δ is irreducible. The representation of the full orthogonal group obtained by setting $\Delta(-E_{2k+1}) = \pm 1$ is, à fortiori, irreducible.

Case 2. $n = 2k$.

Here the normalised element of volume for the doubly covered rotation group is obtained from (9.86) by division by 2^k:

$$(10.16)\quad d\tau = [\{c(k-1, \cdots, 0)\}^2 \div (2\pi)^k k!\, 2^{2k-1}] d(\theta_1, \cdots, \theta_k).$$

Hence

$$\frac{1}{V}\int \{\chi(\Delta)\}^2 d\tau = \int [\{c(k-\tfrac{1}{2},\cdots,\tfrac{1}{2})\}^2 \div (2\pi)^k k!\, 2^{2k-1}]\, d(\theta_1,\cdots,\theta_k)$$

(since $2\cos\theta/2\cos p\theta = \cos(p+\tfrac{1}{2})\theta + \cos(p-\tfrac{1}{2})\theta$). On writing $\theta_j = 2\phi_j$ we obtain

$$\frac{1}{V}\int \{\chi(\Delta)\}^2 d\tau = \int [\{c(2k-1, 2k-3,\cdots,1)\}^2 \div (2\pi)^k k!\, 2^{k-1}]\, d(\phi_1,\cdots,\phi_k)$$

where the range of integration for each angle ϕ is from 0 to 2π. By the same reasoning as before the value of the integral is two so that Δ is the sum of two irreducible representations Δ' and Δ''. The leading term of $\chi(\Delta)$ is, by (10. 13) $e^{i(\theta_1+\cdots+\theta_k)/2}$ and so $\chi(\Delta)$ must contain, in addition to this term, all the terms obtained from it by changing the signs of an *even* number of the angles $\theta_1,\cdots,\theta_k$; after separating out from $\chi(\Delta)$ the 2^{k-1} terms thus seen to belong to one of the irreducible representations contained in Δ there remain 2^{k-1} terms, namely $e^{i(\theta_1+\cdots+\theta_{k-1}-\theta_k)/2}$ and the terms derived from this by changing the signs of an *even* number of the angles $\theta_1,\cdots,\theta_k$. Since Δ contains two irreducible representations each of the two sets of terms must furnish the characters of one of these irreducible representations. From the very definition of each of the sets of terms it is clear that the first set is $2^{k-1}(\cos\theta_1/2\cdots\cos\theta_k/2 + i^k\sin\theta_1/2\cdots\sin\theta_k/2)$ whilst the second is $2^{k-1}(\cos\theta_1/2\cdots\cos\theta_k/2 - i^k\sin\theta_1/2\cdots\sin\theta_k/2)$

$$(10.\,17)\quad \begin{cases} \chi(\Delta') = 2^{k-1}(\cos\theta_1/2\cdots\cos\theta_k/2 + i^k\sin\theta_1/2\cdots\sin\theta_k/2) \\ \chi(\Delta'') = 2^{k-1}(\cos\theta_1/2\cdots\cos\theta_k/2 - i^k\sin\theta_1/2\cdots\sin\theta_k/2). \end{cases}$$

On multiplication by $2c(k-1,\cdots,1,0)$ it is clear that these may be put in the alternative form

$$(10.\,18)\quad \begin{aligned} 2c(k-1,\cdots,1,0)\,\chi(\Delta') &= c(k-\tfrac{1}{2},\cdots,\tfrac{1}{2}) + s(k-\tfrac{1}{2},\cdots,\tfrac{1}{2}) \\ 2c(k-1,\cdots,1,0)\,\chi(\Delta'') &= c(k-\tfrac{1}{2},\cdots,\tfrac{1}{2}) - s(k-\tfrac{1}{2},\cdots,\tfrac{1}{2}). \end{aligned}$$

Similarly the character of the irreducible two-valued representation Δ of the $n = 2k+1$ dimensional rotation group may be put in the form

$$(10.\,19)\quad \chi(\Delta) = 2^k\cos\theta_1/2\cdots\cos\theta_k/2 = s(k,\cdots,1) \div s(k-\tfrac{1}{2},\cdots,\tfrac{1}{2}).$$

The representation Δ of the full $2n$-dimensional real orthogonal group is *irreducible*; this is an immediate consequence of the fact that the value of $\chi(\Delta)$ for any $2n \times 2n$ real orthogonal matrix of determinant -1 is zero. In fact if this is admitted it is clear that the integral $\frac{1}{V}\int \{\chi(\Delta)\}^2 d\tau$ taken over the full orthogonal group, must be 1; for its has the value 2 when taken over the rotation subgroup and the volume of the full group is twice that of the rotation subgroup. To show that $\chi(\Delta)$ is zero for any improper $2n \times 2n$ real orthogonal matrix of determinant -1 we turn to the canonical representative Θ (p. 229) of a class of the full orthogonal group which contains an improper element:

$$\Theta = C_1 + \cdots + C_{k-1} + F$$

where $F = \begin{pmatrix} 1 & 0 \\ 0 & -1 \end{pmatrix}$. Since $\Delta(F) = \begin{pmatrix} 0 & 1 \\ 1 & 0 \end{pmatrix}$, by (10.7), it follows at once that

$$\Delta(\Theta) = \begin{pmatrix} e^{i\theta_1/2} & 0 \\ 0 & e^{-i\theta_1/2} \end{pmatrix} \times \cdots \times \begin{pmatrix} e^{i\theta_{k-1}/2} & 0 \\ 0 & e^{-i\theta_{k-1}/2} \end{pmatrix} \times \begin{pmatrix} 0 & 1 \\ 1 & 0 \end{pmatrix}$$

and since the trace of $\begin{pmatrix} 0 & 1 \\ 1 & 0 \end{pmatrix}$ is zero the trace of $\Delta(\Theta)$ is zero (the trace of a Kronecker product being the product of the traces of the various factors).

4. The two-valued representations of the *n*-dimensional rotation group R_n.

The representation Δ has the property that when the matrix X of the group is varied continuously in such a way that the angles $(\theta_1, \cdots, \theta_k)$ are each increased by 2π (so that X returns to its original value) $\Delta(X)$ does not return to its original value but attains the value $-\Delta(X)$. We shall see in the next section that all continuous representations of the orthogonal group are either one-valued or two-valued (in the above sense); in the present section we consider the characters of any continuous two-valued representation. By a verbatim repetition of the argument on pp. 265-6 it follows that the character $\chi(X)$ of any continuous two-valued representation of R_n is a linear combination of expressions

$$\sigma_{(\lambda+\frac{1}{2})} = \Sigma e^{i(\lambda_1+\frac{1}{2})\theta_1 + (\lambda_2+\frac{1}{2})\theta_2 + \cdots + (\lambda_k+\frac{1}{2})\theta_k}$$

where $(\lambda) = (\lambda_1, \cdots, \lambda_k)$ is any set of k integers (the notation being such that $\lambda_1 \geq \lambda_2 \geq \cdots \geq \lambda_k \geq 0$ if $n = 2k+1$ is odd and such that $\lambda_1 \geq \lambda_2 \geq \cdots \geq \lambda_{k-1} \geq |\lambda_k| \geq 0$ if $n = 2k$ is even). The summation involved in the definition of $\sigma_{(\lambda+\frac{1}{2})}$ is, when n is odd, over all those permutations and changes of sign of $(\theta_1, \cdots, \theta_k)$ which actually change the term $e^{i(\lambda_1+\frac{1}{2})\theta_1 + \cdots + (\lambda_k+\frac{1}{2})\theta_k}$; whilst when n is even only *even* numbers of changes of sign of the angles $(\theta_1, \cdots, \theta_k)$ are allowed. Whether or not n is even there is associated with each set (λ) a one-valued representation $\Gamma_{(\lambda)}$ whose character $\{\lambda\}'$ has $\sigma_{(\lambda)}$ as its leading term (cf. p. 266 and the formulae (9.75), (9.85)). It follows that the character of $\Delta \times \Gamma_{(\lambda)}$ has $\sigma_{(\lambda+\frac{1}{2})}$ as its leading term; and, on analysing $\Delta \times \Gamma_{(\lambda)}$ into its irreducible components, that there exists a simple character $\chi_{(\lambda+\frac{1}{2})}$ whose leading term is $\sigma_{(\lambda+\frac{1}{2})}$. Hence (by the argument on p. 267) each $\sigma_{(\lambda+\frac{1}{2})}$ may be expressed, by a recurrence method, as a linear combination, with integral coefficients, of the simple characters $\chi_{(\lambda+\frac{1}{2})}$ the first term in this linear combination being $\chi_{(\lambda+\frac{1}{2})}$ with the numerical coefficient unity. There is no ambiguity as to the simple characters $\chi_{(\lambda+\frac{1}{2})}$; for *any* simple two-valued character must have a constant multiple of some $\sigma_{(\lambda+\frac{1}{2})}$ as its leading term and so a linear combination of this simple character and $\chi_{(\lambda+\frac{1}{2})}$ must be equivalent to a linear combination of simple characters with lower leading terms. The simple characters being linearly independent (owing to the orthogonality relations) it follows that the simple character whose leading term is a multiple of $\sigma_{(\lambda+\frac{1}{2})}$ must be $\chi_{(\lambda+\frac{1}{2})}$, the multiple being unity.

Any linear combination, with integral coefficients, of the quantities $\sigma_{(\lambda+\frac{1}{2})}$ is a linear combination, with integral coefficients, of the simple characters $\chi_{(\lambda+\frac{1}{2})}$. We now proceed to determine these simple characters themselves treating separately the cases n odd, and n even.

Case 1. $n = 2k + 1$.

The determinant $s(l_1 + 1, \cdots, l_k + 1)$ is divisible by $c(k - 1, \cdots, 1, 0)$ (pp. 289-90) and it is also divisible by $(2i)^k \sin \theta_1/2 \cdots \sin \theta_k/2$ (since $\sin p\theta$ is divisible by $\sin \theta$ and hence by $\sin \theta/2$). Hence the quotient $s(l_1 + 1, \cdots, l_k + 1) \div (2i)^k \sin \theta_1/2 \cdots \sin \theta_k/2 \; c(k - 1, \cdots, 1, 0)$ or, equivalently, $s(l_1 + 1, \cdots, l_k + 1) \div s(k - \frac{1}{2}, \cdots, \frac{1}{2})$ is a polynomial with integral coefficients in the quantities $e^{\pm i\theta_j/2}$ which is a symmetric and even function of the angles $(\theta_1, \cdots, \theta_k)$. It is, accordingly, a linear combination, with integral coefficients, of the quantities $\sigma_{(\lambda+\frac{1}{2})}$ and, hence, a linear combination with integral coefficients of the simple two-valued characters $\chi_{(\lambda+\frac{1}{2})}$. We wish to show that it is actually a simple character itself and to do this calculate the integral of its squared modulus over the group. Using the form (10.15) for the normalised element of volume of the doubly covered group our integral appears as

$$\int [\,|\, s(l_1 + 1, \cdots, l_k + 1)|^2 \div (2\pi)^k k!\, 2^{2k}]\, d(\theta_1, \cdots, \theta_k)$$

and this is unity by the argument on p. 309 (which was used to prove the irreducibility of the representation Δ). Hence the characters of the irreducible two-valued representations of the $2k+1$ dimensional rotation group are given by the formula:

$$(10.20)\qquad \chi_{(\lambda+\frac{1}{2})} = s(l_1+1,\cdots,l_k+1) \div s(k-\tfrac{1}{2},\cdots,\tfrac{1}{2})$$

where, as usual,

$$l_1 = \lambda_1 + (k-1),\quad l_2 = \lambda_2 + k - 2,\cdots, l_k = \lambda_k.$$

There are no other two-valued irreducible representations. It follows at once from (10.13) and (9.85) that the Kronecker product $\Delta \times \Gamma_{(\lambda)}$ is reducible with the following components (the result being an immediate consequence of the relation $2\cos\theta/2 \sin(l_p+\frac{1}{2})\theta = \sin(l_p+1)\theta + \sin l_p\theta$)

$$(10.21)\qquad \Delta \times \Gamma_{(\lambda)} = \Sigma\Gamma_{(p+\frac{1}{2})}$$

the summation on the right being over the 2^k sets (p) which are obtainable from the set (λ) by either replacing any λ_j by $\lambda_j - 1$ or by leaving it unaltered (it being understood that any set p for which the normal non-increasing order is not preserved or which contains a negative number is dropped).

The rule for analysing the product of $\Gamma_{(\lambda)}$ by Δ may be stated in the following convenient form: the first term in the analysis of $\Delta \times \Gamma_{(\lambda)}$ is obtained by adding $\frac{1}{2}$ to each λ_j; the other terms are obtained by subtracting 1 from one or more of the subscripts in this first term. E. g.

$$\Delta \times \Gamma_1 = \Gamma_{3/2,(1/2)^{k-1}} + \Gamma_{(1/2)^k};$$
$$\Delta \times \Gamma_{1^2} = \Gamma_{(3/2)^2(1/2)^{k-2}} + \Gamma_{3/2,(1/2)^{k-1}} + \Gamma_{(1/2)^k}.$$

It follows from (10.20), (10.13) and (9.85) that the same rule is applicable to the product $\Delta \times \Gamma_{(\lambda+\frac{1}{2})}$ (which product is a one-valued representation). The formula (10.14) for $\Delta \times \Delta$ is a particular case of this rule, Δ being $\Gamma_{(1/2)^k}$ (cf. (10.19)).

The dimension of the two-valued representation $\Gamma_{(\lambda+\frac{1}{2})}$ follows readily from (10.20) by evaluation of $\chi_{(\lambda+\frac{1}{2})}$ at the unit element (for which $\theta_1 = \theta_2 = \cdots = \theta_k = 0$). The reasoning will be sufficiently evident on considering the case $k=3$ $(n=7)$.

$$\text{Here } s(p_1,p_2,p_3) = (2i)^3 \begin{vmatrix} \sin p_1\theta_1 & \sin p_1\theta_2 & \sin p_1\theta_3 \\ \sin p_2\theta_1 & \sin p_2\theta_2 & \sin p_2\theta_3 \\ \sin p_3\theta_1 & \sin p_3\theta_2 & \sin p_3\theta_3 \end{vmatrix}$$

$$= (2i)^3 p_1p_2p_3\theta_1\theta_2\theta_3 \begin{vmatrix} 1-p_1^2\theta_1^2/3!+\cdots & 1-p_1^2\theta_2^2/3!+\cdots & 1-p_1^2\theta_3^2/3!+\cdots \\ 1-p_2^2\theta_1^2/3!+\cdots & 1-p_2^2\theta_2^2/3!+\cdots & 1-p_2^2\theta_3^2/3!+\cdots \\ 1-p_3^2\theta_1^2/3!+\cdots & 1-p_3^2\theta_2^2/3!+\cdots & 1-p_3^2\theta_3^2/3!+\cdots \end{vmatrix}$$

The lowest order terms in the expansion of the three row determinant just written are

$$-\frac{1}{3!5!}\begin{vmatrix} 1 & p_1^2 & p_1^4 \\ 1 & p_2^2 & p_2^4 \\ 1 & p_3^2 & p_3^4 \end{vmatrix}(\theta_2^2\theta_3^4-\theta_3^2\theta_2^4+\theta_3^2\theta_1^4-\theta_1^2\theta_3^4+\theta_1^2\theta_2^4-\theta_2^2\theta_1^4)$$

$$=-\frac{1}{3!}\frac{1}{5!}\Delta(p^2)\Delta(\theta^2) \text{ where } \Delta(p^2)=(p_1^2-p_2^2)(p_1^2-p_3^2)(p_2^2-p_3^2),$$

$\Delta(\theta^2)=(\theta_1^2-\theta_2^2)(\theta_1^2-\theta_3^2)(\theta_2^2-\theta_3^2)$. Hence the term independent of θ in the power series expansion of $s(p)\div s(q)$ near $\theta_1=0,\cdots,\theta_k=0$ is $p_1\cdots p_k\Delta(p^2)\div q_1\cdots q_k\Delta(q^2)$. From this result and (10.20) we see that the dimension $d_{(\lambda+\frac{1}{2})}$ of $\Gamma_{(\lambda+\frac{1}{2})}$ is given by the formula

$$(10.22)\qquad d_{(\lambda+\frac{1}{2})}=\prod_1^k(l_p+1)\cdot\Delta\{(l_p+1)^2\}\div\prod_1^k(p-\tfrac{1}{2})\Delta\{(p-\tfrac{1}{2})^2\}.$$

For $n=3$, $k=1$ we have the result

$$d_{(\lambda+\frac{1}{2})}=(\lambda+1)\div\tfrac{1}{2}=2(\lambda+1)$$

so that as λ takes the values $0,1,2,\cdots$ the two-valued representations have the *even* dimensions $2,4,6,8,\cdots$ (the one-valued representations having the odd dimensions $1,3,5,\cdots$).

For $n=5$, $k=2$ we have

$$\begin{aligned} d_{(\lambda_1+\frac{1}{2},\,\lambda_2+\frac{1}{2})} &= \tfrac{2}{3}(l_1+1)(l_2+1)(l_1-l_2)(l_1+l_2+2) \\ &= \tfrac{2}{3}(\lambda_1+2)(\lambda_2+1)(\lambda_1-\lambda_2+1)(\lambda_1+\lambda_2+3). \end{aligned}$$

E. g., $d_{(3/2)^2}=20$; $d_{(3/2,1/2)}=16$; $d_{(1/2)^2}=4$. Since Γ_{1^2} has the dimension 10 (by (9.47)) we have the check by dimensions:

$$4\times 10=20+16+4$$

on the formula

$$\Delta\times\Gamma_{(1^2)}=\Gamma_{(3/2)^2(1/2)^{k-2}}+\Gamma_{(3/2)(1/2)^{k-1}}+\Gamma_{(1/2)^k}.$$

If we repeat the argument of pp. 288-91 for $n=2k+1$ instead of, as there, for $n=2k$ the only difference is that we must use $g_p=f_p\div(1-t_p)$ instead of f_p. This means that the p_j occurring in the expression (9.78) for $\{\lambda\}'''$ must be replaced by $p'_j=p_j-p_{j-1}$; we denote the resulting determinant of the k-th order by $\{\lambda\}^{\text{iv}}$. Thus, from (9.80),

$$s(l+1)\div c(k-1,\cdots,1,0)=(2i)^k\sin\theta_1\cdots\sin\theta_k\{\lambda+1\}^{\text{iv}}.$$

It follows, from (10.20), that $\chi_{(\lambda+\frac{1}{2})}$ may be put in the form

$$\chi_{(\lambda+\frac{1}{2})}=2^k\cos\theta_1/2\cdots\cos\theta_k/2\,\{\lambda+1\}^{\text{iv}}.$$

Since $f(t) = (1 - t) \prod_1^k (1 - 2\cos\theta_p t + t^2)$ we have

$$\tfrac{1}{2} f(-1) = \{2^k \cos\theta_1/2 \cdots \cos\theta_k/2\}^2$$

so that $2^k \cos\theta_1/2 \cdots \cos\theta_k/2 = \sqrt{\tfrac{1}{2} f(-1)} = \sqrt{\tfrac{1}{2}\det(E_n + X)}$. Hence

$$(10.23) \qquad \chi_{(\lambda+\frac{1}{2})} = 2^k \cos\theta_1/2 \cdots \cos\theta_k/2 \{\lambda + 1\}^{\text{iv}} = \sqrt{\tfrac{1}{2}\det(E_n + X)}\,\{\lambda + 1\}^{\text{iv}}$$

where

$$(10.24) \qquad \{\lambda + 1\}^{\text{iv}} = \begin{vmatrix} p_{\lambda_1} - p_{\lambda_1 - 1}, & p_{\lambda_1+1} - p_{\lambda_1-2}, & \cdots & p_{\lambda_1+k-1} - p_{\lambda_1-k} \\ \cdot & & & \cdot \\ \cdot & & & \cdot \\ p_{\lambda_k - k+1} - p_{\lambda_k - k} & \cdot & \cdots & p_{\lambda_k} - p_{\lambda_k - 2k+1} \end{vmatrix}.$$

Case 2. $n = 2k$.

Here we consider first the two valued representations of the full orthogonal group.

Since $s(l_1, \cdots, l_k)$ is divisible by $c(k-1, \cdots, 1, 0)$ (pp. 289-90) it follows that $c(l_1 + \frac{1}{2}, \cdots, l_k + \frac{1}{2})$ is divisible by $c(k-1, \cdots, 0)$; we have merely to multiply $c(l_1 + \frac{1}{2}, \cdots, l_k + \frac{1}{2})$ by $(2i)^k \sin\theta_1/2 \cdots \sin\theta_k/2$ when we obtain an aggregate of terms of the type $s(p_1, \cdots, p_k)$; since $c(k-1, \cdots, 1, 0)$ does not have a factor in common with $\sin\theta_1/2 \cdots \sin\theta_k/2$ the result follows. The quotient $c(l_1 + \frac{1}{2}, \cdots, l_k + \frac{1}{2}) \div c(k-1, \cdots, 1, 0)$ is a linear combination with integral coefficients of the quantities $\sigma_{(p+\frac{1}{2})}$ the leading term being $\sigma_{(\lambda+\frac{1}{2})}$. It follows, on using the normalised element of volume (10.16), and by repeating the argument on pages 309-10 that the quantities

$$(10.25) \qquad \chi_{(\lambda+\frac{1}{2})} = c(l_1 + \tfrac{1}{2}, \cdots, l_k + \tfrac{1}{2}) \div c(k-1, \cdots, 1, 0)$$

are simple characters of the *full* orthogonal group; whilst they are *compound* characters of the rotation subgroup being the sum of exactly two simple characters $\chi'_{(\lambda+\frac{1}{2})}$ and $\chi''_{(\lambda+\frac{1}{2})}$ of this rotation subgroup. These simple characters are given by

$$(10.26) \qquad \begin{aligned} \chi'_{(\lambda+\frac{1}{2})} &= \{c(l_1 + \tfrac{1}{2}, \cdots, l_k + \tfrac{1}{2}) + s(l_1 + \tfrac{1}{2}, \cdots, l_k + \tfrac{1}{2})\} \\ &\qquad \div 2c(k-1, \cdots, 1, 0) \\ \chi''_{(\lambda+\frac{1}{2})} &= \{c(l_1 + \tfrac{1}{2}, \cdots, l_k + \tfrac{1}{2}) - s(l_1 + \tfrac{1}{2}, \cdots, l_k + \tfrac{1}{2})\} \\ &\qquad \div 2c(k-1, \cdots, 1, 0). \end{aligned}$$

In fact $s(l_1 + \frac{1}{2}, \cdots, l_k + \frac{1}{2})$ is at once seen (on multiplying it by $2^k \cos\theta_1/2 \cdots \cos\theta_k/2$) to be divisible by $c(k-1, \cdots, 1, 0)$ and so $\chi'_{(\lambda+\frac{1}{2})}$, $\chi''_{(\lambda+\frac{1}{2})}$ are linear combinations of simple characters. On forming the squared modulus and integrating over the rotation group the squared terms each yield 2 whilst the product term (which is present if k is even) yields zero. Hence

$$\frac{1}{V}\int |\chi'_{(\lambda+\frac{1}{2})}|^2\, d\tau = \frac{1}{V}\int |\chi''_{(\lambda+\frac{1}{2})}|^2\, d\tau = 1.$$

At the unit element $\chi'_{(\lambda+\frac{1}{2})}$ and $\chi''_{(\lambda+\frac{1}{2})}$ have the same value which must, therefore, be positive (since it is one-half the value of $\chi_{(\lambda+\frac{1}{2})}$ at the unit element i. e. one-half the dimension of the irreducible representation $\Gamma_{(\lambda+\frac{1}{2})}$ of the full orthogonal group). Hence $\chi'_{(\lambda+\frac{1}{2})}$, $\chi''_{(\lambda+\frac{1}{2})}$ are actually simple characters; their sum being $\chi_{(\lambda+\frac{1}{2})}$ we see that $\Gamma_{(\lambda+\frac{1}{2})}$ is analysable into the sum of two irreducible representations, $\Gamma'_{(\lambda+\frac{1}{2})}$ and $\Gamma''_{(\lambda+\frac{1}{2})}$ of the same dimension.

The dimension of the irreducible representation $\Gamma_{(\lambda+\frac{1}{2})}$ of the full orthogonal group, whose characters are furnished by (10. 25), follows on evaluating $\chi_{(\lambda+\frac{1}{2})}$ at the unit element. By the same reasoning as that used to derive (10. 22) we find

$$(10.\,27) \qquad d_{(\lambda+\frac{1}{2})} = 2\Delta\{(l_p+\tfrac{1}{2})^2\} \div \Delta\{(p-1)^2\}$$

(the presence of the factor 2 being due to the fact that $c_p = 2\cos p\theta$, $p > 0$ whilst $c_0 = 1$, not 2). The common dimension of the irreducible representations $\Gamma'_{(\lambda+\frac{1}{2})}$, $\Gamma''_{(\lambda+\frac{1}{2})}$ of the rotation subgroup is:

$$(10.\,28) \quad d'_{(\lambda+\frac{1}{2})} = d''_{(\lambda+\frac{1}{2})} = \tfrac{1}{2}d_{(\lambda+\frac{1}{2})} = \Delta\{(l_p+\tfrac{1}{2})^2\} \div \Delta\{(p-1)^2\}.$$

From (10. 25) we see that $\Delta \times \Gamma_{(\lambda+\frac{1}{2})}$ is a reducible one-valued representation of the full orthogonal group whose analysis is furnished by the rule given on p. 313 for the case $n = 2k+1$; similarly $\Delta \times \Gamma_{(\lambda)}$ is a reducible two-valued representation whose analysis is given by the same rule.

By repeating the argument given when $n = 2k+1$ we see that there are no other continuous two-valued representations of the full orthogonal $2k$ dimensional group than the representations $\Gamma_{(\lambda+\frac{1}{2})}$: the set of irreducible two-valued representations $\Gamma_{(\lambda+\frac{1}{2})}$ of the full orthogonal group is complete. Furthermore the set of irreducible two-valued representations $\Gamma'_{(\lambda+\frac{1}{2})}$, $\Gamma''_{(\lambda+\frac{1}{2})}$ of the rotation subgroup is complete (cf. pp. 311-13).

We have seen (p. 245) that

$$(1-2\cos\theta_j t_p + t_p^2)^{-1} = 1 + 2\sum_1^\infty \{\cos q\theta_j + \cos(q-2)\theta_j + \cdots\} t_p^q,$$

and this implies that

$$(1 - t_p)(1 - 2\cos\theta_j t_p + t_p^2)^{-1}$$
$$= 1 + 2\sum_1^{\infty}\{\cos q\theta_j - \cos(q-1)\theta_j + \cdots\}t_p^q.$$

The coefficient of t_p^q is readily shown, on multiplying it by $\cos\theta_j/2$ to be $\cos(q+\frac{1}{2})\theta_j \div \cos\theta_j/2$ and so

$$\frac{2(1-t_p)\cos\theta_j/2}{1-2\cos\theta_j t_p + t_p^2} = \sum_0^{\infty} c_{q+\frac{1}{2}}(\theta_j)t_p^q.$$

From this it follows by the reasoning given on p. 289 that

$$(10.28)\quad 2^{k(k-1)}\Delta(\cos\theta)2^k\cos\theta_1/2\cdots\cos\theta_n/2\prod_{p=1}^{k}(1-t_p)\prod_{\substack{p<q\\1}}^{k}(1-t_pt_q)$$
$$\div f_1\cdots f_k = \Sigma c(l+\tfrac{1}{2})\{\lambda\}(\boldsymbol{t}).$$

But $(1-t_p)/f_p = \sum_0^{\infty} p''_{j_p}t_p^{j_p}$ where $p''_q = p_q - p_{q-1}$ so that

$$\prod_1^k(1-t_p)f_p^{-1} = \sum_{(j)=0}^{\infty} p''_{j_1}\cdots p''_{j_k}t_1^{j_1}\cdots t_p^{j_p}.$$

On multiplication by $\Delta_k(\boldsymbol{t})L_k(\boldsymbol{t})$ we obtain on the right a sum of products of determinants $A(l_1,\cdots,l_k)$ by determinants $\{\lambda\}^{\text{v}}$

$$\{\lambda\}^{\text{v}} = \begin{vmatrix} p''_{\lambda_1} & p''_{\lambda_1+1}+p''_{\lambda_1-1} & \cdots & p''_{\lambda_1+k-1}+p''_{\lambda_1-k+1} \\ \cdot & & & \cdot \\ \cdot & & & \cdot \\ p''_{\lambda_k-k+1} & \cdot & \cdots & p''_{\lambda_k}+p''_{\lambda_k-2k+2} \end{vmatrix}$$

or, equivalently,

$$(10.30)\quad \{\lambda\}^{\text{v}} = \begin{vmatrix} p_{\lambda_1}-p_{\lambda_1-1} & p_{\lambda_1+1}-p_{\lambda_1-2} & \cdots & p_{\lambda_1+k-1}-p_{\lambda_1-k} \\ \cdot & \cdot & & \cdot \\ \cdot & \cdot & & \cdot \\ p_{\lambda_k-k+1}-p_{\lambda_k-k} & \cdot & \cdots & p_{\lambda_k}-p_{\lambda_k-2k+1} \end{vmatrix}$$

so that $\{\lambda\}^{\text{v}} = \{\lambda+1\}^{\text{iv}}$. On division through by $\Delta_k(\boldsymbol{t})$ we obtain

$$\prod_{p=1}^{k}(1-t_p)\prod_{\substack{p<q\\1}}^{k}(1-t_pt_q)\div f_1\cdots f_k = \Sigma\{\lambda\}^{\text{v}}\{\lambda\}(\boldsymbol{t})$$

and a comparison of this with (10.29) yields

$$c(l+\tfrac{1}{2})\div c(k-1,\cdots,1,0) = 2^k\cos\theta_1/2\cdots\cos\theta_k/2\ \{\lambda\}^{\text{v}}.$$

It follows from (10.25) that the characters of the irreducible two-valued representations $\Gamma_{(\lambda+\frac{1}{2})}$ of the full $2k$ dimensional orthogonal group may be expressed in the form

$$(10.31) \qquad \chi_{(\lambda+\frac{1}{2})} = 2^k \cos\theta_1/2 \cdots \cos\theta_k/2 \ \{\lambda\}^{\text{v}} = \sqrt{\det(E_n+X)}\{\lambda\}^{\text{v}}$$

where $\{\lambda\}^{\text{v}}$ is given by (10.30); (since $f(t)=\prod_1^k (1-2\cos\theta_p t+t^2)$, $2^k\cos\theta_1/2\cdots\cos\theta_k/2=\sqrt{f(-1)}=\sqrt{\det(E_n+X)}$).

A repetition of the argument just given, with the single difference that we deal with $(1+t_p)\div f_p$ rather than $(1-t_p)\div f_p$, enables us to show that

$$s(l+\tfrac{1}{2})\div c(k-1,\cdots,1,0)=(2i)^k\sin\theta_1/2\cdots\sin\theta_k/2\,\{\lambda\}^{\text{vi}}$$

where

$$(10.32) \qquad \{\lambda\}^{\text{vi}} = \begin{vmatrix} p_{\lambda_1}+p_{\lambda_1-1} & p_{\lambda_1+1}+p_{\lambda_1+2} & \cdots & p_{\lambda_1+k-1}+p_{\lambda_1-k} \\ \cdot & \cdot & & \cdot \\ \cdot & \cdot & & \cdot \\ p_{\lambda_k-k+1}+p_{\lambda_k-k} & \cdot & \cdots & p_{\lambda_k}+p_{\lambda_k-2k+1} \end{vmatrix}.$$

It follows from (10.26) that the characters of the irreducible two-valued representations $\Gamma'_{(\lambda+\frac{1}{2})}$ and $\Gamma''_{(\lambda+\frac{1}{2})}$ of the $2k$ dimensional rotation group may be written in the form

$$(10.33) \qquad \begin{aligned} \chi'_{(\lambda+\frac{1}{2})} &= 2^{k-1}[\cos\theta_1/2\cdots\cos\theta_k/2\,\{\lambda\}^{\text{v}} \\ &\qquad + i^k\sin\theta_1/2\cdots\sin\theta_k/2\,\{\lambda\}^{\text{vi}}] \\ &= \tfrac{1}{2}[\sqrt{\det(E_n+X)}\{\lambda\}^{\text{v}} + i^k\sqrt{\det(E_n-X)}\{\lambda\}^{\text{vi}}] \end{aligned}$$

$$(10.34) \qquad \begin{aligned} \chi''_{(\lambda+\frac{1}{2})} &= 2^{k-1}[\cos\theta_1/2\cdots\cos\theta_k/2\,\{\lambda\}^{\text{v}} \\ &\qquad - i^k\sin\theta_1/2\cdots\sin\theta_k/2\,\{\lambda\}^{\text{vi}}] \\ &= \tfrac{1}{2}[\sqrt{\det(E_n+X)}\{\lambda\}^{\text{v}} - i^k\sqrt{\det(E_n-X)}\{\lambda\}^{\text{vi}}]. \end{aligned}$$

5. The topology of the real n-dimensional rotation group.

Each element $X=e^S$ of the real n-dimensional rotation group R_n may be represented by a point p in a representative Cartesian real space of n^2 dimensions (p. 52). Since $X'X=E_n$ all points p lie at the same distance $\sqrt{n}$ from the origin o of the representative space and so the points p which correspond to elements X of R_n may be said to lie on a spherical spread, of dimension $\dfrac{n(n-1)}{2}$, in the n^2 dimensional representative space. The continuous curve $p(t)$, where $X(t)=e^{tS}$, connects, as t varies from 0 to 1 the unit element E_n with X; (we shall agree that the abbreviation: X is connected with E: stands for the longer statement: the representative point of X is connected with the representative point of E). However the points X of R_n do not, as we shall see, constitute a *simply connected* spread: there exist closed curves on this spread which cannot be contracted continuously to a point, it being understood that the closed curve remains on the rotation spread during the contraction. It is the purpose of the present section to show that the rotation spread (i. e. the locus of the representative points of elements X of R_n) is *doubly* connected: every closed curve on this spread belongs to one or the other of two types—it may either be continuously contracted to a point or it belongs to a type of curves no one of which may be continuously contracted to a point but such that any one curve of the type may be continuously deformed into any other. Before proceeding to the proof of this fundamental result we observe that we may, without loss of generality, assume that all our closed curves begin and end at the unit point (= the representative point of E_n). In fact if C is the closed curve $\{X(t)\}$ beginning and ending at $X(0) = e^S$ the curve $\Gamma = \{X^{-1}(0)X(t)\}$ may be obtained from C by continuous deformation; we have merely to set $\Gamma(\tau) = e^{-\tau S}X(t)$ and let τ vary continuously from 0 to 1; and $\Gamma = \Gamma(1)$ begins and ends at the unit point.

The essential part of the proof of our theorem that the representative spread of R_n is doubly connected is the factorisation (already given by Euler in the case $n = 3$) of X into a product of plane rotations (a plane rotation being an n-dimensional rotation in which all the variables but two are unaffected). We shall denote by $T_{p,q}(\theta), p < q$, the plane rotation $x \rightarrow x'$ where $x'_p = \cos\theta\, x_p + \sin\theta\, x_q$; $x'_q = -\sin\theta\, x_p + \cos\theta\, x_q$; $x'_r = x_r$; $r \neq p$; $r \neq q$. Denoting by $(x_s{}^r)$ the element in the r-th row and s-th column of X the element in the first row and second column of $XT_{1,2}(\theta)$ is $x_1{}^1 \sin\theta + x_2{}^1 \cos\theta$ and on setting $\theta = \theta_2 = \arctan(-x_2{}^1/x_1{}^1)$ we see that the element in the first row and second column of $XT_{1,2}(\theta_2)$ is zero. On multiplying by $T_{1,3}(\theta_3)$ we arrange, similarly, that the element in the first row and third column of $XT_{1,2}(\theta_2)T_{1,3}(\theta_3)$ is zero, the element in the first row and second column being still zero since it is the same as the element in the first row and second column of $XT_{1,2}(\theta_2)$. Proceeding in this way we see that the elements in the first row of $XT_{1,2}(\theta_2)T_{1,3}(\theta_3)\cdots T_{1,n}(\theta_n)$, after the first, may be made zero, by proper choice of $(\theta_2,\cdots,\theta_n)$. The element in the first row and first column of $XT_{1,2}(\theta_2)\cdots T_{1,n}(\theta_n)$ is then ± 1 since this matrix is an element of R_n (so that the sum of the squares of the elements in the first row is unity). If it is -1 we make it $+1$ by replacing θ_n by $\theta_n + \pi$. Since $T_{p,q}(-\theta) = \{T_{p,q}(\theta)\}^{-1}$ we see that

$$(10.35) \qquad X = ZT_{1,n}(\phi_n)T_{1,n-1}(\phi_{n-1}) \cdots T_{1,2}(\phi_2); \qquad \phi_k = -\theta_k$$

where Z is of the form $Z = \begin{pmatrix} 1 & 0 \\ 0 & X_{n-1} \end{pmatrix}$, X_{n-1} an element of the $n-1$ dimensional rotation group R_{n-1}. On proceeding with X_{n-1} as we did for X_n (or, equivalently, by induction from $n-1$ to n) we see that X may be factored into a product of plane rotations the number of factors being $(n-1) + (n-2) + \cdots + 1 = \dfrac{n(n-1)}{2}$. When $n = 3$ there are three factors:

$$X = T_{2,3}(\theta)T_{1,3}(\phi_3)T_{1,2}(\phi_2).$$

The factorisation furnished by Euler, in the case $n = 3$, was similar but slightly different. By the same argument as that given above we may write X in the form

$$X = \tilde{Z}T_{1,2}(\tilde{\phi}_2)T_{2,3}(\tilde{\phi}_3) \cdots T_{n-1,n}(\tilde{\phi}_n)$$

where $\tilde{Z}$ has the same form as Z. When $n = 3$ we find

$$X = T_{2,3}(\tilde{\theta})T_{1,2}(\tilde{\phi}_2)T_{2,3}(\tilde{\phi})$$

which is Euler's factorisation (cf. (10.2)). The variant (due to Brauer) described by (10.35) is, however, more convenient for our present purpose.

The factorisation (10.35) is by no means *unique*; It will suffice to determine the degree of ambiguity when $X = E_n$. In this case the element in the first row and last column of $ZT_{1,n}(\phi_n)$, being the same as the element in the first row and last column of $X = E_n$ must be zero; and the elements in the first row and remaining columns of $ZT_{1,n}(\phi_n)$, with the exception of the first, are all zero also since they are the same as the corresponding elements of Z. Hence the element in the first row and column of $ZT_{1,n}(\phi_n)$ is ± 1 (since $ZT_{1,n}(\phi_n)$ is an element of R_n, so that the sum of the squares of the elements in the first row is unity). From the definition of Z it follows that the element in the first row and column of $T_{1,n}(\phi_n) = \pm 1$ so that $\phi_n \equiv 0$ or π (mod 2π). We next consider $ZT_{1,n}(\phi_n)T_{1,n-1}(\phi_{n-1})$; the elements in the first row and $n-1$-st and n-th columns are zero, being the same as those of $X = E_n$ whilst the elements in the first row and remaining columns, save the first, are zero, being the same as the corresponding elements of $ZT_{1,n}(\phi_n)$. Hence the element in the first row and column of $ZT_{1,n}(\phi_n)T_{1,n-1}(\phi_{n-1}) = \pm 1$ implying that the element in the first row and column of $T_{1,n-1}(\phi_{n-1})$

$= \pm 1$ so that $\phi_{n-1} \equiv 0$ or $\pi \pmod{2\pi}$. Proceeding in this way we see that all the ϕ_k, $k = 2, \cdots, n$, $\equiv 0$ or $\pi \pmod{2\pi}$. Since the element in the first row and column of the product $ZT_{1,n}(\phi_n) \cdots T_{1,2}(\phi_2) = E_n$ is $+1$ only an *even* number of the $\phi_2, \cdots, \phi_n$ are $\equiv \pi \pmod{2\pi}$. The factors for which $\phi_k \equiv 0$ may be omitted in the factorisation since the corresponding $T_{1,k}(\phi_k) = E_n$.

We now consider an arbitrary closed path beginning and ending at E_n. At the beginning point we adopt the factorisation $Z = E_n$; $\phi_k = 0$, $k = 2, \cdots, n$ and we have to examine what we can say about the factorisation when we are back at the unit point; or when we deform the closed path continuously in any way. Such a continuous deformation, for instance, would be obtained by adding to the original closed path a path open or closed beginning at E and traced *twice* once in one sense and once in the opposite sense. Let ϕ_p, ϕ_q be the first pair of angles counted in the order $n, n-1, \cdots, 2$ which are congruent to π and consider the path traced out by the element

$$Y = ZT_{q,p}(\pi)T_{q,p}(\theta)T_{1,p}(\theta_p)T_{1,q}(\theta_q)T_{1,q-1}(\phi_{q-1}) \cdots T_{1,2}(\phi_2)$$

of R_n as θ, θ_p, θ_q vary as follows

(a) all three start with the value π and θ_p varies from π to $3\pi/2$, θ and θ_q being held $= \pi$;

(b) θ_p maintaining the value $3\pi/2$, θ and θ_q vary from π to 2π always remaining equal;

(c) θ_p varies from $3\pi/2$ to 2π, θ and θ_q being held $= 2\pi$.

Now $T_{1,p}(3\pi/2)T_{1,q}(\theta_q) = T_{q,p}(-\theta_q)T_{1,p}(3\pi/2)$ it being sufficient to check this when $p = 3$, $q = 2$; the check is furnished by

$$\begin{pmatrix} 0 & 0 & -1 \\ 0 & 1 & 0 \\ 1 & 0 & 0 \end{pmatrix}\begin{pmatrix} \cos\theta_q & \sin\theta_q & 0 \\ -\sin\theta_q & \cos\theta_q & 0 \\ 0 & 0 & 1 \end{pmatrix} = \begin{pmatrix} 0 & 0 & -1 \\ -\sin\theta_q & \cos\theta_q & 0 \\ \cos\theta_q & \sin\theta_q & 0 \end{pmatrix}$$

$$\begin{pmatrix} 1 & 0 & 0 \\ 0 & \cos\theta_q & -\sin\theta_q \\ 0 & \sin\theta_q & \cos\theta_q \end{pmatrix}\begin{pmatrix} 0 & 0 & -1 \\ 0 & 1 & 0 \\ 1 & 0 & 0 \end{pmatrix} = \begin{pmatrix} 0 & 0 & -1 \\ -\sin\theta_q & \cos\theta_q & 0 \\ \cos\theta_q & \sin\theta_q & 0 \end{pmatrix}$$

Hence Y remains fixed as the angles θ, θ_q trace the path (b). Again $T_{q,p}(\pi)T_{1,p}(\theta_p) = T_{1,p}(\pi - \theta_p)T_{1,q}(\pi)$; the check being furnished when $p = 3$, $q = 2$ by

$$\begin{pmatrix}1 & 0 & 0\\ 0 & -1 & 0\\ 0 & 0 & -1\end{pmatrix}\begin{pmatrix}\cos\theta_p & 0 & \sin\theta_p\\ 0 & 1 & 0\\ -\sin\theta_p & 0 & \cos\theta_p\end{pmatrix}=\begin{pmatrix}\cos\theta_p & 0 & \sin\theta_p\\ 0 & -1 & 0\\ \sin\theta_p & 0 & -\cos\theta_p\end{pmatrix}$$

$$\begin{pmatrix}-\cos\theta_p & 0 & \sin\theta_p\\ 0 & 1 & 0\\ -\sin\theta_p & 0 & -\cos\theta_p\end{pmatrix}\begin{pmatrix}-1 & 0 & 0\\ 0 & -1 & 0\\ 0 & 0 & 1\end{pmatrix}=\begin{pmatrix}\cos\theta_p & 0 & \sin\theta_p\\ 0 & -1 & 0\\ \sin\theta_p & 0 & -\cos\theta_p\end{pmatrix}.$$

Hence Y traces in (a) the same path as in (c) but in opposite senses. Hence *any* closed path starting and ending at E_n may be continuously deformed into one for which all ϕ_k start and end at 0 (mod 2π) the factor Z then necessarily starting and ending at E_n. The path traced out by X may be continuously deformed into one found by letting $T_{1,n}(\phi_n), \cdots, T_{1,2}(\phi_2)$, Z trace out their paths independently of each other one after the other; all but the factor which is varying being held constant whilst that one is being varied. If we denote by α the closed curve traced out by $T_{1,2}(\phi)$ as ϕ varies from 0 to 2π the various factors $T_{1,n}(\phi_n), \cdots, T_{1,3}(\phi_3)$ trace out curves which may be continuously deformed into α traced once or oftener in either sense. Thus $T_{1,3}(\theta)$ is the transform of $T_{1,2}(\theta)$ by the element $\begin{pmatrix}1 & 0 & 0 & \cdot\\ 0 & 0 & 1 & \cdot\\ 0 & -1 & 0 & \cdot\\ \cdot & \cdot & \cdot & E_{n-3}\end{pmatrix}$ of R so that as ϕ_3 varies from 0 to 2π, $T_{1,3}(\phi_3)$ traces out a curve which is obtainable from α by continuous deformation; in fact, if A, B are any fixed elements of R, the curve traced out by $Y = AXB$ is obtainable by a continuous deformation from the curve traced out by X. However we do not know that ϕ_3 varies from 0 to 2π; we only know that it varies from 0 to 0 (mod 2π) i. e. from 0 to $2m_3\pi$ where m_3 is an integer, positive, negative or zero. Hence $T_{1,3}(\phi_3)$ traces out a curve which may be obtained from α^{m_3} by continuous deformation; α^{m_3} denoting α traced out m_3 times in the same sense as α if $m_3 > 0$ and in the opposite sense if $m_3 < 0$. The factor Z is of the type $\begin{pmatrix}1 & 0\\ 0 & X_{n-1}\end{pmatrix}$ and we therefore know that the curve traced out by X may be deformed continuously into a power of α if we assume this already known for elements X_{n-1} of R_{n-1}. The theorem being trivial for $n = 2$ we know, by an induction argument from $n-1$ to n, that the path traced out by X is continuously deformable into a power of α. But $T_{1,3}(\pi)T_{1,2}(\phi)T_{1,3}(\pi) = T_{1,2}(-\phi)$ so that the curve traced by $T_{1,2}(\phi)$ in one sense is continuously deformable into the same curve traced in the opposite sense. Hence if the power of α is *even* the curve traced by X may be continuously contracted to a point; whilst if it is odd the curve traced out by X may be deformed continuously into the curve α. Hence the n-dimensional rotation matrices occupy a spread which is either doubly or simply connected; the latter alternative occurring only if α, i. e. the curve traced out by $T_{1,2}(\phi)$ as ϕ varies from 0 to 2π, can be continuously contracted to a point. As a matter of fact α can *not* be continuously contracted to a point but this, being a negative statement, is not easy to prove directly. We obtain an indirect proof by noticing that if the rotation spread were simply connected any analytic function (without branch points) defined over it would be uniform (= single valued). If, then, we can construct an analytic function, without branch points, defined over the rotation spread, which is *not* uniform we shall have proved that the rotation spread is not simply connected. It is clear that such an analytic function is at most doubly valued since any closed curve on the rotation spread, traced twice in the same sense, may be continuously contracted to a point; for α^2 is continuously contractible to a point.

In order to construct a two-valued analytic function, without branch points, on the rotation spread we first observe that every continuous representation $\Gamma = \{D(X)\}$ of R is an analytic function (not necessarily uniform) of the elements of X. In fact this is evident when $n = 2$; for if we write

$$X = \begin{pmatrix} \cos\theta & \sin\theta \\ -\sin\theta & \cos\theta \end{pmatrix}, \quad D(X) = F(\theta)$$

the continuous matrix $F(\theta)$ satisfies the equation $F(\theta)F(\phi) = F(\theta+\phi)$ so that the elements of $F(\theta)$ are analytic functions of θ of the type $\Sigma p_j(\theta)e^{\alpha_j\theta}$ where the $p_j(\theta)$ are polynomials in θ and the α_j are constants (see the corresponding argument for the unimodular group on p. 185). The result follows, for any n, from the formula (10. 35) by the principle of induction; for (10. 35) forces

$$D(X) = D(Z)D\{T_{1,n}(\phi_n)\}\cdots D\{T_{1,2}(\phi_2)\}$$

and the arguments $\phi_n, \cdots, \phi_2$ are analytic functions (not necessarily uniform, but without singularities) of the elements of X (forcing by (10. 35) the elements of Z to be analytic functions of the elements of X). Hence the elements of any continuous representation $\{D(X)\}$ of R are analytic functions (not necessarily uniform) of the elements of X (or, equivalently, of the elements of S where $X = e^S$). We know that any analytic function defined over R is at most doubly valued and on repeating the argument of p. 265 (with the omission of the word *periodic*) we see that each element of $D(\Lambda)$ is a linear combination of expressions of the type $e^{i(m_1\theta_1 + \cdots + m_k\theta_k)}$ where the coefficients $m_1, \cdots, m_k$ are *either* all integers, positive, negative or zero or all *half-integers*, i. e. half an *odd* integer, positive, negative or zero; the first alternative occurring when the representation is uniform (= single valued) and the second when it is doubly valued.

Since every continuous representation of R is either irreducible or analysable (being bounded and, hence, equivalent to a unitary representation) we may confine our attention to irreducible representations $\Gamma = \{D(X)\}$. If X_1 and X_2 are any two elements of R in the neighborhood of E_n we consider the basic representation relation

$$D(X_1)D(X_2) = D(X_1X_2);$$

holding X_2 fixed we let X_1 trace out a closed curve and denote by $\tilde{D}(X_1)$ the matrix obtained in this way by analytic continuation from $D(X_1)$. Thus

$$\tilde{D}(X_1)D(X_2) = \tilde{D}(X_1X_2).$$

Similarly holding X_1 fixed and letting X_2 trace out a closed path which may be continuously deformed into the path traced out by X_1 (so that X_1X_2 traces out in the two cases: first when X_1 varies and X_2 is held fixed and second when X_2 varies and X_1 is held fixed: curves which are continuously deformable into each other) we obtain

$$D(X_1)D(X_2) = \tilde{D}(X_1X_2).$$

On letting X_1 again trace out the same closed path as before, X_2 being fixed, this last equation yields (since the curve traced out by X_1X_2, twice in the same sense, is continuously contractable to a point,

$$D(X_1)\tilde{D}(X_2) = D(X_1X_2).$$

On setting $X_2 = E_n$ we find from the first two relations

$$\tilde{D}(X_1)D(E_n) = D(X_1)\tilde{D}(E_n) = \tilde{D}(X_1),$$

and on setting both X_1 and $X_2 = E_n$ in the third relation

$$\{\tilde{D}(E_n)\}^2 = D(E_n) = E_d;\ d \text{ being the dimension of } \Gamma.$$

On setting $X_1 = E_n$ in our first relation we have $\tilde{D}(E_n)D(X_2) = \tilde{D}(X_2)$ and this implies $\tilde{D}(E_n)D(X_1) = \tilde{D}(X_1) = D(X_1)\tilde{D}(E_n)$ so that $\tilde{D}(E_n)$ must be a scalar matrix by Schur's lemma (since it commutes with the matrices of an irreducible collection). Hence $\tilde{D}(E_n) = \pm E_d$ and $\tilde{D}(X_1) = \pm D(X_1)$. It follows, by analytic continuation, that this relation holds identically:

$$\tilde{D}(X) = \pm D(X).$$

We have seen in the preceding section that there actually exist two-valued representations and this proves that the rotation group is not simply connected.

6. The covering group of the real *n*-dimensional rotation group.

When we speak, as we have done in previous sections of this chapter, of two-valued representations of the rotation group we realise that the term is a misnomer. All representations of any group are, by definition, one-valued; what is meant by the phrase "two-valued" is that there exists a new group, which we term the covering group of the rotation group, such that the so-called two-valued representations of the rotation group are actual (hence one-valued) representations of this covering group. The rotation group is isomorphic to the covering group, i. e. to each element of the covering group there corresponds a definite element of the rotation group in such a way that to the product of any two elements of the covering group corresponds the product of the two corresponding elements of the rotation group. But the isomorphism is not simple: the same element of the rotation group corresponds to more than one element (in fact to precisely two elements) of the covering group. In a representation, therefore, of the covering group two distinct elements of the representation, corresponding to two distinct elements of the covering group, may correspond to one and the same element of the rotation group; this will certainly happen when the two distinct elements of the covering group are such that they correspond to the same element of the rotation group.

The elements of the covering group are defined as follows: Let $X = e^S$ be any element of the n-dimensional rotation group and let x be the representative point of X in the n^2-dimensional representative Euclidean space (so that x lies on a $n(n-1)/2$ dimensional spherical spread O in this space). Then X may be connected with E_n by the path $X(t) = e^{St}$, $0 \leq t \leq 1$. We regard as elements of our covering group the classes of paths connecting the unit point e (which represents E_n) with the various points x. We say classes of paths, rather than simply paths, because any two paths which can be deformed continuously into one another are regarded as identical. The result of the previous section may be expressed as follows: to each element X of the rotation group correspond precisely two elements of the covering group. We denote a path connecting e with x by $\widehat{ex}$ and the class of all paths which are continuously deformable into this path by ξ; so that ξ is an element of the covering group of the rotation group which corresponds to the element X of this rotation group.

To show that the aggregate of elements ξ actually constitutes a group, to which the rotation group is isomorphic, we must first define a law of combination $\eta\xi$ with respect to which the elements ξ constitute a group. We do this as follows. Let $\widehat{ex}$ be any member of the class ξ of paths connecting E_n and X and let $X(t)$ be the elements of the rotation group defined by the points of $\widehat{ex}$, $0 \leq t \leq 1$. If Y is any element whatsoever of the rotation group we denote by $y \cdot \widehat{ex}$ the path defined by the matrices $YX(t)$, $0 \leq t \leq 1$. Thus $y \cdot \widehat{ex}$ is a path beginning at y and ending at yx_1 (the representative point of $YX_1 = YX(1)$). Further if $\widehat{xy}$, $\widehat{yz}$ are any two paths (of which the end point of the first is the beginning point of the second) we denote by $\widehat{xy} \times \widehat{yz}$ the path $\widehat{xz}$ found by first tracing $\widehat{xy}$ and following this by $\widehat{yz}$. These notations having been explained the law of combination is as follows: let $\widehat{ex}$ be a member of the class ξ and $\widehat{ey}$ a member of the class η then $\eta\xi$ is the class ζ which contains the path $\widehat{ez} = \widehat{ey} \times y \cdot \widehat{ex}$ $(z = yx)$. It is clear that if $\widehat{ex}$ is replaced by any other member $(\widehat{ex})'$ of ξ and if $\widehat{ey}$ is replaced by any other member $(\widehat{ey})'$ of η the new path $(ez)'$ belongs to ζ. For $(\widehat{ex})' \sim \widehat{ex}$ (the notation $\sim$ implying membership in the same class) forces $y \cdot (\widehat{ex})' \sim y \cdot \widehat{ex}$; in fact the continuous deformation which sends $x(t)$ into $x'(t)$ induces a continuous deformation which sends $yx(t)$ into $yx'(t)$. Also the law of path multiplication $\widehat{xy} \times \widehat{yz}$ is evidently such that $(\widehat{xy})' \sim (\widehat{xy})$, $(\widehat{yz})' \sim (\widehat{yz})$ forces $(\widehat{xy})' \times (\widehat{yz})' \sim (\widehat{xy}) \times (\widehat{yz})$ — the necessary continuous deformation being found by first deforming $(\widehat{xy})$ into $(\widehat{xy})'$ and following this by a deformation of $(\widehat{yz})$ into $(\widehat{yz})'$. To show that the aggregate of elements ξ with the law of combination $\eta\xi$ constitutes a group we must prove (a) the associative law (b) the existence of a left unit and (c) the existence of a left inverse.

(a) $\zeta(\eta\xi)$ is the class containing the path

$$\widehat{ez} \times z(\widehat{ey} \times y \cdot \widehat{ex}) = \widehat{ez} \times z \cdot \widehat{ey} \times zy \cdot \widehat{ex}$$

whilst $(\zeta\eta)\xi$ is the class containing the path

$$(\widehat{ez} \times z \cdot \widehat{ey}) \times zy \cdot \widehat{ex} = \widehat{ez} \times z \cdot \widehat{ey} \times zy \cdot \widehat{ex}.$$

Hence $\zeta(\eta\xi) = (\zeta\eta)\xi$ proving the associative law.

(b) The path consisting of the single point e acts as a left unit in path multiplication: $e \cdot \widehat{ex} = \widehat{ex}$. Denoting the class containing this path by ϵ we have $\epsilon\xi = \xi$.

(c) As the left inverse of ξ we may take the class ξ^{-1} containing the path $x^{-1} \cdot \widehat{xe}$ where $\widehat{ex}$ is a path belonging to ξ. In fact $\xi^{-1}\xi$ is then the class which contains the path $x^{-1} \cdot \widehat{xe} \times x^{-1} \cdot ex = x^{-1}(\widehat{xe} + \widehat{ex}) \sim \widehat{ee} = \epsilon$.

The product $\eta\xi$ is a class of paths whose end points are uniquely determined (being e and yx). To yx corresponds the uniquely determined element YX of the rotation group. Hence the rotation group is isomorphic to the covering group. To E_n correspond the two classes containing the curves $\alpha^0 = \widehat{ee}$ and α^1 of the previous section. These two elements constitute a subgroup of the covering group which is known as the fundamental group of the covered rotation group: *the fundamental group of the n-dimensional rotation group is the symmetric group on two letters.*

CHAPTER ELEVEN

THE CRYSTALLOGRAPHIC GROUPS

We shall discuss in this chapter those subgroups of the three-dimensional real orthogonal group which are of importance in the theory of crystallography and of molecular structure and shall show how their irreducible representations are determined.

1. The finite subgroups of the three-dimensional rotation group.

We have seen (p. 299) that the unimodular two-dimensional unitary group furnishes a (two-valued) representation of the three-dimensional rotation group. This fact is so fundamental for our present purpose that it seems desirable to treat it in some detail so as to obtain the explicit expressions for the elements of the unimodular two-dimensional matrix U in terms of the parameters of the three-dimensional rotation matrix O. Let O describe a rotation through an angle θ about an axis whose direction cosines are (l, m, n); then we have seen (p. 237) that $O = e^S$ where S is the skew-symmetric matrix

$$S = \theta \begin{pmatrix} 0 & -n & m \\ n & 0 & -l \\ -m & l & 0 \end{pmatrix}$$

and $l^2 + m^2 + n^2 = 1$; hence (p. 237)

$$O = e^S = E_3 + \frac{\sin\theta}{\theta} S + \frac{1 - \cos\theta}{\theta^2} S^2.$$

We now write $\lambda = l \sin\theta/2$, $\mu = m \sin\theta/2$, $\nu = n \sin\theta/2$, $\rho = \cos\theta/2$ (so that $\lambda^2 + \mu^2 + \nu^2 + \rho^2 = 1$) and then O appears in the form

$$(11.1)\quad O = \begin{pmatrix} \rho^2 + \lambda^2 - \mu^2 - \nu^2 & 2(\lambda\mu - \nu\rho) & 2(\lambda\nu + \mu\rho) \\ 2(\mu\lambda + \nu\rho) & \rho^2 + \mu^2 - \nu^2 - \lambda^2 & 2(\mu\nu - \lambda\rho) \\ 2(\nu\lambda - \mu\rho) & 2(\nu\mu + \lambda\rho) & \rho^2 + \nu^2 - \lambda^2 - \mu^2 \end{pmatrix}.$$

It is convenient to present O in a new basis. On writing $\xi = Tx$ the transformation $x \to x' = Ox$ appears in the form $\xi \to \xi' = TOT^{-1}\xi$ and we take as the transforming matrix T the following:

$$(11.2)\qquad T = \begin{pmatrix} 1 & i & 0 \\ 0 & 0 & 1 \\ -1 & i & 0 \end{pmatrix}$$

so that $\xi = x + iy$; $\eta = z$; $\zeta = -x + iy$. An easy calculation yields

$$R = TOT^{-1}$$

$$(11.3) \quad = \begin{pmatrix} (i\nu+\rho)^2 & -2(i\nu+\rho)(i\lambda-\mu) & (i\lambda-\mu)^2 \\ -(i\nu+\rho)(i\lambda+\mu) & \rho^2+\nu^2-\lambda^2-\mu^2 & (i\nu-\rho)(i\lambda-\mu) \\ (i\lambda+\mu)^2 & 2(i\lambda+\mu)(i\nu-\rho) & (i\nu-\rho)^2 \end{pmatrix}$$

and it is at once evident that R is the symmetrized Kronecker square of the unimodular two-dimensional unitary matrix

$$(11.4) \qquad U = \pm \begin{pmatrix} \rho + i\nu & \mu - i\lambda \\ -(\mu + i\lambda) & \rho - i\nu \end{pmatrix}.$$

The geometrical interpretation of this algebraic result is found in the stereographic projection of the unit sphere $x^2 + y^2 + z^2 = 1$ from the South Pole $(0, 0, -1)$ on the equatorial plane $z = 0$. Denoting points on this equatorial plane by complex numbers w it is at once clear that $w = (x + iy)(1 + z) = \xi/(1 + z)$ and that $w\bar{w} = \dfrac{1 - z}{1 + z}\cdot$ It follows from (11.3), since $\xi' = R\xi$ that

$$(11.5) \qquad w' = \frac{(\rho + i\nu)w + (\mu - i\lambda)}{-(\mu + i\lambda)w + \rho - i\nu}$$

so that each rotation $x \to x' = Ox$ of the unit sphere $x^2 + y^2 + z^2 = 1$ appears, under stereographic projection of the sphere upon the equatorial plane, as the linear-fractional transformation (11. 5) of this equatorial plane. In order, therefore, to determine all possible finite subgroups of the three-dimensional rotation group, it is merely necessary to determine all finite subgroups of the linear fractional group $w \to w'$ of (11. 5). We denote any element of this group G by the associated matrix U of (11. 4) ($\pm U$ being regarded as identical). Thus the carrier space in which U operates is a *ray-space* rather than a linear vector space; the vectors $x = (x^1, x^2)$ and $mx = (mx^1, mx^2)$, m any complex number, being regarded as identical. Each element U of G other than the identity E_2 possesses two characteristic rays either of which determines the other (since the scalar product $x^*{}_2 x_1$ of the two characteristic vectors of U is zero). We term these characteristic rays the *poles* of U. If the characteristic matrix of U is X we have $UX = X\Lambda$ where $\Lambda = \begin{pmatrix} e^{i\theta} & 0 \\ 0 & e^{-i\theta} \end{pmatrix}$ and it is clear that all elements of G having the same poles constitute, together with E_2, an Abelian subgroup of G

(since they can all be presented simultaneously in their canonical form $\Lambda = \begin{pmatrix} e^{i\theta} & 0 \\ 0 & e^{-i\theta} \end{pmatrix}$).

If H is a finite subgroup of G those elements of H which possess common poles constitute an Abelian subgroup K of H; and it is easy to see that K is cyclic. In fact let U be that element of K other than E_2 for which θ, $0 < \theta < 2\pi$, is least; then for any other element V of K the angle ϕ must be an integral multiple of θ. For otherwise we could find an integer m such that $0 < \phi - m\theta < \theta$ and VU^{-m} would be an element of K with angle $\phi - m\theta < \theta$, contrary to hypothesis. Hence $K = \{E_2, U, U^2, \cdots\}$ and we shall denote the order of this cyclic group by k (the poles of U being said to belong to K and to be of order k). Let H be of order n and let K be of index j in h $(n = kj)$:

$$H = K_1 + K_2 + \cdots + K_j$$

where $K_1 = K$, $K_2 = V_2K, \cdots, K_j = V_jK$ are the left-cosets of K in H. Let x_1 be a pole of U: $Ux_1 = x_1$ ($x_1 = mx_1$, m any complex number!); then $VUV^{-1} \cdot Vx_1 = Vx_1$ so that Vx_1 is a pole of VUV^{-1} and belongs to the cyclic group VKV^{-1} of order k. The various poles $x_1, x_2 = V_2x_1, \cdots, x_j = V_jx_1$ are all distinct; for $V_px_1 = V_qx_1$ would imply that x_1 is a pole of $V_q^{-1}V_p$ or, equivalently, that $V_q^{-1}V_p$ is in K contrary to the constructive definition of left-cosets. We term the set of j poles $(x_1, \cdots, x_j)$, each of order k, a set of equivalent poles. Each element of H sends any one of a set of equivalent poles into one of the same set (hence the name); in fact if W is an arbitrary element of H, $Wx_p = WV_px_1$ and WV_p, being an element of H, lies in one of the cosets, K_q, say, of K in H. Hence $Wx_p = V_qx_1 = x_q$. Again Wx_r and Wx_s are different, $r \neq s$, as their equality would imply, on operating by W^{-1}, $x_r = x_s$. Hence H induces a group of permutations on the j equivalent poles. If we denote the second pole of U by $x_{1'}$, $x_{1'}$ may or may not appear in the set of equivalent poles determined by x_1; but if $x_{1'}$ does appear so also will $x_{2'}, \cdots, x_{j'}$ (so that j must be even). In fact $Vx_1 = x_a$ forces $Vx_{1'} = x_{a'}$ since Vx_1, $Vx_{1'}$ are the two poles of VUV^{-1}. If, then, $x_{1'}$ does not appear in the set the j conjugate groups $V_pKV_p^{-1}$ have no element in common other than the identity whilst if $x_{1'}$ appears we have merely $j/2$ groups conjugate (in H) to K. Now each of the elements of H, other than the identity element E_2, has two poles so that we have $2n - 2$ in all (each pole counted as often as it appears). But each pole of a set of $j = n/k$ equivalent poles belongs to the $k - 1$ elements, other than the identity, of a cyclic subgroup K of order k of H. Hence we obtain, on summing over the various sets of equivalent poles,

$$\sum_1^r (n/k_p)(k_p - 1) = 2n - 2$$

r denoting the number of such sets. On division by n we obtain the basic relation

$$\sum_{p=1}^{r} 1/k_p = r - 2 + 2/n. \tag{11.6}$$

Since each $k_p \geq 2$ the left-hand side $\leq r/2$ so that $r \leq 4 - 4/n$; also each $k_p \leq n$ so that the left-hand side $\leq r/n$ which implies, on multiplying through by n, $r \geq 2$. Thus there are only two possibilities for r, namely, $r = 2$ and $r = 3$.

Case 1. $r = 2$.

Here $1/k_1 + 1/k_2 = 2/n$ and since $k_1 \leq n$, $k_2 \leq n$ we must have $k_1 = k_2 = n$. Hence n is arbitrary and $H = K$ so that H is a cyclic group $(E, U, \cdots, U^{n-1})$ of order n. All elements of H have the same two poles each of order n. The corresponding subgroup of the three dimensional rotation group is the set of n rotations about a common axis through the angles $2p\pi/n$, $p = 0, 1, \cdots, n - 1$.

Case 2. $r = 3$.

Here $1/k_1 + 1/k_2 + 1/k_3 = 1 + 2/n$ and so at least one of the three numbers $(k_1, k_2, k_3) = 2$. Denoting this one by k_1 we have

$$1/k_2 + 1/k_3 = 1/2 + 2/n.$$

If one of the numbers (k_2, k_3) also $= 2$ we denote it by k_2 and we see then that $n = 2k_3$ must be even. H has a cyclic subgroup K of order $n/2$ and this subgroup determines a set of 2 equivalent poles each of order $n/2$. K is a normal divisor of H (being of index 2) and so the two poles $(x_1, x_{1'})$ of the equivalent set both belong to K. The elements of H which are not in K are all of period 2 (since $k_1 = k_2 = 2$) and any one of these permutes the two poles $(x_1, x_{1'})$ of order $n/2$. The corresponding subgroup of the three-dimensional rotation group is the group consisting of

(a) the set of $n/2$ rotations through the angles $4p\pi/n$, $p = 0, 1, \cdots, n-1$ about a common axis NS; and

(b) the set of $n/2$ rotations obtained by following each of the $n/2$ rotations of (a) by a rotation through π around an axis perpendicular to the axis NS. This group is known as the *dihedral* group of even order n.

Of particular importance is the case $n = 4$ (the *four* group). Here $H = (E_2, U, V, VU)$ where U is of period 2. Since UV is in the group and is distinct from E_2, U, V we must have $UV = VU$. When U is presented in canonical form $\mu = 0 = \nu$, by (11.4) and since U is of period 2 its $\theta = \pi$ so that $\rho = \cos \theta/2 = 0$. Hence the canonical form of U is

$$U = \begin{pmatrix} i & 0 \\ 0 & -i \end{pmatrix}.$$

Since V permutes the poles $(1, 0)$, $(0, 1)$ of U and is of period 2 it must be either $\begin{pmatrix} 0 & -1 \\ 1 & 0 \end{pmatrix}$ or $\begin{pmatrix} 0 & i \\ i & 0 \end{pmatrix}$. It is indifferent which choice we make the other being $UV = VU$. Hence the canonical presentation of the dihedral group of order 4 (the four-group) is

$$(11.7) \quad E_2 = \begin{pmatrix} 1 & 0 \\ 0 & 1 \end{pmatrix};\ U = \begin{pmatrix} i & 0 \\ 0 & -i \end{pmatrix};\ V = \begin{pmatrix} 0 & -1 \\ 1 & 0 \end{pmatrix};\ UV = VU = \begin{pmatrix} 0 & i \\ i & 0 \end{pmatrix}$$

(after calculating UV one must always remember that $-U = U$, by convention).

If neither of the numbers $(k_2, k_3) = 2$ one at least of them $= 3$. Denote this one by k_2 so that $1/k_3 = 1/6 + 2/n$. Hence $k_3 < 6$ so that we have three possibilities

1) $k_3 = 3;\quad n = 12$
2) $k_3 = 4;\quad n = 24$
3) $k_3 = 5;\quad n = 60.$

In particular we see that if we have a finite subgroup of the three-dimensional group of odd order it must be cyclic; if it is of even order (the order not being 12, 24 or 60) and not cyclic it must be dihedral.

Before proceeding to a discussion of these groups it is convenient to call attention to the following definition. If K is any subgroup of a finite group H the set of elements U of H which transform K into itself:

$$UKU^{-1} = K$$

constitute a subgroup of H which contains K as an invariant subgroup. It is known as the normalizer N of K (in H). If K is an invariant subgroup of H, $N = H$; whilst if K coincides with p of its conjugate groups $V_q K V_q^{-1}$, $q = 1, \cdots, j$, the order of the normalizer is kp.

We first consider the case 1) for which $k_3 = 3$ $(k_1 = 2, k_2 = 3)$; $n = 12$. Since $k_1 = 2$ there is a set of six equivalent poles and since the other two sets of equivalent poles are each of order 3 the set of six equivalent poles must be of the type $(1, 1', 2, 2', 3, 3')$. The normalizer N of K must, therefore, be of order 4. If $K = (E_2, U)$, $N = (E_2, U, V, VU)$ where $Vx_1 = x'_1$. It is clear that N is not cyclic since x_1 is not a pole of V and all elements (other than E_2) of a cyclic group have the same poles. Hence N is dihedral (= the four-group) and V is of period 2 and commutative with U. We now consider the set of 4 equivalent poles (z_1, z_2, z_3, z_4) determined by the cyclic group $K = (E_2, S, S^2)$ corresponding to $k_3 = 3$. S effects a permutation on (z_1, z_2, z_3, z_4) containing the unary cycle (1); this permutation cannot contain a binary cycle since then S^2 would contain three unary cycles which is absurd since S^2 has exactly two poles. Thus $S \to (234)$ and no one of the numbers 2, 3, 4 can be the "prime" of any other; e. g., if $3 = 2'$, $S(z_2) = z_{2'}$ forces $S(z_{2'}) = z_2$ and $S \to (22')$. Thus the normalizer of K is K itself and K has four conjugate groups in H the only common element of any two of which is the identity. Hence H contains 8 elements of period 3, three of period 2 (namely U, V, UV) and the identity (the last four constituting the *common* normalizer of each of the three cyclic subgroups of order 2). Since no one of (z_1, z_2, z_3, z_4) is a pole of U, U effects a permutation (12)(34), say, and V and UV effect permutations of the same type. Writing $V \to (13)(24)$, $UV \to (14)(23)$ we see that H is (simply isomorphic to) the alternating group on four letters. Since the common normalizer N of each of the three cyclic subgroups $\{E_2, U\}$, $\{E_2, V\}$, $\{E_2, UV\}$ of order 2 does not contain any element of period 3 the three elements SUS^{-1}, SVS^{-1}, $SUVS^{-1}$ constitute a cyclic permutation of the three elements U, V, UV and S^2 effects the other cyclic permutation. Hence we may, without lack of generality, write $SUS^{-1} = V$; $SVS^{-1} = UV$. On setting $S = \begin{pmatrix} \alpha & \beta \\ -\bar{\beta} & \bar{\alpha} \end{pmatrix}$ (with $\alpha\bar{\alpha} + \beta\bar{\beta} = 1$) and adopting the canonical presentation (11. 7) of the four-group $(1, U, V, UV)$ we find from $SU = VS$ that $\beta = \pm i\alpha$ and from $SV = UVS$, $\bar{\alpha} = \pm i\alpha$ so that $\alpha = \pm \beta$. Hence $\alpha\bar{\alpha} = \frac{1}{2}$ and $\bar{\alpha} = \pm i\alpha$ so that $\alpha^2 = \pm 1/2i$. There are four possibilities according to the various sign choices (in agreement with the fact that four of the 8 elements of period 3 effect the permutation $U \to V$, $V \to UV$, $UV \to U$). Adopting the sign-pair $\alpha = -i\alpha$, $\beta = i\alpha$ we find

$$(11.8) \quad S = \frac{1}{\sqrt{2}} \begin{pmatrix} e^{i\pi/4} & -e^{i\pi/4} \\ e^{-i\pi/4} & e^{-i\pi/4} \end{pmatrix} = \begin{pmatrix} \dfrac{1+i}{2} & -\dfrac{1+i}{2} \\ \dfrac{1-i}{2} & \dfrac{1-i}{2} \end{pmatrix}.$$

The corresponding values of (θ, l, m, n) are $(2\pi/3,\ 1/\sqrt{3},\ 1/\sqrt{3},\ 1/\sqrt{3})$. The corresponding subgroup of the three-dimensional rotation group is realised as follows: consider the 8 corners of a cube and denote the four corners of one face by $1, 4', 2, 3'$, the corners 1, 2 (and $3', 4'$)

being diagonally opposite each other. Let the four other corners be denoted by $1', 4, 2', 3$ the corners $(1. 1')$ being diametrically opposite each other and so on. Then the twelve rotations which send the tetrahedron $(1, 2, 3, 4)$ into itself constitute a realization of H. Here U, V, UV are rotations through π about the lines joining the mid-points of opposite faces of the cube (or, equivalently, the mid-points of opposite edges of the tetrahedron) whilst the 8 elements of period 3 are rotations through $\pm 2\pi/3$ about the diagonals of the cube. This realisation of H is known as the *tetrahedral* group. The *essential* result of the discussion just given is the proof of the fact that there is, aside from the cyclic and dihedral groups, only *one* finite subgroup of order 12 of the rotation group.

We now pass to the case $k_3 = 4$ $(k_1 = 2, k_2 = 3), n = 24$. Corresponding to $k_3 = 4$ we have a cyclic subgroup of H of order 4 and an associated set of six equivalent poles of order 4; since all poles of order 4 must be found in this set $(k_1 \neq 4, k_2 \neq 4)$ this set is of the type $(x_1, x_2, x_3, x_{1'}, x_{2'}, x_{3'})$ and so K has an normalizer in H a group of order 8 which (being non-cyclic) is necessarily dihedral:

$$N = (K, VK); \quad K = (E_2, U, U^2, U^3).$$

V, in common with all the elements of the coset VK is of period 2 and $U^2 = S$ is also of period 2. Since K belongs to a set of 3 conjugate subgroups (no two of which has an element in common save E_2) H contains 6 elements of period 4 and three elements (S, S', S'') of period 2 which belong to the same class of H (since when K is transformed into one of its conjugates K' the *single* element S of period 2 in K must be transformed into the *single* element S' of period 2 in K'). Since $k_1 = 2$ we have a cyclic subgroup of order 2 of H and an associated set of 12 equivalent poles of the type $(1, \cdots, 6, 1', \cdots, 6')$. Hence in addition to the three elements S, S', S'' of period 2, whose poles are of order 4, H contains 6 elements of order 2 (belonging to the same class of H) whose poles are of order 2. Corresponding to $k_3 = 3$ we have a set of 8 equivalent poles of the type $(1, 2, 3, 4, 1', 2', 3', 4')$ so that the cyclic subgroup K (of order 3) belongs to a set of 4 conjugate subgroups of K (no two of which have an element in common save E_2). Hence H contains 8 elements of order 3 and this exhausts the elements of H (E_2, 9 elements of period 2, 8 of period 3, 6 of period 4). If neither S' nor S'' appeared amongst the four elements of period 2 in the coset VK all the elements of this coset would be of period 2 with poles of order 2; and hence the elements in the corresponding coset $(VK)'$ of either of the two conjugate subgroups, $\{K\}'$ say, would also all be of period 2 with poles of order 2. Hence the two sets VK and $(VK)'$ would have at least *two* common elements since there are 8 elements in the two sets and there are only six elements of period 2 with poles of order 2; denoting one of the two common elements by V the two sets VK, VK' have at least one element, other than V, in common. But this is impossible since K and K' have no element, other than E_2 in common. Hence either S' or S'' is in the coset VK. Let us denote by S' that one of these two elements which lies in VK (it will appear immediately that *both* S' and S'' are in VK); S' being in the normalizer of K transforms S (the only element of period 2 in K) into itself so that S' commutes with S:

$$SS' = S'S \text{ (so that } SS' \text{ is of period 2).}$$

Under the various elements of H the element SS' of period 2 transforms into one of the set of three elements $SS', S'S'', S''S$; in fact if $SS' \to S'S''$ then $S'S \to S''S'$ so that $S'S'' = S''S'$ and so on. Hence SS' must be one of the three elements S, S', S'' of period 2 (the other 6 elements of period 2 belonging to a class of six elements). Hence $SS' = S'' = S'S$. Multiplication on the left by S gives $S' = SS''$; and multiplication on the right by S gives $S''S = S'$. Similarly $S = S''S' = S'S''$. Hence the four elements (E_2, S, S', S'') form a group of order 4 which (not being cyclic) is the four-group and which is an invariant subgroup of H. Now no one of the 8 elements of period 3 can belong to the normalizer of the group $\{E_2, S\}$ of order 2; for if W, of period 3, commuted with S, of period 2 the product WS would be of period 6 and there are no elements of period 6 in H. Applying the same argument to $\{E_2, S'\}$, $\{E_2, S''\}$ we see that any one of the 8 elements of period 3 effects a cyclic permutation of (S, S', S''). On writing S, S', S'' in the normal form (11. 7) we find that one of the 8 elements of order 3 is of the form

$$W = \frac{1}{\sqrt{2}} \begin{pmatrix} e^{i\pi/4} & -e^{i\pi/4} \\ e^{-i\pi/4} & e^{-i\pi/4} \end{pmatrix}$$

of (11. 8). The complete set of 8 elements is got by multiplying the four group

$$E_2 = \begin{pmatrix} 1 & 0 \\ 0 & 1 \end{pmatrix}; \quad S = \begin{pmatrix} i & 0 \\ 0 & -i \end{pmatrix}; \quad S' = \begin{pmatrix} 0 & -1 \\ 1 & 0 \end{pmatrix}; \quad S'' = \begin{pmatrix} 0 & i \\ i & 0 \end{pmatrix}$$

by W and W^2. Hence H contains the tetrahedral group as a subgroup of order 2 (hence invariant). To obtain the other 12 elements of H we observe that $U\,(S = U^2)$ is of the form $\begin{pmatrix} \alpha & 0 \\ 0 & \alpha^{-1} \end{pmatrix}$ since it has the same poles $(1,0)$, $(0,1)$ as S. Then $S = U^2$ yields $\alpha^2 = \pm i$ so that $\alpha = e^{\pm i\pi/4}$. There is no lack of generality in taking the $+$ sign since the other sign gives U^3 (the reciprocal of U). Hence

$$U = \begin{pmatrix} e^{i\pi/4} & 0 \\ 0 & e^{-i\pi/4} \end{pmatrix}.$$

Thus there is only one non-cyclic, non-dihedral subgroup of order 24 of the three-dimensional rotation group. In addition to the twelve rotations of the tetrahedral group it contains six rotations through angles $\pm \pi/2$ about the lines joining the mid-points of opposite faces of the fundamental cube and in addition six rotations through the angle π about the six joins of opposite edges of the cube. The group is known as the *octahedral* group since it sends the regular octahedron whose corners are the mid-points of the faces of the fundamental cube into itself. The octahedral group is simply isomorphic to the symmetric group on four letters. All of its operations permute the four diagonals of the basic cube and the isomorphism is given by: $S \rightarrow (12)(34)$; $S' \rightarrow (23)(14)$; $S'' \rightarrow (31)(24)$; $W \rightarrow (234)$; $U \rightarrow (1234)$.

We shall not discuss in detail the remaining case $k_1 = 2, k_2 = 3, k_3 = 5, n = 60$ for it is of no importance, as we shall see in the next section, for the theory of crystallography. It has a set of 12 equivalent poles of order 5, a set of 20 equivalent poles of order 3 and a set of 30 equivalent poles of order 2. It is simply isomorphic to the alternating group on 5 letters and is known as the *icosahedral* group since its realisation as a subgroup of the 3-dimensional rotation group is the group of sixty rotations sending a regular icosahedron into itself. Amongst the sixty elements are 24 of period 5 (rotations through $\pm 2\pi/5$, $\pm 4\pi/5$ about the six axes joining opposite corners of the icosahedron); 20 of period 3 (rotations through $\pm 2\pi/3$ about the 10 axes joining the mid-points of opposite faces of the icosahedron); and 15 of period 2 (rotations through π about the 15 axes joining the mid-points of opposite edges of the icosahedron).

2. The crystallographic groups.

Let (u, v, w) be a set of non-coplanar vectors and consider their linear combinations with *integral* (positive, negative or zero) coefficients. If all these vectors have a common initial point (not necessarily the origin) their end points are said to be the points of a space lattice. We understand by the term *crystallographic group* a finite subgroup of the full real orthogonal group each element of which sends each and every point of a space lattice into a point of the same lattice. We shall first consider the crystallographic groups of the *first kind* i. e. those which are subgroups of the rotation group so that all their elements are proper (i. e. of determinant $+1$). Each such group, being a finite subgroup of the rotation group, must be one of the various types discussed in the previous section. Not all of these, however, are possible crystallographic groups; in fact no pole of an element of a crystallographic group of the first kind can be of order > 6. To see this let θ be the angle of rotation of an element O (other than the identity) of a crystallographic group of the first kind and let p be a point of the space lattice having the property that no point of the lattice (other than the origin if the origin happens to belong to the lattice) is nearer the origin than p. Denote $O(p)$, $O^{-1}(p)$ by p' and p''. Then the point p''' defined by

$$\overrightarrow{pp'''} = \overrightarrow{pp'} + \overrightarrow{pp''}$$

belongs to the space lattice. It will be nearer the origin than p, without coinciding with the origin, if $0 < \theta < \pi/3$ or if $\pi/3 < \theta < \pi/2$. Hence the order of the poles of O cannot surpass 6 and if it is less than 6 it cannot surpass 4. The only possible orders are, accordingly, 2, 3, 4 and 6. Thus, as has been remarked above, no crystallographic group of the first kind can contain as a subgroup the icosahedral group (since this group contains elements whose poles are of order 5). Since the trace of a (proper) orthogonal matrix whose angle of rotation is θ is $1 + 2\cos\theta$ we have only the following five possibilities for the trace of an element O of a crystallographic group of the first kind.

1. $Tr\, O = 3$ $(O = E_3)$; 2. $Tr\, O = -1$ (O an element of period 2, $\theta = \pi$); 3. $Tr O = 0$ (O an element of period 3, $\theta = 2\pi/3$); 4. $Tr\, O = 1$ (O an element of period 4, $\theta = \pi/2$); 5. $Tr\, O = 2$ (O an element of period 6, $\theta = \pi/3$).

We denote our crystallographic group by H and regard it as a representation of itself in order to apply the theory of group representations. The representation of H, furnished by H itself, may or may not be reducible. If it is reducible the components, as representations of a finite group, are unitary (any representation equivalent to a unitary representation being, as usual, termed unitary); but they may not be real. If they are real they are orthogonal since "real, unitary" is the same as "real, orthogonal." Let us suppose, to start, that H is reducible and contains, when reduced, three real components each necessarily of dimension 1 since the sum of the dimensions is 3. Since each component is real and of finite period the 1×1 matrices of this component must be ± 1 so that each element of this component is either the identity or of period 2. There are at most four distinct elements in H (since we must either take all signs + or one + and two — in order that each element of H be proper). If there are 4 elements in H, H is the four group (consisting of the identity and three rotations through π one about each of the coordinate axes); if there are but two elements in H it is the cyclic group of order two consisting of the identity and a rotation through π about one of the coordinate axes. It is clear that each of these groups sends any lattice having the origin as one of its points and its vectors (u, v, w) each parallel to one of the coordinate axes into itself. We have thus, so far, two crystallographic groups of the first kind. The two group is denoted by C_2 (to denote that it is a cyclic group of order 2) and the four-group by D_2 to denote that it is a dihedral group realised by adjoining to C_2 a rotation through π about an axis perpendicular to the axis of C_2. Both groups C_2 and D_2, being Abelian, have only one-dimensional irreducible representations. The characters of these have been given on pp. 99 and 103.

We next consider the case where H furnishes an irreducible representation of itself. Since the characters $\chi(O)$ of H are real the sum of their squares is the order h of H. We denote by (n_2, n_3, n_4, n_5) the number of elements of H of periods $(2, 3, 4, 6)$ respectively. Then, since $\chi(E_3) = 3$,

$$9 + n_2 + n_4 + 4n_5 = h = 1 + n_2 + n_3 + n_4 + n_5$$

so that $n_3 = 8 + 3n_5$ implying $h \geqq 9$. Also H cannot be cyclic (all irreducible representations of a cyclic group being one-dimensional, a cyclic group being Abelian) nor can it be dihedral. In fact *a dihedral group D_n of order $2n$ possesses no irreducible representations of dimension > 2.* To see this let $\epsilon = e^{2\pi i/n}$, $n > 2$, and construct the 2×2 matrices $A = \begin{pmatrix} \epsilon & 0 \\ 0 & \epsilon^{-1} \end{pmatrix}$, $B = \begin{pmatrix} 0 & 1 \\ 1 & 0 \end{pmatrix}$. Then the group $(E_2, A, \cdots, A^{n-1}; B, BA, \cdots, BA^{n-1})$ is a two-dimensional representation of D_n. The characters of this representation are all real and the sum of their squares $= \sum_0^{n-1} \epsilon^{2j} + \sum_0^{n-1} \epsilon^{-2j} + 2n = 2n$ (since the sum of the squares of the roots of $x^n - 1 = 0$ is zero and since ϵ^{-1} runs over these roots when ϵ does). Hence the representation is irreducible. On using ϵ^j, $j = 2, \cdots, n-1$ we obtain $(n-2)$ 2×2 representations of D_n. If any one of these 2-dimensional representations were reducible it would be Abelian since all its matrices could be presented simultaneously in diagonal form. On setting $A_j = \begin{pmatrix} \epsilon^j & 0 \\ 0 & \epsilon^{-j} \end{pmatrix}$ it is clear that $BA_jB^{-1} = A_j^{-1}$ so that in order that our two-dimensional representation be reducible we must have $\epsilon^j = \epsilon^{-j}$, i. e., $\epsilon^{2j} = 1$ so that n must be even. If n is odd $(= 2m + 1)$ we obtain, by giving j, in turn, the values $1, 2, \cdots, m$, m irreducible two-dimensional representations (no two of which are equivalent since the character of A_j, namely $2 \cos 2j\pi/n$, is different from that of A_k, namely $2 \cos 2k\pi/n$, $k \neq j = 1, \cdots, m$). In addition to these two-dimensional irreducible representations we have two one-dimensional representations namely the identity representation and the alternating representation (in which 1 is attached to each element of the cyclic subgroup C_n and -1 to each other element). The fact that the sum of the squares of these various irreducible representations, namely $4m + 2$, is the order $2n$ of the group assures us that there are no other irreducible representations. If n is even, $= 2m$, we obtain $m - 1$ irreducible 2-dimensional representations by setting $j = 1, \cdots, m - 1$ and one reducible 2×2 representation by setting $j = m$. In all we have $m - 1$ two-dimensional irreducible representations and 4 one-dimensional representations no two of these $m + 3$ representations being equivalent. The sum of the squares of their dimensions being $4m = 2n$ we know that there are no other irreducible representations.

Returning, then, to our irreducible group H of dimension > 9 we know that it must be either the tetrahedral group ($h = 12$) or the octahedral group ($h = 24$), since these are the only non-cyclic, non-dihedral crystallographic groups of the first kind (the corresponding lattice being built from the fundamental cube $1, 2, 3, 4, 1', 2', 3', 4'$ of p. 334). Thus we have two additional crystallographic groups of the first kind T, of order 12, and O, of order 24, each of which furnishes an irreducible representation (of dimension 3) of itself. We have given the character table of T, which is simply isomorphic to the alternating group on 4 letters on p. 175; and of O, which is simply isomorphic to the symmetric group on 4 letters on p. 142.

Before proceeding to a discussion of the remaining cases, namely, that in which the representation of H is reducible containing two components and that in which H is reducible containing three components not all of which are real it is convenient to establish a theorem connecting the order of a finite group with the characters of a given representation of the group. For any irreducible representation of a finite group H the sum of its characters is divisible by the order h of H; the quotient being unity for the identical representation and zero for all others, since this quotient tells how often the identity representation is contained in the given representation. Since *any* representation of H is a linear combination with (positive or zero) integral coefficients of irreducible representations the sum of the characters of any representation Γ of H is divisible by h. The squared characters of Γ are the characters of $\Gamma \times \Gamma$

so that the sum of these squared characters is divisible by h; similarly the sum of the cubed characters (which are the characters of $\Gamma \times \Gamma \times \Gamma$) is divisible by h and so on. Thus the sum over all elements of H of any polynomial with integral coefficients (positive, negative or zero) in the character χ of any representation of H is divisible by h. If there are r distinct characters $v^{(1)}, \cdots, v^{(r)}$ and m_j denotes the number of elements of H for which $\chi = v^{(j)}$ we have $\sum_1^r m_j f(v^{(j)})$ divisible by h where f is any polynomial in χ with integral coefficients. If all characters χ^j are integral we may choose for $f(\chi)$ the product $(\chi - v^{(2)})(\chi - v^{(3)}) \cdots (\chi - v^{(r)})$ and we find that

(11.9) $\quad m_1(v^{(1)} - v^{(2)})(v^{(1)} - v^{(3)}) \cdots (v^{(1)} - v^{(r)})$ is divisible by h.

We now consider the representation of H which is furnished by H itself and denote by χ the characters of one of its irreducible components. Then the quantities $\bar{\chi}$ are the characters of an irreducible representation of H (the conjugate representation) and it is clear that H contains these two representations equally often. For H contains the irreducible representation, whose characters are χ, $1/h \sum TrO\chi(O)$ times (the summation being over the elements O of H) and this is the same as $1/h \sum Tr(O)\bar{\chi}(O)$ simply because $Tr(O)$ is real. It follows that if H is reducible it must contain at least one *real* component of dimension 1; for at least one of its components is one-dimensional and if this is not real all the components are one-dimensional, a second one-dimensional component being the conjugate complex of the first. The third component is, then, certainly real since the sum of all three (being TrO) is real. This real component (being unitary) has all its elements ± 1. If an element O carries the value $+1$ for its real one-dimensional component, the characters of the remaining two-dimensional component A (which may or may not be reducible) have the following possible values (see p. 337): 1. $TrA = 2 (O = E_3)$; 2. $TrA = -2$ (O an element of period 2, $\theta = \pi$); 3. $TrA = -1$ (O an element of period 3, $\theta = 2\pi/3$); 4. $TrA = 0$ (O an element of period 4, $\theta = \pi/2$); 5. $TrA = 1$ (O an element of period 6, $\theta = \pi/3$). There remains a sixth possibility occurring when O has the value -1 for its real one-dimensional component; each matrix A of the two-dimensional (unitary) component must have determinant -1 so that it is of the form $\begin{pmatrix} \alpha & +\bar{\beta} \\ \beta & -\bar{\alpha} \end{pmatrix}$, $\alpha\bar{\alpha} + \beta\bar{\beta} = 1$; since $TrO = TrA - 1$ is real α is real. Hence the characteristic numbers of A are ± 1 and the sixth possibility is: 6. $TrA = 0$ (O an element of period 2, $\theta = \pi$). This sixth case can only occur when the two-dimensional component is *irreducible*; in fact if it were reducible it would contain two conjugate complex one-dimensional representations so that the characters of the two representations could not be ± 1. We denote by $(n_1, n_2, n_3, n_4, n_5, n_6)$ the number of elements of the various types. Since all elements of O are distinct all matrices A are distinct; for an equality between two of the matrices A would force the corresponding one-dimensional real components to be equal and hence the two corresponding elements O of H to be equal. Hence $n_1(A = E_2) = 1$; $n_2(A = -E_2) = 0$ or 1.

We first consider the case where the two-dimensional representation $\{A\}$ is reducible, the one-dimensional components being conjugate complex (and not real; the case where H contains 3 real one-dimensional components having been already discussed). Then $n_6 = 0$ and we deal with the two cases $n_2 = 0$, $n_2 = 1$.

1) $n_2 = 0$; this implies $n_4 = 0$, $n_5 = 0$, since the square of an element of order 4 or the cube of an element of order 6, would be $-E_2$. On setting $m_1 = n_1 = 1$, $v^{(1)} = 2$, $v^{(2)} = -1$ in (11.9) we find that 3 is divisible by h. Hence $h = 3$ and we have the cyclic group C_3 (the plane lattice containing the points $1, \omega, \omega^2$ ($\omega = e^{2\pi i/3}$) being sent into itself by C_3, the space lattice obtained by parallel displacement of this lattice in a direction perpendicular to its plane is sent into itself by C_3).

2) $n_2 = 1$. Here the reducibility of the representation $\{A\}$ gives $\Sigma n_j(\chi^j)^2 = 2h$ which coupled with $\Sigma n_j = h$ gives $\Sigma n_j\{(\chi^j)^2 - 1\} = h$. On setting $n_1 = 1$, $n_2 = 1$ we obtain $h = 6 - n_4$ so that $h \leq 6$. From $\Sigma n_j(\chi^j)^2 = 2h$ we obtain $h \geq 4$. Since $h \neq 5$ we have only two possibilities:

   a) $h = 4$, $n_4 = 2$. This is the cyclic group C_4; the plane lattice containing the points $1, \pm i$ being sent into itself by C_4.

   b) $h = 6$, $n_4 = 0$, $n_3 + n_5 = 4$. Since to each element A of period 3 (or 6) corresponds an element $-A$ of period 6 (or 3) we must have $n_3 = n_5 = 2$. The group is the cyclic group C_6; the corresponding plane lattice containing the points $1, -\omega^2, \omega$.

Dealing next with the case where $\{A\}$ is irreducible we again treat separately the cases $n_2 = 0, 1$.

a) $n_2 = 0$. The irreducibility of $\{A\}$ gives $\Sigma n_j(\chi^j)^2 = h$ which coupled with $\Sigma n_j = h$ yields $\Sigma n_j\{(\chi^j)^2 - 1\} = 0$, i. e. $n_4 + n_6 = 3$ so that $h \geq 4$ (since $n_1 = 1$). From (11.9) we see since $v^{(1)} = 2$,

$v^{(2)} = -1$, $v^{(3)} = 0$, $v^{(4)} = 1$ that h is a divisor of 6. Hence $h = 6$ so that $n_4 = 0$ (4 not being a divisor of 6) $n_6 = 3$ so that H contains three elements of period 2. H cannot be cyclic (for it would have then only two elements of period 2). Hence $n_5 = 0$, $n_3 = 2$ so that H is the dihedral group D_3 the corresponding lattice containing the points $(\cos 2\pi/3, \pm \sin 2\pi/3, 0)$, $(0, 0, 1)$. D_3 is simply isomorphic to the symmetric group on 3 letters and we have given its character table on p. 100.

b) $n_2 = 1$. On setting $v^{(1)} = 2$, $v^{(2)} = -2$, $v^{(3)} = -1$, $v^{(4)} = 0$, $v^{(5)} = 1$ we see from (11.9) that h is a divisor of 24. From $h = \Sigma\, n_j (\chi^j)^2$ $h \geq 8$. Since H is reducible $h \neq 24$ (the only allowable group of this order being the *irreducible* octahedral group). Hence $h = 8$ or $h = 12$ and we have either D_4 or D_6 (the tetrahedral group $h = 12$ being ruled out since H is reducible and the cyclic groups C_8, C_{12} being ruled out since no pole of an element of H can be of order > 6). D_4 has one irreducible representation of dimension 2 and 4 of dimension 1 and $n_2 = 1$, $n_3 = 0$, $n_4 = 2$, $n_5 = 0$, $n_6 = 4$; whilst D_6 has two irreducible representations of dimension 2 and four of dimension 1 and $n_2 = 1$, $n_3 = 2$, $n_4 = 0$, $n_5 = 2$, $n_6 = 6$.

We have now exhausted all possibilities for crystallographic groups of the first kind. There are eleven different groups (including the identity):

$$E;\ C_2, D_2;\ T, O;\ C_3, C_4, C_6;\ D_3, D_4, D_6.$$

The four sets (following the identity E) correspond to the following situations:

C_2, D_2;	H reducible into 3 real components
T, O;	H irreducible
C_3, C_4, C_6;	H reducible into 3 components one real and the other two conjugate complex
D_3, D_4, D_6;	H reducible into two components.

From each of these eleven crystallographic groups of the first kind we obtain a new group of double the order by adding the elements $-O$, where O is any element of H. The elements $-O$ are all improper and the crystallographic group of the first kind is a subgroup of index two (hence invariant) of the "extended" group $\{H, -H\}$. We may denote the elements H by (O, E_3) and the improper elements by $(O, -E_3)$ and it is clear that the "extended" crystallographic group of the first kind is merely the direct product of the original crystallographic group of the first kind by the cyclic two-group $I = (E_3, -E_3)$. The lattices associated with these extended crystallographic groups are symmetric about the origin (the group containing the element $-E_3$). If the crystallographic group contains a rotation through π: $x \to x' = -x$; $y \to y' = -y$; $z \to z' = z$ the extended group will contain the product of this by $-E_3$ i. e. the reflection $x \to x' = x$; $y \to y' = y$; $z \to z' = -z$ in the "horizontal" plane $z = 0$. We denote the extended group by adding the label h (= reflection in a plane perpendicular to the axis of rotation) to the symbol for the crystallographic group of the first kind: Thus $C_{2,h}, D_{2,h}$; $T_h, O_h, C_{4,h}, C_{6,h}, D_{4,h}, D_{6,h}$. The two groups C_3 and D_3 do not contain a rotation through π about the vertical axis but D_3 contains a rotation through π about a horizontal axis so that the group found by extending D_3 contains a reflection in a vertical plane i. e. a plane through the axis of the cyclic subgroup C_3 of D_3. We denote, accordingly, the extended group by $D_{3,v}$; the extended group of C_3 we denote simply by $\bar{C}_3$ so that $\bar{C}_3$ is a cyclic group of order 6 generated by $-L$, $(L^3 = E_3)$. Thus we have the following eleven crystallographic groups containing the central reflection $-E_3$:

$$\{E_3, -E_3\};\ C_{2,h}, D_{2,h};\ T_h, O_h;\ \bar{C}_3, C_{4,h}, C_{6,h};\ D_{3,v}, D_{4,h}, D_{6,h}.$$

It is clear that the remaining crystallographic groups cannot contain the central reflection $-E_3$. In fact if a crystallographic group is not of the first kind its proper elements constitute a subgroup of index two so that if it contains $-E_3$ it must be of the type $(H, -H)$ just discussed. Let us consider then a possible crystallographic group K which is not of the first kind, (hence, of even order), and which does not contain the central reflection $-E_3$. Let $\{H\}$ be its subgroup of index two formed by its proper elements (so that $\{H\}$ is a crystallographic group of the first kind). Then if O is in H, $-O$ is not in K (for if it were $-O \cdot O^{-1} = -E_3$ would be in K). If, then, A is any improper element of K, so that each improper element of K is of the form AO, O in H, $-AO$ is a rotation which is not in H. The collection $\{H, -AH\}$ constitutes accordingly, a crystallographic group of the first kind of the same (even) order as K; this crystallographic group being such that it has a subgroup of index 2. Conversely from any crystallographic group of even order and possessing a subgroup of index 2: $\{H, -AH\}$ we obtain a crystallographic group $\{H, AH\}$ containing improper elements but not containing the central reflection $-E_3$ (since E_3 is not contained in the coset $-AH$ of H). If our crystallographic group of even order possesses several subgroups of index 2 we obtain several crystallographic groups from it in this way and we have to examine whether or not these are distinct. From C_2 we obtain the group (E_3, S) where S is the reflection $x \to x' = x;\ y \to y' = y;\ z \to z' = -z$ in the horizontal plane $z = 0$. From C_4 we obtain the cyclic group $\bar{C}_2$ of order 4 generated by $x \to x' = y;\ y \to y' = -x;\ z \to z' = -z$. From C_6 we obtain $C_{3,h}$ for C_6 contains the element $x \to x' = -x;\ y \to y' = -y;\ z \to z' = z$ outside its cyclic subgroup and so our new group contains $x \to x' = x,\ y \to y' = y,\ z \to z' = -z$ i. e. the reflection in the horizontal plane $z = 0$. $C_{3,h}$ is a cyclic group of order 6 generated by the element $x \to x' = \frac{1}{2}(-x + \sqrt{3}y);\ y \to y' = \frac{1}{2}(\sqrt{3}x + y);\ z \to z' = -z$. From D_3 we obtain $C_{3,v}$ since D_3 contains $x \to x' = x;\ y \to y' = -y,\ z \to z' = -z$ so that our new group contains $x \to x' = -x;\ y \to y' = y;\ z \to z' = z$. From O we obtain, similarly, T_v. The four-group D_2 has three subgroups of index 2; let us denote the four elements of D_2 as follows:

$$(x, y, z);\ (-x, -y, z);\ (x, -y, -z);\ (-x, y, -z)$$

where the symbol $(-x, -y, z)$, for example, denotes the rotation $x \to x' = -x;\ y \to y' = -y;\ z \to z' = z$. If we take (x, y, z), $(-x, -y, z)$ as our H our new crystallographic group is

$$(x, y, z);\ (-x, -y, z);\ (-x, y, z);\ (x, -y, z)$$

which is a $C_{2,v}$ (the C_2 around the z axis with the added reflection $x \to x' = -x;\ y \to y' = y;\ z \to z' = z$ in the yz plane). If we take (x, y, z), $(x, -y, -z)$ as our H we obtain

$$(x, y, z);\ (x - y, -z);\ (x, y, -z);\ (x - y, z)$$

which is again a $C_{2,v}$ (rotation through π about the x axis followed by a reflexion in the xy plane). Both groups are the same being transformable one into the other by the permutation matrix $x \to x' = z$, $y \to y' = y;\ z \to z' = x$. Similarly if we take the third C_2 for H we obtain the same $C_{2,v}$. Thus D_2 yields only one crystallographic group $C_{2,v}$. The remaining crystallographic groups of the first kind possessing subgroups of index 2 are D_4 and D_6. Each of them yields *two* new crystallographic groups. Let us first discuss D_4. This dihedral group of order 8 has 5 irreducible representations one of dimension 2 and four of dimension 1 (p. 339). Let L denote the element of order 4 and M the element of order 2 which generate D_4 thus: $C_4 = (E_3, L, L^2, L^3)$; $D_4 = \{C_4, MC_4\}$; $L^4 = E$, $M^2 = E$. Then $MLM = L^3$, $ML^2M = L^2$, $ML^3M = L$ and the five classes of D_4 are E_3; (L, L^3); L^2; (M, ML^2); (ML, ML^3). In addition to the cyclic subgroup of index 2 we have two other subgroups of index 2; (E_3, L^2, M, ML^2), (E_3, L^2, ML^3, ML). The cyclic subgroup yields the crystallographic group $C_{4,v}$ since $-M$ is the reflexion $x \to x' = -x$; $y \to y' = y$; $z \to z' = z$ in a vertical plane. The other two groups are

$$(E_3, L^2, M, ML^2; \; -L, -L^3, -ML^3, -ML)$$

and
$$(E_3, L^2, ML^3, ML; \; -L, -L^3, -ML^2, -M).$$

These are simply isomorphic in the order written so that each is a representation of the other. Now M, being a rotation through π has the trace -1 whilst ML, being the substitution $x \to x' = -y$; $y \to y' = -x$; $z \to z' = -z$ has also the trace -1 so that the characters of the two classes (M, ML^2), (ML, ML^3) of D_4, in the representation of D_4 which is furnished by D_4 itself are the same namely -1. Hence the two groups just written down are equivalent (since, as representations of each other they have the same characters). This group yielded by D_4 (other than the $C_{4,v}$) is a $D_{2,v}$. In fact the substitutions $(E_3, L^2, M, ML^2;$ $-L, -L^3, -ML^3, -ML)$ are (x, y, z), $(-x, -y, z)$, $(x -y, -z)$, $(-z, y, z)$; $(y, -x, -z)$, $(-y, x, -z)$, $(-y, -x, z)$, (y, x, z); the first four constitute a D_2 and the last is a reflection in the vertical plane $x - y = 0$. $D_{2,v}$ is a dihedral group of order 8 whose cyclic subgroup is generated by the element $-L$. Finally D_6, of order twelve, has two irreducible two-dimensional representations and four one-dimensional representations (p. 339). The six classes are

$$E_3, \; (L, L^5), \; (L^2, L^4), \; L^3, \; (M, ML^2, ML^4), \; (ML, ML^3, ML^5),$$

with characters 3, 2, 0, -1, -1, -1 respectively. In addition to the cyclic subgroup of index 2 which leads to the new crystallographic group $C_{6,v}$ we have the two subgroups of index 2:

$$(E_3, L^2, L^4, M, ML^2, ML^4)$$
$$(E_3, L^2, L^4, ML, ML^3, ML^5).$$

We thus obtain the two groups

$$(E_3, L^2, L^4, M, ML^2, ML^4, -L, -L^3, -L^5, -ML, -ML^3, -ML^5)$$
$$(E_3, L^2, L^4, ML^5, ML, ML^3, -L, -L^3, -L^5, -M, -ML^2, -ML^4)$$

which are simply isomorphic, in the order written. Each may be regarded as a representation of the other and since they have the same characters they are equivalent. They furnish a $D_{3,h}$; in fact the first six, say, $(E_3, L^2, L^4, M, ML^2, ML^4)$ constitute a D_3 whilst $-L^3$ is the reflection

$$x \to x' = -x; \; y \to y' = y; \; z \to z' = -z$$

in the horizontal plane $z = 0$.

Resuming, then, there are in all 32 crystallographic groups. Of these

11 are of the first kind i. e. contain only rotations; 11 contain the central reflection $-E_3$ and 10 do not contain this central reflection but contain improper elements.

3. The character tables of the 32 crystallographic groups.

Although there are 32 distinct crystallographic groups this does not mean that there are 32 different character tables. Several of the 32 groups may be simply isomorphic so that they all have the same character table. The groups differ in the sense that they are different representations of the same abstract group. For convenience of reference we shall denote in this section the group $(E_3, -E_3)$, which consists of the identity and the central reflection, by the symbol I (= inversion) and the group which consists of the identity and a plane reflection by the symbol S.

Of the 31 crystallographic groups other than the identity three, namely C_2, I and S are all representations of the two-group (= group of permutations on two letters). This contains two classes and has two irreducible representations Γ_1, Γ_2 each of dimension one. Γ_1 the identity representation, has the characters $(1, 1)$ and Γ_2, the alternating representation, has the characters $(1, -1)$. The characters of C_2, I, S are, respectively $(3, -1)$, $(3, -3)$, $(3, 1)$ so that

$$C_2 = \Gamma_1 + 2\Gamma_2; \quad I = 3\Gamma_2; \quad S = 2\Gamma_1 + \Gamma_2.$$

Of the remaining 28 crystallographic groups three, namely, D_2, $C_{2,h}$, $C_{2,v}$ are the four-group. This group has four irreducible representations all of dimension one and we have given its character table on p. 103; we rederive it here so as to prepare for the more complicated groups to follow. Denoting C_2 by (E, L), $L^2 = E$ and setting $M^2 = E$, $ML = LM$ the four-group is $(E, L; M, ML)$. We obtain, by the method of p. 338, the two-dimensional representation $(E_2, -E_2; B, -B)$ where $B = \begin{pmatrix} 0 & 1 \\ 1 & 0 \end{pmatrix}$. The diagonal canonical form of B is $\begin{pmatrix} 1 & 0 \\ 0 & -1 \end{pmatrix}$, since the characteristic numbers of B are ± 1. Hence the two-dimensional representation is the sum of the two one-dimensional representations

$$\Gamma_3 = (1, -1, 1, -1); \quad \Gamma_4 = (1, -1, -1, 1).$$

These together with the identity representation $\Gamma_1 = (1, 1, 1, 1)$ and the alternating representation $\Gamma_2 = (1, 1, -1, -1)$ constitute the four irreducible representations of the four-group. The characters of D_2, $C_{2,h}$, $C_{2,v}$ being, respectively, $(3, -1, -1, -1)$, $(3, -1, 1, -3)$, $(3, -1, 1, 1)$ we have

$$D_2 = \Gamma_2 + \Gamma_3 + \Gamma_4; \quad C_{2,h} = \Gamma_2 + 2\Gamma_3; \quad C_{2,v} = \Gamma_1 + \Gamma_3 + \Gamma_4.$$

There is but one crystallographic group C_3 isomorphic to the cyclic group of order 3. This cyclic group has three irreducible representations all of dimension one, their characters being

$$\Gamma_1 = (1, 1, 1); \quad \Gamma_2 = (1, \omega, \omega^2); \quad \Gamma_3 = (1, \omega^2, \omega); \quad \omega = e^{2\pi i/3}.$$

Since the characters of C_3 are $(3, 0, 0)$ we have

$$C_3 = \Gamma_1 + \Gamma_2 + \Gamma_3.$$

Of the remaining 24 groups two, namely, D_3, $C_{3,v}$ are simply isomorphic to the symmetric group on three letters: $(E, L, L^2; M, ML, ML^2)$, $L^3 = E$, $M^2 = E$, $ML = L^2M$. Each of these two groups has, therefore, three irreducible representations one of dimension 2 and two of dimension 1. Arranging the classes in the order E, (L, L^2), (M, ML, ML^2); Γ_1, the identity representation, has the characters $(1, 1, 1)$; Γ_2, the alternating representation, has the characters $(1, 1, -1)$; and Γ_3, the two-dimensional representation, has the characters $(2, -1, 0)$. Since the characters of D_3, $C_{3,v}$ are, respectively, $(3, 0, -1)$, $(3, 0, 1)$ we have

$$D_3 = \Gamma_2 + \Gamma_3; \quad C_{3,v} = \Gamma_1 + \Gamma_3.$$

Of the remaining 22 groups two, namely, C_4 and $\bar{C}_2$ are simply isomorphic to the cyclic group of order 4. Each of these has, accordingly, four irreducible representations all of dimension 1, their characters being

$$\Gamma_1 = (1, 1, 1, 1); \quad \Gamma_2 = (1, i, -1, -i);$$
$$\Gamma_3 = (1, -1, 1, -1); \quad \Gamma_4(1, -i, -1, i).$$

The characters of C_4 and $\bar{C}_2$ being $(3, 1, -1, 1)$ and $(3, -1, -1, -1)$ respectively, we have

$$C_4 = \Gamma_1 + \Gamma_2 + \Gamma_4; \quad \bar{C}_2 = \Gamma_2 + \Gamma_3 + \Gamma_4.$$

Of the remaining 20 groups three, namely D_4, $C_{4,v}$, $D_{2,v}$ are simply isomorphic to the dihedral group of order 8. Each of these groups has, accordingly, 5 irreducible representations one of dimension 2 and four of dimension one. On denoting the dihedral group of order 8 by $(C_4; MC_4)$ where $C_4 = (E, L, L^2, L^3)$, $L^4 = E$, $M^2 = E$ and arranging the classes in the order E, (L, L^3), L^2, (M, ML^2), (ML, ML^3) the character table of the group is as follows (Γ_1 = the identity representation, Γ_2, the alternating representation, Γ_3, Γ_4 = the two one-dimensional representations into which one of the two-dimensional representations breaks down, and Γ_5 = the two-dimensional representation).

Character Table for the dihedral group of order 8.

	(E)	(L, L^3)	(L^2)	(M, ML^2)	(ML, ML^3)
Γ_1	1	1	1	1	1
Γ_2	1	1	1	-1	-1
Γ_3	1	-1	1	1	-1
Γ_4	1	-1	1	-1	1
Γ_5	2	0	-2	0	0

The characters of D_4, $C_{4,v}$ and $D_{2,v}$ are $(3,1,-1,-1,-1)$, $(3,1,-1,1,1)$ and $(3,-1,-1,1,-1)$, respectively, so that

$$D_4 = \Gamma_2 + \Gamma_5; \quad C_{4,v} = \Gamma_1 + \Gamma_5; \quad D_{2,v} = \Gamma_3 + \Gamma_5.$$

Of the remaining 17 groups three, namely $C_6, \bar{C}_3, C_{3,h}$ are simply isomorphic to the cyclic group of order 6. Each of these groups has, accordingly six irreducible representations all of dimension 1 with the characters:

$$\Gamma_1 = (1, 1, 1, 1, 1, 1); \quad \Gamma_2 = (1, -\omega^2, \omega, -1, \omega^2, -\omega)$$
$$\Gamma_3 = (1, \omega, \omega^2, 1, \omega, \omega^2); \quad \Gamma_4 = (1, -1, 1, -1, 1, -1)$$
$$\Gamma_5 = (1, \omega^2, \omega, 1, \omega^2, \omega); \quad \Gamma_6 = (1, -\omega, \omega^2, -1, \omega, -\omega^2)$$

where $\omega = e^{2\pi i/3}$. The characters of $C_6, \bar{C}_3, C_{3,h}$ being $(3, 2, 0, -1, 0, 2)$, $(3, 0, 0, -3, 0, 0)$ and $(3, -2, 0, 1, 0, -2)$ we have

$$C_6 = \Gamma_1 + \Gamma_2 + \Gamma_6; \quad \bar{C}_3 = \Gamma_2 + \Gamma_4 + \Gamma_6; \quad C_{3,h} = \Gamma_3 + \Gamma_4 + \Gamma_5.$$

Of the remaining 14 groups four, namely, D_6, $C_{6,v}$, $D_{3,v}$ and $D_{3,h}$ are simply isomorphic to the dihedral group of order 12. They have accordingly (p. 339) six irreducible representations of which 2 are two-dimensional and 4 one-dimensional. On denoting the dihedral group of order 12 by (C_6, MC_6), where $C_6 = (E, L, L^2, L^3, L^4, L^5)$, $L^6 = E$, $M^2 = E$ and writing the six-classes in the order E, (L, L^5), (L^2, L^4), L^3, (M, ML^2, ML^4), (ML, ML^3, ML^5) the character table is as follows (Γ_1 denoting the identity representation, Γ_2 the alternating representation, Γ_3, Γ_4 the two one-dimensional representations contained in the reducible 2×2 representation, and Γ_5, Γ_6 the 2 two-dimensional irreducible representations)

Character table for the dihedral group of order 12.

	E	(L, L^5)	(L^2, L^4)	L^3	(M, ML^2, ML^4)	(ML, ML^3, ML^5)
Γ_1	1	1	1	1	1	1
Γ_2	1	1	1	1	-1	-1
Γ_3	1	-1	1	-1	1	-1
Γ_4	1	-1	1	-1	-1	1
Γ_5	2	1	-1	-2	0	0
Γ_6	2	-1	-1	2	0	0

Since the characters of D_6, $C_{6,v}$, $D_{3,v}$, $D_{3,h}$ are $(3, 2, 0, -1, -1, -1)$, $3, 2, 0, -1, 1, 1)$, $(3, 0, 0, -3, -1, 1)$ and $(3, -2, 0, 1, 1, -1)$, respectively, we have

$$D_6 = \Gamma_2 + \Gamma_5; \quad C_{6,v} = \Gamma_1 + \Gamma_5; \quad D_{3,v} = \Gamma_4 + \Gamma_5; \quad D_{3,h} = \Gamma_3 + \Gamma_6.$$

Of the remaining 10 groups one, namely T, is simply isomorphic to the alternating group on four letters. It has four irreducible representations of which one is of dimension 3 the other 3 being one-dimensional. We have given the character table on p. 175. T is itself irreducible being the three dimensional irreducible representation.

Of the remaining 9 groups two, namely, O and T_v are simply isomorphic to the symmetric group on 4 letters. Each of these two groups has, accordingly, 5 irreducible representations of which two are of dimension 3, one is of dimension 2 and 2 are of dimension 1. We have given the character table on p. 142; O is that three-dimensional irreducible representation whose characters are $(3, -1, 0, -1, 1)$ whilst T_v is the other three-dimensional irreducible representation whose characters are $(3, 1, 0, -1, -1)$.

The remaining 7 groups are $D_{2,h}$, T_h, O_h, $C_{4,h}$, $C_{6,h}$, $D_{4,h}$ $D_{6,h}$. Each is the direct product of the corresponding one of the crystallographic groups (D_2, T, O, C_4, C_6, D_4, D_6) of the first kind by the two-group $I = (E_3, -E_3)$. Each has, accordingly, twice as many irreducible representations as the corresponding group of the first kind, the characters of these being obtained by the rule given on p. 101. Thus, for instance, if A denotes the 6×6 character table for D_6 given above then the 12×12 table for $D_{6,h}$ is $\begin{pmatrix} A & A \\ A & -A \end{pmatrix}$.

4. The symmetrized Kronecker square of an irreducible representation of a crystallographic group.

The character tables for the various crystallographic groups are so simple (most of the irreducible representations being of dimension one) that it is a trivial matter to analyse the Kronecker product of any two (not necessarily distinct) irreducible representations of one of these crystallographic groups. E. g., from the character table of the group D_6, p. 349 we read

$$\Gamma_5 \times \Gamma_5 = \Gamma_1 + \Gamma_2 + \Gamma_6 = \Gamma_6 \times \Gamma_6; \quad \Gamma_5 \times \Gamma_6 = \Gamma_3 + \Gamma_4 + \Gamma_5.$$

The Kronecker square of an irreducible representation with real characters always contains the identity representation exactly once. In fact this is a general property of any irreducible representation with real characters of any finite group; for the irreducibility of Γ gives $\Sigma \chi\bar{\chi} = g$, the order of the group, and the reality of the characters forces $\Sigma \chi^2 = g$. But $(1/g)\Sigma\chi^2$ is precisely the number of times that $\Gamma \times \Gamma$ contains the identity representation.

It is important for some purposes to have the symmetrized Kronecker square $[\Gamma]_{(2)}$ (see p. 72) of an irreducible representation of a crystallographic group. Denoting by s_1 the characters of Γ those of $[\Gamma]_{(2)}$ are given (p. 90) by

$$q_2(\boldsymbol{s}) = \tfrac{1}{2}(s_1{}^2 + s_2)$$

where $s_1{}^2$ furnishes the characters of the ordinary Kronecker square $\Gamma \times \Gamma = [\Gamma]_2$. The quantities s_2 (being the sum of the squares of the characteristic numbers of a typical matrix A of Γ) are the characters $\chi(A^2)$. Thus the analysis of $[\Gamma]_{(2)}$ is readily obtained. In the case of the dihedral group of order 8 (whose character table is given on p. 348) we have for Γ_5

$$s_1{}^2 = (4, 0, 4, 0, 0); \quad s_2 = (2, -2, 2, 2, 2)$$

so that $q_2(\boldsymbol{s}) = (3, -1, 3, 1, 1)$ implying

$$[\Gamma_5]_{(2)} = \Gamma_1 + \Gamma_3 + \Gamma_4.$$

Similarly for the dihedral group of order 12 whose character table is given on p. 349. For Γ_5 we have $s_1{}^2 = (4, 1, 1, 4, 0, 0)$, $s_2 = (2, -1, -1, 2, 2, 2)$ so that $q_2(\boldsymbol{s}) = (3, 0, 0, 3, 1, 1)$ implying

$$[\Gamma_5]_{(2)} = \Gamma_1 + \Gamma_6.$$

For Γ_6 we have $s_1{}^2 = (4, 1, 1, 4, 0, 0)$, $s_2 = (2, -1, -1, 2, 2, 2)$ so that $[\Gamma_6]_{(2)}$ has the same analysis as $[\Gamma_5]_{(2)}$:

$$[\Gamma_6]_{(2)} = \Gamma_1 + \Gamma_6.$$

For the three-dimensional representation T of the tetrahedral group, whose character table has been given on p. 175, we have $s_1{}^2 = (9, 1, 0, 0)$, $s_2 = (3, 3, 0, 0)$ so that $q_2(\boldsymbol{s}) = (6, 2, 0, 0)$ implying

$$[T]_{(2)} = \Gamma_1 + \Gamma_2 + \Gamma_3 + T.$$

For the two-dimensional representation Γ_3 of the octahedral group, whose character table has been given on p. 142, we have

$$s_1{}^2 = (4, 0, 1, 4, 0)\,; \quad s_2 = (2, 2, -1, 2, 2)$$

so that $q_2(\boldsymbol{s}) = (3, 1, 0, 3, 1)$ implying

$$[\Gamma_3]_{(2)} = \Gamma_1 + \Gamma_3.$$

For the three-dimensional representation O we have $s_1{}^2 = (9, 1, 0, 1, 1)$; $s_2 = (3, 3, 0, 3, -1)$ so that $q_2(\boldsymbol{s}) = (6, 2, 0, 2, 0)$ implying

$$[O]_{(2)} = \Gamma_1 + \Gamma_3 + O.$$

For the three-dimensional representation T_v we have the same analysis

$$[T_v]_{(2)} = \Gamma_1 + \Gamma_3 + O.$$

CHAPTER TWELVE

THE LORENTZ GROUP

We shall discuss in this chapter the Lorentz group and its representations and shall see that, in contrast to the situation for the orthogonal group, the proper Lorentz group is not connected but consists of two separated connected pieces.

1. The four-dimensional Lorentz group.

The matrix of the quadratic form

$$x'Fx = -(x^0)^2 + (x^1)^2 + (x^2)^2 + (x^3)^2$$

is

$$(12.1) \qquad F = \begin{pmatrix} -1 & 0 & 0 & 0 \\ 0 & 1 & 0 & 0 \\ 0 & 0 & 1 & 0 \\ 0 & 0 & 0 & 1 \end{pmatrix} = \begin{pmatrix} -E_1 & 0 \\ 0 & E_3 \end{pmatrix}$$

and we say that a real homogeneous linear transformation

$$(12.2) \qquad x \to y = Lx$$

is a Lorentz transformation if it leaves the quadratic form $x'Fx$ invariant; L is termed a Lorentz matrix. Since under (12.2) $x'Fx$ goes over into $y'Fy = x'L'FLx$ the criterion for a Lorentz matrix is

$$(12.3) \qquad L'FL = F.$$

It is clear from the very definition that the collection $\{L\}$ of Lorentz matrices constitute a group G', the unit element being E_4. From (12.3) we read $(\det L)^2 = 1$ (since $\det L' = \det L$) and so $\det L = \pm 1$. Also F is a Lorentz matrix (since $F' = F, F^2 = E_4$) of determinant -1 so that, if M is a Lorentz matrix of determinant -1, $L = FM$ is a Lorentz matrix of determinant $+1$ and $M = FL$. The collection $\{L\}$ of Lorentz matrices of determinant $+1$ constitute a subgroup G of the full Lorentz group known as the proper Lorentz group (the Lorentz matrix L being termed proper when its determinant $= +1$); G is of index 2 in G' and is, accordingly, an invariant subgroup.

On writing (12.3) in the form $L' = FL^{-1}F$ we see, from the group property of Lorentz matrices, that L' is, with L, a Lorentz matrix. On equating the elements in the first row and column of both sides of (12.3) we find

$$(12.4) \qquad (l_1{}^1)^2 - (l_2{}^1)^2 - (l_3{}^1)^2 - (l_4{}^1)^2 = 1$$

so that $(l_1^1)^2 \geq 1$ or, equivalently, $|l_1^1| \geq 1$. Hence there are two types of Lorentz matrices, namely, those for which $l_1^1 \geq 1$ and those for which $l_1^1 \leq -1$. If we have two matrices L, K of the first type so also is their product LK; in fact the element in the first row and column of $LK = l_1^1k_1^1 + l_2^1k_1^2 + l_3^1k_1^3 + l_4^1k_1^4$ and $(l_2^1k_1^2 + l_3^1k_1^3 + l_4^1k_1^4)^2 \leq \{(l_2^1)^2 + (l_3^1)^2 + (l_4^1)^2\}\{(k_1^2)^2 + (k_1^3)^2 + (k_1^4)^2\}$. From (12.4) we have $(l_2^1)^2 + (l_3^1)^2 + (l_4^1)^2 < (l_1^1)^2$ and on writing this relation (which is valid for *any* Lorentz matrix L) for the Lorentz matrix K' we have $(k_1^2)^2 + (k_1^3)^2 + (k_1^4)^2 < (k_1^1)^2$ so that $|l_2^1k_1^2 + l_3^1k_1^3 + l_4^1k_1^4| < l_1^1k_1^1$ proving that the element in the first row and column of $LK > 0$ (a result which implies that it is also ≥ 1). It is clear that $-E_4$ is a Lorentz matrix and if L is a Lorentz matrix for which $l_1^1 \geq 1$, $-L$ is a Lorentz matrix for which $l_1^1 \leq -1$. Hence the subgroup G'_+ of the full Lorentz group G' which consists of all those Lorentz matrices for which $l_1^1 \geq 1$ is of index two (and hence is an invariant subgroup). Similarly the subgroup G_+ of the proper Lorentz group G which consists of all those proper Lorentz matrices for which $l_1^1 \geq 1$ is of index two (and hence is an invariant subgroup). The two cosets of G'_+ in G', or of G_+ in G, are quite disconnected; in fact if L is any member of G'_+ and M is any element of G' which is not in G'_+ the element in the first row and column of $L - M \geq 2$ so that $|L - M| \geq 2$ (the equality holding, for example, when $L = E_4, M = F$). We shall see in the next section that each element of G_+ may be connected with E_4 by a continuous curve lying entirely in G_+; and this implies, on taking the negatives of the matrices involved, that the coset of G_+ in G is connected each element being connectible with $-E_4$ by means of a continuous curve lying in this coset. Thus G splits up into two disjoint connected pieces; and as G_+ is separated from its coset in G'_+ (simply because the determinant of a matrix is a continuous function of its elements) it follows that G' breaks up into 4 separated pieces

1) G_+; every element connected with E_4
2) The coset $-G_+$ of G_+ in G; every element connected with $-E_4$
3) FG_+; every element connected with F
4) $-FG_+$; every element connected with $-F$.

2. The two-valued two-dimensional unimodular representation of G_+.

Let H be the 2×2 Hermitian matrix

$$H = \begin{pmatrix} x^0 + x^1 & x^2 + ix^3 \\ x^2 - ix^3 & x^0 - x^1 \end{pmatrix}; \quad x^0, x^1, x^2, x^3 \text{ real}$$

and let A be any unimodular 2×2 matrix. On writing $K = AHA^*$ it is clear that K is Hermitian and that $\det K = \det H$ so that if

$$K = \begin{pmatrix} y^0 + y^1 & y^2 + iy^3 \\ y^2 - iy^3 & y^0 - y^1 \end{pmatrix}; \quad y^0, y^1, y^2, y^3 \text{ real}$$

the transformation $H \to K = AHA^*$ induces a real homogeneous linear transformation $x \to y = Lx$ which has the property that

$$\begin{aligned} -(y^0)^2 + (y^1)^2 + (y^2)^2 + (y^3)^2 \ (= -\det K) \\ = -(x^0)^2 + (x^1)^2 + (x^2)^2 + (x^3)^2 \ (= -\det H). \end{aligned}$$

We write

$$h^1 = x^0 + x^1, \quad h^2 = x^2 - ix^3, \quad h^3 = x^2 + ix^3, \quad h^4 = x^0 - x^1$$

i. e.

$$h = Tx; \quad x = T^{-1}h$$

where

$$T = \begin{pmatrix} 1 & 1 & 0 & 0 \\ 0 & 0 & 1 & -i \\ 0 & 0 & 1 & i \\ 1 & -1 & 0 & 0 \end{pmatrix} \qquad T^{-1} = \tfrac{1}{2} \begin{pmatrix} 1 & 0 & 0 & 1 \\ 1 & 0 & 0 & -1 \\ 0 & 1 & 1 & 0 \\ 0 & i & -i & 0 \end{pmatrix}$$

so that $h \to k = Ty = TLx = TLT^{-1}h$.

But the transformation $H \to K = AHA^*$ implies $h \to k = (A \times \bar{A})h$ so that

$$TLT^{-1} = A \times \bar{A}; \quad L = T^{-1}(A \times \bar{A})T.$$

The 4×4 matrix $A \times \bar{A}$ is

$$(12.5) \qquad A \times \bar{A} = \begin{pmatrix} a_1{}^1\bar{a}_1{}^1 & a_1{}^1\bar{a}_2{}^1 & a_2{}^1\bar{a}_1{}^1 & a_2{}^1\bar{a}_2{}^1 \\ a_1{}^1\bar{a}_1{}^2 & a_1{}^1\bar{a}_2{}^2 & a_2{}^1\bar{a}_1{}^2 & a_2{}^1\bar{a}_2{}^2 \\ a_1{}^2\bar{a}_1{}^1 & a_1{}^2\bar{a}_2{}^1 & a_2{}^2\bar{a}_1{}^1 & a_2{}^2\bar{a}_2{}^1 \\ a_1{}^2\bar{a}_1{}^2 & a_1{}^2\bar{a}_2{}^2 & a_2{}^2\bar{a}_1{}^2 & a_2{}^2\bar{a}_2{}^2 \end{pmatrix}$$

and a simple calculation shows that the element in the first row and column of $L = T^{-1}(A \times \bar{A})T$ is $\frac{1}{2}(a_1{}^1\bar{a}_1{}^1 + a_1{}^2\bar{a}_1{}^2 + a_2{}^1\bar{a}_2{}^1 + a_2{}^2\bar{a}_2{}^2)$. Since this $\geqq 0$ it must be $\geqq 1$ and we see that all Lorentz matrices which furnish, by means of the equation

$$(12.6) \qquad L = T^{-1}(A \times \bar{A})T$$

a representation of the 2×2 unimodular group $\{A\}$ belong to the subgroup G'_+ of the full real Lorentz group G'. Furthermore

$$\begin{aligned} \det(A \times \bar{A}) &= \det(A \times E_2) \cdot (E_2 \times \bar{A}) \\ &= \det(E_2 \times A) \cdot \det(E_2 \times \bar{A}) \end{aligned}$$

(since $A \times E_2$ is transformable, by means of a permutation matrix into $E_2 \times A$)

$$= (\det A)^2 \times (\det \bar{A})^2 = 1.$$

Hence the matrices $L = T^{-1}(A \times \bar{A})T$ belong to the subgroup G_+ of the *proper* Lorentz group G. It remains to show that they *exhaust* this subgroup G_+, i. e. that G furnishes a representation of the 2×2 unimodular group $\{A\}$, and that, conversely, the 2×2 unimodular group $\{A\}$ furnishes a two-valued representation $(L \to \pm A)$ of the subgroup G_+ of the proper Lorentz group G.

Before doing this we shall show that every Lorentz matrix which is of the type $L = T^{-1}(A \times \bar{A})T$ may be put in the form $L = e^{SF}$ where S is a skew-symmetric real matrix; and, conversely, that every matrix of the type e^{SF} is a Lorentz matrix of the type $T^{-1}(A \times \bar{A})T$. This theorem together with the theorem that G_+ is exhausted by the matrices $L = T^{-1}(A \times \bar{A})T$ imply that G_+ is connected. In fact $L = e^{SF}$ is connected with E_4 by the elements $L(t) = e^{tSF}$, $0 \leq t \leq 1$, of G_+. We first observe that any 2×2 unimodular matrix A may be written in the form $A = e^B$. In fact if A can be reduced to diagonal form: $PAP^{-1} = \begin{pmatrix} \lambda & 0 \\ 0 & \lambda^{-1} \end{pmatrix}$ we have merely to set $PBP^{-1} = \begin{pmatrix} \log \lambda & 0 \\ 0 & -\log \lambda \end{pmatrix}$. If A cannot be presented in diagonal form its characteristic numbers must be equal (and hence both $+1$ or -1); if they are both $+1$ we can find a P so that $PAP^{-1} = \begin{pmatrix} 1 & 1 \\ 0 & 1 \end{pmatrix}$ and then it suffices to set $PBP^{-1} = \begin{pmatrix} 0 & 1 \\ 0 & 0 \end{pmatrix}$. For the square of this is the zero matrix so that $e^{PBP^{-1}} = E_2 + PBP^{-1} = PAP^{-1}$ implying $e^B = A$. Finally if both characteristic numbers of $A = -1$ we deal with $-A$ obtaining $e^C = -A$ which implies $e^B = A$ where $B = C + i\pi E_2$. Since $\pm A$ yield the same L we may choose the sign which gives $Tr\, B = 0$ and we shall suppose this agreed on.

On setting, then, $A = e^B$ we observe that this implies

$$A \times E_2 = e^{B \times E_2}; \quad E_2 \times \bar{A} = e^{E_2 \times \bar{B}}$$

(for $(B \times E_2)\ (B \times E_2) = (B^2 \times E_2)$ etc.). Hence

$$(A \times \bar{A}) = (A \times E_2)(E_2 \times \bar{A}) = e^{(B \times E_2)} \cdot e^{(E_2 \times \bar{B})}$$
$$= e^{(B \times E_2) + (E_2 \times \bar{B})}$$

(since the matrices $B \times E_2$ and $E_2 \times \bar{B}$ commute) so that

$$L = T^{-1}(A \times A)T = e^{T^{-1}[(B \times E_2) + (E_2 \times \bar{B})]T}.$$

An elementary computation yields

$$(12.7)\quad T^{-1}(B\times E_2)T$$
$$=\frac{1}{2}\begin{pmatrix} b_1{}^1+b_2{}^2 & b_1{}^1-b_2{}^2 & b_2{}^1+b_1{}^2 & i(b_2{}^1-b_1{}^2) \\ b_1{}^1-b_2{}^2 & b_1{}^1+b_2{}^2 & b_2{}^1-b_1{}^2 & i(b_2{}^1+b_1{}^2) \\ b_2{}^1+b_1{}^2 & b_1{}^2-b_2{}^1 & b_1{}^1+b_2{}^2 & i(b_2{}^2-b_1{}^1) \\ i(b_2{}^1-b_1{}^2) & -i(b_2{}^1+b_1{}^2) & i(b_1{}^1-b_2{}^2) & b_1{}^1+b_2{}^2 \end{pmatrix}$$

$T^{-1}(E_2\times \bar{B})T=$ conjugate complex of $T^{-1}(E_2\times B)T$.

Since $b_1{}^1+b_2{}^2=0$ it follows that

$$L=e^{SF}$$

where S is the skew symmetric real matrix

$$S=\begin{pmatrix} 0 & p & q & r \\ -p & 0 & n & -m \\ -q & -n & 0 & l \\ -r & m & -l & 0 \end{pmatrix}$$

$p=R\cdot P$ (= real part of) $b_1{}^1-b_2{}^2$; $q=R\cdot P(b_1{}^2+b_2{}^1)$
$r=I\cdot P$ (= imaginary part of) $b_1{}^2-b_2{}^1$; $l=I\cdot P(b_1{}^1-b_2{}^2)$
$m=I\cdot P(b_1{}^2+b_2{}^1)$; $n=RP\cdot(b_2{}^1-b_1{}^2)$.

(Observe that the $R\cdot P$ and $I\cdot P$ of a complex number are both *real*, the $I\cdot P$ being the coefficient of i). Conversely given S we have

$$b_1{}^1-b_2{}^2=p+il;\quad b_2{}^1+b_1{}^2=q+im;$$
$$b_2{}^1-b_1{}^2=n-ir \text{ and } b_1{}^1+b_2{}^2=0$$

so that

$$(12.8)\quad \begin{aligned} b_1{}^1&=\tfrac{1}{2}(p+il);\quad b_2{}^2=-\tfrac{1}{2}(p+il) \\ b_2{}^1&=\tfrac{1}{2}\{q+n+i(m-r)\};\quad b_1{}^2=\tfrac{1}{2}\{q-n+i(m+r)\}. \end{aligned}$$

Hence every e^{SF} is an element of G_+ of the type

$$e^{SF}=L=T^{-1}(A\times\bar{A})T$$

and every element of G_+ of the type $L=T^{-1}(A\times\bar{A})T$ may be written in the form e^{SF}.

We have now to prove the result that G_+ is exhausted by the elements L of the type $L=T^{-1}(A\times\bar{A})T$. This is done by means of a factorisation of an arbitrary element L of G_+ into a product of "plane" Lorentz matrices which is essentially the same as the factorisation (10.2) of a proper orthogonal matrix. We denote by $L_j(\theta)$, $j=1,2,3$, the "plane" element of G_4:

$$\begin{matrix} x'_0 = \cosh\theta\, x_0 + \sinh\theta\, x_j \\ x'_j = \sinh\theta\, x_0 + \cosh\theta\, x_j \end{matrix}\; ; \quad x'_r = x_r \qquad (r \neq 0, r \neq j).$$

If L is any element of G_+ the element in the first row and second column of $LL_1(\theta)$ is $l_1{}^1 \sinh\theta + l_2{}^1 \cosh\theta$ and since $l_1{}^1 > l_2{}^1$ we can determine a real $\theta(=\theta_1)$ so that this is zero. Proceeding in this way we can determine $\theta_1, \theta_2, \theta_3$, all real, so that $LL_1(\theta_1)L_2(\theta_2)L_3(\theta_3)$ has all its elements in the first row, save the first, zero. Since this product is an element of G_+ the element in the first row and column must be $+1$ so that

$$LL_1(\theta_1)L_2(\theta_2)L_3(\theta_3) = \begin{pmatrix} 1 & 0 \\ 0 & O_3 \end{pmatrix}.$$

Since O_3 can be factored into a product of three plane rotations (which are also plane Lorentz matrices) we see that

$$L = \begin{pmatrix} 1 & 0 \\ 0 & O_3 \end{pmatrix} L_3(-\theta_3)L_2(-\theta_2)L_1(-\theta_1) \tag{12.9}$$

may be written as the product of six plane Lorentz matrices. To a plane Lorentz matrix of the type $L_1(\theta)$ corresponds a 2×2 unimodular matrix A_1:

$$A_1(\theta) = \begin{pmatrix} e^{\theta/2} & 0 \\ 0 & e^{-\theta/2} \end{pmatrix}$$

whilst to a plane Lorentz matrix of the type $L_2(\theta)$ corresponds the 2×2 unimodular matrix

$$A_2(\theta) = \begin{pmatrix} \cosh\theta/2 & \sinh\theta/2 \\ \sinh\theta/2 & \cosh\theta/2 \end{pmatrix}$$

and to a plane Lorentz matrix of the type $L_3(\theta)$ corresponds the 2×2 unimodular matrix

$$A_3(\theta) = \begin{pmatrix} \cosh\theta/2 & -i\sinh\theta/2 \\ i\sinh\theta/2 & \cosh\theta/2 \end{pmatrix}$$

(all of which statements are readily verifiable by means of (12. 5) and (12. 6).) To each of the three "plane" factors of $\begin{pmatrix} 1 & 0 \\ 0 & O_3 \end{pmatrix}$ corresponds a 2×2 unimodular *unitary* matrix V (cf. the derivation of (10. 2)) and so to L corresponds an A, namely,

$$A = UA_3(-\theta_3)A_2(-\theta_2)A_1(-\theta_1)$$

(for the matrices L of G_+ which correspond, by means of (12. 6), to the 2×2 unimodular matrices $\{A\}$ constitute a representation of the 2×2

unimodular group $\{A\}$). Hence every element of G_+ is of the type (12.6) or, equivalently, every element of G_+ is of the type e^{SF} and conversely.

3. The theory of semi-vectors.

It follows from (12.6) that

$$TLT^{-1} = A \times \bar{A} = (A \times E_2)(E_2 \times \bar{A}) = (E_2 \times \bar{A})(A \times E_2)$$

so that $L = MN = NM$ where

$$(12.10) \qquad M = T^{-1}(A \times E_2)T; \quad N = T^{-1}(E_2 \times \bar{A})T.$$

The collection of matrices $\{M\}$ constitute a group which is simply isomorphic to the group $\{A\}$ of 2×2 unimodular matrices; in fact $\{M\}$ can be presented by a proper choice of basis in the form

$$(12.11) \qquad M = E_2 \times A = \begin{pmatrix} A & 0 \\ 0 & A \end{pmatrix}.$$

Similarly N can be presented by a proper choice of basis in the form

$$N = E_2 \times \bar{A} = \begin{pmatrix} \bar{A} & 0 \\ 0 & \bar{A} \end{pmatrix}.$$

Now the transformation $x \to y = Mx$ implies $H \to K = AH$ and since $\det A = 1$ it follows that M is a complex Lorentz matrix, i. e. a matrix with *complex* elements for which $M'FM = F$. Similarly N is a complex Lorentz matrix. The collections $\{M\}$ and $\{N\}$ constitute subgroups of the complex Lorentz group (for $(A \times E_2)(B \times E_2) = (AB \times E_2)$ etc.) and each element of $\{M\}$ is commutative with each element of $\{N\}$ for

$$(A \times E_2)(E_2 \times \bar{B}) = (A \times \bar{B}) = (E_2 \times \bar{B})(A \times E_2).$$

A vector x in the common carrier space of $\{M\}$ and $\{N\}$ has been called (by Einstein and Mayer) a semi-vector for the following reason: if $x \to y = Nx$ and $y \to z = My$ (where M and N are furnished by (12.10)) then $x \to z = MNx = Lx$ where L is a proper real Lorentz matrix for which $l_1^1 \geq 1$; and all real Lorentz matrices of this type are obtainable in this way. To get the proper Lorentz matrices for which $l_1^1 \leq -1$ it is evidently sufficient to follow the transformation M by the transformation $-N$. It is clear that $\pm M$ yield the same L and that the theory of semi-vectors is merely a description of the two-valued representation of G_+ by the 2×2 unimodular group (cf. (12.11)). It may be observed that if we follow $x \to y = Mx$ by any element of the other group we obtain $x \to z = Lx$ where L is now a *complex* Lorentz matrix. Indeed

$$L = T^{-1}(A \times \bar{B})T$$

and this implies

$$H \to K = AHB^*$$

so that $\det K = \det H$.

The matrix M of (12.10) may be written in the form e^{S_1F} where $S_1F = T^{-1}(B \times E_2)T$ is given by (12.7). It is important to observe the special nature of S_1F: it is of the type

$$(12.12) \quad S_1F = \begin{pmatrix} 0 & il & im & in \\ il & 0 & n & -m \\ im & -n & 0 & l \\ in & m & -l & 0 \end{pmatrix};$$

where $l = i(b_2{}^2 - b_1{}^1)$; $m = -i(b_2{}^1 + b_1{}^2)$; $n = b_2{}^1 - b_1{}^2$.

An easy calculation yields $S_1FS_1F = -(l^2 + m^2 + n^2)E_2$ so that if we write $l^2 + m^2 + n^2 = \theta^2$

$$e^{S_1F} = \cos\theta\, E_2 + (\sin\theta/\theta)S_1F = \cos\theta\, E_2 + \sin\theta\, I$$

where $I = S_1F/\theta$, $I^2 = -E_2$. Similarly each matrix N can be written in the form $N = e^{S_2F}$ where now S_2F is again special in the sense that $S_2FS_2F = -(p^2 + q^2 + r^2)E_2 = -\phi^2E_2$ so that $e^{S_2F} = \cos\phi E_2 + \sin\phi J$, $J^2 = -E_2$ but

$$(12.13) \quad S_2F = \begin{pmatrix} 0 & -ip & -iq & -ir \\ -ip & 0 & r & -q \\ -iq & -r & 0 & p \\ -ir & q & -p & 0 \end{pmatrix}.$$

$$\text{Since } S_1FS_2F = \begin{pmatrix} lp + mq + nr & i(nq - mr) & i(lr - np) & i(mp - lq) \\ -i(nq - mr) & lp - mq - nr & (lq + mp) & (lr + np) \\ -i(lr - np) & lq + mp & mq - nr - lp & mr + nq \\ -i(mp - lq) & lr + np & mr + nq & nr - lp - mq \end{pmatrix}.$$

S_1F and S_2F commute: $S_1FS_2F = S_2FS_1F$ (for an interchange of S_1F and S_2F is equivalent to an interchange of (l, m, n) and (p, q, r) coupled with a change of i to $-i$); this fact merely reflects the commutativity of M and N.

4. The derivation of irreducible representations of the Lorentz group from irreducible representations of the attached orthogonal group.

On denoting by B the 4×4 symmetric, unitary matrix

$$B=\begin{pmatrix} i & 0 \\ 0 & E_3 \end{pmatrix} \tag{12.14}$$

it is clear that $F=B^2=B^{-2}$ so that the relation (12.3) may be written in the form $BL'B^{-1}\cdot B^{-1}LB=E_4$ or, equivalently, $O'O=E_4$ where

$$O=B^{-1}LB. \tag{12.15}$$

Hence as L runs over the full (real) Lorentz group G', O runs over a subgroup of the full (complex) 4×4 orthogonal group. We have seen (cf. the derivation of (12.9)) that any element of G' may be factored in the form

$$L=\begin{pmatrix} \pm 1 & 0 \\ 0 & O_3 \end{pmatrix} L_3(\phi_3)L_2(\phi_2)L_1(\phi_1)$$

where L_1, L_2, L_3 are plane Lorentz matrices and ϕ_1, ϕ_2, ϕ_3 are real; O_3 being a, proper or improper, 3×3 real orthogonal matrix. If we assign to ϕ_1, ϕ_2, ϕ_3 pure imaginary values $\phi_1=i\psi_1$, $\phi_2=i\psi_2$, $\phi_3=i\psi_3$, ψ_1, ψ_2, ψ_3 real, L_1, L_2, L_3 are no longer Lorentz matrices but they are unitary matrices. Thus, for instance,

$$L_1(\phi_1)=L_1(i\psi_1)=U_1(\psi_1)=\begin{pmatrix} \cos\psi_1 & i\sin\psi_1 & 0 & 0 \\ i\sin\psi_1 & \cos\psi_1 & 0 & 0 \\ 0 & 0 & 1 & 0 \\ 0 & 0 & 0 & 1 \end{pmatrix}.$$

Since B is unitary it follows that the O of (12.15) is unitary when the parameters (ϕ_1, ϕ_2, ϕ_3) which occur in the specification of L are assigned purely imaginary values. Since O is orthogonal it must be real (for $O^*=O'$ implies $\bar{O}=O$). Hence we obtain a real orthogonal group by assigning purely imaginary values to the parameters ϕ_1, ϕ_2, ϕ_3 of L (the remaining three of the six parameters of L being assigned real values). Conversely if O is any element of the 4×4 real orthogonal group with parameters $(\psi_1, \psi_2, \psi_3, \phi_4, \phi_5, \phi_6)$ and we assign to the parameters (ψ_1, ψ_2, ψ_3) purely imaginary values, the remaining three being kept real, we obtain, from (12.15) an element L of the real Lorentz group. The correspondence between O and L is evidently not one to one; when any one of the three parameters ψ_1, ψ_2, ψ_3 is increased by an integral multiple of 2π we obtain the same element O but when one of the three parameters (ϕ_1, ϕ_2, ϕ_3) of L is increased by an integral multiple of 2π we do not obtain the same value of L.

Let now $\Gamma = \{D(\psi)\}$ be any representation of the 4×4 real orthogonal group. Then by assigning to ψ_1, ψ_2, ψ_3 purely imaginary values we obtain a representation $\tilde{\Gamma}$ of G'. The basic result we need here is that *if* Γ *is irreducible so also is* $\tilde{\Gamma}$. The reason for this is clear: The (assumed) reducibility of $\tilde{\Gamma}$ finds its expression in the vanishing of certain analytic functions of the six parameters $(\phi_1, \cdots, \phi_6)$ of a typical element L of G'. But if these analytic functions vanish when the six parameters are assigned arbitrary real values they must vanish identically; i. e. they must vanish when the six parameters are assigned arbitrary complex values. In particular they vanish when (ϕ_1, ϕ_2, ϕ_3) are assigned pure imaginary values the remaining three being kept real. But this would imply the reducibility of Γ. Hence we obtain from any *irreducible* representation of the 4×4 real orthogonal group an *irreducible* representation of the full Lorentz group by the mere formal process of assigning purely imaginary values to the first three parameters ψ_1, ψ_2, ψ_3. The same argument shows that the representations of G' obtained in this way from reducible representations of the 4×4 real orthogonal group are reducible and *completely reducible* (simply because any reducible representation of the real orthogonal group is completely reducible). The same argument yields the orthogonality relations; the equivalence of representations having the same characters and so on.

It is important to realise the somewhat striking nature of these results. The parametric region for the Lorentz group extends to infinity: $-\infty < \phi_j < \infty$, $j = 1, 2, 3$ and so the concept of group-integration is not available (the total "volume" of the group being infinite). We express this fact by the statement that the Lorentz group is not *compact*. However we are able to obtain the results stated by placing the burden on a closely related group, namely, the 4×4 real orthogonal group. The *closeness* of the relationship being simply that we obtain one group by assigning real values to certain parameters whilst we obtain the related group by assigning purely imaginary values to these same parameters. This closely related group is compact (in fact unitary) and we are able to invoke the results flowing from the powerful method of group integration. The device applied here is termed by Weyl the "unitary trick." Whilst realising its importance we must also be aware of its limitations. Just because the trigonometric functions are periodic (which is merely another way of saying "just because the real orthogonal group is compact") we obtain only very special representations of the Lorentz group from the known representations of the orthogonal group; namely those which arise from periodic functions of the parameters ψ_1, ψ_2, ψ_3. This point will be made clear by considering the 2×2 proper Lorentz group. A typical element L is of the type $L = \pm\begin{pmatrix} \cosh\phi & \sinh\phi \\ \sinh\phi & \cosh\phi \end{pmatrix}$ and the associated element O of the proper 2×2 real orthogonal group is $\pm\begin{pmatrix} \cos\psi & \sin\psi \\ -\sin\psi & \cos\psi \end{pmatrix}$. The irreducible representations of this latter group are all one-dimensional and of the type

$$D = e^{2\pi i m\psi}$$

where m is an *integer*, positive, negative or zero. From these we obtain the one-dimensional representations

$$D(\phi) = e^{2\pi m\phi};\ m \text{ an integer},$$

of the Lorentz group but we fail to secure the representations where m is any complex number other than an integer. Nor have we proven the complete reducibility of any reducible representation of the Lorentz group. For example

$$D(\phi) = e^{\alpha\phi}\begin{pmatrix} 1 & \phi \\ 0 & 1 \end{pmatrix};\ \alpha \text{ an arbitrary complex number};$$

is a reducible two-dimensional representation of the two-dimensional Lorentz group which is not completely reducible.

REFERENCES

The following list of books and papers is not intended to be, in any sense, a complete bibliography of the Theory of Group Representations. It consists mainly of sources which we have ourselves found helpful and which we recommend to the reader seeking further information.

A. BOOKS.

(1) W. Burnside, *Theory of Groups of Finite Order*, 2nd Edition, Cambridge University Press (1911).(Dover, New York)

(2) L. E. Dickson, *Modern Algebraic Theories*,(Dover, New York) (1926).

(3) R. Fricke, *Lehrbuch der Algebra*, Bd. I, II, Vieweg & Sohn, Braunschweig, (1924) and (1926).

(4) H. Hilton, *An Introduction to the Theory of Groups of Finite Order*, Clarendon Press, Oxford, (1908).

(5) ———, *Mathematical Crystallography and the Theory of Groups of Movements*, Clarendon Press, Oxford, (1903).(Dover, New York)

(6) O. Schreier and E. Sperner, *Einführung in die analytische Geometrie und Algebra*, Bd. I, II, B. G. Teubner, Leipzig, (1931) and (1935).

(7) I. Schur, *Die algebraischen Grundlagen der Darstellungstheorie der Gruppen*, Zurich Lectures, (1936).

(8) A. Speiser, *Theorie der Gruppen von endlicher Ordnung*, Dritte Auflage, Springer, Berlin, (1937).

(9) B. L. van der Waerden, *Die gruppentheoretische Methode in der Quantenmechanik*, Springer, Berlin, (1932).

(10) ———, *Gruppen von linearen Transformationen*, *Ergebnisse der Math.*, **4**, Heft 2, Springer, Berlin, (1935).

(11) J. H. M. Wedderburn, *Lectures on Matrices*, American Mathematical Society, (1934).

(12) H. Weyl, *The Theory of Groups and Quantum Mechanics*, E. P. Dutton, New York, (1931). (Dover, New York)

(13) ———, *The Classical Groups, their Invariants and Representations*, Princeton University Press (1938).

(14) E. P. Wigner, *Gruppentheorie und ihre Anwendung auf die Quantenmechanik der Atomspektren*, Vieweg & Sohn, Braunschweig, (1931).

B. PAPERS.

(15) H. Auerbach, "Sur les groupes bornés de substitutions linéaires, *Comptes Rendus, Acad. Sci., Paris*, **195** (1932), pp. 1367-1369.

(16) H. Bethe, "Termaufspaltung in Kristallen," *Ann. der Physik*, 5 Folge, **3** (1929), pp. 133-208.

(17) R. Brauer, "Uber die Darstellung der Drehungsgruppe durch Gruppen linearer Substitutionen," *Inaugural–Dissertation*, Berlin, (1925).

(18) ———, "Die stetigen Darstellungen der komplexen orthogonalen Gruppe," *Berliner Berichte*, (1929), pp. 626-638.

(19) R. Brauer and I. Schur, "Zum Irreduzibilitätsbegriff in der Theorie der Gruppen linearer homogener Substitutionen," *Berliner Berichte*, (1930), pp. 209-229.

(20) R. Brauer and H. Weyl, "Spinors in *n*-dimensions," *American Journal of Mathematics*, **57** (1935), pp. 425-449.

(21) A. H. Clifford, "Representations induced in an invariant subgroup," *Annals of Mathematics*, **38** (1937), pp. 533-550.

(22) A. Einstein and W. Mayer, "Semi-Vektoren und Spinoren," *Berliner Berichte*, (1932), pp. 522-550.

(23) H. Ferns, "The irreducible representations of a group and its fundamental region," *Transactions of the Royal Society of Canada*, 3rd Ser., Section III, **28** (1934), pp. 35-60.

(24) G. Frobenius, "Über Gruppencharaktere," *Berliner Berichte*, (1896), pp. 985-1021.

(25) ———, "Über Relationen zwischen den Charakteren einer Gruppe und denen ihrer Untergruppen," *Berliner Berichte*, (1898), pp. 501-515.

(26) ———, "Über die Darstellung der endlichen Gruppen durch lineare Substitutionen, I, *Berliner Berichte*, (1897), pp. 994-1015; II, *Berliner Berichte*, (1899), pp. 482-500.

(27) ———, "Über die Composition der Charaktere einer Gruppe," *Berliner Berichte*, (1899), pp. 330-339.

(28) ———, "Über die Charaktere der symmetrischen Gruppe," *Berliner Berichte*, (1900), pp. 516-534.

(29) ———, "Über die Charaktere der alternierenden Gruppe," *Berliner Berichte*, (1901), pp. 303-315.

(30) ———, "Über die charakteristischen Einheiten der symmetrischen Gruppe," *Berliner Berichte*, (1903), pp. 328-358.

(31) ———, "Über die Charaktere der mehrfach transitiven Gruppen," *Berliner Berichte*, (1904), pp. 558-571.

(32) ———, "Gruppentheoretische Ableitung der 32 Kristallklassen," *Berliner Berichte*, (1911), pp. 681-691.

(33) G. Frobenius and I. Schur, "Über die reelen Darstellungen der endlichen Gruppen," *Berliner Berichte*, (1906), pp. 186-208.

(34) ———, "Über die Äquivalenz der Gruppen linearer Substitutionen," *Berliner Berichte*, (1906), pp. 209-217.

(35) D. E. Littlewood, "Group characters and the structure of groups," *Proceedings of the London Mathematical Society*, (2), **39** (1935), pp. 150-199.

(36) ———, "Some properties of *S*-functions," *Proceedings of the London Mathematical Society*, (2), **40** (1936), pp. 49-70.

(37) D. E. Littlewood and A. R. Richardson, "Group characters and algebra," *Philosophical Transactions of the Royal Society of London*, (A), **233** (1934), pp. 99-141.

(38) D. E. Littlewood and A. R. Richardson, "Immanants of some special matrices," *Quarterly Journal* (*Oxford Ser.*), **5** (1934), pp. 269-282.

(39) ———, "Some special S-functions and q-series," *Quarterly Journal* (*Oxford Ser.*), **6** (1935), pp. 184-198.

(40) H. Minkowski, *Gesammelte Abhandlungen,* Bd. II, Teubner, Leipzig, (1911), pp. 131-229.

(41) F. D. Murnaghan, "On the representations of the symmetric group," *American Journal of Mathematics,* **59** (1937), pp. 437-488.

(42) ———, "The characters of the symmetric group," *American Journal of Mathematics,* **59** (1937), pp. 739-753.

(43) ———, "The analysis of the direct product of irreducible representations of the symmetric groups," *American Journal of Mathematics,* **60** (1938), pp. 44-65.

(44) ———, "The analysis of the Kronecker product of irreducible representations of the symmetric group," *American Journal of Mathematics,* **60** (1938), pp. 761-784.

(45) J. von Neumann, "Über die analytischen Eigenschaften von Gruppen linearer Transformationen und ihrer Darstellungen," *Mathematische Zeitschrift,* **30** (1929), pp. 3-46.

(46) G. Polya, "Über die Funktionalgleichung der Exponentialfunktion im Matrizenkalkül," *Berliner Berichte,* (1928), pp. 96-99.

(47) G. de B. Robinson, "On the fundamental region of an orthogonal representation of a finite group," *Proceedings of the London Mathematical Society,* (2), **43** (1937), pp. 289-301.

(48) ———, "On the representations of the symmetric group," *American Journal of Mathematics,* **60** (1938), pp. 745-760.

(49) I. Schur, "Über eine Klasse von Matrizen die sich einer gegebenen Matrix zuordnen lassen," *Inaugural–Dissertation,* Berlin, (1901).

(50) ———, "Neue Begrundung der Theorie der Gruppencharaktere," *Berliner Berichte,* (1905), pp. 406-432.

(51) ———, "Über die Darstellung der symmetrischen Gruppe durch lineare homogene Substitutionen," *Berliner Berichte,* (1908), pp. 664-678.

(52) ———. "Neue Anwendungen der Integralrechnung auf Probleme der Invariantentheorie," I, *Berliner Berichte,* (1924), pp. 189-208; II, *ibid.* (1924), pp. 297-321; III, *ibid.* (1924), pp. 346-355.

(53) ———, "Über die rationalen Darstellungen der allgemeinen linearen Gruppe," *Berliner Berichte,* (1927), pp. 58-75.

(54) ———, "Über die stetigen Darstellungen der allgemeinen linearen Gruppe," *Berliner Berichte,* (1928), pp. 100-124.

(55) W. Specht, "Die irreduciblen Darstellungen der symmetrischen Gruppe," *Mathematische Zeitschrift,* **39** (1935), pp. 696-711.

(56) ———, "Zur Darstellungstheorie der symmetrischen Gruppe," *Mathematische Zeitschrift,* **42** (1937), pp. 774-779.

(57) ———, "Darstellungstheorie der affinen Gruppe," *Mathematische Zeitschrift,* **43** (1937), pp. 120-160.

(58) W. Specht, "Darstellungstheorie der alternierenden Gruppe," *Mathematische Zeitschrift,* **43** (1937), pp. 553-572.

(59) H. Weyl, "Theorie der Darstellung kontinuierlicher halb-einfacher Gruppen durch lineare Transformationen," I, *Mathematische Zeitschrift,* **23** (1925), pp. 271-309; II, *Mathematische Zeitschrift,* **24** (1926), pp. 328-376; III, *Mathematische Zeitschrift,* **24** (1926), pp. 377-395.

(60) A. Young, "Quantitative substitutional analysis," Part I, *Proceedings of the London Mathematical Society* (1), **33** (1901), pp. 97-146; Part II, *ibid.* (1), **34** (1902), pp. 361-397; Part III, *ibid.* (2), **28** (1928), pp. 255-292; Part IV, *ibid.* (2), **31** (1930), pp. 253-272; Part V, *ibid.* (2), **31** (1930), pp. 273-288; Part VI, *ibid.* (2), **34** (1932), pp. 196-230; Part VII, *ibid.* (2), **36** (1933), pp. 304-368; Part VIII, *ibid.* (2), **37** (1934), pp. 441-495.

(61) M. Zia-ud-Din, "The characters of the symmetric group of order 11!," *Proceedings of the London Mathematical Society,* (2), **39** (1935), pp. 200-204.

(62) ———, "The characters of the symmetric group of degrees 12 and 13," *Proceedings of the London Mathematical Society,* (2), **42** (1937), pp. 340-355.

INDEX

Catalogue of Dover SCIENCE BOOKS

BOOKS THAT EXPLAIN SCIENCE

THE NATURE OF LIGHT AND COLOUR IN THE OPEN AIR, M. Minnaert. Why is falling snow sometimes black? What causes mirages, the fata morgana, multiple suns and moons in the sky; how are shadows formed? Prof. Minnaert of U. of Utrecht answers these and similar questions in optics, light, colour, for non-specialists. Particularly valuable to nature, science students, painters, photographers. "Can best be described in one word—fascinating!" Physics Today. Translated by H. M. Kremer-Priest, K. Jay. 202 illustrations, including 42 photos. xvi + 362pp. 5⅜ x 8. T196 Paperbound **$1.95**

THE RESTLESS UNIVERSE, Max Born. New enlarged version of this remarkably readable account by a Nobel laureate. Moving from sub-atomic particles to universe, the author explains in very simple terms the latest theories of wave mechanics. Partial contents: air and its relatives, electrons and ions, waves and particles, electronic structure of the atom, nuclear physics. Nearly 1000 illustrations, including 7 animated sequences. 325pp. 6 x 9. T412 Paperbound **$2.00**

MATTER AND LIGHT, THE NEW PHYSICS, L. de Broglie. Non-technical papers by a Nobel laureate explain electromagnetic theory, relativity, matter, light, radiation, wave mechanics, quantum physics, philosophy of science. Einstein, Planck, Bohr, others explained so easily that no mathematical training is needed for all but 2 of the 21 chapters. "Easy simplicity and lucidity . . . should make this source-book of modern physcis available to a wide public," Saturday Review. Unabridged. 300pp. 5⅜ x 8. T35 Paperbound **$1.60**

THE COMMON SENSE OF THE EXACT SCIENCES, W. K. Clifford. Introduction by James Newman, edited by Karl Pearson. For 70 years this has been a guide to classical scientific, mathematical thought. Explains with unusual clarity basic concepts such as extension of meaning of symbols, characteristics of surface boundaries, properties of plane figures, vectors, Cartesian method of determining position, etc. Long preface by Bertrand Russell. Bibliography of Clifford. Corrected. 130 diagrams redrawn. 249pp. 5⅜ x 8. T61 Paperbound **$1.60**

THE EVOLUTION OF SCIENTIFIC THOUGHT FROM NEWTON TO EINSTEIN, A. d'Abro. Einstein's special, general theories of relativity, with historical implications, analyzed in non-technical terms. Excellent accounts of contributions of Newton, Riemann, Weyl, Planck, Eddington, Maxwell, Lorentz, etc., are treated in terms of space, time, equations of electromagnetics, finiteness of universe, methodology of science. "Has become a standard work," Nature. 21 diagrams. 482pp. 5⅜ x 8. T2 Paperbound **$2.00**

BRIDGES AND THEIR BUILDERS, D. Steinman, S. R. Watson. Engineers, historians, everyone ever fascinated by great spans will find this an endless source of information and interest. Dr. Steinman, recent recipient of Louis Levy Medal, is one of the great bridge architects, engineers of all time. His analysis of great bridges of history is both authoritative and easily followed. Greek, Roman, medieval, oriental bridges; modern works such as Brooklyn Bridge, Golden Gate Bridge, etc. described in terms of history, constructional principles, artistry, function. Most comprehensive, accurate semi-popular history of bridges in print in English. New, greatly revised, enlarged edition. 23 photographs, 26 line drawings. xvii + 401pp. 5⅜ x 8. T431 Paperbound **$1.95**

CONCERNING THE NATURE OF THINGS, Sir William Bragg. Christmas lectures at Royal Society by Nobel laureate, dealing with atoms, gases, liquids, and various types of crystals. No scientific background is needed to understand this remarkably clear introduction to basic processes and aspects of modern science. "More interesting than any bestseller," London Morning Post. 32pp. of photos. 57 figures. xii + 232pp. 5⅜ x 8. T31 Paperbound **$1.35**

THE RISE OF THE NEW PHYSICS, A. d'Abro. Half million word exposition, formerly titled "The Decline of Mechanism," for readers not versed in higher mathematics. Only thorough explanation in everyday language of core of modern mathematical physical theory, treating both classical, modern views. Scientifically impeccable coverage of thought from Newtonian system through theories of Dirac, Heisenberg, Fermi's statistics. Combines history, exposition; broad but unified, detailed view, with constant comparison of classical, modern views. "A must for anyone doing serious study in the physical sciences," J. of the Franklin Inst. "Extraordinary faculty . . . to explain ideas and theories . . . in language of everyday life," Isis. Part I of set: philosophy of science, from practice of Newton, Maxwell, Poincaré, Einstein, etc. Modes of thought, experiment, causality, etc. Part II: 100 pp. on grammar, vocabulary of mathematics, discussions of functions, groups, series, Fourier series, etc. Remainder treats concrete, detailed coverage of both classical, quantum physics: analytic mechanics, Hamilton's principle, electromagnetic waves, thermodynamics, Brownian movement, special relativity, Bohr's atom, de Broglie's wave mechanics, Heisenberg's uncertainty, scores of other important topics. Covers discoveries, theories of d'Alembert, Born, Cantor, Debye, Euler, Foucault, Galois, Gauss, Hadamard, Kelvin, Kepler Laplace, Maxwell, Pauli, Rayleigh Volterra, Weyl, more than 180 others. 97 illustrations. ix + 982pp. 5⅜ x 8.
T3 Vol. 1 Paperbound **$2.00**
T4 Vol. II Paperbound **$2.00**

SPINNING TOPS AND GYROSCOPIC MOTION, John Perry. Well-known classic of science still unsurpassed for lucid, accurate, delightful exposition. How quasi-rigidity is induced in flexible, fluid bodies by rapid motions; why gyrostat falls, top rises; nature, effect of internal fluidity on rotating bodies; etc. Appendixes describe practical use of gyroscopes in ships, compasses, monorail transportation. 62 figures. 128pp. 5⅜ x 8.
T416 Paperbound **$1.00**

FOUNDATIONS OF PHYSICS, R. B. Lindsay, H. Margenau. Excellent bridge between semi-popular and technical writings. Discussion of methods of physical description, construction of theory; valuable to physicist with elementary calculus. Gives meaning to data, tools of modern physics. Contents: symbolism, mathematical equations; space and time; foundations of mechanics; probability; physics, continua; electron theory; relativity; quantum mechanics; causality; etc. "Thorough and yet not overdetailed. Unreservedly recommended," Nature. Unabridged corrected edition. 35 illustrations. xi + 537pp. 5⅜ x 8. S377 Paperbound **$2.45**

FADS AND FALLACIES IN THE NAME OF SCIENCE, Martin Gardner. Formerly entitled "In the Name of Science," the standard account of various cults, quack systems, delusions which have masqueraded as science: hollow earth fanatics, orgone sex energy, dianetics, Atlantis, Forteanism, flying saucers, medical fallacies like zone therapy, etc. New chapter on Bridey Murphy, psionics, other recent manifestations. A fair reasoned appraisal of eccentric theory which provides excellent innoculation. "Should be read by everyone, scientist or non-scientist alike," R. T. Birge, Prof. Emeritus of Physics, Univ. of Calif; Former Pres., Amer. Physical Soc. x + 365pp. 5⅜ x 8. T394 Paperbound **$1.50**

ON MATHEMATICS AND MATHEMATICIANS, R. E. Moritz. A 10 year labor of love by discerning, discriminating Prof. Moritz, this collection conveys the full sense of mathematics and personalities of great mathematicians. Anecdotes, aphorisms, reminiscences, philosophies, definitions, speculations, biographical insights, etc. by great mathematicians, writers: Descartes, Mill, Locke, Kant, Coleridge, Whitehead, etc. Glimpses into lives of great mathematicians, from Archimedes to Euler, Gauss, Weierstrass. To mathematicians, a superb browsing-book. To laymen, exciting revelation of fullness of mathematics. Extensive cross index. 410pp. 5⅜ x 8. T489 Paperbound **$1.95**

GUIDE TO THE LITERATURE OF MATHEMATICS AND PHYSICS, N. G. Parke III. Over 5000 entries under approximately 120 major subject headings, of selected most important books, monographs, periodicals, articles in English, plus important works in German, French, Italian, Spanish, Russian. (many recently available works). Covers every branch of physics, math, related engineering. Includes author, title, edition, publisher, place, date, number of volumes, number of pages. 40 page introduction on basic problems of research, study provides useful information on organization, use of libraries, psychology of learning, etc. Will save you hours of time. 2nd revised edition. Indices of authors, subjects. 464pp. 5⅜ x 8. S447 Paperbound **$2.49**

THE STRANGE STORY OF THE QUANTUM, An Account for the General Reader of the Growth of Ideas Underlying Our Present Atomic Knowledge, B. Hoffmann. Presents lucidly, expertly, with barest amount of mathematics, problems and theories which led to modern quantum physics. Begins with late 1800's when discrepancies were noticed; with illuminating analogies, examples, goes through concepts of Planck, Einstein, Pauli, Schroedinger, Dirac, Sommerfield, Feynman, etc. New postscript through 1958. "Of the books attempting an account of the history and contents of modern atomic physics which have come to my attention, this is the best," H. Margenau, Yale U., in Amer. J. of Physics. 2nd edition. 32 tables, illustrations. 275pp. 5⅜ x 8. T518 Paperbound **$1.45**

HISTORY OF SCIENCE AND PHILOSOPHY OF SCIENCE

THE VALUE OF SCIENCE, Henri Poincaré. Many of most mature ideas of "last scientific universalist" for both beginning, advanced workers. Nature of scientific truth, whether order is innate in universe or imposed by man, logical thought vs. intuition (relating to Weierstrass, Lie, Riemann, etc), time and space (relativity, psychological time, simultaneity), Herz's concept of force, values within disciplines of Maxwell, Carnot, Mayer, Newton, Lorentz, etc. iii + 147pp. 5⅜ x 8. S469 Paperbound **$1.35**

PHILOSOPHY AND THE PHYSICISTS, L. S. Stebbing. Philosophical aspects of modern science examined in terms of lively critical attack on ideas of Jeans, Eddington. Tasks of science, causality, determinism, probability, relation of world physics to that of everyday experience, philosophical significance of Planck-Bohr concept of discontinuous energy levels, inferences to be drawn from Uncertainty Principle, implications of "becoming" involved in 2nd law of thermodynamics, other problems posed by discarding of Laplacean determinism. 285pp. 5⅜ x 8. T480 Paperbound **$1.65**

THE PRINCIPLES OF SCIENCE, A TREATISE ON LOGIC AND THE SCIENTIFIC METHOD, W. S. Jevons. Milestone in development of symbolic logic remains stimulating contribution to investigation of inferential validity in sciences. Treats inductive, deductive logic, theory of number, probability, limits of scientific method; significantly advances Boole's logic, contains detailed introduction to nature and methods of probability in physics, astronomy, everyday affairs, etc. In introduction, Ernest Nagel of Columbia U. says, "[Jevons] continues to be of interest as an attempt to articulate the logic of scientific inquiry." liii + 786pp. 5⅜ x 8. S446 Paperbound **$2.98**

A HISTORY OF ASTRONOMY FROM THALES TO KEPLER, J. L. E. Dreyer. Only work in English to give complete history of cosmological views from prehistoric times to Kepler. Partial contents: Near Eastern astronomical systems, Early Greeks, Homocentric spheres of Euxodus, Epicycles, Ptolemaic system, Medieval cosmology, Copernicus, Kepler, much more. "Especially useful to teachers and students of the history of science . . . unsurpassed in its field," Isis. Formerly "A History of Planetary Systems from Thales to Kepler." Revised foreword by W. H. Stahl. xvii + 430pp. 5⅜ x 8. S79 Paperbound **$1.98**

A CONCISE HISTORY OF MATHEMATICS, D. Struik. Lucid study of development of ideas, techniques, from Ancient Near East, Greece, Islamic science, Middle Ages, Renaissance, modern times. Important mathematicians described in detail. Treatment not anecdotal, but analytical development of ideas. Non-technical—no math training needed. "Rich in content, thoughtful in interpretations," U.S. Quarterly Booklist. 60 illustrations including Greek, Egyptian manuscripts, portraits of 31 mathematicians. 2nd edition. xix + 299pp. 5⅜ x 8. S255 Paperbound **$1.75**

THE PHILOSOPHICAL WRITINGS OF PEIRCE, edited by Justus Buchler. A carefully balanced expositon of Peirce's complete system, written by Peirce himself. It covers such matters as scientific method, pure chance vs. law, symbolic logic, theory of signs, pragmatism, experiment, and other topics. "Excellent selection . . . gives more than adequate evidence of the range and greatness," Personalist. Formerly entitled "The Philosophy of Peirce." xvi + 368pp. T217 Paperbound **$1.95**

SCIENCE AND METHOD, Henri Poincaré. Procedure of scientific discovery, methodology, experiment, idea-germination—processes by which discoveries come into being. Most significant and interesting aspects of development, application of ideas. Chapters cover selection of facts, chance, mathematical reasoning, mathematics and logic; Whitehead, Russell, Cantor, the new mechanics, etc. 288pp. 5⅜ x 8. S222 Paperbound **$1.35**

SCIENCE AND HYPOTHESIS, Henri Poincaré. Creative psychology in science. How such concepts as number, magnitude, space, force, classical mechanics developed, how modern scientist uses them in his thought. Hypothesis in physics, theories of modern physics. Introduction by Sir James Larmor. "Few mathematicians have had the breadth of vision of Poincaré, and none is his superior in the gift of clear exposition," E. T. Bell. 272pp. 5⅜ x 8. S221 Paperbound **$1.35**

ESSAYS IN EXPERIMENTAL LOGIC, John Dewey. Stimulating series of essays by one of most influential minds in American philosophy presents some of his most mature thoughts on wide range of subjects. Partial contents: Relationship between inquiry and experience; dependence of knowledge upon thought; character logic; judgments of practice, data, and meanings; stimuli of thought, etc. viii + 444pp. 5⅜ x 8. T73 Paperbound **$1.95**

WHAT IS SCIENCE, Norman Campbell. Excellent introduction explains scientific method, role of mathematics, types of scientific laws. Contents: 2 aspects of science, science and nature, laws of chance, discovery of laws, explanation of laws, measurement and numerical laws, applications of science. 192pp. 5⅜ x 8. S43 Paperbound **$1.25**

FROM EUCLID TO EDDINGTON: A STUDY OF THE CONCEPTIONS OF THE EXTERNAL WORLD, Sir Edmund Whittaker. Foremost British scientist traces development of theories of natural philosophy from western rediscovery of Euclid to Eddington, Einstein, Dirac, etc. 5 major divisions: Space, Time and Movement; Concepts of Classical Physics; Concepts of Quantum Mechanics; Eddington Universe. Contrasts inadequacy of classical physics to understand physical world with present day attempts of relativity, non-Euclidean geometry, space curvature, etc. 212pp. 5⅜ x 8. T491 Paperbound **$1.35**

THE ANALYSIS OF MATTER, Bertrand Russell. How do our senses accord with the new physics? This volume covers such topics as logical analysis of physics, prerelativity physics, causality, scientific inference, physics and perception, special and general relativity, Weyl's theory, tensors, invariants and their physical interpretation, periodicity and qualitative series. "The most thorough treatment of the subject that has yet been published," The Nation. Introduction by L. E. Denonn. 422pp. 5⅜ x 8. T231 Paperbound **$1.95**

LANGUAGE, TRUTH, AND LOGIC, A. Ayer. A clear introduction to the Vienna and Cambridge schools of Logical Positivism. Specific tests to evaluate validity of ideas, etc. Contents: function of philosophy, elimination of metaphysics, nature of analysis, a priori, truth and probability, etc. 10th printing. "I should like to have written it myself," Bertrand Russell. 160pp. 5⅜ x 8. T10 Paperbound **$1.25**

THE PSYCHOLOGY OF INVENTION IN THE MATHEMATICAL FIELD, J. Hadamard. Where do ideas come from? What role does the unconscious play? Are ideas best developed by mathematical reasoning, word reasoning, visualization? What are the methods used by Einstein, Poincaré, Galton, Riemann? How can these techniques be applied by others? One of the world's leading mathematicians discusses these and other questions. xiii + 145pp. 5⅜ x 8. T107 Paperbound **$1.25**

GUIDE TO PHILOSOPHY, C. E. M. Joad. By one of the ablest expositors of all time, this is not simply a history or a typological survey, but an examination of central problems in terms of answers afforded by the greatest thinkers: Plato, Aristotle, Scholastics, Leibniz, Kant, Whitehead, Russell, and many others. Especially valuable to persons in the physical sciences; over 100 pages devoted to Jeans, Eddington, and others, the philosophy of modern physics, scientific materialism, pragmatism, etc. Classified bibliography. 592pp. 5⅜ x 8. T50 Paperbound **$2.00**

SUBSTANCE AND FUNCTION, and **EINSTEIN'S THEORY OF RELATIVITY, Ernst Cassirer.** Two books bound as one. Cassirer establishes a philosophy of the exact sciences that takes into consideration new developments in mathematics, shows historical connections. Partial contents: Aristotelian logic, Mill's analysis, Helmholtz and Kronecker, Russell and cardinal numbers, Euclidean vs. non-Euclidean geometry, Einstein's relativity. Bibliography. Index. xxi + 464pp. 5⅜ x 8. T50 Paperbound **$2.00**

FOUNDATIONS OF GEOMETRY, Bertrand Russell. Nobel laureate analyzes basic problems in the overlap area between mathematics and philosophy: the nature of geometrical knowledge, the nature of geometry, and the applications of geometry to space. Covers history of non-Euclidean geometry, philosophic interpretations of geometry, especially Kant, projective and metrical geometry. Most interesting as the solution offered in 1897 by a great mind to a problem still current. New introduction by Prof. Morris Kline, N.Y. University. "Admirably clear, precise, and elegantly reasoned analysis," International Math. News. xii + 201pp. 5⅜ x 8. S233 Paperbound **$1.60**

THE NATURE OF PHYSICAL THEORY, P. W. Bridgman. How modern physics looks to a highly unorthodox physicist—a Nobel laureate. Pointing out many absurdities of science, demonstrating inadequacies of various physical theories, weighs and analyzes contributions of Einstein, Bohr, Heisenberg, many others. A non-technical consideration of correlation of science and reality. xi + 138pp. 5⅜ x 8. S33 Paperbound **$1.25**

EXPERIMENT AND THEORY IN PHYSICS, Max Born. A Nobel laureate examines the nature and value of the counterclaims of experiment and theory in physics. Synthetic versus analytical scientific advances are analyzed in works of Einstein, Bohr, Heisenberg, Planck, Eddington, Milne, others, by a fellow scientist. 44pp. 5⅜ x 8. S308 Paperbound **60¢**

A SHORT HISTORY OF ANATOMY AND PHYSIOLOGY FROM THE GREEKS TO HARVEY, Charles Singer. Corrected edition of "The Evolution of Anatomy." Classic traces anatomy, physiology from prescientific times through Greek, Roman periods, dark ages, Renaissance, to beginning of modern concepts. Centers on individuals, movements, that definitely advanced anatomical knowledge. Plato, Diocles, Erasistratus, Galen, da Vinci, etc. Special section on Vesalius. 20 plates. 270 extremely interesting illustrations of ancient, Medieval, Renaissance, Oriental origin. xii + 209pp. 5⅜ x 8. T389 Paperbound **$1.75**

SPACE-TIME-MATTER, Hermann Weyl. "The standard treatise on the general theory of relativity," (Nature), by world renowned scientist. Deep, clear discussion of logical coherence of general theory, introducing all needed tools: Maxwell, analytical geometry, non-Euclidean geometry, tensor calculus, etc. Basis is classical space-time, before absorption of relativity. Contents: Euclidean space, mathematical form, metrical continuum, general theory, etc. 15 diagrams. xviii + 330pp. 5⅜ x 8. S267 Paperbound **$1.75**

MATTER AND MOTION, James Clerk Maxwell. Excellent exposition begins with simple particles, proceeds gradually to physical systems beyond complete analysis; motion, force, properties of centre of mass of material system; work, energy, gravitation, etc. Written with all Maxwell's original insights and clarity. Notes by E. Larmor. 17 diagrams. 178pp. 5⅜ x 8. S188 Paperbound **$1.25**

PRINCIPLES OF MECHANICS, Heinrich Hertz. Last work by the great 19th century physicist is not only a classic, but of great interest in the logic of science. Creating a new system of mechanics based upon space, time, and mass, it returns to axiomatic analysis, understanding of the formal or structural aspects of science, taking into account logic, observation, a priori elements. Of great historical importance to Poincaré, Carnap, Einstein, Milne. A 20 page introduction by R. S. Cohen, Wesleyan University, analyzes the implications of Hertz's thought and the logic of science. 13 page introduction by Helmholtz. xlii + 274pp. 5⅜ x 8. S316 Clothbound **$3.50**
S317 Paperbound **$1.75**

FROM MAGIC TO SCIENCE, Charles Singer. A great historian examines aspects of science from Roman Empire through Renaissance. Includes perhaps best discussion of early herbals, penetrating physiological interpretation of "The Visions of Hildegarde of Bingen." Also examines Arabian, Galenic influences; Pythagoras' sphere, Paracelsus; reawakening of science under Leonardo da Vinci, Vesalius; Lorica of Gildas the Briton; etc. Frequent quotations with translations from contemporary manuscripts. Unabridged, corrected edition. 158 unusual illustrations from Classical, Medieval sources. xxvii + 365pp. 5⅜ x 8. T390 Paperbound **$2.00**

A HISTORY OF THE CALCULUS, AND ITS CONCEPTUAL DEVELOPMENT, Carl B. Boyer. Provides laymen, mathematicians a detailed history of the development of the calculus, from beginnings in antiquity to final elaboration as mathematical abstraction. Gives a sense of mathematics not as technique, but as habit of mind, in progression of ideas of Zeno, Plato, Pythagoras, Eudoxus, Arabic and Scholastic mathematicians, Newton, Leibniz, Taylor, Descartes, Euler, Lagrange, Cantor, Weierstrass, and others. This first comprehensive, critical history of the calculus was originally entitled "The Concepts of the Calculus." Foreword by R. Courant. 22 figures. 25 page bibliography. v + 364pp. 5⅜ x 8. S509 Paperbound **$2.00**

A DIDEROT PICTORIAL ENCYCLOPEDIA OF TRADES AND INDUSTRY, Manufacturing and the Technical Arts in Plates Selected from "L'Encyclopédie ou Dictionnaire Raisonné des Sciences, des Arts, et des Métiers" of Denis Diderot. Edited with text by C. Gillispie. First modern selection of plates from high-point of 18th century French engraving. Storehouse of technological information to historian of arts and science. Over 2,000 illustrations on 485 full page plates, most of them original size, show trades, industries of fascinating era in such great detail that modern reconstructions might be made of them. Plates teem with men, women, children performing thousands of operations; show sequence, general operations, closeups, details of machinery. Illustrates such important, interesting trades, industries as sowing, harvesting, beekeeping, tobacco processing, fishing, arts of war, mining, smelting, casting iron, extracting mercury, making gunpowder, cannons, bells, shoeing horses, tanning, papermaking, printing, dying, over 45 more categories. Professor Gillispie of Princeton supplies full commentary on all plates, identifies operations, tools, processes, etc. Material is presented in lively, lucid fashion. Of great interest to all studying history of science, technology. Heavy library cloth. 920pp. 9 x 12. T421 2 volume set **$18.50**

DE MAGNETE, William Gilbert. Classic work on magnetism, founded new science. Gilbert was first to use word "electricity," to recognize mass as distinct from weight, to discover effect of heat on magnetic bodies; invented an electroscope, differentiated between static electricity and magnetism, conceived of earth as magnet. This lively work, by first great experimental scientist, is not only a valuable historical landmark, but a delightfully easy to follow record of a searching, ingenious mind. Translated by P. F. Mottelay. 25 page biographical memoir. 90 figures. lix + 368pp. 5⅜ x 8. S470 Paperbound **$2.00**

HISTORY OF MATHEMATICS, D. E. Smith. Most comprehensive, non-technical history of math in English. Discusses lives and works of over a thousand major, minor figures, with footnotes giving technical information outside book's scheme, and indicating disputed matters. Vol. I: A chronological examination, from primitive concepts through Egypt, Babylonia, Greece, the Orient, Rome, the Middle Ages, The Renaissance, and to 1900. Vol. II: The development of ideas in specific fields and problems, up through elementary calculus. "Marks an epoch . . . will modify the entire teaching of the history of science," George Sarton. 2 volumes, total of 510 illustrations, 1355pp. 5⅜ x 8. Set boxed in attractive container. T429, 430 Paperbound, the set **$5.00**

THE PHILOSOPHY OF SPACE AND TIME, H. Reichenbach. An important landmark in development of empiricist conception of geometry, covering foundations of geometry, time theory, consequences of Einstein's relativity, including: relations between theory and observations; coordinate definitions; relations between topological and metrical properties of space; psychological problem of visual intuition of non-Euclidean structures; many more topics important to modern science and philosophy. Majority of ideas require only knowledge of intermediate math. "Still the best book in the field," Rudolf Carnap. Introduction by R. Carnap. 49 figures. xviii + 296pp. 5⅜ x 8. S443 Paperbound **$2.00**

FOUNDATIONS OF SCIENCE: THE PHILOSOPHY OF THEORY AND EXPERIMENT, N. Campbell. A critique of the most fundamental concepts of science, particularly physics. Examines why certain propositions are accepted without question, demarcates science from philosophy, etc. Part I analyzes presuppositions of scientific thought: existence of material world, nature of laws, probability, etc; part 2 covers nature of experiment and applications of mathematics: conditions for measurement, relations between numerical laws and theories, error, etc. An appendix covers problems arising from relativity, force, motion, space, time. A classic in its field. "A real grasp of what science is," Higher Educational Journal. xiii + 565pp. 5⅝ x 8⅜. S372 Paperbound **$2.95**

THE STUDY OF THE HISTORY OF MATHEMATICS and **THE STUDY OF THE HISTORY OF SCIENCE, G. Sarton.** Excellent introductions, orientation, for beginning or mature worker. Describes duty of mathematical historian, incessant efforts and genius of previous generations. Explains how today's discipline differs from previous methods. 200 item bibliography with critical evaluations, best available biographies of modern mathematicians, best treatises on historical methods is especially valuable. 10 illustrations. 2 volumes bound as one. 113pp. + 75pp. 5⅜ x 8. T240 Paperbound **$1.25**

MATHEMATICAL PUZZLES

MATHEMATICAL PUZZLES OF SAM LOYD, selected and edited by **Martin Gardner.** 117 choice puzzles by greatest American puzzle creator and innovator, from his famous "Cyclopedia of Puzzles." All unique style, historical flavor of originals. Based on arithmetic, algebra, probability, game theory, route tracing, topology, sliding block, operations research, geometrical dissection. Includes famous "14-15" puzzle which was national craze, "Horse of a Different Color" which sold millions of copies. 120 line drawings, diagrams. Solutions. xx + 167pp. 5⅜ x 8. T498 Paperbound **$1.00**

SYMBOLIC LOGIC and THE GAME OF LOGIC, Lewis Carroll. "Symbolic Logic" is not concerned with modern symbolic logic, but is instead a collection of over 380 problems posed with charm and imagination, using the syllogism, and a fascinating diagrammatic method of drawing conclusions. In "The Game of Logic" Carroll's whimsical imagination devises a logical game played with 2 diagrams and counters (included) to manipulate hundreds of tricky syllogisms. The final section, "Hit or Miss" is a lagniappe of 101 additional puzzles in the delightful Carroll manner. Until this reprint edition, both of these books were rarities costing up to $15 each. Symbolic Logic: Index. xxxi + 199pp. The Game of Logic: 96pp. 2 vols. bound as one. 5⅜ x 8. T492 Paperbound **$1.50**

PILLOW PROBLEMS and A TANGLED TALE, Lewis Carroll. One of the rarest of all Carroll's works, "Pillow Problems" contains 72 original math puzzles, all typically ingenious. Particularly fascinating are Carroll's answers which remain exactly as he thought them out, reflecting his actual mental process. The problems in "A Tangled Tale" are in story form, originally appearing as a monthly magazine serial. Carroll not only gives the solutions, but uses answers sent in by readers to discuss wrong approaches and misleading paths, and grades them for insight. Both of these books were rarities until this edition, "Pillow Problems" costing up to $25, and "A Tangled Tale" $15. Pillow Problems: Preface and Introduction by Lewis Carroll. xx + 109pp. A Tangled Tale: 6 illustrations. 152pp. Two vols. bound as one. 5⅜ x 8. T493 Paperbound **$1.50**

NEW WORD PUZZLES, G. L. Kaufman. 100 brand new challenging puzzles on words, combinations, never before published. Most are new types invented by author, for beginners and experts both. Squares of letters follow chess moves to build words; symmetrical designs made of synonyms; rhymed crostics; double word squares; syllable puzzles where you fill in missing syllables instead of missing letter; many other types, all new. Solutions. "Excellent," Recreation. 100 puzzles. 196 figures. vi + 122pp. 5⅜ x 8. T344 Paperbound **$1.00**

MATHEMATICAL EXCURSIONS, H. A. Merrill. Fun, recreation, insights into elementary problem solving. Math expert guides you on by-paths not generally travelled in elementary math courses—divide by inspection, Russian peasant multiplication; memory systems for pi; odd, even magic squares; dyadic systems; square roots by geometry; Tchebichev's machine; dozens more. Solutions to more difficult ones. "Brain stirring stuff . . . a classic," Genie. 50 illustrations. 145pp. 5⅜ x 8. T350 Paperbound **$1.00**

THE BOOK OF MODERN PUZZLES, G. L. Kaufman. Over 150 puzzles, absolutely all new material based on same appeal as crosswords, deduction puzzles, but with different principles, techniques. 2-minute teasers, word labyrinths, design, pattern, logic, observation puzzles, puzzles testing ability to apply general knowledge to peculiar situations, many others. Solutions. 116 illustrations. 192pp. 5⅜ x 8. T143 Paperbound **$1.00**

MATHEMAGIC, MAGIC PUZZLES, AND GAMES WITH NUMBERS, R. V. Heath. Over 60 puzzles, stunts, on properties of numbers. Easy techniques for multiplying large numbers mentally, identifying unknown numbers, finding date of any day in any year. Includes The Lost Digit, 3 Acrobats, Psychic Bridge, magic squares, triangles, cubes, others not easily found elsewhere. Edited by J. S. Meyer. 76 illustrations. 128pp. 5⅜ x 8. T110 Paperbound **$1.00**

DOVER SCIENCE BOOKS

PUZZLE QUIZ AND STUNT FUN, J. Meyer. 238 high-priority puzzles, stunts, tricks—math puzzles like The Clever Carpenter, Atom Bomb, Please Help Alice; mysteries, deductions like The Bridge of Sighs, Secret Code; observation puzzlers like The American Flag, Playing Cards, Telephone Dial; over 200 others with magic squares, tongue twisters, puns, anagrams. Solutions. Revised, enlarged edition of "Fun-To-Do." Over 100 illustrations. 238 puzzles, stunts, tricks. 256pp. 5⅜ x 8. T337 Paperbound **$1.00**

101 PUZZLES IN THOUGHT AND LOGIC, C. R. Wylie, Jr. For readers who enjoy challenge, stimulation of logical puzzles without specialized math or scientific knowledge. Problems entirely new, range from relatively easy to brainteasers for hours of subtle entertainment. Detective puzzles, find the lying fisherman, how a blind man identifies color by logic, many more. Easy-to-understand introduction to logic of puzzle solving and general scientific method. 128pp. 5⅜ x 8. T367 Paperbound **$1.00**

CRYPTANALYSIS, H. F. Gaines. Standard elementary, intermediate text for serious students. Not just old material, but much not generally known, except to experts. Concealment, Transposition, Substitution ciphers; Vigenere, Kasiski, Playfair, multafid, dozens of other techniques. Formerly "Elementary Cryptanalysis." Appendix with sequence charts, letter frequencies in English, 5 other languages, English word frequencies. Bibliography. 167 codes. New to this edition: solutions to codes. vi + 230pp. 5⅜ x 8⅜. T97 Paperbound **$1.95**

CRYPTOGRAPY, L. D. Smith. Excellent elementary introduction to enciphering, deciphering secret writing. Explains transposition, substitution ciphers; codes; solutions; geometrical patterns, route transcription, columnar transposition, other methods. Mixed cipher systems; single, polyalphabetical substitutions; mechanical devices; Vigenere; etc. Enciphering Japanese; explanation of Baconian biliteral cipher; frequency tables. Over 150 problems. Bibliography. Index. 164pp. 5⅜ x 8. T247 Paperbound **$1.00**

MATHEMATICS, MAGIC AND MYSTERY, M. Gardner. Card tricks, metal mathematics, stage mind-reading, other "magic" explained as applications of probability, sets, number theory, etc. Creative examination of laws, applications. Scores of new tricks, insights. 115 sections on cards, dice, coins; vanishing tricks, many others. No sleight of hand—math guarantees success. "Could hardly get more entertainment . . . easy to follow," Mathematics Teacher. 115 illustrations. xii + 174pp. 5⅜ x 8. T335 Paperbound **$1.00**

AMUSEMENTS IN MATHEMATICS, H. E. Dudeney. Foremost British originator of math puzzles, always witty, intriguing, paradoxical in this classic. One of largest collections. More than 430 puzzles, problems, paradoxes. Mazes, games, problems on number manipulations, unicursal, other route problems, puzzles on measuring, weighing, packing, age, kinship, chessboards, joiners', crossing river, plane figure dissection, many others. Solutions. More than 450 illustrations. viii + 258pp. 5⅜ x 8. T473 Paperbound **$1.25**

THE CANTERBURY PUZZLES H. E. Dudeney. Chaucer's pilgrims set one another problems in story form. Also Adventures of the Puzzle Club, the Strange Escape of the King's Jester, the Monks of Riddlewell, the Squire's Christmas Puzzle Party, others. All puzzles are original, based on dissecting plane figures, arithmetic, algebra, elementary calculus, other branches of mathematics, and purely logical ingenuity. "The limit of ingenuity and intricacy," The Observer. Over 110 puzzles, full solutions. 150 illustrations. viii + 225 pp. 5⅜ x 8. T474 Paperbound **$1.25**

MATHEMATICAL PUZZLES FOR BEGINNERS AND ENTHUSIASTS, G. Mott-Smith. 188 puzzles to test mental agility. Inference, interpretation, algebra, dissection of plane figures, geometry, properties of numbers, decimation, permutations, probability, all are in these delightful problems. Includes the Odic Force, How to Draw an Ellipse, Spider's Cousin, more than 180 others. Detailed solutions. Appendix with square roots, triangular numbers, primes, etc. 135 illustrations. 2nd revised edition. 248pp. 5⅜ x 8. T198 Paperbound **$1.00**

MATHEMATICAL RECREATIONS, M. Kraitchik. Some 250 puzzles, problems, demonstrations of recreation mathematics on relatively advanced level. Unusual historical problems from Greek, Medieval, Arabic, Hindu sources; modern problems on "mathematics without numbers," geometry, topology, arithmetic, etc. Pastimes derived from figurative, Mersenne, Fermat numbers: fairy chess; latruncles: reversi; etc. Full solutions. Excellent insights into special fields of math. "Strongly recommended to all who are interested in the lighter side of mathematics," Mathematical Gaz. 181 illustrations. 330pp. 5⅜ x 8. T163 Paperbound **$1.75**

FICTION

FLATLAND, E. A. Abbott. A perennially popular science-fiction classic about life in a 2-dimensional world, and the impingement of higher dimensions. Political, satiric, humorous, moral overtones. This land where women are straight lines and the lowest and most dangerous classes are isosceles triangles with 3° vertices conveys brilliantly a feeling for many concepts of modern science. 7th edition. New introduction by Banesh Hoffmann. 128pp. 5⅜ x 8. T1 Paperbound **$1.00**

SEVEN SCIENCE FICTION NOVELS OF H. G. WELLS. Complete texts, unabridged, of seven of Wells' greatest novels: The War of the Worlds, The Invisible Man, The Island of Dr. Moreau, The Food of the Gods, First Men in the Moon, In the Days of the Comet, The Time Machine. Still considered by many experts to be the best science-fiction ever written, they will offer amusements and instruction to the scientific minded reader. "The great master," Sky and Telescope. 1051pp. 5⅜ x 8. T264 Clothbound **$3.95**

28 SCIENCE FICTION STORIES OF H. G. WELLS. Unabridged! This enormous omnibus contains 2 full length novels—Men Like Gods, Star Begotten—plus 26 short stories of space, time, invention, biology, etc. The Crystal Egg, The Country of the Blind, Empire of the Ants, The Man Who Could Work Miracles, Aepyornis Island, A Story of the Days to Come, and 20 others "A master . . . not surpassed by . . . writers of today," The English Journal. 915pp. 5⅜ x 8. T265 Clothbound **$3.95**

FIVE ADVENTURE NOVELS OF H. RIDER HAGGARD. All the mystery and adventure of darkest Africa captured accurately by a man who lived among Zulus for years, who knew African ethnology, folkways as did few of his contemporaries. They have been regarded as examples of the very best high adventure by such critics as Orwell, Andrew Lang, Kipling. Contents: She, King Solomon's Mines, Allan Quatermain, Allan's Wife, Maiwa's Revenge. "Could spin a yarn so full of suspense and color that you couldn't put the story down," Sat. Review. 821pp. 5⅜ x 8. T108 Clothbound **$3.95**

CHESS AND CHECKERS

LEARN CHESS FROM THE MASTERS, Fred Reinfeld. Easiest, most instructive way to improve your game—play 10 games against such masters as Marshall, Znosko-Borovsky, Bronstein, Najdorf, etc., with each move graded by easy system. Includes ratings for alternate moves possible. Games selected for interest, clarity, easily isolated principles. Covers Ruy Lopez, Dutch Defense, Vienna Game openings; subtle, intricate middle game variations; all-important end game. Full annotations. Formerly "Chess by Yourself." 91 diagrams. viii + 144pp. 5⅜ x 8. T362 Paperbound **$1.00**

REINFELD ON THE END GAME IN CHESS, Fred Reinfeld. Analyzes 62 end games by Alekhine, Flohr, Tarrasch, Morphy, Capablanca, Rubinstein, Lasker, Reshevsky, other masters. Only 1st rate book with extensive coverage of error—tell exactly what is wrong with each move you might have made. Centers around transitions from middle play to end play. King and pawn, minor pieces, queen endings; blockage, weak, passed pawns, etc. "Excellent . . . a boon," Chess Life. Formerly "Practical End Play." 62 figures. vi + 177pp. 5⅜ x 8. T417 Paperbound **$1.25**

HYPERMODERN CHESS as developed in the games of its greatest exponent, ARON NIMZOVICH, edited by Fred Reinfeld. An intensely original player, analyst, Nimzovich's approaches startled, often angered the chess world. This volume, designed for the average player, shows how his iconoclastic methods won him victories over Alekhine, Lasker, Marshall, Rubinstein, Spielmann, others, and infused new life into the game. Use his methods to startle opponents, invigorate play. "Annotations and introductions to each game . . . are excellent," Times (London). 180 diagrams. viii + 220pp. 5⅜ x 8. T448 Paperbound **$1.35**

THE ADVENTURE OF CHESS, Edward Lasker. Lively reader, by one of America's finest chess masters, including: history of chess, from ancient Indian 4-handed game of Chaturanga to great players of today; such delights and oddities as Maelzel's chess-playing automaton that beat Napoleon 3 times; etc. One of most valuable features is author's personal recollections of men he has played against—Nimzovich, Emanuel Lasker, Capablanca, Alekhine, etc. Discussion of chess-playing machines (newly revised). 5 page chess primer. 11 illustrations. 53 diagrams. 296pp. 5⅜ x 8. S510 Paperbound **$1.45**

THE ART OF CHESS, James Mason. Unabridged reprinting of latest revised edition of most famous general study ever written. Mason, early 20th century master, teaches beginning, intermediate player over 90 openings; middle game, end game, to see more moves ahead, to plan purposefully, attack, sacrifice, defend, exchange, govern general strategy. "Classic . . . one of the clearest and best developed studies," Publishers Weekly. Also included, a complete supplement by F. Reinfeld, "How Do You Play Chess?", invaluable to beginners for its lively question-and-answer method. 448 diagrams. 1947 Reinfeld-Bernstein text. Bibliography. xvi + 340pp. 5⅜ x 8. T463 Paperbound **$1.85**

MORPHY'S GAMES OF CHESS, edited by P. W. Sergeant. Put boldness into your game by flowing brilliant, forceful moves of the greatest chess player of all time. 300 of Morphy's best games, carefully annotated to reveal principles. 54 classics against masters like Anderssen, Harrwitz, Bird, Paulsen, and others. 52 games at odds; 54 blindfold games; plus over 100 others. Follow his interpretation of Dutch Defense, Evans Gambit, Giuoco Piano, Ruy Lopez, many more. Unabridged reissue of latest revised edition. New introduction by F. Reinfeld. Annotations, introduction by Sergeant. 235 diagrams. x + 352pp. 5⅜ x 8. T386 Paperbound **$1.75**

WIN AT CHECKERS, M. Hopper. (Formerly "Checkers.") Former World's Unrestricted Checker Champion discusses principles of game, expert's shots, traps, problems for beginner, standard openings, locating best move, end game, opening "blitzkrieg" moves to draw when behind, etc. Over 100 detailed questions, answers anticipate problems. Appendix. 75 problems with solutions, diagrams. 79 figures. xi + 107pp. 5⅜ x 8. T363 Paperbound **$1.00**

HOW TO FORCE CHECKMATE, Fred Reinfeld. If you have trouble finishing off your opponent, here is a collection of lightning strokes and combinations from actual tournament play. Starts with 1-move checkmates, works up to 3-move mates. Develops ability to lock ahead, gain new insights into combinations, complex or deceptive positions; ways to estimate weaknesses, strengths of you and your opponent. "A good deal of amusement and instruction," Times, (London). 300 diagrams. Solutions to all positions. Formerly "Challenge to Chess Players." 111pp. 5⅜ x 8. T417 Paperbound **$1.25**

A TREASURY OF CHESS LORE, edited by Fred Reinfeld. Delightful collection of anecdotes, short stories, aphorisms by, about masters; poems, accounts of games, tournaments, photographs; hundreds of humorous, pithy, satirical, wise, historical episodes, comments, word portraits. Fascinating "must" for chess players; revealing and perhaps seductive to those who wonder what their friends see in game. 49 photographs (14 full page plates). 12 diagrams. xi + 306pp. 5⅜ x 8. T458 Paperbound **$1.75**

WIN AT CHESS, Fred Reinfeld. 300 practical chess situations, to sharpen your eye, test skill against masters. Start with simple examples, progress at own pace to complexities. This selected series of crucial moments in chess will stimulate imagination, develop stronger, more versatile game. Simple grading system enables you to judge progress. "Extensive use of diagrams is a great attraction," Chess. 300 diagrams. Notes, solutions to every situation. Formerly "Chess Quiz." vi + 120pp. 5⅜ x 8. T433 Paperbound **$1.00**

MATHEMATICS: ELEMENTARY TO INTERMEDIATE

HOW TO CALCULATE QUICKLY, H. Sticker. Tried and true method to help mathematics of everyday life. Awakens "number sense"—ability to see relationships between numbers as whole quantities. A serious course of over 9000 problems and their solutions through techniques not taught in schools: left-to-right multiplications, new fast division, etc. 10 minutes a day will double or triple calculation speed. Excellent for scientist at home in higher math, but dissatisfied with speed and accuracy in lower math. 256pp. 5 x 7¼. Paperbound **$1.00**

FAMOUS PROBLEMS OF ELEMENTARY GEOMETRY, Felix Klein. Expanded version of 1894 Easter lectures at Göttingen. 3 problems of classical geometry: squaring the circle, trisecting angle, doubling cube, considered with full modern implications: transcendental numbers, pi, etc. "A modern classic . . . no knowledge of higher mathematics is required," Scientia. Notes by R. Archibald. 16 figures. xi + 92pp. 5⅜ x 8. T298 Paperbound **$1.00**

HIGHER MATHEMATICS FOR STUDENTS OF CHEMISTRY AND PHYSICS, J. W. Mellor. Practical, not abstract, building problems out of familiar laboratory material. Covers differential calculus, coordinate, analytical geometry, functions, integral calculus, infinite series, numerical equations, differential equations, Fourier's theorem probability, theory of errors, calculus of variations, determinants. "If the reader is not familiar with this book, it will repay him to examine it," Chem. and Engineering News. 800 problems. 189 figures. xxi + 641pp. 5⅜ x 8. S193 Paperbound **$2.25**

TRIGONOMETRY REFRESHER FOR TECHNICAL MEN, A. A. Klaf. 913 detailed questions, answers cover most important aspects of plane, spherical trigonometry—particularly useful in clearing up difficulties in special areas. Part I: plane trig, angles, quadrants, functions, graphical representation, interpolation, equations, logs, solution of triangle, use of slide rule, etc. Next 188 pages discuss applications to navigation, surveying, elasticity, architecture, other special fields. Part 3: spherical trig, applications to terrestrial, astronomical problems. Methods of time-saving, simplification of principal angles, make book most useful. 913 questions answered. 1738 problems, answers to odd numbers. 494 figures. 24 pages of formulas, functions. x + 629pp. 5⅜ x 8. T371 Paperbound **$2.00**

CALCULUS REFRESHER FOR TECHNICAL MEN, A. A. Klaf. 756 questions examine most important aspects of integral, differential calculus. Part I: simple differential calculus, constants, variables, functions, increments, logs, curves, etc. Part 2: fundamental ideas of integrations, inspection, substitution, areas, volumes, mean value, double, triple integration, etc. Practical aspects stressed. 50 pages illustrate applications to specific problems of civil, nautical engineering, electricity, stress, strain, elasticity, similar fields. 756 questions answered. 566 problems, mostly answered. 36pp. of useful constants, formulas. v + 431pp. 5⅜ x 8. T370 Paperbound **$2.00**

MONOGRAPHS ON TOPICS OF MODERN MATHEMATICS, edited by J. W. A. Young. Advanced mathematics for persons who have forgotten, or not gone beyond, high school algebra. 9 monographs on foundation of geometry, modern pure geometry, non-Euclidean geometry, fundamental propositions of algebra, algebraic equations, functions, calculus, theory of numbers, etc. Each monograph gives proofs of important results, and descriptions of leading methods, to provide wide coverage. "Of high merit," Scientific American. New introduction by Prof. M. Kline, N.Y. Univ. 100 diagrams. xvi + 416pp. 6⅛ x 9¼.
S289 Paperbound **$2.00**

MATHEMATICS IN ACTION, O. G. Sutton. Excellent middle level application of mathematics to study of universe, demonstrates how math is applied to ballistics, theory of computing machines, waves, wave-like phenomena, theory of fluid flow, meteorological problems, statistics, flight, similar phenomena. No knowledge of advanced math required. Differential equations, Fourier series, group concepts, Eigenfunctions, Planck's constant, airfoil theory, and similar topics explained so clearly in everyday language that almost anyone can derive benefit from reading this even if much of high-school math is forgotten. 2nd edition. 88 figures. viii + 236pp. 5⅜ x 8. T450 Clothbound **$3.50**

ELEMENTARY MATHEMATICS FROM AN ADVANCED STANDPOINT, Felix Klein. Classic text, an outgrowth of Klein's famous integration and survey course at Göttingen. Using one field to interpret, adjust another, it covers basic topics in each area, with extensive analysis. Especially valuable in areas of modern mathematics. "A great mathematician, inspiring teacher, . . . deep insight," Bul., Amer. Math Soc.

Vol. I. ARITHMETIC, ALGEBRA, ANALYSIS. Introduces concept of function immediately, enlivens discussion with graphical, geometric methods. Partial contents: natural numbers, special properties, complex numbers. Real equations with real unknowns, complex quantities. Logarithmic, exponential functions, infinitesimal calculus. Transcendence of e and pi, theory of assemblages. Index. 125 figures. ix + 274pp. 5⅜ x 8. S151 Paperbound **$1.75**

Vol. II. GEOMETRY. Comprehensive view, accompanies space perception inherent in geometry with analytic formulas which facilitate precise formulation. Partial contents: Simplest geometric manifold; line segments, Grassman determinant principles, classication of configurations of space. Geometric transformations: affine, projective, higher point transformations, theory of the imaginary. Systematic discussion of geometry and its foundations. 141 illustrations. ix + 214pp. 5⅜ x 8. S151 Paperbound **$1.75**

A TREATISE ON PLANE AND ADVANCED TRIGONOMETRY, E. W. Hobson. Extraordinarily wide coverage, going beyond usual college level, one of few works covering advanced trig in full detail. By a great expositor with unerring anticipation of potentially difficult points. Includes circular functions; expansion of functions of multiple angle; trig tables; relations between sides, angles of triangles; complex numbers; etc. Many problems fully solved. "The best work on the subject," Nature. Formerly entitled "A Treatise on Plane Trigonometry." 689 examples. 66 figures. xvi + 383pp. 5⅜ x 8. S353 Paperbound **$1.95**

NON-EUCLIDEAN GEOMETRY, Roberto Bonola. The standard coverage of non-Euclidean geometry. Examines from both a historical and mathematical point of view geometries which have arisen from a study of Euclid's 5th postulate on parallel lines. Also included are complete texts, translated, of Bolyai's "Theory of Absolute Space," Lobachevsky's "Theory of Parallels." 180 diagrams. 431pp. 5⅜ x 8. S27 Paperbound **$1.95**

GEOMETRY OF FOUR DIMENSIONS, H. P. Manning. Unique in English as a clear, concise introduction. Treatment is synthetic, mostly Euclidean, though in hyperplanes and hyperspheres at infinity, non-Euclidean geometry is used. Historical introduction. Foundations of 4-dimensional geometry. Perpendicularity, simple angles. Angles of planes, higher order. Symmetry, order, motion; hyperpyramids, hypercones, hyperspheres; figures with parallel elements; volume, hypervolume in space; regular polyhedroids. Glossary. 78 figures. ix + 348pp. 5⅜ x 8. S182 Paperbound **$1.95**

MATHEMATICS: INTERMEDIATE TO ADVANCED

GEOMETRY (EUCLIDEAN AND NON-EUCLIDEAN)

THE GEOMETRY OF RENÉ DESCARTES. With this book, Descartes founded analytical geometry. Original French text, with Descartes's own diagrams, and excellent Smith-Latham translation. Contains: Problems the Construction of Which Requires only Straight Lines and Circles; On the Nature of Curved Lines; On the Construction of Solid or Supersolid Problems. Diagrams. 258pp. 5⅜ x 8. S68 Paperbound **$1.50**

THE WORKS OF ARCHIMEDES, edited by T. L. Heath. All the known works of the great Greek mathematician, including the recently discovered Method of Archimedes. Contains: On Sphere and Cylinder, Measurement of a Circle, Spirals, Conoids, Spheroids, etc. Definitive edition of greatest mathematical intellect of ancient world. 186 page study by Heath discusses Archimedes and history of Greek mathematics. 563pp. 5⅜ x 8. S9 Paperbound **$2.00**

COLLECTED WORKS OF BERNARD RIEMANN. Important sourcebook, first to contain complete text of 1892 "Werke" and the 1902 supplement, unabridged. 31 monographs, 3 complete lecture courses, 15 miscellaneous papers which have been of enormous importance in relativity, topology, theory of complex variables, other areas of mathematics. Edited by R. Dedekind, H. Weber, M. Noether, W. Wirtinger. German text; English introduction by Hans Lewy. 690pp. 5⅜ x 8. S226 Paperbound **$2.85**

THE THIRTEEN BOOKS OF EUCLID'S ELEMENTS, edited by Sir Thomas Heath. Definitive edition of one of very greatest classics of Western world. Complete translation of Heiberg text, plus spurious Book XIV. 150 page introduction on Greek, Medieval mathematics, Euclid, texts, commentators, etc. Elaborate critical apparatus parallels text, analyzing each definition, postulate, proposition, covering textual matters, refutations, supports, extrapolations, etc. This is the full Euclid. Unabridged reproduction of Cambridge U. 2nd edition. 3 volumes. 995 figures. 1426pp. 5⅜ x 8. S88, 89, 90, 3 volume set, paperbound **$6.00**

AN INTRODUCTION TO GEOMETRY OF N DIMENSIONS, D. M. Y. Sommerville. Presupposes no previous knowledge of field. Only book in English devoted exclusively to higher dimensional geometry. Discusses fundamental ideas of incidence, parallelism, perpendicularity, angles between linear space, enumerative geometry, analytical geometry from projective and metric views, polytopes, elementary ideas in analysis situs, content of hyperspacial figures. 60 diagrams. 196pp. 5⅜ x 8. S494 Paperbound **$1.50**

ELEMENTS OF NON-EUCLIDEAN GEOMETRY, D. M. Y. Sommerville. Unique in proceeding step-by-step. Requires only good knowledge of high-school geometry and algebra, to grasp elementary hyperbolic, elliptic, analytic non-Euclidean Geometries; space curvature and its implications; radical axes; homopethic centres and systems of circles; parataxy and parallelism; Gauss' proof of defect area theorem; much more, with exceptional clarity. 126 problems at chapter ends. 133 figures. xvi + 274pp. 5⅜ x 8. S460 Paperbound **$1.50**

THE FOUNDATIONS OF EUCLIDEAN GEOMETRY, H. G. Forder. First connected, rigorous account in light of modern analysis, establishing propositions without recourse to empiricism, without multiplying hypotheses. Based on tools of 19th and 20th century mathematicians, who made it possible to remedy gaps and complexities, recognize problems not earlier discerned. Begins with important relationship of number systems in geometrical figures. Considers classes, relations, linear order, natural numbers, axioms for magnitudes, groups, quasi-fields, fields, non-Archimedian systems, the axiom system (at length), particular axioms (two chapters on the Parallel Axioms), constructions, congruence, similarity, etc. Lists: axioms employed, constructions, symbols in frequent use. 295pp. 5⅜ x 8. S481 Paperbound **$2.00**

CALCULUS, FUNCTION THEORY (REAL AND COMPLEX), FOURIER THEORY

FIVE VOLUME "THEORY OF FUNCTIONS" SET BY KONRAD KNOPP. Provides complete, readily followed account of theory of functions. Proofs given concisely, yet without sacrifice of completeness or rigor. These volumes used as texts by such universities as M.I.T., Chicago, N.Y. City College, many others. "Excellent introduction . . . remarkably readable, concise, clear, rigorous," J. of the American Statistical Association.

ELEMENTS OF THE THEORY OF FUNCTIONS, Konrad Knopp. Provides background for further volumes in this set, or texts on similar level. Partial contents: Foundations, system of complex numbers and Gaussian plane of numbers, Riemann sphere of numbers, mapping by linear functions, normal forms, the logarithm, cyclometric functions, binomial series. "Not only for the young student, but also for the student who knows all about what is in it," Mathematical Journal. 140pp. 5⅜ x 8. S154 Paperbound **$1.35**

THEORY OF FUNCTIONS, PART I, Konrad Knopp. With volume II, provides coverage of basic concepts and theorems. Partial contents: numbers and points, functions of a complex variable, integral of a continuous function, Cauchy's intergral theorem, Cauchy's integral formulae, series with variable terms, expansion and analytic function in a power series, analytic continuation and complete definition of analytic functions, Laurent expansion, types of singularities. vii + 146pp. 5⅜ x 8. S156 Paperbound **$1.35**

THEORY OF FUNCTIONS, PART II, Konrad Knopp. Application and further development of general theory, special topics. Single valued functions, entire, Weierstrass. Meromorphic functions: Mittag-Leffler. Periodic functions. Multiple valued functions. Riemann surfaces. Algebraic functions. Analytical configurations, Riemann surface. x + 150pp. 5⅜ x 8. S157 Paperbound **$1.35**

PROBLEM BOOK IN THE THEORY OF FUNCTIONS, VOLUME I, Konrad Knopp. Problems in elementary theory, for use with Knopp's "Theory of Functions," or any other text. Arranged according to increasing difficulty. Fundamental concepts, sequences of numbers and infinite series, complex variable, integral theorems, development in series, conformal mapping. Answers. viii + 126pp. 5⅜ x 8. S 158 **Paperbound $1.35**

PROBLEM BOOK IN THE THEORY OF FUNCTIONS, VOLUME II, Konrad Knopp. Advanced theory of functions, to be used with Knopp's "Theory of Functions," or comparable text. Singularities, entire and meromorphic functions, periodic, analytic, continuation, multiple-valued functions, Riemann surfaces, conformal mapping. Includes section of elementary problems. "The difficult task of selecting . . . problems just within the reach of the beginner is here masterfully accomplished," AM. MATH. SOC. Answers. 138pp. 5⅜ x 8. S159 Paperbound **$1.35**

ADVANCED CALCULUS, E. B. Wilson. Still recognized as one of most comprehensive, useful texts. Immense amount of well-represented, fundamental material, including chapters on vector functions, ordinary differential equations, special functions, calculus of variations, etc., which are excellent introductions to these areas. Requires only one year of calculus. Over 1300 exercises cover both pure math and applications to engineering and physical problems. Ideal reference, refresher. 54 page introductory review. ix + 566pp. 5⅜ x 8. S504 Paperbound **$2.45**

LECTURES ON THE THEORY OF ELLIPTIC FUNCTIONS, H. Hancock. Reissue of only book in English with so extensive a coverage, especially of Abel, Jacobi, Legendre, Weierstrass, Hermite, Liouville, and Riemann. Unusual fullness of treatment, plus applications as well as theory in discussing universe of elliptic integrals, originating in works of Abel and Jacobi. Use is made of Riemann to provide most general theory. 40-page table of formulas. 76 figures. xxiii + 498pp. 5⅜ x 8. S483 Paperbound **$2.55**

THEORY OF FUNCTIONALS AND OF INTEGRAL AND INTEGRO-DIFFERENTIAL EQUATIONS, Vito Volterra. Unabridged republication of only English translation, General theory of functions depending on continuous set of values of another function. Based on author's concept of transition from finite number of variables to a continually infinite number. Includes much material on calculus of variations. Begins with fundamentals, examines generalization of analytic functions, functional derivative equations, applications, other directions of theory, etc. New introduction by G. C. Evans. Biography, criticism of Volterra's work by E. Whittaker. xxxx + 226pp. 5⅜ x 8. S502 Paperbound **$1.75**

AN INTRODUCTION TO FOURIER METHODS AND THE LAPLACE TRANSFORMATION, Philip Franklin. Concentrates on essentials, gives broad view, suitable for most applications. Requires only knowledge of calculus. Covers complex qualities with methods of computing elementary functions for complex values of argument and finding approximations by charts; Fourier series; harmonic anaylsis; much more. Methods are related to physical problems of heat flow, vibrations, electrical transmission, electromagnetic radiation, etc. 828 problems, answers. Formerly entitled "Fourier Methods." x + 289pp. 5⅜ x 8. S452 Paperbound **$1.75**

THE ANALYTICAL THEORY OF HEAT, Joseph Fourier. This book, which revolutionized mathematical physics, has been used by generations of mathematicians and physicists interested in heat or application of Fourier integral. Covers cause and reflection of rays of heat, radiant heating, heating of closed spaces, use of trigonometric series in theory of heat, Fourier integral, etc. Translated by Alexander Freeman. 20 figures. xxii + 466pp. 5⅜ x 8. S93 Paperbound **$2.00**

ELLIPTIC INTEGRALS, H. Hancock. Invaluable in work involving differential equations with cubics, quatrics under root sign, where elementary calculus methods are inadequate. Practical solutions to problems in mathematics, engineering, physics; differential equations requiring integration of Lamé's, Briot's, or Bouquet's equations; determination of arc of ellipse, hyperbola, lemiscate; solutions of problems in elastics; motion of a projectile under resistance varying as the cube of the velocity; pendulums; more. Exposition in accordance with Legendre-Jacobi theory. Rigorous discussion of Legendre transformations. 20 figures. 5 place table. 104pp. 5⅜ x 8. S484 Paperbound **$1.25**

THE TAYLOR SERIES, AN INTRODUCTION TO THE THEORY OF FUNCTIONS OF A COMPLEX VARIABLE, P. Dienes. Uses Taylor series to approach theory of functions, using ordinary calculus only, except in last 2 chapters. Starts with introduction to real variable and complex algebra, derives properties of infinite series, complex differentiation, integration, etc. Covers biuniform mapping, overconvergence and gap theorems, Taylor series on its circle of convergence, etc. Unabridged corrected reissue of first edition. 186 examples, many fully worked out. 67 figures. xii + 555pp. 5⅜ x 8. S391 Paperbound **$2.75**

LINEAR INTEGRAL EQUATIONS, W. V. Lovitt. Systematic survey of general theory, with some application to differential equations, calculus of variations, problems of math, physics. Includes: integral equation of 2nd kind by successive substitutions; Fredholm's equation as ratio of 2 integral series in lambda, applications of the Fredholm theory, Hilbert-Schmidt theory of symmetric kernels, application, etc. Neumann, Dirichlet, vibratory problems. ix + 253pp. 5⅜ x 8. S175 Clothbound **$3.50**
S176 Paperbound **$1.60**

TRIGONOMETRICAL SERIES, Antoni Zygmund. On modern advanced level. Contains carefully organized analyses of trigonometric, orthogonal, Fourier systems of functions, with clear adequate descriptions of summability of Fourier series, proximation theory, conjugate series, convergence, divergence of Fourier series. Especially valuable for Russian, Eastern European coverage. 329pp. 5⅜ x 8. S290 Paperbound **$1.50**

THE LAWS OF THOUGHT, George Boole. This book founded symbolic logic some 100 years ago. It is the 1st significant attempt to apply logic to all aspects of human endeavour. Partial contents: derivation of laws, signs and laws, interpretations, eliminations, conditions of a perfect method, analysis, Aristotelian logic, probability, and similar topics. xvii + 424pp. 5⅜ x 8. S28 Paperbound **$2.00**

SYMBOLIC LOGIC, C. I. Lewis, C. H. Langford. 2nd revised edition of probably most cited book in symbolic logic. Wide coverage of entire field; one of fullest treatments of paradoxes; plus much material not available elsewhere. Basic to volume is distinction between logic of extensions and intensions. Considerable emphasis on converse substitution, while matrix system presents supposition of variety of non-Aristotelian logics. Especially valuable sections on strict limitations, existence theorems. Partial contents: Boole-Schroeder algebra; truth value systems, the matrix method; implication and deductibility; general theory of propositions; etc. "Most valuable," Times, London. 506pp. 5⅜ x 8. S170 Paperbound **$2.00**

GROUP THEORY AND LINEAR ALGEBRA, SETS, ETC.

LECTURES ON THE ICOSAHEDRON AND THE SOLUTION OF EQUATIONS OF THE FIFTH DEGREE, Felix Klein. Solution of quintics in terms of rotations of regular icosahedron around its axes of symmetry. A classic, indispensable source for those interested in higher algebra, geometry, crystallography. Considerable explanatory material included. 230 footnotes, mostly bibliography. "Classical monograph . . . detailed, readable book," Math. Gazette. 2nd edition. xvi + 289pp. 5⅜ x 8. S314 Paperbound **$1.85**

INTRODUCTION TO THE THEORY OF GROUPS OF FINITE ORDER, R. Carmichael. Examines fundamental theorems and their applications. Beginning with sets, systems, permutations, etc., progresses in easy stages through important types of groups: Abelian, prime power, permutation, etc. Except 1 chapter where matrices are desirable, no higher math is needed. 783 exercises, problems. xvi + 447pp. 5⅜ x 8. S299 Clothbound **$3.95**
S300 Paperbound **$2.00**

THEORY OF GROUPS OF FINITE ORDER, W. Burnside. First published some 40 years ago, still one of clearest introductions. Partial contents: permutations, groups independent of representation, composition series of a group, isomorphism of a group with itself, Abelian groups, prime power groups, permutation groups, invariants of groups of linear substitution, graphical representation, etc. "Clear and detailed discussion . . . numerous problems which are instructive," Design News. xxiv + 512pp. 5⅜ x 8. S38 Paperbound **$2.45**

COMPUTATIONAL METHODS OF LINEAR ALGEBRA, V. N. Faddeeva, translated by C. D. Benster. 1st English translation of unique, valuable work, only one in English presenting systematic exposition of most important methods of linear algebra—classical, contemporary. Details of deriving numerical solutions of problems in mathematical physics. Theory and practice. Includes survey of necessary background, most important methods of solution, for exact, iterative groups. One of most valuable features is 23 tables, triple checked for accuracy, unavailable elsewhere. Translator's note. x + 252pp. 5⅜ x 8. S424 Paperbound **$1.95**

THE CONTINUUM AND OTHER TYPES OF SERIAL ORDER, E. V. Huntington. This famous book gives a systematic elementary account of the modern theory of the continuum as a type of serial order. Based on the Cantor-Dedekind ordinal theory, which requires no technical knowledge of higher mathematics, it offers an easily followed analysis of ordered classes, discrete and dense series, continuous series, Cantor's transfinite numbers. "Admirable introduction to the rigorous theory of the continuum . . . reading easy," Science Progress. 2nd edition. viii + 82pp. 5⅜ x 8. S129 Clothbound **$2.75**
S130 Paperbound **$1.00**

THEORY OF SETS, E. Kamke. Clearest, amplest introduction in English, well suited for independent study. Subdivisions of main theory, such as theory of sets of points, are discussed, but emphasis is on general theory. Partial contents: rudiments of set theory, arbitrary sets, their cardinal numbers, ordered sets, their order types, well-ordered sets, their cardinal numbers. vii + 144pp. 5⅜ x 8. S141 Paperbound **$1.35**

CONTRIBUTIONS TO THE FOUNDING OF THE THEORY OF TRANSFINITE NUMBERS, Georg Cantor. These papers founded a new branch of mathematics. The famous articles of 1895-7 are translated, with an 82-page introduction by P. E. B. Jourdain dealing with Cantor, the background of his discoveries, their results, future possibiilties. ix + 211pp. 5⅜ x 8. S45 Paperbound **$1.25**

DATE DUE			